AN ENCYCLOPEDIA
OF
MODERN AMERICAN HUMOR

BENNETT CERF

An Encyclopedia of Modern American Humor

Good for a Laugh

Laughter, Incorporated

Shake Well before Using

Anything for a Laugh

Laughing Stock

Try and Stop Me

An Encyclopedia of

MODERN AMERICAN HUMOR

Edited by

BENNETT CERF

Drawings by Doug Anderson

Hanover House

DOUBLEDAY & COMPANY, INC.

Garden City, New York

Library of Congress Catalog Card Number 54–11449
Copyright, 1954, by Doubleday & Company, Inc.
Printed in the United States

ACKNOWLEDGMENTS

Copyrighted material cannot be reprinted without the blessing of the authors and publishers controlling same. Since fully ninety per cent of this particular compilation *is* copyrighted, the entire project would have died aborning had the necessary permissions been withheld. The Editor is duly grateful for the co-operation of everybody concerned. Detailed acknowledgments will be found in their proper places.

Contents

FOREWORD

THE last successful compilation of this sort that appeared on the market was A *Subtreasury of American Humor*. It was edited by E. B. White and his wife, Katharine. Mrs. White has been a moving force in the operation of *The New Yorker* magazine from the day it first was published—and *The New Yorker* is in a class by itself in periodicals leaning toward the lighter side of life. E. B. White is not only a recognized authority on the baffling subject of "what's funny," but one of the country's all-time greats in humorous writing himself. On the face of it, any attempt to produce a new anthology similar in nature to the Whites' might be considered sheer presumption.

But A *Subtreasury* was published a full thirteen years ago. As humor goes, that is an eternity. Since 1941, a brand-new crop of first-class humorists has appeared to brighten our horizon. Thomas Heggen, Max Shulman, Russell Lynes, Cleveland Amory, H. Allen Smith, John Crosby, and Art Buchwald are only a few of them.

Aiming therefore at a collection that includes, perforce, some stand-bys that could not conceivably be omitted, but that highlights, wherever possible, achievements of the brash and bouncy newcomers, I feel that this volume will justify its existence. (I even added at the last moment excerpts from a brand-new first novel by Mac Hyman—as hilarious a book, I believe, as has come along in years.)

In attempting, for the first time, to divide the contents on a regional basis, I was astonished to discover how much of our contemporary humor centers about New York City, although the Deep South, by virtue of a tradition-scorning and unfettered group of young scriveners, is closing in by leaps and bounds. Those stories that could be assigned to no specific locale have been grouped under headings like "Anywhere, U.S.A.," "This Side of Parodies," "Growing Pains," and "Beyond the Twelve-Mile Limit."

The section labeled "The Next Verse You Hear" is necessarily the briefest kind of sampling of modern American light poetry, a field in which we excel. And "A Whiff of Grease Paint" is just a passing bow in the direction of the rich and fascinating world of the stage, motion pictures, radio, and television. There wasn't room for more. I am deliberately cutting short this introduction, in fact, because I know as a publisher, that the reader wants as much space as possible devoted to actual selections, and can dispense happily with yawn-provoking theories by the editor on the baffling subject of just what does make people laugh. Space was at a particular premium in this volume; I am sick at heart over some of the pieces that had to be omitted.

I began this anthology as a diversion. As I progressed, it became an obsession. Reading, night after night, the complete short stories of such master craftsmen as Ring Lardner, F. Scott Fitzgerald, Dorothy Parker, John O'Hara, and Roark Bradford constituted the most exhilarating and absorbing task I ever have undertaken.

Some of the stories finally selected are so "off-beat" that many readers may consider their inclusion arbitrary, if not ridiculous. But "humor" is an elastic word. Many a story decidedly on the grim side remains essentially true to the comic spirit.

It was my violent distaste for early American humor, so dependent on bad spelling and faulty grammar for its effect, that made me begin the collection with selections from Mark Twain (and *not* the, to me, vastly overrated *Jumping Frog of Calaveras County*). It was my own background of undergraduate humor (I edited the Columbia *Jester* way back in 1919)—and constant exposure to the flip wisecracks of contemporary wits that inclined me possibly a bit too far to suit some tastes in the direction of humor that ignores subtlety and finesse, but makes a reader slap his sides with convulsive glee. For me, a hearty "belly laugh" is one of the most beautiful sounds in the world.

Finally, this "encyclopedia" is intended to prove that there still exist a powerful lot of Americans who know how to laugh and make others laugh—intentionally. There couldn't be a better time to remind ourselves of the fact. Any country that can produce, in the span of two decades, such superb humorists as James Thurber, E. B. White, Frank Sullivan, S. J. Perelman, Clarence Day, Wolcott Gibbs, Robert Benchley, and all the newer luminaries proudly rounded up in these pages, has no need to worry about its sense of humor.

Possibly we haven't been laughing quite *enough* in recent months —or at exactly the right things.

Possibly this collection will help just a little to rectify the situation.

BENNETT CERF

Mt. Kisco, New York.
September, 1954.

I. ANYWHERE, U. S. A.

Cornelia Otis Skinner

ON SKATING

IT IS my cross in life to be completely unathletic. At college I was a member of the seventh hockey team. Hockey was compulsory; there were only seven teams and the seventh rarely met, because there was no one bad enough to meet them. The instructor who taught us fencing, after the first lesson, advised me to take up folk dancing, and the night after I got over the horse in gym, my class gave me a dinner. True, at school I was at the head of an awkward squad that had to do deep-breathing exercises during the recess period, but after a month a new athletic teacher decided we weren't worth the trouble and turned us into a raw egg and Sanatogen list. Since that remote time, no poet has ever sought the inspired word more avidly than I the form of exercise I can pursue without looking like one of the Fratellini brothers. I ought to realize that it is a fruitless quest, and stick to yeast and vibrating machines; but now and again the urge re-awakens and I embrace some new sport with desperate ambition, only to sink into a neurasthenia of wondering if perhaps I'm not suffering from rickets. However, there seems to be nothing wrong with me physically. My heart is the kind doctors call in other doctors to listen to; my blood pressure is doing whatever a blood pressure should; and, unless I attempt some set form of exercise, I apparently co-ordinate.

Elise listened to me with compassion. She too suffered from having a spirit of the White Maid of Astolat imprisoned in the body of a great bouncing outdoor girl. Moreover, as she had been eating too well, she was losing the bouncing quality and felt that something should be done about it. The previous winter she had taken up golf at Wanamaker's and I had turned my hand (or rather my ankle) at soft shoe dancing. But Elise found that the subway gave her sinus trouble and my instructor told me that if only I'd started younger he'd have been able to "place" me in burlesque; so we again found ourselves thrown on a sporting world without a muscle between us.

It was a cold day and we were walking in the Park. The long clean hiss of skates cutting new ice rose from the pond. It sounded fresh and wholesome above the roar and rumble of the Great City, as a milk churn would sound in a cocktail bar. A handful of people was gliding about the white surface below us in delicious cadence.

"Do you know how to skate?" asked Elise.

"Do you know how to walk a tight rope?" I replied. We admitted we neither of us knew how to do either but would like to learn and of the two pastimes skating seemed the more practical.

"It seems a lot to learn for so short a season," I ventured.

"But think what a help it would be at St. Moritz."

The fact that neither Elise nor I can go abroad except in the middle of summer did not in the least dim our ardor.

"We might come here tomorrow," I suggested.

"We'll have to take some indoor lessons first." Elise appeared to know all about it.

"Where? At Ned Wayburn's?"

"No. One goes to a sort of academy and hires an instructor." And we arranged to meet next day at the Palais de Glace or whatever our city's glorified ice-house calls itself.

After twenty-four hours I must admit the nap had a bit worn off (if there is a nap on ice). The marble approach to the skating edifice with its uniformed guard and gold paneled walls had more of a Roxy than a Hans Brinker atmosphere. I advanced to the "guichet" and found myself asking for a seat on the parterre (a location, I ruefully reflected, in which I was only too likely and too frequently to be). Someone handed me a pink ticket and timidly I entered the chilly building.

An orchestra was playing the "Blue Danube," apparently assuming that stately river froze over every winter, and to its measure some two dozen couples were twirling swiftly and gracefully about a vast arena. Silent pairs glided around the outer edge, a wild youth was racing past them as if he'd been carrying the good news from Ghent to Aix and had lost the way, and in the center a little group of serious skaters were studying the intricacies of the figure eight, seemingly mistaking it for the Einstein theory. My heart was pounding with what I told myself was delight. "What a sport! What a sport!" I thought (or tried to), breathing deep of the ammonia-scented air and endeavoring to hear the music above the sudden roar of an elevated train. I was standing near the instructors. I knew they were instructors because their caps said so. Stalwart fellows they were, clad in uniforms of Lincoln green. They looked like Robin Hood's Merrie Men, except that they weren't especially merrie.

Elise arrived. She was going to a wedding later and was wearing a chiffon-velvet dress, a broadtail coat and white kid gloves. I asked her if she wasn't a little overdressed, but she said she thought not, and, as a concession to sport, changed the white kid gloves for a pair of gray mittens. We stood for a time uncertain what to do, until the kindly soul who kept the appointment book told us the young lady in the dressing room would fit us to skates. A shudder went through me as if she had said thumbscrews.

The young lady in the dressing room was colored and bored with life. Our entrance was an interruption to her perusal of a tabloid. She asked us resentfully what size skates we wore. (She might as well have asked what size diving bell I required.) After glancing scornfully at my foot she called to a hidden confederate, "Marie! Send up a large pair!" Marie told her to come and get them, and she shambled away leaving me feeling like someone who, trying to purchase a dress in the misses' department, is told she will find what she wants at Lane Bryant. After a bit she impassively returned with two objects of torture—high laced shoes that I suspected had been left there by a Boston welfare worker, and fastened to their soles a glittering example of the steel-forger's art that weighed incredibly. After thrusting my feet into the boots she laced them so tightly I was about to scream when she took a button hook from her belt and pulled the laces until she'd made an excellent tourniquet at each ankle.

"Aren't you stopping the circulation?" I suggested.

"I guess so," she replied and I thought what a pity I hadn't been bitten by a rattlesnake. "You don't feel the cold, see," she explained. She was right. After ten minutes I didn't feel anything.

The operation was repeated on Elise, who bore it bravely; after which the young lady returned to her tabloid and left us sitting helplessly on the bench.

"How do your new shoes hurt?" croaked Elise.

"Very well, thank you," I replied. "I suppose we'd better go on in."

"How?" asked Elise. "Do we coast down this wooden passageway?"

"No. We walk, of course."

"Don't be funny. Someone will have to carry me."

"You don't expect to be carried about the ice, do you?" I retorted. "Come on, Elise, it isn't far." And I sprang courageously to my feet, which turned out not to be where they usually were—a surprise that precipitated me back onto the bench.

"A well-equipped place like this ought to have wheel chairs," I said savagely.

"Hold the wall," came the tired voice of the young lady.

"How can you hold a wall!" snarled Elise. She had risen and was swaying like a helmsman in a gale.

"If worse comes to worst we can always crawl," I said and wondered what one did in case of fire.

Lurching, clutching at benches and one another, we managed to progress down the passageway with the grace of trained bears and emerge near the group of instructors in Lincoln green. The appointment-book lady called out that someone named Kelly was to take Elise, and I saw her go away pale but gallant. There was some muttered conversation among the Merrie Men as to who was to take me. The chosen instructor apparently didn't feel adequate. At length a great creature, the Little John of the band, loomed up to me and said "I'll take you, lady," as Hercules might have said, "Allow me, Atlas."

"I hate to bother you," I murmured.

"It's a pleasure," replied my gallant and steered me toward the ice. Here he paused, crossed my arms and, after doing the same with his own, seized my hands in a vise-like grip. I wondered if he wanted to play "Wringing the dish-rag," but with a swift spring he sailed onto the ice and yanked me after him irretrievably into the frozen waste. For a few moments things looked very bad indeed and the instructor and I looked even worse. We bent violently to one side, then to the other, then bowed forward several times like Moslems salaaming Mecca. Now I was ahead of my partner, now behind him; the next second found me wrapped about him like a drunkard about a lamp-post. He meantime was maintaining his equilibrium and murmuring "Steady! Steady!" as if he thought I was Twenty Grand. At moments we were arm's length apart, only to come together in a passionate embrace that made me feel he ought to ask me to marry him. My ankles, meantime, were giving me all the support of india rubber. They bent and turned as I never knew they could and most of the time I was progressing on the side of my shoe.

"How is it you ain't never skated when you was a kid?" my Merrie Man panted. We had traversed the length of the room and were pausing for breath. For lack of a better excuse I said I had always lived in Cuba and wondered what I'd do if he started speaking to me in Spanish.

"Couldn't you let yourself go more?" he asked.

"Go where?" I inquired, but he didn't seem to know. There was an awkward pause. In an attempt to be chatty, I asked him what his name was. "Call me M." he answered and I said I would, feeling that here indeed was an element of mystery.

"Come on," said M. and we started the second lap. This was as spectacular as the first. Something seemed to be pulling my feet forward and my head backward and a mirror showed me the unfortunate image of myself executing a sort of Nordic cakewalk while the solicitous M. endeavored to divert my convulsions in the right direction. Once more we paused for breath. In the interval I caught sight of Elise. She was bending forward in the attitude of someone looking for a four-leaf clover and was daintily if uncertainly *walking*, lifting her foot a good six inches with every step. At times her arms, and consequently those of Mr. Kelly flew up in a manner that reminded one of the more animated figures of the Mazurka. This threw them at a perilous angle and I maliciously hoped the orchestra might play "Slide, Kelly, Slide." I called to her in what I considered a cheery tone but she gave me in reply only a dirty look.

"Shall we try again?" M. was saying, and once more we lurched forth. This time I managed to steer a straighter course. "You'll do all right," he said not unkindly.

"Oh, do you think so?" I simpered.

"Do you like to dance?" he asked abruptly.

"Yes," I faltered. "Do you?" And feeling that no price was too great to pay, I wondered if he were about to ask me to dinner at the Persian Room. But he only repeated, "Then you'll do all right."

Fired with ambition I started again. By now both of my feet had gone to sleep, and the calves of my legs were only half awake. I was quite numb all over and cheered myself with the thought that no fall could be more painful than the present state of my person. With the courage of despair I set forth at a swifter pace. Unfortunately that unseen force again pulled my head and feet in diametrically opposed directions and once more I was precipitated into the cakewalk, this time with such energy that I found myself going backward in time to the band which was rendering a lively fox trot. M. too seemed to have caught the spirit of the dance, albeit unwillingly, and was backing with me at increasing speed, shouting "Careful!" with as much efficacy as a Paris gendarme calls "*Attention!*" to the traffic.

Faster and faster we flew in a movement that must be difficult for even the most expert. I was aware of people stopping to watch, of flying bits of ice, of Elise's face blanched and horrified; then, in perfect unison, we struck the surface and landed, facing each other tailor-fashion, in the position of two people about to play "Pease Porridge Hot!" Our manœuvre made a considerable stir and a small band of Merrie Men rushed out, as at the sound of Robin's horn, to our rescue. Firm hands seized and lifted me onto that completely uncontrollable part of my anatomy, my feet, and somebody said "There you are!" as if I didn't know. Unfortunately no bones were broken, so I had to continue my lesson; but Elise, who had witnessed my tumbling act, suddenly remembered she had a date, waved a mitten at me and departed.

The remainder of the time passed uneventfully enough. M., that prince of diplomats, never once referring to our débâcle, patiently steered me, lurching, heaving, now waving my arms as if semaphoring, now bowing as a sovereign to my subjects. I tried the theory of mental images. I thought of Charlotte, of beautiful mad Tartars skimming over the ice of whatever mad Tartars skim over the ice of, of Rear-Admiral Byrd sailing over the Pole; but my power of imagination was defeated by my lack of co-ordination and the reflection of myself in passing mirrors. After half an hour that seemed interminable, M. expressed the opinion that I had done enough for the day. Surely the day had done more than enough for me, and I was only too relieved to be shoved to the edge and deposited on the wooden runway. Thence I made my way in a quaint and somewhat primitive rhythm to the dressing-room.

The colored young lady sighed deeply and unlaced the Iron Maidens. Tales of Northern exposure and frozen members that drop off assailed me and I half expected her to remove my feet with the boots. They appeared, however, still to be attached, though completely paralyzed and bearing across each instep curious markings that made them look like waffles. This interesting design showed plainly through my chiffon hose and lasted most of the day, but I was lucky to have escaped with no further injury.

Since then, Elise and I have returned a few times to the strong arms of M. and Kelly. We have not, however, as yet come into our own—though we have succeeded in coming into everything and everybody in the ice palace. I feel there is too much of the Latin in me to excel in so Nordic a sport, although M. keeps assuring me that if I can dance I ought to do—do what, he doesn't say; and, what's more, I have an idea he is entertaining the petty suspicion that I don't even dance. Elise and I have lately discussed taking up some sport that doesn't hurt so, to re-establish our self-confidence; and, the season being winter, and the month for such things being no nearer than June, we are considering canoeing.

Dorothy Parker

THE SEXES

THE young man with the scenic cravat glanced nervously down the sofa at the girl in the fringed dress. She was examining her handkerchief; it might have been the first one of its kind she had seen, so deep was her interest in its material, form, and possibilities. The young man cleared his throat, without necessity or success, producing a small, syncopated noise.

"Want a cigarette?" he said.

"No, thank you," she said. "Thank you ever so much just the same."

"Sorry I've only got these kind," he said. "You got any of your own?"

"I really don't know," she said. "I probably have, thank you."

"Because if you haven't," he said, "it wouldn't take me a minute to go up to the corner and get you some."

"Oh, thank you, but I wouldn't have you go to all that trouble for anything," she said. "It's awfully sweet of you to think of it. Thank you ever so much."

"Will you for God's sakes stop thanking me?" he said.

"Really," she said, "I didn't know I was saying anything out of the way. I'm awfully sorry if I hurt your feelings. I know what it feels like to get your feelings hurt. I'm sure I didn't realize it was an insult to say 'thank you' to a person. I'm not exactly in the habit of having people swear at me because I say 'thank you' to them."

"I did not swear at you!" he said.

"Oh, you didn't?" she said. "I see."

"My God," he said, "all I said, I simply asked you if I couldn't go out and get you some cigarettes. Is there anything in that to get up in the air about?"

"Who's up in the air?" she said. "I'm sure I didn't know it was a criminal offense to say I wouldn't dream of giving you all that trouble. I'm afraid I must be awfully stupid, or something."

"Do you want me to go out and get you some cigarettes; or don't you?" he said.

"Goodness," she said, "if you want to go so much, please don't feel you have to stay here. I wouldn't have you feel you had to stay for anything."

"Ah, don't be that way, will you?" he said.

"Be what way?" she said. "I'm not being any way."

"What's the matter?" he said.

"Why, nothing," she said. "Why?"

"You've been funny all evening," he said. "Hardly said a word to me, ever since I came in."

"I'm terribly sorry you haven't been having a good time," she said. "For goodness' sakes, don't feel you have to stay here and be bored. I'm sure there are millions of places you could be having a lot more fun. The only thing, I'm a little bit sorry I didn't know before, that's all. When you said you were coming over tonight, I broke a lot of dates to go to the theater and everything. But it doesn't make a bit of difference. I'd much rather have you go and have a good time. It isn't very pleasant to sit here and feel you're boring a person to death."

"I'm not bored!" he said. "I don't want to go any place! Ah, honey, won't you tell me what's the matter? Ah, please."

"I haven't the faintest idea what you're talking about," she said. "There isn't a thing on earth the matter. I don't know what you mean."

"Yes, you do," he said. "There's something the trouble. Is it anything I've done, or anything?"

"Goodness," she said, "I'm sure it isn't any of my business, anything you do. I certainly wouldn't feel I had any right to criticize."

"Will you stop talking like that?" he said. "Will you, please?"

"Talking like what?" she said.

"You know," he said. "That's the way you were talking over the telephone today, too. You were so snotty when I called you up, I was afraid to talk to you."

"I beg your pardon," she said. "What did you say I was?"

"Well, I'm sorry," he said. "I didn't mean to say that. You get me so balled up."

"You see," she said, "I'm really not in the habit of hearing language like that. I've never had a thing like that said to me in my life."

"I told you I was sorry, didn't I?" he said. "Honest, honey, I didn't mean it. I don't know how I came to say a thing like that. Will you excuse me? Please?"

"Oh, certainly," she said. "Goodness, don't feel you have to apologize to me. It doesn't make any difference at all. It just seems a little bit funny to have somebody you were in the habit of thinking was a gentleman come to your home and use language like that to you, that's all. But it doesn't make the slightest bit of difference."

"I guess nothing I say makes any difference to you," he said. "You seem to be sore at me."

"I'm sore at you?" she said. "I can't understand what put that idea in your head. Why should I be sore at you?"

"That's what I'm asking you," he said. "Won't you tell me what I've done? Have I done something to hurt your feelings, honey? The way you were, over the phone, you had me worried all day. I couldn't do a lick of work."

"I certainly wouldn't like to feel," she said, "that I was interfering with your work. I know there are lots of girls that don't think anything of doing things like that, but I think it's terrible. It certainly isn't very nice to sit here and have someone tell you you interfere with his business."

"I didn't say that!" he said. "I didn't say it!"

"Oh, didn't you?" she said. "Well, that was the impression I got. It must be my stupidity."

"I guess maybe I better go," he said. "I can't get right. Everything I say seems to make you sorer and sorer. Would you rather I'd go?"

"Please do just exactly whatever you like," she said. "I'm sure the last thing I want to do is have you stay here when you'd rather be some place else. Why don't you go some place where you won't be bored? Why don't you go up to Florence Leaming's? I know she'd love to have you."

"I don't want to go up to Florence Leaming's!" he said. "What would I want to go up to Florence Leaming's for? She gives me a pain."

"Oh, really?" she said. "She didn't seem to be giving you so much of a pain at Elsie's party last night, I notice. I notice you couldn't even talk to anybody else, that's how much of a pain she gave you."

"Yeah, and you know why I was talking to her?" he said.

"Why, I suppose you think she's attractive," she said. "I suppose some people do. It's perfectly natural. Some people think she's quite pretty."

"I don't know whether she's pretty or not," he said. "I wouldn't know her if I saw her again. Why I was talking to her was you wouldn't even give me a tumble, last night. I came up and tried to talk to you, and you just said, 'Oh, how do you do'—just like that, 'Oh, how do you do'—and you turned right away and wouldn't look at me."

"I wouldn't look at you?" she said. "Oh, that's awfully funny. Oh, that's marvelous. You don't mind if I laugh, do you?"

"Go ahead and laugh your head off," he said. "But you wouldn't."

"Well, the minute you came in the room," she said, "you started making such a fuss over Florence Leaming, I thought you never wanted to see anybody else. You two seemed to be having such a wonderful time together, goodness knows I wouldn't have butted in for anything."

"My God," he said, "this what's-her-name girl came up and began talking to me before I even saw anybody else, and what could I do? I couldn't sock her in the nose, could I?"

"I certainly didn't see you try," she said.

"You saw me try to talk to you, didn't you?" he said. "And what did you do? 'Oh, how do you do.' Then this what's-her-name came up again, and there I was, stuck. Florence Leaming! I think she's terrible. Know what I think of her? I think she's a damn little fool. That's what I think of her."

"Well, of course," she said, "that's the impression she always gave me, but I don't know. I've heard people say she's pretty. Honestly I have."

"Why, she can't be pretty in the same room with you," he said.

"She has got an awfully funny nose," she said. "I really feel sorry for a girl with a nose like that."

"She's got a terrible nose," he said. "You've got a beautiful nose. Gee, you've got a pretty nose."

"Oh, I have not," she said. "You're crazy."

"And beautiful eyes," he said, "and beautiful hair and a beautiful mouth. And beautiful hands. Let me have one of the little hands. Ah, look atta little hand! Who's got the prettiest hands in the world? Who's the sweetest girl in the world?"

"I don't know," she said. "Who?"

"You don't know!" he said. "You do so, too, know."

"I do not," she said. "Who? Florence Leaming?"

"Oh, Florence Leaming, my eye!" he said. "Getting sore about Florence Leaming! And me not sleeping all last night and not doing a stroke of work all day because you wouldn't speak to me! A girl like you getting sore about a girl like Florence Leaming!"

"I think you're just perfectly crazy," she said. "I was not sore! What on earth ever made you think I was? You're simply crazy. Ow, my new pearl beads! Wait a second till I take them off. There!"

Joe H. Palmer

BY ANY OTHER NAME

THERE was once a time when an owner could name his horse anything he pleased. It was not a very good time, because jokes around a racetrack have usually been remarkable for their broadness and not for the rapierlike quality of their wit, and some of the names in the early volumes of the English racing calendar are not adaptable to mixed company unless it is of an unusually intimate sort. Sometimes not even then.

There was also once a time when it wasn't necessary to name a horse at all. This was not a very good time either, because you can see how, if the horse of the year appeared only as "Mr. Chenery's b.c., by Princequillo," you might easily lose track of him. If you call him Hill Prince you remember better.

In these days The Jockey Club exercises what it considers, often

From *This Was Racing*, by Joe Palmer, copyright, 1953, by A. S. Barnes & Company, Inc., New York.

wrongly, strict supervision over names. You get a name under the following conditions:

It must contain no more than three words.

It must contain no more than fourteen letters, including spaces.

It must not duplicate the name of any horse which has been in racing or in the stud within fifteen years, and must not duplicate the name of any prominent horse regardless of time.

It must not offend against propriety or good taste.

It must catch the registrar of The Jockey Club when he isn't swamped with work.

If any of these conditions is violated, the application for the name is sent back to the owner, who swears for a while and then often puts together some meaningless combination of letters or syllables on the ground that such an idiocy has never been committed before, and the name can consequently be obtained. This is why so many horses have bad names.

The ideal name is one which means something, even if not much, is reasonably euphonious, has a touch of color to it, and keeps you in mind of the breeding of the animal. As examples there are Hill Prince, by Princequillo-Hildene; Greek Song, by Heliopolis-Sylvan Song, and Greek Ship, by Heliopolis-Boat. As a matter of fact, Heliopolis was not a city in Greece, as everyone seems to think. There were two of them, one in Syria and one in Lower Egypt. But the name is Greek, so virtue is served.

The classical example in this corner was the product of Mrs. Helen Hay Whitney, who used unusual care and got unusual results in the naming of horses. This was Singing Wood, by Royal Minstrel-Glade, for surely you have not forgotten so much of your Anglo-Saxon as not to remember that "singing wood" was an Anglo-Saxon "kenning," or nickname, for a harp. It was a beautiful name, and it was no more than just that Singing Wood should have won the Futurity in his year.

Sometimes there's a story behind the names, not always publicly revealed. Sometimes it's plain enough, though, as in the case of Oil Capitol's dam, Never Again, which was originally named New Deal. This was possible because she was foaled in France; over here, once she had raced, the name could not have been changed.

Last year when a two-year-old named Champion Liar appeared, there was some speculation about its namesake, the issue being confused because there were so many candidates. It turned out to represent a change in the foreign policy of Mr. Isidor Bieber, who had bred a long string of foals out of the dam, Maaja. These were, in order, named Russian Valor, Russian Action, Empty Noose, Appease Not and Champion Liar, and you can discern a perceptible swing in Mr. Bieber's opinion between Stalingrad and Lake Success.

There was a man some years ago who named his horses very unattractively. I seem to remember Ugly Mary and Losing Clon as examples. He approached this on a practical level. He said with those names female hunch players would not bet on them, and he would get better odds when they won.

On the score of good taste, by which The Jockey Club means anything that would have been acceptable to Queen Victoria in her declining years, the registrar tries to hit all curve balls thrown at him, but he misses some. One of the best curve-ball pitchers he has to contend with is a Jockey Club member, Alfred Vanderbilt.

I can remember when a New York delegation to Pimlico made a moderate killing on one of Mr. Vanderbilt's horses, False Front. The plunge was taken partly because we were drinking martinis on the clubhouse porch, but largely because we admired the subtlety of the name. The dam's name was Superficial.

Some owners ask help from the public. John H. Clark of Lexington, Ky., who operates a horse agency, has recently sent a list of his yearlings to all his clients, requesting suggestions for names. The yearlings are all by Eternal Bull, and I understand that the names of a good many sports columnists and racing writers have been submitted.

Joe H. Palmer

THE ODDS WERE RIGHT

THIS is a parable which concerns the late W. T. (Fatty) Anderson, who, in the phrase which O. Henry lifted from a more venerable author, amused himself by going to and fro upon the earth,

From *This Was Racing*, by Joe Palmer, copyright, 1953, by A. S. Barnes & Company, Inc., New York.

and walking up and down in it. There is a trainer named W. T. Anderson now, but this is not the same man.

He did not have to keep it straight in his mind if he was a gourmet or a gourmand, because he was both. There is a tale they tell of an eating contest he had against a man who claimed to be champion of Cuba. The tale varies as to how many miles of water were scraped clean of shellfish and how much poultry laid down its life for this experiment, but most versions come together with the introduction of two huge apple pies. The Cuban champion went on the ropes after two large slices and was assisted out. Anderson ate his own placidly, then reached across the table for the section left by his antagonist. He hesitated for a moment and then called the waiter. He wanted a piece of cheese to put on it.

He liked to race horses and did, but he was modest about it. He wanted publicity so little that it was the devil and all to get him to race them in his own name, as the rules of racing require. The idea was not any fraud, for he was merely trying to get a horse and a bookmaker ready at the same time, and his name on the program produced a certain wariness in the ring.

He got ruled off for this several times, but he was never convinced. "You couldn't make him stop it," a crony of Anderson's told me. "He did it once at the Fair Grounds and didn't tell even me." He thought a minute and added, "And I owned half the horse."

You may gather that Anderson was interested in matters of chance. He took Carlaris down for the Coffroth Handicap at Tijuana and bet virtually all he had on him, which was a good deal at the time, prudently saving out $3,000 to get home on with his stable if he lost. But on the morning of the race, Gene Normille, whom he didn't like, ran into him after breakfast.

"Five to three he doesn't," said Normille.

Out came the shipping money. Down came Carlaris, by seven.

Once it was a little different. You would not have heard of Raceland. This was a track built in the early '20s at Ashland, Ky., for the purpose of discouraging inflation and the payment of grocery bills by the coal miners and lumberjacks of the Kentucky and West Virginia mountains.

It didn't work out. The mountaineers proved to be sensible people, who would spend money on copper worms for their stills, or for cartridges, or for labor saving devices, such as wives and mules. ("It's a wonderful country for men and dawgs," a mountain woman once said to a man who admired the view from her kitchen porch, "but it's hell on women and mules.") They did not see any sense in betting on horses, and Raceland fell ungracefully on its face after two years.

But during the two years Anderson and a friend went up. They had a horse running that was pretty sure to win, and they left $3,000 with a commissioner in Cincinnati to be spread around.

"But look," said the companion, "this is a new track and it's trying to make friends. For heaven's sake don't do anything up here."

Anderson assented and kept his word, more or less. All he did was pad the mutuels. At minor tracks, where the handle isn't anything much, a relatively small amount of money bet around the real favorite will chase his price from a legitimate 7 to 5 up to around 6 to 1. So Anderson threw several thousand dollars away betting on horses that would lose, so that he would get 6 to 1 on his $3,000 in Cincinnati.

It worked beautifully, and the horse trotted home. In the midst of a victory celebration, however, there came a call from Cincinnati. The new track, it appeared, was not included in the wire service, and bookmakers wouldn't accept bets on horses there. So not only was the $18,000 profit a mirage, but Anderson had thrown away his own money making a false price. He took it cheerfully. It was an honest mistake.

But the story I was getting to started with a poker game in Havana, in which our hero, because of the mistaken assumption that three queens was the high hand, came out into the cold gray light of morning with several hundred miles of water and a $5 bill between him and his homeland.

On the way to his hotel he met a man carrying a large fish.

"What kind of fish is that?" he asked.

"Red snapper," said the fisherman.

"For five dollars it's not," said Anderson.

It developed that the fish was on the way to be sold, and it was agreed that the decision of the fishmonger would be final.

"What kind of fish is this?" said the fisherman, tossing it down on a block.

"No jokes in the morning," said the buyer. "You've been fishing these waters for years and you ought to know. Get on with you."

"Never mind that," said the fisherman. "To decide a bet, what kind of a fish is it?"

"It's a red snapper," said the merchant. "You know cursed well it is."

Anderson handed over the $5 bill.

"You win," he said, "but it was still a good bet. I had every other kind of fish in the ocean running for me."

So there is a moral. Anybody can make a losing bet; just be sure you get the right odds.

Corey Ford

HOW TO GUESS YOUR AGE

IT SEEMS to me that they are building staircases steeper than they used to. The risers are higher, or there are more of them, or something. Maybe this is because it is so much farther today from the first to the second floor, but I've noticed it is getting harder to make two steps at a time any more. Nowadays it is all I can do to make one step at a time.

Another thing I've noticed is the small print they're using lately. Newspapers are getting farther and farther away when I hold them, and I have to squint to make them out. The other day I had to back halfway out of a telephone booth in order to read the number on the coin box. It is obviously ridiculous to suggest that a person my age needs glasses, but the only other way I can find out what's going on is to have somebody read aloud to me, and that's not too satisfactory because people speak in such low voices these days that I can't hear them very well.

Everything is farther than it used to be. It's twice the distance from my house to the station now, and they've added a fair-sized hill that I never noticed before. The trains leave sooner too. I've given up running for them, because they start faster these days when I try to catch them. You can't depend on timetables any more, and it's no use asking the conductor. I ask him a dozen times a trip if the next station is where I get off, and he always says it isn't. How can you trust a conductor like that? Usually I gather up my bundles and put on my hat and coat and stand in the aisle a couple of stops away, just to make sure I don't go past my destination. Sometimes I make doubly sure by getting off at the station ahead.

A lot of other things are different lately. Barbers no longer hold up a mirror behind me when they've finished, so I can see the back of my head, and my wife has been taking care of the tickets lately when we go to the theater. They don't use the same material in clothes any more, either. I've noticed that all my suits have a tendency to shrink, especially in certain places such as around the waist or in the seat of the pants, and the laces they put in shoes nowadays are harder to reach.

Revolving doors revolve much faster than they used to. I have to let a couple of openings go past me before I jump in, and by the time I get up nerve enough to jump out again I'm right back in the street where I started. It's the same with golf. I'm giving it up because these modern golf balls they sell are so hard to pick up when I stoop over. I've had to quit driving, too; the restrooms in filling stations are getting farther and farther apart. Usually I just stay home at night and read the papers, particularly the obituary columns. It's funny how much more interesting the obituary columns have been getting lately.

Even the weather is changing. It's colder in winter and the summers are hotter than they used to be. I'd go away, if it wasn't so far. Snow is heavier when I try to shovel it, and I have to put on rubbers whenever I go out, because rain today is wetter than the rain we used to get. Draughts are more severe too. It must be the way they build windows now.

People are changing too. For one thing, they're younger than they used to be when I was their age. I went back recently to an alumni reunion at the college I graduated from in 1943—that is, 1933—I mean, 1923—and I was shocked to see the mere tots they're admitting as students these days. The average age of the freshman class couldn't have been more than seven. They seem to be more polite than in my time, though; several undergraduates called me "Sir," and one of them asked me if he could help me across the street.

On the other hand, people my own age are so much older than I am. I realize that my generation is approaching middle age (I define middle age roughly as the period between 21 and 110) but there is no excuse for my classmates tottering into a state of advanced senility. I ran into my old roommate at the bar, and he'd changed so much that he didn't recognize me. "You've put on a little weight, George," I said.

"It's this modern food," George said. "It seems to be more fattening."

"How about another martini?" I said. "Have you noticed how much weaker the martinis are these days?"

"Everything is different," said George. "Even the food you get. It's more fattening."

"How long since I've seen you, George?" I said. "It must be several years."

"I think the last time was right after the election," said George.

"What election was that?"

George thought for a moment. "Harding."

I ordered a couple more martinis. "Have you noticed these martinis are weaker than they used to be?" I said.

"It isn't like the good old days," George said. "Remember when we'd go down to the speak, and order some Orange Blossoms, and maybe pick up a couple of flappers? Boy, could they neck! Hot diggety!"

"You used to be quite a cake-eater, George," I said. "Do you still do the Black Bottom?"

"I put on too much weight," said George. "This food nowadays seems to be more fattening."

"I know," I said, "you mentioned that just a minute ago."

"Did I?" said George.

"How about another martini?" I said. "Have you noticed the martinis aren't as strong as they used to be?"

"Yes," said George, "you said that twice before."

"Oh," I said. . . .

I got to thinking about poor old George while I was shaving this morning, and I stopped for a moment and looked at my own reflection in the mirror.

They don't seem to use the same kind of glass in mirrors any more.

Corey Ford

THE OFFICE PARTY

THERE are several methods of getting through the Christmas holidays. One is to board a ship in San Francisco and sail for the Orient, arranging to cross the International Dateline at midnight on Christmas Eve. As a result, the next day on the calendar will be December 26, and your Christmas will have been a total blank.

Another way to make your Christmas a total blank is to attend an Office Party the day before . . .

The annual Office Party starts along about noon on December 24 and ends two or three months later, depending how long it takes the boss to find out who set fire to his wastebasket, threw the water cooler out of the window, and betrayed Miss O'Malley in the men's washroom. By the time the entire Accounting Department has been dismissed and the painters have finished doing over the two lower floors which were ruined when somebody turned on the sprinkler system at the festivities' height, the moment has arrived to start planning *next* year's party, which everyone vows will be even more hilarious than the last one. *Next* year all the guests will be supplied with shin guards and hockey sticks.

Usually the merrymaking begins in a modest way, with some paper cups and a bottle of Pretty Good Stuff that Mr. Freem, in Office Supplies, received from a salesman who was anxious to land the roller-towel concession for the following year. While a few associates drop by to wish Mr. Freem a merry Yule and sample his P.G.S., Mr. Freem's secretary receives her annual Christmas remembrance from Mr. Freem. She accepts this gift in stony silence, owing to the fact that her employer forgot all about getting her anything until the last minute, as usual, and hastily sent her out an hour ago with five dollars and the coy instructions to buy herself something she likes but not to look at it because it's supposed to be a surprise. (Mr. Freem's secretary has settled on a particularly virulent perfume, which she knows Mr. Freem can't stand.)

Precisely at noon a sound of sleigh bells is heard, and Mr. Twitchell, the boss, emerges from his sanctum in an ill-fitting Santa Claus suit, a white beard, and a jovial smile that fools no one. Mr. Twitchell is a great believer in cementing employer-staff relationships, and as an example of co-operation between the brass and the underlings he has not only supplied refreshments for the occasion but has deducted 10 per cent from everyone's pay check to cover the cost so they'll all feel this is their party too. After a few opening remarks, in which Mr. Twitchell puts everybody in the proper holiday mood by explaining that production has slumped so badly there won't be any Christmas bonus this year, he waves his arm toward the door, and a boy from the drugstore enters with a tray of pimento-cheese sandwiches. Mr. Twitchell beams and lights a cigar, inadvertently setting fire to his false beard and thus supplying the only genuine laugh of the day.

The next hour or so is devoted to shaking hands and getting acquainted. After all, the main idea of an Office Party is for the different branches of the organization to get to know each other better, because the L. C. Twitchell Company is really just one big happy family and the sooner we all forget our restraint and get on a first-name basis with each other, the better time we'll have or Mr. Twitchell will know the reason why. The only trouble is that each branch of the organization has the private conviction that all the other branches are manned by imbeciles and crooks, and conversation between them is limited to such expressions of Yuletide cheer as "Well, you fellows in Promotion must have quite a drag, getting that new air-conditioning outfit for your floor," or "I hear a lot of heads are going to roll in Personnel the first of the year." To make matters worse, nobody is quite sure who anybody else is, and that stranger to whom you have just confided that the organization's weak link is the Front Office will presently turn out to be none other than Mr. Furbish, the first vice-president and a brother-in-law of the boss.

The only thing to do, under these circumstances, is to get good and loaded as fast as possible. After sufficient champagne has been mixed with sufficient rye, the ice is broken, and the celebrants are not only calling each other by their first names, but are adding certain endearing epithets which they have kept bottled up all year. For example, that mild, soft-spoken Mr. Murgatroyd of the Accounting Department has just backed his immediate superior into a corner and is telling him in a loud voice that he ought to know for his own good what people are saying about him, they all think he is nothing but a stuffed shirt and why doesn't he try and act like a human being for a change? (Mr. Murgatroyd will awaken in a cold sweat next morning and try to remember what he said.)

Little Miss Meeker, who isn't used to cocktails, is contributing to the general merriment by paddling barefoot in the drinking fountain. Mr. Trench of Sales, having pursued his secretary around the desks with a sprig of mistletoe, has cornered her behind the filing cabinet and is assuring her in maudlin tones that his wife doesn't understand him. (As a result of these confidences, his secretary will be transferred shortly to the Chicago branch.) Mr. Phinney, the conscientious office manager, is wandering from room to room with a harried expression, retrieving the stub of a cigarette which some merrymaker has left burning on the edge of a desk, or picking up an empty highball glass and wiping off the ring of moisture from the mahogany bookcase. Mr. Phinney greets the Office Party each year with all the enthusiasm he would display toward a return attack of sciatica.

By midafternoon the party is a shambles. Paper cups, parts of sandwiches, and an occasional girdle litter the floor. Four shirt-sleeved individuals from the Traffic Department, perspiring freely, have organized a quartet and are rendering such nostalgic Christmas carols as "Jack, Jack, the Sailor Chap" and "O'Reilly's Daughter." Miss Meeker has passed out cold, with her head in a wastebasket, and the upright members of the staff are drawing lots to see which one will get her back to Staten Island. (Miss Meeker will be discovered in Van Cortlandt Park two days later, wandering around in a dazed condition.) Several fist fights have broken out in the men's room, and a first-aid station has been set up in the reception hall for the treatment of abrasions, minor contusions, and black-and-blue marks on stenographers' thighs. Mr. Twitchell remains cold sober, observing the celebrants through his pince-nez glasses and jotting down their names grimly in his little black book. Tomorrow will be Christmas, and maybe Santa Claus will leave a little pink slip in *your* stocking.

By the time the affair breaks up along toward midnight, at the request of the building superintendent and a squadron of police, so much ill will has been generated among the staff that it will take at least twelve months for the organization to get back to normal, and then it will be time for next year's Office Party.

The only solution I know is to stage an Office Party of your own on

December 23, two days before Christmas. If you get sufficiently fried, you may wander by mistake into the wrong Office Party the following noon. Not only will the proceedings be about the same as the party in your own office, but you won't get fired.

And a Merry Christmas to you, courtesy of the L. C. Twitchell Company.

Edward Streeter

EXCERPTS FROM
FATHER OF THE BRIDE

TOMORROW'S MY DAUGHTER'S WEDDING DAY

T HE DAY before the wedding came at last.

When one concentrates fiercely and at length on an event in the distant future it eventually becomes fixed in the mind as something forever remote. As a result it is a shock to awake some morning and find that the distant future has suddenly become the immediate present. It is like a foolish rumor about a lion in the district, which no one takes seriously until the beast springs at you from behind a lilac bush.

The wedding rehearsal was scheduled for five-thirty. Mr. Banks set out for the office exhibiting a nonchalance that he did not feel. Yes, of course, he would take the three-ten from town. There was nothing to get so excited about. Beneath the surface, however, he was distinctly nervous. He felt like a man moving beneath powerful floodlights.

The floodlight operator must have been off duty during his trip to town, however. The same apathetic faces greeted him at the station with the same apathetic comments about the weather, their health, or their lack of it. As the train pulled out of Fairview Manor, Reggie Fry lurched into the seat beside him and spent three stations describing an intricate real-estate deal in the course of which he had outwitted and discomfited the best brains in the business. Mr. Banks could stand it no longer.

"My daughter's getting married tomorrow," he said simply.

"Really?" said Mr. Fry. "Didn't know you had a daughter. Time flies, eh? I hope she's got a place to live after she's married. It's a bad situation. Getting worse. The Real-Estate Board put out some interesting figures about it in their last bulletin. I've got it here somewhere. Here it is. Now just let me read you these few paragraphs. This is on the volume of building of one-family homes in the mid-continent states during the first quarter."

Mr. Banks shuddered and gave himself up to his thoughts.

He would have found it hard to describe just what he expected when he arrived at the office. Obviously he had not anticipated organized cheering as he came in the door, yet it depressed him to have Miss Rooney nod to him from the switchboard and say, "MorningMrBanksnicemorning," just as she did on the other three hundred working days of the year.

Even his partners failed to grasp the significance of current events. As each one drifted into Mr. Banks' office during the morning he offered some fatuous remark about not falling down in the aisle or trying to bend over in his cutaway. Then, having made their concessions to the trivia of life, they concentrated on the task of dumping on his desk every unanswerable and boring problem they could dig out of their pending files. They reminded Mr. Banks of executives cleaning out their desks before leaving for their summer vacations.

During the moments when his partners were not bedeviling him the outside world took up the torch. The cream of the dullest and most long-winded of Mr. Banks' clients flocked into his office for no other apparent reason than to make sheep eyes at him and fill up an idle hour with the sound of their own voices.

The only positive note was the telephone. Whenever Mr. Banks thought about that morning during later years it was his telephone buzzer which sounded the motif of the nightmare cacophony.

"Darling, the worst thing. Old Mr. McQuade is down at the station. —McQuade, dear. I don't know. He's some relative of *yours*.—Well, it's no use arguing about that *now*. He's down at the station and he wants to know where he's supposed to *go*. Where in the world am I going to put him?"

Only the presence of a customer mooning beside his desk restrained Mr. Banks from detailed instructions.

"Hello. Is this you, Stanley?—This is Ella. *Ella.*—Is this Stanley Banks?—This is *Ella.* Yes. How *are* you? We came down the last minute as a surprise. Now we don't want you to bother your *head* about us. Just tell us how the trains run to Fairview Manor and how to get from the station to your house. If you haven't room to put us up we can go *anywhere* at all. The last thing we want to do is put you to any trouble. I guess you've got troubles enough just now." (Hysterical laughter.)

The sheep-eyed gentleman beside Mr. Banks' desk looked at him anxiously. "I hope that wasn't bad news," he said.

"No, no," said Mr. Banks. "I've got a daughter getting married tomorrow."

"Oh, of course. Quite," said the sheep-eyed gentleman and resumed his narrative.

"Darling, I'm so sorry to bother you again but I'm almost crazy. You can't imagine what's happened. The Bennett boy has come down with measles and they can't take in Cousin Laura and Bob. What in the *world* are we—I know, dear, but I thought you might have some *ideas.*"

By twelve-thirty he could stand it no longer. Shoving a pile of papers into a desk drawer, he rang for Miss Bellamy. "I'm getting the hell out of here," he said defiantly. The phone rang. "I'm gone."

"So sorry," murmured Miss Bellamy into the mouthpiece. "He was called away very hurriedly. He just this moment left the office. No, I don't think I could catch him. I know how sorry he'll be. He wanted to talk to you. Yes, I'll certainly tell him." She hung up the receiver. "It's that Mr. Wadley you've been trying to get for three days."

"That fellow has no judgment," said Mr. Banks.

"Yes indeed," said Miss Bellamy soothingly. "Now I have everything ready in this envelope. Here's a list of all the ushers and bridesmaids and where they're staying and their telephone numbers. And then here's a full set of church seating lists. There's one for each usher with his name typed on it and special instructions for those who have special jobs. I've put in some extra copies just in case. Oh, yes, and I've phoned all the papers just to make sure they remember and—well —I guess that's all till I see you in church."

Miss Bellamy looked suddenly deflated and wistful. Mr. Banks had never seen her like that before. For one terrible moment he thought she was going to cry.

"You've been wonderful," he said awkwardly. "Wonderful. I'll never forget it." He left quickly as the phone started to ring.

Several days earlier Miss Bellamy had sent crisp little notes to all the ushers and bridesmaids, attempting to impress upon their scattered minds that the rehearsal would be at five-thirty at St. George's Church and the importance of being prompt.

Mr. Banks had insisted on being there fifteen minutes ahead of time. He wanted this wedding well rehearsed—no sloppy business—and he felt somehow that if he and Mrs. Banks were early it would expedite things. To his dismay he found the church in complete darkness. The Reverend Mr. Galsworthy and the organist were nowhere about. The smoothly functioning machinery of St. George's was at dead center and the self-starter was missing.

Mr. Banks had pictured the organist busily warming up his instrument with a burst of arpeggios and Mr. Galsworthy nervously pacing the aisle, measuring distances, putting markers in his book and making a few final notes. Not even Mr. Tringle, the sexton, was puttering around.

He finally located Mr. Tringle in the cellar of the rectory gluing the back of a broken chair. "Good gracious," he exclaimed. "That late a'ready? Maybe we best go up an' put on the lights."

The first bridesmaid turned up at a quarter to six. She was a wispy little number who seemed to have been left out of everything to date and was obviously terrified at the thought of what lay ahead. The organist strolled in several minutes later.

"Are you sure," asked Mrs. Banks anxiously, "that you know what you are going to play at the wedding?"

"Oh, yes," said the organist. He was an earnest-looking young man with heavy horn spectacles. "Oh, quite. This is the Broadhurst wedding, isn't it?"

The knuckles of Mr. Banks' hand grew white as he clutched the end of the pew. "No," he said gently.

"This is the *Banks* wedding—and it's *tomorrow*," he added with subtle sarcasm.

"Surely," agreed the organist and disappeared through the gloom of the side aisle.

By six-thirty Kay and all but four of the bridal party had appeared. The minister was still absent. The groom was still absent. The ushers and bridesmaids who had made the great sacrifice stood in small groups glaring at Mr. Banks with unconcealed hostility. It was evident that each and all had torn themselves away from agreeable situations for what they clearly considered to be an old-fashioned whim of Mr.

Banks'. By their attitude they said, "You got us here. You ruined our fun. Now what are you going to do about it?"

It made Mr. Banks nervous. He distributed the seating lists to the ushers and made a little talk about over all strategy. Somehow it didn't go very well. They listened to him with the detached boredom of tourists harangued by a Grand Canyon guide. Their aspirations were obviously elsewhere.

"I wonder where Mr. Galsworthy is?" asked Mr. Banks for the tenth time.

"Oh, he's somewhere. He's always late," said Mr. Tringle amiably. "I run the rehearsal."

"But some of the bridal party aren't here yet," protested Mr. Banks. "The groom isn't here. Nobody's here."

"Some of the bridal party is never here," said Mr. Tringle. "The groom don't do nothing in weddings. Everything goes all right. You see. Don't worry. Now if you young ladies will line up in pairs outside that there door—"

They lined up, tittering and unwilling, as people line up for a group photograph which nobody wants taken. Once in place they unlined immediately. Mr. Tringle pushed them back like errant cattle. "O.K., Fritz," he yelled irreligiously. The organ suddenly gave a series of bumps and broke into the wedding march. Mrs. Banks watched nervously from a pew.

"It's too fast," she cried hopelessly as the skeleton procession dashed past her. "You're running. It's awful."

"You want to do it again?" asked Mr. Tringle, rubbing his hands with the air of one who has staged a great dramatic spectacle. "It comes O.K. next time. Take it easy. Line up now. Hey, you. Big girl. You get in back row this time so's they can see the other bridesmaids. O.K., Fritz, shoot," he bawled.

They were off again. It wasn't the way Mr. Banks had pictured it. In fact, it reminded him more of the mob scene in the *Vagabond King* than a wedding rehearsal. He gave a sigh of relief as he saw the Reverend Galsworthy enter the church, trotting like a pony and exuding geniality. Now they would get the situation in hand.

"Well, well, well," said Mr. Galsworthy. "All over, I see. That means I'm just in time. So sorry. Had a meeting. Mr. Tringle's an old hand, though." He put his arm around Mr. Tringle's shoulder and squeezed him with impersonal affection. "Do they know their stuff, Mr. Tringle? Good. Well, I'm sure it will all go off very smoothly and that it will be a beautiful wedding."

Mr. Banks could hardly believe what he heard. "But they haven't really begun to rehearse. Four of the bridal party aren't even here yet and the groom isn't here either. They tried it a couple of times and it was awful."

Mr. Galsworthy looked at his watch and clucked.

"They do all right," said Mr. Tringle. "O.K. tomorrow."

"Good," said Mr. Galsworthy. "Good. I have a meeting now. As for the groom—well, the groom is not very important at weddings, is he, my dear?" He smiled benignly at the wispy bridesmaid under the impression that she was the bride-to-be.

"You're not nervous, are you, dear?" he continued, taking the wispy girl's hand in his. "No, of course not. Have your young man call me in the morning. I'll put him through his paces. I hate to rush, but I must. Don't worry. Everything will be fine."

Mr. Banks opened his mouth. "But—" A secretarial-looking person bustled down the aisle. "Mrs. Banks? There's a phone call for you in the Rector's office. I believe it's the groom's father and mother. They're at your house and they want to know if the rehearsal's over. I think the groom is with them."

"Sure," said Mr. Tringle cheerily. "Rehearsal's all over. Tell 'em to take it easy. Everybody'll be right home."

"Don't forget to have the groom call me in the morning," said Mr. Galsworthy. "Now don't worry. It will go beautifully tomorrow. I know. You see I've done this before."

"But—" began Mr. Banks. Then he looked around. The bridal party had disappeared, bearing Kay and the wispy girl with them. Mr. and Mrs. Banks shook hands cordially with Mr. Galsworthy and followed them.

On the way out Mr. Banks noted that most of Miss Bellamy's beautifully typed seating lists had been laid on the seats of pews and abandoned. He gathered them up. With the extras there might be enough for a redistribution.

"I do hope—" said Mrs. Banks.

"So do I," agreed her husband.

They went home to dress for the party at the Club.

ALL OVER

THE LAST guest had gone. The last damp hand had been wrung. The bridal party had disappeared noisily to seek bigger and newer adventure. The Dunstans had left. The relatives had returned to the oblivion from which they had emerged. Mr. and Mrs. Banks were alone with the wreckage.

They sat limply in two armchairs which Mr. Banks had dragged down from upstairs. The rug was covered with confetti. The few casual tables which Mr. Massoula had left in the living room were garnished with gray rings. Here and there on the white paint of the sills were the dark signatures of cigarettes. The floral background of the reception line obliterated the fireplace. They stared at it in silence.

"She did look lovely in that going-away suit," said Mrs. Banks dreamily. "Didn't you think it was good-looking?"

Mr. Banks couldn't remember it very well. He knew she had had on something tan. There his detail stopped. But her face was etched forever on his memory as she stood on the landing waiting to throw the bride's bouquet.

"She's a darling," he said.

"Queer the Griswolds didn't come," mused Mrs. Banks. "They accepted and Jane told me they were coming."

"I don't see how you know whether they came or not."

"I know everybody that was here and everybody that wasn't," said Mrs. Banks complacently.

Mr. Banks did not question it. This woman who couldn't remember the details of the most elementary problem for five minutes would remember now and forever everyone who came, everyone who didn't—and also those who crashed the gate.

"My God," exclaimed Mrs. Banks, pressing her hand over her face. "We forgot to ask the Storers."

"We couldn't have," said Mr. Banks.

"We did, though."

"That's terrible. Couldn't we pretend we sent them an invitation? You could call Esther tomorrow and ask her why she didn't come."

"I might at that," said Mrs. Banks.

There was a brief silence. "What are we going to do with all those presents?" asked Mr. Banks.

"I don't know. Somebody's got to pack them, I suppose. I think I'll just leave them as they are for a while."

"I guess that's the best thing," said Mr. Banks.

They lapsed into exhausted silence. In the brain of each a projector was unreeling the film of the day's events. It would have amazed them if they could have known how different the films were.

In another compartment of Mr. Banks' brain an adding machine was relentlessly at work. The figures came pouring out and each time they were greater than before.

"Didn't the decorations in the church look too lovely?" asked Mrs. Banks.

Mr. Banks was startled to discover that he had not even noticed if there were any decorations in the church. It was a relief to know that someone had checked on that dog-robber Tim.

"They were beautiful," he said simply.

"Mr. Tim did a wonderful job considering how little money we gave him to work with," said Mrs. Banks. Her husband started, then pressed his lips together and made no comment.

"I suppose," said Mrs. Banks, "we ought to get out the vacuum cleaner and not leave this whole mess for Delilah tomorrow. I'll go up and change my dress."

Mr. Banks followed her upstairs glumly. Like a fog blowing in from the sea, he could feel the first wisps of depression fingering into his soul.

Here was the place where she had stood. He paused and looked over the rail at the confetti-strewn hall. Queer about places and houses. They remained the same yet they were never the same. By no stretch of the imagination was this the spot from which Kay had tossed her flowers to the waving arms below.

He continued up the stairs, thinking of all the money and energy that was wasted each year visiting the scenes of great events under the impression that they were still the same places.

At the door of the spare room where the presents were on display, he paused, then lit the light and went in. This morning it had been a gay, exciting place, full of anticipation and promise of things to come. The animating spirit was gone. Now it was just a bare room with card tables along the walls covered with china and glassware. It was as impersonal as a store.

He tried to shake off the cloud that was settling over him. In the bathroom a single bottle of champagne rested quietly in the wash-basin. It had been put there by someone just before Mr. Massoula ran out. Heaven knew what for. It was still cold. For a moment he debated whether to open it. Then he turned, went downstairs and got out the vacuum cleaner.

An hour later the last particle of confetti had been transferred to the bulging back of the machine. They sat once more in their chairs in the living room gazing with exhausted faces at the banked greens in front of the fireplace.

On the floor near the edge of the rug Mr. Banks spied a few bits of confetti that the cleaner had overlooked. He rose to pick them up. There seemed to be more just under the edge. He turned back the corner and disclosed a solid mat of multicolored paper.

Without comment he dropped the rug back into place. Mrs. Banks was watching, but said nothing. He went quietly up to the bathroom and drew the cork in the last remaining bottle. From the spare room he selected two of Kay's new champagne glasses and returned to his wife.

Carefully he filled the two glasses and handed one to Mrs. Banks. Behind the floral background the clock on the mantle struck twelve. The whistle of a train from the city hooted in the distance as it rounded the curve into the Fairview Manor station. A dog was barking somewhere.

"How," said Mr. Banks raising his glass.

"How," said Mrs. Banks.

Robert Benchley

LADIES' WILD

IN THE exclusive set (no diphtheria cases allowed) in which I travel, I am known as a heel in the matter of parlor games. I will drink with them, wrassle with them and, now and again, leer at the ladies, but when they bring out the bundles of pencils and the pads of paper and start putting down all the things they can think of beginning with "W," or enumerating each other's bad qualities on a scale of 100 (no hard-feeling results, mind you—just life-long enmity), I tiptoe noisily out of the room and say: "The hell with you."

For this reason, I am not usually included in any little games that may be planned in advance. If they foresee an evening of "Consequences" coming over them, they whisper "Get Benchley out of the

From *After 1903 What?*, copyright, 1938, by Robert Benchley. Reprinted by permission of Harper & Brothers.

house. Get him a horse to ride, or some beads to string—anything to get him out of the way." For, I forgot to tell you, not only am I a non-participant in parlor games, but I am a militant non-participant. I heckle from the sidelines. I throw stones and spit at the players. Hence the nickname: "Sweet Old Bob," or sometimes just the initials.

One night last summer, I detected, from the general stir among the ladies and more effete gents, that I was being eased out of the house. This meant that the gaming was about to begin. But instead of the usual clatter of pencils among the *croupiers,* I saw someone sneaking in with a tray of poker chips. They almost had me out the door when I discovered what was up.

"Well, so long, Bob," they said. "Good bowling to you."

"What's this?" I came back into the room. "Are those poker chips?"

"Sure, they're poker chips. It's all right to play poker, isn't it? The reform administration's gone out."

I assumed a hurt air. In fact, I didn't have to assume it. I was hurt.

"I don't suppose I'm good enough to play poker with you," I said. "All I'm good enough for is to furnish the liquor and the dancing girls."

"Why, we thought you didn't like games. You always act like such a goddamned heel whenever a game is suggested."

"My dear people," I said, trying to be calm, "there are games and games. 'Twenty Questions' is one game, if you will, but poker—why, poker is a man's game. It's my dish. I'm an old newspaperman, you know. Poker is the breath of life to a newspaperman." (As a matter of fact, I never played poker once when I was on a newspaper, and was never allowed to do more than kibitz at the Thanatopsis games of Broun, Adams, Kaufman, and that bunch, but poker is still my favorite game in a small way, or at least it *was.*)

Then there was a great scrambling to get me a chair, and sell me chips. "Old Bob's going to play!" was the cry. "Old Bob likes poker!" People came in from the next room to see what the commotion was, and one woman said that, if I was going to play, she had a headache. (I had ruined a game of "Who Am I?" for her once by blowing out a fuse from the coat-closet.)

As for me, I acted the part to the hilt. I took off my coat, unbuttoned my vest so that just the watch-chain connected it, lighted my pipe, and kept my hat on the back of my head.

"This is the real poker costume," I said. "The way we used to play it down on the old Trib. There ought to be a City News ticker over in the corner to make it seem like home."

"I'm afraid he's going to be too good for us," said one of the more timid ladies. "We play for very small stakes, you know."

"The money doesn't matter," I laughed. "It's the game. And anyway," I added modestly, "I haven't played for a long time. You'll probably take me good." (I wish now that I had made book on that prediction.)

It was to be Dealer's Choice, which should have given me a tip-off right there, with three women at the table, one the dealer.

"This," she announced, looking up into space as if for inspiration, "is going to be 'Hay Fever.'"

"I beg pardon," I said leaning forward.

"'Hay Fever,'" explained one of the men. "The girls like it. One card up, two down, the last two up. One-eyed Jacks, sevens, and nines wild. High-low."

"I thought this was going to be poker," I said.

"From then on you play it just like regular poker," said the dealer.

From then on! My God! Just like regular poker!

Having established myself as an old poker-fan, I didn't want to break down and cry at the very start, so I played the hand through. I say I "played" it. I sat looking at my cards, peeking now and then just to throw a bluff that I knew what I was doing. One-eyed Jacks, sevens, and nines wild, I kept saying that to myself, and puffing very hard at my pipe. After a minute of owlish deliberation, I folded.

The next hand was to be "Whistle Up Your Windpipe," another one which the girls had introduced into the group and which the men, weak-kneed sissies that they were, had allowed to become regulation. This was seven-card stud, first and last cards up, deuces, treys, and red-haired Queens wild, high-low-and-medium. I figured out that I had a very nice straight, bet it as I would have bet a straight in the old days, and was beaten to eleven dollars and sixty cents by a royal straight flush. Amid general laughter, I was told that an ordinary straight in these games is worth no more than a pair of sixes in regular poker. A royal straight flush usually wins. Well, it usually won in the old days, too.

By the time the deal came to me, my pipe had gone out and I had taken my hat off. Between clenched teeth I announced: "And this, my frands, is going to be something *you* may not have heard of. This is going to be *old-fashioned draw-poker*, with *nothing* wild." The women had to have it explained to them, and remarked that they didn't see much fun in that. However, the hand was played. Nobody had anything (in comparison to what they had been having in the boom days), and nobody bet. The hand was over in a minute and a half, amid terrific silence.

That was the chief horror of this epidemic of "Whistle Up Your Windpipe," "Beezy-Weezy," and "Mice Afloat." It made old-fashioned stud seem tame, even to me. Every time it came to me, I elected the old game, just out of spite, but nobody's heart was in it. I became the spoil-sport of the party again, and once or twice I caught them trying to slip the deal past me, as if by mistake. Even a round of jack-pots netted nothing in the way of excitement, and even when I won one on a full-house, there was no savour to the victory, as I had to explain to the women what a full-house was. They thought that I was making up my own rules. Nothing as small as a full-house had ever been seen in that game.

The Big Newspaper Man was taken for exactly sixty-one dollars and eight cents when the game broke up at four A. M. Two of the women were the big winners. They had finally got it down to a game where everything was wild but the black nines, and everyone was trying for "low."

From now on I not only walk out on "Twenty Questions" and "Who Am I?" but, when there are ladies present (God *bless* them!), I walk out on poker. And a fine state of affairs it is when an old newspaperman has to walk out on poker!

Russell Lynes

THE NEW SNOBBISM

THERE was a time not long ago when a snob was a snob and as easy to recognize as a cock pheasant. In the days when Ward McAllister was the arbiter of Newport society and when there were precisely four hundred souls in New York worth knowing and only "nobodies" lived west of the Alleghenies, snobbishness was a nice

From *Snobs*, by Russell Lynes, copyright, 1950, by Harper & Brothers.

clean-cut business that made careers for otherwise unoccupied women and gave purpose to otherwise barren lives. In those days the social order was stratified as tidily as the terracing of an Italian garden, and a man could take his snobs or leave them. But now the social snob, while not extinct, has gone underground (except for professionals such as head waiters and metropolitan-hotel room clerks), and snobbery has emerged in a whole new set of guises, for it is as indigenous to man's nature as ambition and a great deal easier to exercise.

Snobbery has assumed so many guises, in fact, that it is, I believe, time that someone attempt to impose order on what is at best a confused situation. There are a few basic categories of snobs that seem to include most of the more common species that one is likely to encounter, or, indeed, to be. None of these categories is new; there have always been, I presume, snobs of every sort,[1] but now that the pre-eminence of the social variety has been submerged in a wave of political and economic egalitarianism, and now that we find ourselves in an era in which the social scientists believe that it is somehow good for us to be ticketed and classified, let us sort out the most common practitioners of the sneer.

The Intellectual Snob is of such distinguished lineage and comes from such established precedent that he is dignified by a mention in Webster's ("one who repels the advances of those whom he regards as his inferiors; as, an intellectual snob"). The other categories are less well known and less well documented. For convenience, let us call Them the Regional Snobs, the Moral Snobs, the Sensual Snobs, the Emotional Snobs, the Physical Snobs, the Occupational Snobs, and, finally, the Reverse Snobs or Antisnob Snobs. Before we examine these, we should be aware that economic and social boundaries, while they may occasionally serve as guide ropes, are on the whole unimportant in considering the various forms of condescension and the various attitudes of superiority that distinguish the true snob from the merely vain man, woman, or child.

Snobbishness, as we will use the word, implies both an upward and a downward movement—a scramble upward to emulate or outdo those whose position excels one's own, and a look downward on (or sometimes straight through) those less happily endowed than one's self. The true snob never rests; there is always a higher goal to attain, and there are, by the same token, always more and more people to

[1] It is 102 years since William Makepeace Thackeray published his *Book of Snobs*, a series of facetious essays that originally appeared in *Punch*. Mr. Thackeray's snobs are largely of the social sort.

look down upon. The snob is almost by definition insecure in his social (in the larger sense) relationships, and he resorts to snobbishness as a means of massaging his ego. Since scarcely anyone is so secure that his ego does not sometimes need a certain amount of external manipulation, there is scarcely anyone who isn't a snob of some sort. As a matter of fact the gods of the Greeks and the Romans were frightful snobs, morally, physically, and emotionally, and it is not uncommon for civilized peoples to worship snobbery. It is the Christian religion that promoted the virtue of humility for us, and of all the virtues it is the most difficult to come by. Let us not, then, be snobbish about snobs—at least not yet.

It is not my intention to apply the scientific method to the definition of the categories which we shall examine, though each species will be seen to have its subspecies and each subspecies to have many variants. I mean this to be suggestive, merely a sketch that will enable the reader to glimpse the vast possibilities that a methodical study of snobs by a diligent social scientist might uncover.

II

Our first category is the Regional Snobs, commonly known in the South as Virginians, in the West as Californians, and in the East as Bostonians. This, however, should be recognized for what it is, a mere colloquialism. The Regional Snob can come from anywhere, and is readily distinguished by his patronizing attitude toward anywhere else. He lets it be known that there is no place to match the seat of his origin; indeed, he seems surprised or amused that people in other places are so much like people. The Asturians who live in the north of Spain, for example, look with special distaste on the citizens of the neighboring province, Galicia, and they have a saying that "a Galician is the animal that most closely resembles a human being." In Texas it is said that you should never ask a man where he comes from. "If he's a Texan," they say, "he'll tell you. If he's not don't embarrass him." These are not as extreme cases as they might seem. It was recorded a decade ago that a boy who lived on Martha's Vineyard, an island off the Massachusetts coast, was assigned the problem in school of writing a composition about the then Duce of Italy. His paper started with the sentence: "Mussolini is an off-islander."

But let us consider more common types of Regional Snobs. In Vermont, for example, the Regional Snob is generally called a "native" to distinguish him from the group known as "summer people." The aloofness of the Vermont native, a man proud of his thrift, of the bleakness of his winters, and especially of the fact that he has managed to squeeze a living out of rocky hillsides and out of "summer people," [2] has a special laconic quality that is guaranteed to freeze the marrow of, say, a Texan. This kind of Regional snobbism is of the *We've had it tougher than anybody* variety, and is the opposite of the California type which is of the *We know how to live better than you do* kind, or of the Gracious Living types found in the South, notably in Virginia, in South Carolina, and in the New Orleans vicinity.

These types are, more or less, Area Snobs and should be distinguished from the local or home-town varieties which demonstrate certain cultural patterns quite different from those found in general geographical areas. The local snob does not even in many cases recognize his home town as anything very special; his vision may be myopic to the extent of permitting everything beyond the end of his particular street to go out of focus. "The other side of the tracks" is a phrase less frequently heard than it was a generation or so ago. We live in an age of "developments"—real estate developments, housing developments, community developments—of "projects" and of subdivisions, and the railroad tracks have lost some of their social significance in this age of busses and automobiles. So we have subdivision dwellers looking down upon development dwellers, and development dwellers turning their heads away from project dwellers, and project dwellers scornful of tenement dwellers. But the genuine home-town snob is rather more special than any of these.

Boston is too well known for its special brand of provincial hauteur to need discussion here, but the New York brand is less well documented and will serve to demonstrate one of the extreme forms of local snobbism. This is the Cultural Capital variety, or *Anything or anybody of any interest comes here* kind, that makes the New Yorker when visiting in any other city assume an air of condescension that has both an overhead spin and a reverse twist. "You know," the New Yorker[3] will say when visiting a city in the Middle West, "I think it's really terribly interesting *out here.*" It is a wonder that so few New Yorkers get their throats cut in what they think of as (but do not call)

---

[2] And more recently, with the advent of the Ski Snobs, out of "winter people" as well.
[3] Not to be confused with the magazine of the same name. It is not within the scope of this essay to discuss institutional snobbism.

"the provinces." In its most advanced forms Cultural Capital Snobbism will bend all the way over backward and touch its heels with its hair with some such observation as: "I think New Yorkers are the most provincial people in the world, don't you?" The born and bred New Yorker is rare (or at least thinks of himself as rare), and in general the New Yorker by adoption is the more virulent of the species.

At the other end of the scale we find Small Town Snobbism: the *I have lived here longer than anyone* type vies with the type who makes much of the fact that only people who rub elbows with the members of a small community really understand the meaning of life. This latter type, like the Cultural Capital Snob, is usually a member of the community by adoption, having fled from the city in order to discover what he calls "real values." Sometimes the members of this group are summer people gone native who retain certain characteristic attributes of their type such as station wagons, and dress themselves in more elaborately rural costumes (blue jeans, checked wool shirts, even straw hats) than any genuinely rural inhabitant would consider proper or necessary. Another variant of this species is the ex-urbanite who buys a farm in order to "get next to the soil." These might be called the Eternal Verities Snobs, Back to the Land Division, and are very likely to be authors.[4]

Before we proceed to our next category, there is one offshoot of the Regional Snobs which bears brief mention: The World Is My Home species,[5] made up of people who pride themselves on the fact that they are as much at home in Shepheard's Hotel in Cairo as in the Casino at Monte Carlo or in the Ritz Bar in Paris or in the Pump Room in Chicago or in less expensive saloons in any of these places. The members of this category like to think of themselves as "the international set" and are frequently remittance men, decayed nobility, career diplomats, overseas representatives (and their wives) of American industries, wealthy divorcees, or rich refugees. They regard every international problem or crisis chiefly as a personal inconvenience, and every visa in their passports as a mark of sophistication. The natives of any place they visit have no other function but to serve them, and their technique for insulting waiters is unsurpassed. Although the world is their home, they are in one sense the most provincial snobs of all, for their real world consists of a few thousand wanderers, and their horizons are limited to the chips on the table, the bottles on the

---

[4] Indeed, Connecticut and Bucks County have been so overrun by authors that a real farmer can hardly afford to buy land there.

[5] Not to be confused with the One World Snobs.

bar, and the crystals in the chandeliers of hotel dining rooms, and when out of doors they darken their little world with sun glasses.[6] They have an unmitigated scorn for all tourists and are ashamed and embarrassed by their compatriots who travel abroad.

It is probable that as the world grows smaller, Regional Snobbism will increase. It is a logical antidote to political efforts to make man love his neighbor.

III

Like the Regional Snobs, the number of Moral Snobs is legion and they love their neighbors no more dearly. Oscar Wilde, a really accomplished snob, said that "Morality is simply the attitude we adopt toward people we personally dislike." But the Moral Snob carries it further than that; his snobbishness extends to people he doesn't even know. Morality is both a public and a private matter, to be sure, and it is characteristic of the Moral Snob to put a good deal of ornamental fretwork on his public façade and let the private places of his personality be slovenly. To call him a hypocrite would be to attribute vices to his virtues; he is not so positive a character as that. He does not necessarily want to get away with anything, but he is always quite sure that everyone else does, or would if he didn't keep a sharp eye on them.

In our day there are two main categories of Moral Snobs—the Religious Snobs and the Tolerance Snobs. In mentioning the former, I am aware that I am on delicate ground, but the Religious Snobs are identified with no particular sect or creed, and the true believer is rarely, if ever, snobbish about it. The only thing that they seem to have in common is the conviction that those who disapprove of their faith or the methods by which they try to spread it are "bigots." [7]

[6] There are two important variants of this species: (1) the Language Snob, who pretends to five or six languages and sprinkles his conversation with French, Spanish, and German phrases, and (2) the Reverse Language Snob, who prides himself on getting along everywhere with his native tongue on the assumption that anyone who doesn't know it is a fool or worse.

[7] The most extreme example of this type of snobbism I have heard of is credited to the family of the Duc de Levis-Mirepoix, one of the oldest important French titles, that dates back to the ninth century. The family is purported to be descended from the sister of the Virgin Mary, and when the members of the Levis-Mirepoix family pray, they are said to say: "*Ave Maria, ma cousine . . .*"

Sometimes opposed to the Religious Snob and sometimes allied with him is the Tolerance Snob, a species of comparatively recent origin. It should be noted that he turns the tables on the Religious Snob for lack of tolerance toward disbelievers and backsliders, and in such cases he often calls the Religious Snob a "bigot." The bigot is a most useful foil to the Tolerance Snob. But whether he is at logger-heads with the Religious Snob or not, the *I am more tolerant than anybody* Snob has a special predilection for getting his name printed on the letterheads of societies for the prevention and furthering of things.

In contrast with the Moral Snobs are the Sensual Snobs who take special pride in being able to wrest more pleasure per cell from the flesh than anyone else. In this general category which is even more elastic than I mean to make it we find the Food and Drink, the Sex, the Indolence, and the Health and Hygiene Snobs.

The Food and Drink species is almost too common to require more than a passing word. In Food the Herb Snobs while somewhat old-fashioned still persist; but this species, I believe, is less in the ascendancy now than the Pot Luck Snobs, Casserole Division, or the *This is something I just threw together at the last minute* species. The mussels-snails-brains-and-garlic group continues to operate, especially in areas where mussels, snails, brains, and garlic are still considered somewhat outrageous, and the Plain American Food Group ("If you want a good cup of coffee and a decent hamburger, eat in a diner") flourishes in metropolitan areas where good foreign cooking is commonplace.

The Foreign Food Snob often can be identified by his attitude of frustration. The "little place" that he discovered and which used to be so good has always just recently gone to pot. "You know how it is," he says. "The frogs legs Provençal used to be superb, but now the place has got popular, and the food isn't fit to eat any more."

The Drink Snobs are, of all categories, the easiest to identify since the rules are so well established. They insist that their whisky be bonded; they know what proof it is; and they drink it neat or "on the rocks"; their Scotch is "V.O." or "V.V.O."; their martinis are as dry as almost no vermouth can make them (in restaurants where they suspect the martinis may be somewhat amber in hue they order Gibsons and remove the onions); and they always nod at the waiter after looking at the date on a bottle of wine. Only the genuine connoisseur has the self-assurance to send back a bottle of wine. Some Drink Snobs take special pride in the amount they can consume and not show it;

others take special pride in having a worse hangover than anybody ever had before.

The Sex Snobs have been adequately documented by the Physiology Department of Indiana University. It may, however, be interesting to note that the publication of Dr. Kinsey's first volume, *Sexual Behavior in the Human Male*, produced two new manifestations of the Sex Snob: first, those of the *I could tell Kinsey a thing or two* variety; and second, the species that insisted that the excitement about the book was all nonsense—"Why I've known that for years." The attitude of the British toward the Kinsey Report reveals an interesting provincialism. I was told by Dr. Kinsey that in general the reaction of the British professional and, if I may be permitted the phrase, the lay press, was: "No doubt this is all very true about Americans, but we are not interested. The British don't behave like that."

The Indolence Snobs, on the other hand, have been epitomized by an Englishman, Cyril Connolly, in his book, *The Unquiet Grave*. "Others merely live," he wrote; "I vegetate." An interesting counterpart to Mr. Connolly's form of snobbism is to be found in those who make a great show of doing nothing, of sleeping late, of lying in the sun, of always having time to amuse themselves and their friends, and who at the same time produce a great deal of work. These are the people who express their superiority by saying, "I just tossed off this novel in my spare time," or, "I just thought of this new international trade combine over a game of canasta in Miami one evening."

The Health and Hygiene Snobs may more properly belong with the Moral Snobs than with the Sensual Snobs. There is no denying, however, that there is sensual pleasure in the subjugation of the flesh, and that this is part of the routine behavior of the Health and Hygiene Snob. It is a far stronger motive than mere laziness that keeps a man or woman horizontal in the hot sun for a few hours in order to turn first red and then brown; it is certainly not morality that sends men and women to gymnasiums to reduce one portion of the anatomy and exaggerate another; nor is it laziness that makes them diet, abstain from (or at least be ostentatiously moderate about) liquor, and get to bed at what they call "a reasonable hour." It is the delight of being able to look down upon those who, to use their phrase, "don't take proper care of themselves." Sex, of course, enters strongly into this, but then so does a feeling of moral superiority. I have no doubt that the social scientists will in time be able to isolate the Health and Hygiene Snob from the Moral Snob.

While we are on the subject of the body, let us not overlook the

Physical Prowess Snobs, more common among males than among females, but by no means limited to one sex. The Physical Prowess Snob is not necessarily an expert athlete; indeed he is likely not to be. It is the mediocre tennis player, for example, hitting everything hard if inaccurately, who is lofty about the player who may be able to beat him merely by getting the ball back.

No matter what you may think of the Sensual Snobs, it cannot be denied that, unlike the Moral Snobs, they are a great pleasure to themselves.

IV

Since the emotions carry us rapidly in dangerous directions and soon lead us to the darkest corners of man's nature, we must proceed to the dissection of the Emotional Snobs with caution. This is the *I feel things more deeply than anybody* variety, and there is likely to be at least one in every family.

Probably the largest single subdivision of this category is the Love Snob, a type which finds its roots among adolescents, who since they are having their first encounter with sexual love, believe that no one has ever been so in love before. Their intolerance of their juniors is matched only by their scorn for their elders, and this can set a pattern for adult love that is difficult to break. The so-called "great lovers" do not, I believe, belong in the Love Snob category but rather in that of the Sex Snob. It was surely not about the intensity of his emotions that Don Giovanni, with his list of 1,100 ladies, was vain.

The Mother Love Snob, or *I give my all for my children* type, is not uncommon among women who are not Sex Snobs, and it is probable that the second volume of the Kinsey Report may shed some light on this. The Filial Love Snob, or Mom Snob, is not in my experience nearly so common as English authors, such as Geoffrey Gorer, or Americans, such as Philip Wylie, contend that it is. That is not to say that the exploitation of Mom Snobbery by the florists once a year has not given it at least a seasonal boost.

The Marital and/or Soul Mate Snobs are not rare, though they are particularly tiresome because they are, by the very nature of their snobbery, raised to a higher power. Since it takes two to make Soul Mates, they are twice as tiresome as other snobs.

The Popularity Snobs also belong in the Emotional group; in a sense they are everybody's Soul Mate. To use their own vernacular, they have a "way with people" and can "get along with anybody." Theirs is the hauteur of affable condescension, and traditionally the species is common among traveling salesmen, Rotarians, public relations counselors, and politicians, though it would be a mistake not to recognize the far wider ramifications of this type wherever we meet them. Mass demonstrations of Popularity Snobbism are known as conventions.[8] The typical member of this species rarely uses the form "mister" in addressing anyone, no matter how brief or perfunctory the acquaintance. He is strictly a first-name man, and has little respect for anyone's dignity or privacy. He assumes that everybody loves him, and he reasons that there is no privacy in a public love affair.

By contrast the Unpopularity Snob, or *Nobody can get along with me* type, takes two principal forms.[9] The first is an imperious and often petulant species who by dint of the loftiness of his position or intellect makes much of the fact that he can't be bothered with boors and idiots. He works with his door closed; he throws all second-class mail into the wastebasket without opening it; and he never seems to be able to remember anyone's name, or if he does, he mispronounces it. When you meet him, he says "hello," but looks past you, as though you were obstructing his view. The second is the sensitive, or *I'm too special*, type who is "misunderstood" by crass and materialistic people. This species is likely to gravitate in the general direction of the arts and crafts and sooner or later to metropolitan areas.

v

Somewhere between the Emotional Snobs and the Intellectual Snobs[10] are the Sensitivity or Taste Snobs—those who are scornful of any whose aesthetic antennae they consider less receptive than their own. It is customary, I believe, to classify the Art Snobs, the Literary Snobs, and the Musical Snobs with the Intellectual Snobs, but it seems to me that they belong in a limbo between the Emotional and the

[8] College Reunions also figure in this category. They provide opportunities for the temporary renewal of Popularity Snobbism in those who were popular in college but have been slipping ever since.
[9] The persistence of one type of Unpopularity Snob is demonstrated by the number of adults who take special care to make the point that anybody who amounts to anything was "unhappy in school." It is likely to express itself in some such direct statement as "I was the most unpopular boy (girl) in my class."
[10] So commonly known and, as we have noted, so well established as to need no discussion in this brief survey.

Intellectual categories, with plenty of latitude to permit them to jump either way.[11] Furthermore the matter of taste comprehends more than just the arts (and, as we shall see, includes certain other vagaries of man's predilection for lording it over man). But let us take the arts first.

To categorize the Art Snobs into all of their many subdivisions would be an intricate and, I am afraid, tiresome business. We would, for example, have to consider the various shadings that range all the way from the Traditionalist or Permanent Value Snobs to the Modern or *I always keep an open mind* group. There are, however, a few basic behavior patterns that betray the Art Snob at any level. In a gallery he can be observed to stand back from a picture at some distance, his head cocked slightly to one side, and then after a rather long period of gazing (during which he may occasionally squint his eyes) he will approach to within a few inches of the picture and examine the brush-work; he will then return to his former distant position, give the picture another glance, and walk away. The Art Snob can be recognized in the home (*i.e.* your home) by the quick look he gives the pictures on your walls, quick but penetrating, as though he were undressing them. This is followed either by complete and obviously pained silence or by a comment such as, "That's really a very pleasant little water color you have there." In his own house his manner is also slightly deprecating. If you admire a print on his wall, he is likely to say, "I'm glad you like it. It's really not bad considering it is such a late impression." Or if he is in the uppermost reaches of Art Snobs and owns an "old master" which you admire, he will say, "Of course Berenson lists it as a Barna da Sienna, but I've never satisfied myself that it isn't from the hand of one of his pupils."

The Literary Snob has not only read the book you are reading but takes pleasure in telling you the names of all the earlier and more obscure books by the same author, and why each one was superior to the better known one that has come to your attention.

Musical Snobs are in general of two sorts—Classical Snobs and Jazz Snobs. The former can sometimes be identified at concerts because they keep their eyes closed. This can for obvious reasons be misleading, but if closed eyes are accompanied by a regular movement of the

[11] It is interesting to note in connection with the publication of a new (1950) typographically eccentric magazine devoted to taste, that as an undergraduate Thackeray at Cambridge in 1829 contributed to a magazine called the *Snob*. An advertisement described it as follows: "Each number contained only six pages . . . printed on tinted paper of different colors, green, pink, and yellow." The *Snob* lasted for eleven numbers.

hands in time with the music, it is clear that the listener is beating time to himself. This is characteristic of the lowest orders of Classical Snob. If he has a score of the music which he follows while it is being played, he may be a professional musician looking for subtleties of interpretation; he may, on the other hand, merely be a higher order of Classical Snob. The surest way to identify the Classical Snob is to see whether he comes back after the intermission or not; if he stays only for the more difficult or abstruse part of the program and ignores the more popular portion, he is either a snob or a professional critic, or possibly both.

Musical Snobs, Jazz Division, beat time not with their hands but with their feet. They do not talk about records or recordings but about specific choruses, solo passages, or "breaks." They know the dates and numbers of original pressings and occasionally they collect never-played records much the way some book collectors prefer rare copies with uncut pages. They are well grounded in the brand of jazz they refer to as "authentic" (New Orleans, Memphis, Chicago) and they are extremely partisan about what they consider to be "advanced" (Progressive Jazz, Bebop, or even Dixieland). There are some over-tones of social and racial snobbery in the way Jazz Snobs identify them-selves with jazz musicians.

Also among the Taste Snobs are to be found the Clothes Snobs, both male and female. In this instance the female is a good deal more interesting and varied than the male, for while the male "sharp dress-ers" are snobs of a sort, there is only one male Dress Snob who needs to arrest our attention: the Conservative Dress Snob. The buttons on the sleeves of his jacket actually unbutton. There is no padding on his shoulders. The collar of his shirt is a little too high for him, so that it bulges and wrinkles slightly, and it buttons down. He cares deeply about good leather and good tweed, but most of all he cares about being conspicuously inconspicuous.

The female Dress Snobs offer a far more complicated range of types and it requires some temerity on the part of a man to broach this subject at all. In general, however, women seem to fall into the following categories of sartorial superiority:

(1) The Underdressed Snob, who wouldn't be caught dead at a cock-tail party in a cocktail dress, and a similar type, the next on our list. . . .

(2) The Basic Dress Snob, who believes that she has so much person-ality that she can get away anywhere in a simple black ("basic") dress and one piece of "heirloom" jewelry.

(3) The Good Quality Snob, or wearer of muted tweeds, cut almost exactly the same from year to year, often with a hat of the same material. This type is native to the Boston North Shore, the Chicago North Shore, the North Shore of Long Island, to Westchester County, the Philadelphia Main Line, the Peninsula Area of San Francisco, etc. It rides horses and is rare in Southern California, except for Pasadena.

(4) The Band Box Snob—common among professional fashion models and among other young women trying to make their way in the big city. They look as though they had just stepped out of *Vogue* or *Mademoiselle*. They are never ahead of fashion, but they are screamingly up to date.

(5) The Dowdy, or *Who the hell cares about fashion*, Snob.

(6) The Personal Style, or *I know more about my type than the experts*, Snob. This final type considers her taste to be above the whims of mere fashion. She is so chic that she believes that it is un-chic to be merely fashionable.[12]

Good taste is everyone's prerogative (no one willingly confesses to bad taste), and so nearly everyone is a Taste Snob of one sort or another, and often of many sorts at the same time.

VI

Our next category, the Occupational or Job Snobs, are of two sorts: those who are snobbish about the kind of occupation by which they live, and those who are snobbish about how they perform in their occupation. Few women, for example, are snobbish about being housekeepers; many are snobbish about the way they keep house. Many men, on the other hand, are snobbish about the positions they hold and less snobbish about how they perform in them. But first let's take the women. The woman whose dearest ambition is an absolutely well-ordered and efficiently run house looks down upon the woman who firmly believes that it is nonsense to spend so much time over the household that there is not time for what she calls "life." She in turn looks down upon the whole-souled housekeeper. It boils down to a conflict between two aphorisms—"cleanliness is next to godliness" and "a little dirt never hurt anybody"—which, if we weren't careful, would lead us back to our discussion of Moral Snobs. Of course both of these

[12] The outstanding example of this in our time is the Queen Mother of England.

types are looked upon with scorn by the female Career Snob who manages with overbearing aplomb both a job and a household.

The hierarchy within which men work is quite different, and makes quite different demands. The professional man feels somewhat lordly toward the businessman or "money grubber" and considers him lacking in sensibility and intellectual curiosity and near-sighted to the point of seeing nothing beyond the sales chart but the golf course or the bridge table. He is likely to blame the world's ills on the businessman's greed and lack of cultural understanding. The businessman, on the other hand, thinks of many professional men as "dreamers" and "idealists" or even as "pantywaists." This applies especially to artists, writers, actors, musicians, scholars, and editors. The businessman is less likely to be snobbish about physicians, lawyers, and engineers because he considers them, like himself, to be "practical" men. His most unlimited scorn is for bureaucrats who "have never met a payroll."

Performance on the job is less likely to matter than position, as I have said, but there is the Efficiency Snob whose pose is primarily one of crispness. He answers the phone by barking just his last name; he is inclined to have rows of buttons on his telephone or desk and almost no papers. His memoranda are brief to the point of being curt, he considers the word "please" something that has no place among desks and typewriters, and he wants things done "soonest." He thinks of himself as a "trouble shooter" and makes lists of possible troubles to shoot. As each one is shot, it is crossed off the list with a firm black line. Accomplishment is measured by the number of black lines, and everyone who doesn't measure up to his particular standards of efficiency is "hopeless." The reverse of this type, also common, is the man who lives behind a mess of papers, pencils, and paper clips and "can never find anything" and yet manages to get out the work.

The results produced by the Efficiency Snob and the Inefficiency Snob are just about the same.

Performance off the job often reveals the Manual Dexterity Snob who can do complicated mechanical things with his hands and who considers all who can't to be fumbling idiots, and the opposite of this, the All-Thumbs Snob, commonly found among women. Men who are all thumbs are sometimes reticent about it; women rarely are.

VII

We have noted as we went along that almost every kind of snobbism has its opposite; the Moral Snob contrasts with the Sensual Snob, the Manual Dexterity Snob with the All-Thumbs Snob, the Efficiency Snob with the Inefficiency Snob, and so on. But these contrasting sources of the sneer should not be confused with our final category, the Reverse Snob or Antisnob Snob. This is the snob who finds snobbery so distasteful that he (or she) is extremely snobbish about nearly everybody since nearly everybody is a snob about something. This is the man who tries so hard to be "natural," so hard to be "just folks," so hard to avoid having anyone else think he is a snob, that he plays a game which (if I may be forgiven for being a Language Snob for a moment) is *faux naïf.* He would not, for example, ever be caught using a foreign phrase, as I have, lest it be thought pretentious even when it serves better than any other he can think of to convey its meaning. Or if he is forced to use it (or even a foreign name, let's say) he Americanizes its pronunciation lest anyone think him upstage.[13] He makes much of the fact that simple, uneducated people are wiser and nicer than sophisticated and educated people, even wise and nice educated people. He plays down his own education and accomplishments with an elaborate display of modesty and is likely to introduce a very erudite and perceptive observation with the phrase, "Of course I know so little about this I have no right to an opinion," or, "I know this is probably stupid of me, but . . ." Of all the snobs the Reverse Snob is probably the most snobbish; he is so sure of himself that he intentionally puts other people in a position where they have to play his game or feel like snobs themselves. The false simplicity of the Reverse Snob stands in direct and glaring contrast to the genuinely modest man.

By and large it is only the very great who are not snobbish at all. They are the ones who are modest about their accomplishments because they have devoted their lives to achieving some kind of understanding and so have developed a deep tolerance for ignorance. By the same token the serious professionals in any field are not likely to be snobbish about other serious professionals, whether they are doctors or actors or writers or mechanics or businessmen or masons or even,

[13] "They spell it Vinci and pronounce it Vinchy; foreigners always spell better than they pronounce." Mark Twain, *The Innocents Abroad.*

let it be said, housekeepers. As we noted at the outset, it is those who are unsure of themselves and are seeking security in their social relationships who have provided us with this incomplete list of Snobs.

It will not have escaped the reader (and so I might as well admit it) that this cursory attempt to classify and define snobs is an example not only of Intellectual Snobbism but of Moral, Sensual, Occupational, Political, Emotional, and above all of Reverse or Antisnob Snobbism. I am sure there is no greater snob than a snob who thinks he can define a snob.

J. P. McEvoy

FROM HOST TO GUEST IN ONE GENERATION

IT STARTED back in the sixth grade. I liked the sixth grade, especially Rip Van Winkle and the fun he had up in the Catskill Mountains. Someday, I said to myself, I am going to live in the Catskills. . . .

It was the old spinning wheel that got me. I really bought it rather than the house. Later I found it was a prop. For many years after that I saw the same old spinning wheel in many houses for sale—a technique similar to salting a gold mine. But there was a grand smell of nuts and apples and old wood-smoke about the place. And more than that, I had a Catskill right in the back yard.

I was happy. At last I was away from it all. I will keep it a very small house, I said to myself. One bathroom, one guest room. I am 125 miles away from New York City, I said. I will have no visitors, no guests.

So I fixed up a little corncrib for a studio in which to write plays and novels—novels that would electrify the country. Only the sound of falling leaves to lull me, and a faint distant rumble of ninepins. . . .

Now I know that you can't keep a country place from growing. As the children grew larger their room grew smaller. So that meant a wing and a bathroom and that meant more hot water, a larger water heater and a larger furnace, which meant enlarging the basement. And as long as you're enlarging the basement, why not make some store-rooms? Also while you are adding a wing it would be easy to enlarge the kitchen. The old oil stove was too small so we put in a gas stove which meant a little house for the gas cylinders—and why not make it larger and use it for the pumphouse?

Now the house had a wing which unbalanced it so it needed another wing, with a music room. Its windows opened up a view which made a terrace imperative. But a terrace needed a roof to keep off the sun and as long as you had a roof you might as well enclose it, for use in the winter. But not without more radiators, which meant a bigger furnace and a larger basement. Finally I learned to leave a gang of workmen in the basement permanently. They had a camp and lived down there and their singing in the evening after a hard day's work was cheerful indeed.

I forgot the guest room we put in the children's wing for the children's guests. So now we had two guest rooms and in some mysterious way that became known all over New York State. From there it spread rapidly West until in almost any town you went you saw little groups of people gathered, saying, "You know the McEvoys up in the Catskills have some guest rooms. Why don't we drop in on them on our way East?"

The solution is a guest house, I said to no one in particular. But a builder heard me. There was always a builder standing around. And in no time at all I had a guest house. It had guest rooms and a living room which I later learned was also a guest room because my guests brought guests and complained sometimes they had no room for them. Some of the guests fixed up a little kitchen in the guest house and lived there unmolested for weeks. They built their own path to the swimming pool . . .

The swimming pool. While you're at it make it big enough, somebody said. Maybe it was I. So I ordered one 60 feet long and so much dirt came out of the hole I had to hire a gardener to make terraces out of it. After that I had to keep the gardener all year round to take care of the terraces. And then he got married and had a baby so I had to build him a house. The swimming pool was incomplete without a bath house and that meant more plumbing which together with the guest house and the gardener's house overtaxed the septic tank so we had to put in a bigger septic tank which meant moving the garden, enlarging the terraces, hiring another gardener, and putting a wing on the garage with a room in it for him and another bathroom—which meant more plumbing.

All this time I had no place for guests' cars and no rooms for their servants, so I enlarged the garage, adding more servants' rooms upstairs, which meant more plumbing and a still larger septic tank—so the garden grew larger which called for more gardeners, more rooms for gardeners—and more plumbing.

The children and their guests had no place to play except a tennis court and a swimming pool so why not fix up the old barn—very simple, you don't have to spend much money on it. The old barn wound up with a hardwood floor for dancing, a fireplace big enough to roast an ox, a billiard table and a system for amplifying dance records.

The indoor fireplace naturally suggested an outdoor one so a large stone terrace was added with some ovens and a motor-driven rotisserie which could broil a dozen chickens at once. Since it could it did. And that meant more guests because waste is a sin.

But what is a country place without horses? It's pretty nearly all right I can tell you now. But then I was young and didn't know, so I bought a horse. But all of us couldn't ride one horse so soon it was a horse apiece. And you could hardly ask guests to bring their horses from New York. So as we added stalls for more horses we added rooms for more grooms. Sometimes I used to wonder how just one horse could have started that enormous development growing so rapidly in the lower orchard. But I didn't get a chance to do much wondering because I was too busy supporting all this. I built a series of studios to work in but the development soon caught up with me and I had to move farther and farther out into the woods. The mornings I used to devote to writing were now spent in overseeing this busy subdivision. The afternoons were spent in conferences with my contractors and engineers. The nights in poring over my books—checkbooks.

In the same artless fashion the guest list expanded. Now I had permanent guests, semi-permanent guests, week-end guests, guests for the night, drop-in guests, guests on the American Plan, on the European Plan, guests for breakfast only, guests for swimming only, guests for tennis and tea. There were other classifications such as social guests, business guests, old pals, new friends, old teachers, cousins of the governess, shipboard acquaintances and distant relatives. There were guests who came up to see the tulips and were still there to help trim the Christmas tree.

It wasn't exactly a circle—it was a kind of a spiral, and I couldn't see where it was going because I never thought to look. One night I did pause, I remember, because there was a 10-acre parking field near the barn and I was having a party and the servants came in to say there was no more room for the cars. I wondered if maybe this whole thing was getting a little bit out of hand. I left the party several times and went to other parties, but when I came back it was still going with band blaring and lights blazing and the rollicking sound of laughter and screams and breaking glass, occasionally punctuated by the shrill sirens of the state troopers.

That was only one of many times the place was so full I had to go to New York to sleep. Gradually I found myself going there more and more for repose and meditation. And it was then I made a great discovery: that if you really want to be alone and get away from it all take the smallest room in the biggest hotel in the largest city in the world. I remember I woke up and the room was so quiet I was afraid—I wasn't used to this. I called room service and had my breakfast sent up, the waiter clucking over me like a mother hen. I read the morning paper through without one single interruption. There was no knock on the door—no ring on the phone. I was lost in the magic of it all and then I understood—and I loved it. I was a guest!

Why, I could leave all the tumult and the shouting behind me. And by the eternal I will. And by the eternal I did. I sent my secretary up to the country to close the place, pack the children off to school, sell the horses, and break the news gently to the guests that the party was over. She came back pale and wan to report that everything was all right except some of the guests insisted on two weeks' notice, and others had retreated into the woods, dug trenches and were going to put up a fight about it. This situation was adjusted by giving the former notice—and the latter the woods. This destroyed the amateur standing of the remaining guests because now they had to pay taxes on the house they built there.

I have stayed in a lot of other places since I became a guest. The hotel room was all right for a start, but I could hardly make a career out of it. Many friends had invited me to be their guest. But I had been too busy being a perfect host. Now I put the same time and energy into being a perfect guest. From host to guest in one generation—that was the complete cycle I had achieved.

Sometimes I dream I am a host again and I am building bigger and better guest houses. I wake up screaming so loud my host asks me the next day if anything disturbed me during the night. How can I tell him about such a dream? I might start him thinking—the last thing I want. I want my host to be happy. I want him to pass me on to other hosts, equally happy.

For now I am collecting hosts, with all the enthusiasm I once collected guests. Hosts, nothing else. I don't care any more for money; I have no ambition for fame. All I want now is an acre of ground planted in fruit trees and flowers. And in the middle of it a little house. And in the house a guest room. And in the guest room—me!

II. NEW ENGLAND

Frank Sullivan

QUIGLEY 873

PERHAPS no class of scientist is more apt to encounter the unexpected in the course of his work than the student of folklore. My wife and I appreciated this last summer when we discovered the refreshingly unique Lovers' Leap at Wassamattawichez Notch, New Hampshire, which for research purposes we have catalogued as Quigley 873.

My wife, Dr. Johanna Bracegirdle Quigley, and myself (Professor W. Hungerford Quigley) may possibly be recognized as coauthors of "The Role of the Lovers' Leap in American Folklore," the rather monumental study that, we flatter ourselves, has effected a sweeping change in thought on the subject since its publication, a decade ago. We narrowed our field of research to the Lovers' Leap because it seemed to us not only a fascinating but a neglected aspect of folklore, and we have never regretted our decision. Dr. Johanna, a mite more thorough as a scientist than am I, has several times actually made the jump from a Lovers' Leap, just to get the feel of the thing, but on each occasion she used a parachute; I have been adamant on that point.

I might say a word or two here about Lovers' Leaps, for the benefit of readers unfamiliar with the colorful tradition. In North America, which is rich in precipices of all heights, the Lovers' Leap has reached its fullest flower, and in American folklore it is almost always a beautiful Indian maiden and a handsome young brave who, thwarted in their love by parental or tribal opposition, solved their problem trag-

From *The Night the Old Nostalgia Burned Down*, copyright, 1951, by Frank Sullivan. Reprinted by permission of Little, Brown & Company. Originally in *The New Yorker*.

ically by leaping from a ledge at the top of the precipice to the rocks below. The scene later becomes known in legend as a Lovers' Leap. The investigations of Dr. Johanna and myself, up to our discovery of Quigley 873, had revealed eight hundred and seventy-two authentic Lovers' Leaps in the United States and Canada, and we thought we had exhausted the field. The jumps ranged from fifty to three thousand feet and the leaping lovers represented every tribe in the country except the Seminoles, of Florida. Florida, being very flat, affords no facilities for lovers desirous of leaping, and how the star-crossed Seminoles solve their difficulties is a nice problem that Dr. Johanna and I hope one day to probe.

It was during a motor trip in the White Mountains that we discovered Quigley 873. We were bowling along a road near Lake Wassamattawichez on an idyllic June afternoon when, rounding a bend, we saw before us, on the opposite side of the valley, a crag that we both realized instantly might be a Lovers' Leap, and one of the most perfect we had ever encountered—sheer drop, magnificent view, parking space. It had everything!

"It *must* be a Lovers' Leap, but I don't seem to recognize it," I said to Dr. Johanna. Was it possible that we had stumbled on a new Leap? We hardly dared hope.

Well, the thing was to find out, and to do this it was necessary, of course, to locate the oldest inhabitant of North Wassamattawichez, the village nestling in the valley below. My wife and I once differed, though not seriously, on the best method of verifying oldest inhabitants. If a birth certificate was not available, she favored a thorough physical examination by a competent physician, but oldest inhabitants, she found, often displayed a nettling resistance to such a test, and she finally gave up her method and adopted mine, which I do thinks works as well in the long run. My system is simply this: If a native sufficiently advanced in years uses "mebbe" for "maybe," "allus" for "always," and "sezee" for "says he," and if he recalls that his father carried him to the railroad station to watch Lincoln's funeral train pass by, in 1865, then I ask him his age, deduct fifteen years from his answer, and accept him as a bona-fide oldest inhabitant.

Dr. Johanna and I soon found our man, a venerable patriarch named Jonas Atkinson, one hundred and four-minus-fifteen years old, and we engaged him in conversation over a mug of foaming ale at the quaint tavern in the village. By way of breaking the conversational ice, I asked him the traditional question demanded by protocol. "To what do you attribute your great age, Mr. Atkinson?"

"I allus sweat good," he replied, and, gazing into his already empty mug, added slyly, "An' I allus enjoy my ale."

I smiled, and commanded the landlord to fetch more ale.

Dr. Johanna then took up the ball. "My husband and I were attracted by that odd-looking cliff yonder side of the valley," she said with assumed nonchalance. "Has it by any chance got a name?"

"Yep," said Mr. Atkinson. "It's called Lovers' Leap."

The astronomer who has found a new comet or the botanist who has uncovered a hitherto unknown trillium will recognize the excitement that filled us at this confirmation of our hope.

"Lovers' Leap, eh?" said Dr. Johanna, still with pretended indifference. "What ever for?"

"Two Injuns leapt there a long time ago," said Mr. Atkinson.

"Dashed themselves to death on the rocks below, clasped in a last fond embrace?" asked Dr. Johanna, now scarcely able to control her excitement.

"Shucks, no, Sis," said Mr. Atkinson. "Nothin' like that."

Dr. Johanna and I exchanged perplexed glances. "You mean they jumped off that cliff and *lived?*" I asked.

"Didn't say they jumped offen it, Bub," said Mr. Atkinson. "I said they leapt."

"Well, what's the difference?"

"Well, sir, I'll tell ye—Consarn it, I can't. M'throat's gone scratchy on me agin."

"Landlord, more ale!" said I.

"Thankee. Drat this foam. Most of it gits in a feller's beard. Sheer waste o' good ale. Well, sir, it was like this. This maiden an' this here brave from the Wassamattawichez tribe fell in love. Made a fine-lookin' pair, too. He was an all-around athlete and could jump better'n any brave in the tribe, an' they called him Standin' High. She was almost as good as he was at track, so they called her Leapin' Trout. Well, things would o' gone all right, but her father promised her hand to an old buck that happened to have a lot o' wampum. So the kids decided to elope. One day they slipped away an' met down yander in the ravine, all set to light out fer the West. Well, they git jest underneath the cliff thar when who comes rushin' at 'em from one end o' the ravine but a mob o' her folks in hot pursuit. So Leapin' Trout and Standin' High started for th'other end o' the ravine, but who shows up thar but Got Wampum, th'old buck she was supposed to marry, with a mob o' *his* folks. Escape was cut off.

"Leapin' Trout pulled a pizened arrow out o' her quiver an' cried 'At least we can die together!' but her lover stayed her hand. 'Don't puncture yerself,' sezee. 'There is yet a way out.'

" 'Whar?' s'she.

" 'The cliff up thar,' sezee.

" 'Jump fifty feet straight up?' s'she. 'Are you crazy, Standin' High?'

" 'You can do it, with a little help,' sezee. 'I got an idea.'

"There was a log restin' a-teeter across a boulder. He told her to stand on the end that touched the ground.

" 'Now,' sezee, 'when I jump on th'other end, you'll shoot up into the air, and when you do, just hunch and scrunch yerself along all you can an' you'll make the top o' that cliff, understand? It's our on'y chance.'

" 'But you, Standin' High,' s'she, 'what'll become o' you?'

" 'Don't worry about me,' sezee. 'I'll take off right after ye. Come along. We got no time fer argufication.'

"They didn't, nuther, because by now mobs o' kinfolk was comin' down at 'em from both ends o' the gulch, whoopin' and yellin' like savages, and makin' a reg'lar garboil.

"So Leapin' Trout crouched on the grounded end o' the log. Standin' High sprang up onto a big boulder that was nigh. 'Git ready!' sezee. 'Git set! Go!' An' with that he jumps offen the boulder onto th'other end o' the log with all his might, an' up shoots the beautiful Indian maiden like a bat out o' hell. You know, the way the acrobats do it in the circus. An', by gum and by golly, she lands on the edge o' the cliff fifty foot above, teeters there a second, then grabs a bush and hauls herself to safety."

"And what became of Stanley High?" asked Dr. Johanna eagerly.

"*Standin*' High!" corrected Mr. Atkinson. "Well, he can't use the log. He ain't got no friend down thar to catapult *him* up. He has to rely on the stren'th the Lord gave him. So he grabs a fifty-foot pine trunk layin' nearby, gits a good runnin' start, takes off, an' sails into the air in as purty a pole vault as this nation ever see."

"Did he make it?" asked Dr. Johanna.

Mr. Atkinson turned purple and gave out gasping, choking noises. "Landlord, more ale!" I cried. "Hurry!"

Mr. Atkinson quaffed and the spasm passed.

"That ale didn't come a minute too soon, Bub," he said. "Thirsty work, spinnin' these legends."

"Yes, yes, Mr. Atkinson, but tell us—did Standing High make it?"

"Missed it by ten foot."

"A-a-h, what a pity!" Dr. Johanna mourned. "He fell back on the tomahawks of his enemies?"

"I never said that, Sis. He got away all right. But he'd o' bin a gone goose if it hadn't bin fer J. Fenimore Cooper."

"J. Fenimore Cooper?"

"Yep. Standin' High was a great reader, fer an Injun. Allus claimed he learnt everything he knew about Injun lore from J. Fenimore, an' when he left home that mornin' he'd slipped his well-thumbed copy o' 'The Deerslayer' into his pants pocket. That saved his life."

"How?" I asked.

"Well, when old Got Wampum reached the spot, jest after Standin' High took off fer the top o' the cliff, he gave a yell o' baffled rage an' let fly an arrow at his rival's retreatin' form. Old Got Wampum was a good shot."

"He hit Standing High?"

"Right where it done the most good, as things turned out. The arrow passed clean through Cooper's book an' penetrated Standin' High to a depth of mebbe half an inch. Not so deep as a well but deep enough to encourage, as the Bard would say. Standin' High gave a sharp cry an' sprang three more feet into the air."

"And that got him to the top of the cliff?" I asked.

"Nope. He was still shy seven foot."

"So he fell back on the arrows of his foes after all?"

"Not by a durn sight. He grabbed Leapin' Trout by the hair."

"By the hair?"

"Sure. Leapin' Trout had hair seven foot long, like that gal in the fairy tale."

"Rapunzel?" suggested Dr. Johanna.

"Don't mind if I do," said Mr. Atkinson quickly.

I said, "Landlord, more ale!"

"Thankee," said Mr. Atkinson. "Yarnin' suttinly makes a feller spit cotton. Yep, Leapin' Trout got a good hold onto a tree, let her hair down over the cliff, Standin' High grabbed the hair, an' she hauled him up."

"To safety?"

"Yes, Ma'am," said Mr. Atkinson.

"What an utterly charming legend!" said Dr. Johanna, brushing what I fear was a not quite scientific tear from her cheek.

"They didn't leap *offen* that cliff," said Mr. Atkinson. "They leapt onto it. I reckon this here's the on'y Lovers' Leap in reverse in this country, and the on'y one with a happy endin'."

"I can just see old Got Wampum, the disgruntled lover," I chuckled. "I'll bet *his* face was red."

"Why not? He was an Injun," said Mr. Atkinson.

"Did Stanley High and Running Broad live happily ever after?" asked Dr. Johanna.

"Her name was Leapin' Trout," corrected Mr. Atkinson. "Yep, they done all right. Toured fer years with the Pawnee Bill show and retired with a small fortune. I heard tell they had a grandson went to Yale, class of 1922, and he was the best one in all the colleges at vaultin' with the pole."

E. B. White

A WEEKEND WITH THE ANGELS

(*Interlude in a hospital during World War II*)

ONE of the advantages of surgery, to a man at loose ends in Boston, is that it entitles him to a night at a hospital in advance of the operation. In short, it gets him in off the streets. I was instructed to report for my bed not later than three o'clock on Thursday afternoon, although I wasn't to lose my middle turbinate until eight the next morning. That gave me seventeen hours of utter relaxation in comfortable surroundings, dreaming away through the late afternoon, sweating under the arms, wiping my moist palms on the drapes, and marvelling at the strange succession of events that lead a man unerringly into an unimportant misadventure like a nose operation. I had no particular feeling of regret at the idea of giving up a turbinate (which sounded like something the Navy might be able to use in one of its light cruisers); in fact, in a man's middle years there is scarcely a part of the body he would hesitate to turn over to the proper authorities. At my age one jumps at the chance to get rid of something. Half a lifetime with a middle turbinate is enough to satisfy all but the most avid person.

I think the hospital was in Cambridge, but I'm not sure about that, as I was rather depressed on the ride out and when I'm depressed I never look where I'm going. Anyway, it was a very nice place near a small, orderly river (which might easily have been the Charles) and there was a fine big oak just outside my window. The room was tiny but so am I. The bed was a standard crank-up model, complete with drawsheet, rubber pad, and call switch. I had hoped it would have a swan at one end of it, like the boats in the Public Garden, but even without the swan it was a pleasanter accommodation than one can ordinarily expect to get on short notice in Boston.

There seemed no good reason for getting into the bed right away, so I just sat down on a hassock with a copy of the *Atlantic*. After a while a nurse came in.

"I'm Miss Mulqueenie," she said informatively.

"My name is White," I replied. "My temperature is ninety-eight point six, my pulse is seventy-two, and my blood pressure is one hundred and forty over eighty except when I get interested in what I am doing, when it goes up sharply. I'm here for a turbinectomy." Miss Mulqueenie came and sat down by my side. She hung her sphygmomanometer around her neck and drew a pencil and a blank form on me.

"What's your occupation?"

"Writer," I said, searching my memory.

The nurse smiled the knowing smile of a woman who is not easily fooled by men and their little conceits. She then began a careful listing of my clothes and personal effects. About my clothes she seemed a trifle uncertain. "What have you got on underneath your trousers?" she asked, dipping her pencil thoughtfully into her mouth.

"I can't recall," I replied. "It seems ages since I got dressed. This morning seems like a million years ago."

"Well, you must have *some*thing on. What'll I put down?"

"Paisley shawl?" I suggested. She thought a moment and then wrote "underwear" and gave me the list to sign. Then she took my temperature, my blood pressure, and my pulse. My temperature was ninety-eight point six, my pulse was seventy-two, and my blood pressure was one hundred and forty over eighty. "You better get to bed," she said cryptically. And Miss Mulqueenie was gone.

In bed, I felt relaxed and beautiful, as I imagine I shall feel in death. I had not been there long when another nurse appeared. She was in the uniform of a student and her face had the exalted look of a person who is doing a great deal of work and receiving no pay for it—which was, of course, exactly the case. She regarded me closely.

"It says on your card that you're a writer," she began, "but I've never heard of you."

"Did you come in here to harp on my obscurity?" I asked.

"No, I came in here to rub your back." She closed the door and I generously allowed her to rub my back. Later I was given a sedative and slept the uninterrupted sleep of the little-known.

The operation wasn't bad. I quite enjoyed the trip up from my room to the operating parlors, as a closely confined person does enjoy any sort of outing. The morphine had loosened my tongue, and while we waited in the corridor for the surgeon to arrive, the orderly and I let down our hair and had a good chat about fishing tackle. There were several rather distinguished people doing voluntary work in that hospital, and this orderly's face looked familiar. I wouldn't swear to it, but I think it was Governor Saltonstall. You never know whom you'll meet in bed these days. After a few minutes the surgeon was sighted in another part of the building and somebody gave the Governor the go-ahead. He had me halfway through a door leading into an operating room when a nurse caught sight of us. She clicked her tongue in disgust. "No, no," she said, wearily, "that's gall bladder."

The Governor backed me out and we tried our luck in another room. I cautiously put my hand up to my side, where the gall bladder is presumed to be. Everything seemed undisturbed. Soon the surgeon arrived and went to work. Under my skillful direction he removed everything he was supposed to remove and, as far as I could tell, nothing that he wasn't. It was a perfect occasion. It even turned out, in the course of the operation, that *his* father and *my* wife's people were connected—not by blood but in that happy and satisfactory way in which Boston's mystic thread entwines all its sons and daughters.

Because of the war the situation in hospitals is, of course, serious. A civilian feels embarrassed to be there at all, occupying valuable space and wasting the time and strength of the nurses, the student nurses, the nurses' aides, and the Gray Ladies. But I discovered that there is a new spirit in hospitals which, in its own way, is as merciful and resolute as the old, and every bit as mad. A patient, when he enters, receives a booklet reminding him that hospitals are short-handed and asking him not to bother the nurses unnecessarily. If he is a person of any conscience, he takes this quite literally, resolving not to push his call switch unless he is bleeding to death or the room is on fire. He throws himself so violently into the spirit of the emergency that, in the long run, he probably causes just as much trouble as he would have in more relaxed circumstances. I hadn't been off the operating table two hours and was still heavily drugged with morphine and bleeding at the nose when I found myself out of bed, armed with a window pole, engaged in a hand-to-hand encounter with a sticky transom. I enjoyed the nonsensical sensation of being in contact with the enemy. The effort, because of my condition, was rather too much for me, and I just made it back under the covers in time. There was quite a to-do, up and down the halls, when they found I had been out of bed.

As for routine chores, I did them myself, for the most part. Each morning I arose from bed and went at the room, tidying it up and doing all the dozens of things that need doing in an early-morning sickroom. First I would get down and crawl under the bed to retrieve the night's accumulation of blood-soaked paper handkerchiefs, which formed a dismal ring around the scrap basket where I had missed my aim in the dark. Then I'd fold the night blanket neatly and put it away in the bottom drawer of the bureau. I would crank up the bed, take the creases out of the rubber pad, tighten the drawsheet, pat the pillows back into shape, straighten out the *Atlantic Monthly*, and transfer the chrysanthemums into their day vase. Ashtrays had to be emptied, soiled towels removed, the hot-water bottle exhumed from its cold grave at the foot of the bed. One morning, in one of those passionate fits of neatness which overwhelm me from time to time, I spent an hour or so on my hands and knees clearing the room of bobby pins left by a former occupant. It was interesting work but, like all housework, exhausting.

Although there seemed to be, and undoubtedly was, a shortage of help at the hospital, there was one department which was, to my way of thinking, overstaffed. That was the back-rubbing department. There apparently was no schedule or system about back-rubbing—it was just a service a nurse would throw into her routine if she felt like it and had a few minutes to spare. One morning between ten and twelve my back was rubbed three times by as many different angels of mercy. My back, curiously enough, did not need rubbing that morning. I had been up, as usual, doing the housework, and when I finally got things to rights and crawled back into bed at quarter to ten, the blood was coursing through my back. All my back needed was a little while to itself. I took the three rubs without a murmur, but the violence and frequency of the assault increased my nosebleed, and when lunch was brought I was too tired to eat. Right after lunch a nurse I had never seen before, a large, eager girl, waltzed into the room and began peeling the bedclothes off.

"What's up, nurse?" I asked.

"I'm going to rub your back," she replied.

"Look," I said, plucking weakly at the sheets, "what do you say we leave the old backsy-wacksy alone for a few minutes?"

Mostly, however, the days rolled by, hour after hour, and you would never see another living soul. For patriotic reasons I seldom rang and so was seldom visited. Once I had a bath. This was the second morning after the operation. A nurse came in early. Without a word she flung open the door of the commode and extracted a basin, a washcloth, and a piece of soap.

"Can you take your bath?" she asked briskly.

"I always have, in recent years," I replied.

She placed the bathing equipment on the rude table that arched the bed, and handed me a towel. "Take off your uppers and work down. Then roll up your lowers and work up," she snapped. "And don't get the bed wet!"

I waited till she disappeared, then got noiselessly out of bed, removed the basin, emptied it, went into the bathroom which I shared with another fellow, drew a tub, and had a nice bath. Nurses are such formalists.

Of all the memories of this fabulous and salutary weekend, the most haunting is my recollection of the strange visitations of a certain night nurse. She came on duty, I was told, at midnight, and went off at seven. It was her custom to enter my room at a few minutes before five in the morning, when my sleeping potion still held me in thrall, snap on the light, and take a temperature reading. At her entrance I would rouse myself, at enormous physical cost, blink foolishly at the light, and open my mouth to receive, under the thick curly tongue, the thin straight thermometer. The nurse, whose name began with an "A" and ended in a thornbush, would stand in beautiful serenity, gazing peacefully down upon me for the long three minutes required for the recording. Her lips held the faint suggestion of a smile, compounded of scorn and indulgence. Motionless and cool in the lamplight, faithfully discharging her preposterous duty in the awful hour of a day born prematurely, she seemed a creature tinged with madness and beauty. She seemed, but of course could not have been, without flaw. As my drugged senses struggled vainly to catalogue her features, the thermometer would press upward against my tongue and the mercury would begin its long tedious climb toward the normal mark. I have no idea whether she was tall or short, dark or fair, plain or pretty, but in her calm and unreasoning concern about my body heat, at that unconscionable hour, she personified the beauty and lunacy of which life is so subtly blended. On the last morning of my stay I broke the mystical silence that had always before surrounded our ceremony.

"Cousin," I managed to mumble, allowing the thermometer to clash pitilessly against my incisors, "why dost wake me before the dawn for this mild dumbshow?"

She never changed her expression, but I heard words coming surely from her lips. "There's a war on, Bud," she replied. "I got twenty-six readings to take before I go off duty, so just for the heck of it I start with you."

Smiling a tiny proud smile, I raised my right hand and made a V, the way I had seen Churchill do it in the pictures. Then the drug took hold of me again, and when I awoke she was gone. Next day so was I.

Charles W. Morton

PREP SCHOOLS

SAILING is a great vice. Unlike Havana cigars it beguiles children of seven or eight. By early manhood, the addict is beyond recall. Even in his final, veranda years, he continues to talk down East and to denounce the inaccurate terminology of the landsman in all matters of maritime. Takes hold early, bites hard.

A boy of fourteen has been writing occasional letters from a Yankee preparatory school to a young relative of mine. He was a paid hand

From *How to Protect Yourself against Women and Other Vicissitudes*, by Charles W. Morton. Reprinted by permission of J. B. Lippincott Company, Publishers.

last summer on a large sloop, carried a formidable knife on a lanyard and one would judge him an equally good man with a skate sail, ice boat, dhow or junk. In his last letter he was reporting on his grades.

He had flunked a French test, gained a D in English and a C—in mathematics. But his navigation was going very well. "I am glad about that," he writes, "because navigation is something that I can use all my life."

A friend passes along another preparatory school story. His son had been piling up A's at a large school where the headmaster is more noted for his appalling ability to enlarge the endowment than for his acute knowledge of the individuals in his charge. Perhaps through an awareness of this, the headmaster lays some emphasis on having a personal interview once a year with each boy in the school. He can take on about a half a dozen each day, and as an *aide-mémoire* he furtively consults a card which his secretary has just handed him, when the interview begins.

No one has ever seen one of these cards, but it is believed to contain the name of the boy, his parents, and any relatives who happen to be Old Boys of the school. It enables the headmaster to greet the incoming visitor affectionately, by his given name. He usually ends the audience almost immediately by booming genially, "And now, George, are you getting any B's?"

My friend's son is not one to talk himself up, and for two years he merely answered this question in the negative, with an air of polite regret. It naturally disappointed the headmaster, and in his third annual interview the boy was happy to give him a crumb of cheer. Thus, when the headmaster asked hopefully, "Well, George, are you getting any B's?" the boy answered, "Yes sir, one." He did not explain that it was the only mark that low he had ever received, and there was nothing to diminish the headmaster's enthusiasm when he called to the departing boy, "Splendid, splendid—just keep on and maybe you can get some more."

Charles W. Morton

FISHING STORIES

THE time has come to end the senseless competition among writers of fishing stories: the narrator hooks a fish and (*a*) catches it
or (*b*) loses it. The only items in the story that are at all variable are
the species of fish—and hence its size and habitat—and the kind of
tackle used in his wisdom (or folly) by the narrator. These, along with
a few details, would simply be left blank in the standardized fishing
story, to be filled in as the facts warranted. Thus, whether it all took
place at the headwaters of the Orinoco or the narrows of Spectacle
Pond, much pencil chewing and time-consuming thought will be
saved by adherence to the simple rules governing all fishing stories.

The fishing story must begin with a modest statement of the author's credentials: "I've fished for the mighty —— off Acapulco and the
battling —— along the Florida Keys. I've seen a maddened —— swamp
a dory off Wedgeport, but for sheer power and gameness I've seen
nothing that can equal, pound for pound, a ——."

That's a perfectly workable opening paragraph for any fishing story.
If the reader is foolish enough to doubt its validity when applied to
some notoriously inert species, let him remember that the fill-in of the
battle itself will prove everything that the narrator contends. It's bound
to, for the narrator uses just the same fill-in for a rock cod, which
behaves much like a boot full of water, as he would for a fifty-pound
muskellunge.

After presenting his own credentials, the narrator must introduce
his guide. Guides are always terse, monosyllabic men—which saves the
author from writing much improbable dialogue and dialect. They
grunt or they gesture, but that's about all. The narrator must assume
at this point the disarming role of chump and leave the high strategy

to Joe, the guide. ("We never did learn Joe's last name, but he taught us all there was to know about ——s.")

Another purpose of the guide is to wake the author up on that never-to-be-forgotten morning and give him his breakfast: "My head had hardly touched the pillow, so it seemed, before Joe woke me up. The delicious aroma of ——ing —— greeted my nostrils, and I lost no time in getting out of my blankets."

And so to that mysterious locality, known only to Joe, where the narrator has been assured he will have a chance to pit his cunning against the great-granddaddy of all ——s. It makes no difference whether Joe is a Kanaka or a Canadian, or whether they travel by express cruiser, mule, or pirogue—their destination always disappoints the narrator when he gets there: "It looked like the last place in the world to try for ——s, but Joe merely grunted and gestured vaguely at the water. '—— here,' he said. 'Big one.'"

Joe of course was right, the author ruefully confesses. His first lure, a —— (spinner, fly, minnow, or grapnel baited with a small shoat—it's all the same) had hardly touched the water when down went the rod, out screamed the line! It was all the author could do to keep his footing against that first wild rush of the ——.

The next two hours are crammed with action, while the author brings in one gigantic —— after another, certainly the biggest he has ever seen and one of them looking as if it would go for at least —— pounds on the club scales. But hold on. What's wrong with Joe? He seems disgusted. He grunts contemptuously. Bored stiff. The author, still the chump and slow to catch on, presses Joe for comment. Joe grunts. "Big —— still here," Joe replies, gesturing at the water, and the author begins to realize that Joe is talking about a —— of a size never reported in all the annals of —— fishing.

Comes the final cast. Nothing happens. No —— of any size seems to be interested. The length of this interval of writing depends on how much space the author is trying to fill. If need be, he can reminisce of bygone feats against giant clams, electric eels, or things that have nothing to do with ——s.

Suddenly, a few yards beyond the lure, the waters swirl: "Some vast, invisible force was causing a submarine upheaval. Spellbound, I watched a great tail appear for an instant as the monster lazily rolled over and submerged again. I turned to Joe. 'Don't tell me that was a ——!' I whispered. '——s don't get *that* big.' But Joe only grunted. 'Big ——,' he replied."

The author realizes that his tackle is far too light for a —— of this size. Joe had really known what he was talking, or grunting, about. But it's too late now. So: DOWN goes that rod again. OUT screams the line. Even with a —— pound drag, the ——'s rush carries all before it. Crash! The leviathan hurls himself far out of the water and comes down with an echoing splash. The author vainly tries to reel in precious line.

"My rod bent almost double. Pandemonium reigned." Sooner or later, as the line races from the screeching reel, the author does a very foolish thing: "I tried to brake it with my thumb." Naturally enough, he gets a bad burn on his thumb. More leaps, lunges—a page or so of them.

"Suddenly, my line went ominously slack. I began frantically reeling in. '—— gone,' Joe grunted."

True enough. The tale is almost told. Remains only the unbelievable circumstances of the leader when the narrator finally winds it to the surface. Gut, wire, or ⅜-inch log chain, its condition never varies: "*Bitten clean through!* Mute evidence that the —— had met man's challenge—and won!"

They prepare to leave. "But suddenly the waters were convulsed again as the mighty —— broke the surface in all his majesty and, with a final derisive smack of his great tail, disappeared—still the Monarch of ——" (Spectacle Pond, the Upper Orinoco, Hillsboro Inlet, etc., etc.)

Russell Maloney

INFLEXIBLE LOGIC

WHEN the six chimpanzees came into his life, Mr. Bainbridge was thirty-eight years old. He was a bachelor and lived comfortably in a remote part of Connecticut, in a large old house with a carriage drive, a conservatory, a tennis court, and a well-selected library. His income was derived from impeccably situated real estate in New York City, and he spent it soberly, in a manner which could give offence to nobody. Once a year, late in April, his tennis court was resurfaced, and after that anybody in the neighborhood was welcome to use it; his monthly statement from Brentano's seldom ran below seventy-five dollars; every third year, in November, he turned in his old Cadillac coupé for a new one; he ordered his cigars, which were mild and rather moderately priced, in shipments of one thousand, from a tobacconist in Havana; because of the international situation he had cancelled arrangements to travel abroad, and after due thought had decided to spend his travelling allowance on wines, which seemed likely to get scarcer and more expensive if the war lasted. On the whole, Mr. Bainbridge's life was deliberately, and not too unsuccessfully, modelled after that of an English country gentleman of the late eighteenth century, a gentleman interested in the arts and in the expansion of science, and so sure of himself that he didn't care if some people thought him eccentric.

Mr. Bainbridge had many friends in New York, and he spent several days of the month in the city, staying at his club and looking around. Sometimes he called up a girl and took her out to a theatre and a night club. Sometimes he and a couple of classmates got a little tight and went to a prizefight. Mr. Bainbridge also looked in now and then at some of the conservative art galleries, and liked occasionally to go to a concert. And he liked cocktail parties, too, because of the fine footling conversation and the extraordinary number of pretty girls who had nothing else to do with the rest of their evening. It was at a New York cocktail party, however, that Mr. Bainbridge kept his preliminary appointment with doom. At one of the parties given by Hobie Packard, the stockbroker, he learned about the theory of the six chimpanzees.

It was almost six-forty. The people who had intended to have one drink and go had already gone, and the people who intended to stay were fortifying themselves with slightly dried canapés and talking animatedly. A group of stage and radio people had coagulated in one corner, near Packard's Capehart, and were wrangling about various methods of cheating the Collector of Internal Revenue. In another corner was a group of stockbrokers, talking about the greatest stockbroker of them all, Gauguin. Little Marcia Lupton was sitting with a young man, saying earnestly, "Do you really want to know what my greatest ambition is? I want to be myself," and Mr. Bainbridge smiled gently, thinking of the time Marcia had said that to him. Then he heard the voice of Bernard Weiss, the critic, saying, "Of course he wrote one good novel. It's not surprising. After all, we know that if six chimpanzees were set to work pounding six typewriters at random, they would, in a million years, write all the books in the British Museum."

Mr. Bainbridge drifted over to Weiss and was introduced to Weiss's companion, a Mr. Noble. "What's this about a million chimpanzees, Weiss?" he asked.

"Six chimpanzees," Mr. Weiss said. "It's an old cliché of the mathematicians. I thought everybody was told about it in school. Law of averages, you know, or maybe it's permutation and combination. The six chimps, just pounding away at the typewriter keys, would be bound to copy out all the books ever written by man. There are only so many possible combinations of letters and numerals, and they'd produce all of them—see? Of course they'd also turn out a mountain of gibberish, but they'd work the books in, too. All the books in the British Museum."

Mr. Bainbridge was delighted; this was the sort of talk he liked to hear when he came to New York. "Well, but look here," he said, just to keep up his part in the foolish conversation, "what if one of the chimpanzees finally did duplicate a book, right down to the last period, but left that off? Would that count?"

"I suppose not. Probably the chimpanzee would get around to doing the book again, and put the period in."

"What nonsense!" Mr. Noble cried.

"It may be nonsense, but Sir James Jeans believes it," Mr. Weiss said, huffily. "Jeans or Lancelot Hogben. I know I ran across it quite recently."

Mr. Bainbridge was impressed. He read quite a bit of popular science, and both Jeans and Hogben were in his library. "Is that so?" he murmured, no longer feeling frivolous. "Wonder if it has ever actually been tried? I mean, has anybody ever put six chimpanzees in a room with six typewriters and a lot of paper?"

Mr. Weiss glanced at Mr. Bainbridge's empty cocktail glass and said drily, "Probably not."

Nine weeks later, on a winter evening, Mr. Bainbridge was sitting in his study with his friend James Mallard, an assistant professor of mathematics at New Haven. He was plainly nervous as he poured himself a drink and said, "Mallard, I've asked you to come here—Brandy? Cigar?—for a particular reason. You remember that I wrote you some time ago, asking your opinion of . . . of a certain mathematical hypothesis or supposition."

"Yes," Professor Mallard said, briskly. "I remember perfectly. About the six chimpanzees and the British Museum. And I told you it was a perfectly sound popularization of a principle known to every schoolboy who had studied the science of probabilities."

"Precisely," Mr. Bainbridge said. "Well, Mallard, I made up my mind . . . It was not difficult for me, because I have, in spite of that fellow in the White House, been able to give something every year to the Museum of Natural History, and they were naturally glad to oblige me. . . . And after all, the only contribution a layman can make to the progress of science is to assist with the drudgery of experiment. . . . In short, I—"

"I suppose you're trying to tell me that you have procured six chimpanzees and set them to work at typewriters in order to see whether they will eventually write all the books in the British Museum. Is that it?"

"Yes, that's it," Mr. Bainbridge said. "What a mind you have, Mallard. Six fine young males, in perfect condition. I had a—I suppose you'd call it a dormitory—built out in back of the stable. The typewriters are in the conservatory. It's light and airy in there, and I moved most of the plants out. Mr. North, the man who owns the circus very obligingly let me engage one of his best animal men. Really, it was no trouble at all."

Professor Mallard smiled indulgently. "After all, such a thing is not unheard of," he said. "I seem to remember that a man at some university put his graduate students to work flipping coins, to see if heads and tails came up an equal number of times. Of course they did."

Mr. Bainbridge looked at his friend very queerly. "Then you believe that any such principle of the science of probabilities will stand up under an actual test?"

"You had better see for yourself." Mr. Bainbridge led Professor Mallard downstairs, along a corridor, through a disused music room and into a large conservatory. The middle of the floor had been cleared of plants and was occupied by a row of six typewriter tables, each one supporting a hooded machine. At the left of each typewriter was a neat stack of yellow copy paper. Empty wastebaskets were under each table. The chairs were the unpadded, spring-backed kind favored by experienced stenographers. A large bunch of ripe bananas was hanging in one corner, and in another stood a Great Bear water-cooler and a rack of Lily cups. Six piles of typescript, each about a foot high, were ranged along the wall on an improvised shelf. Mr. Bainbridge picked up one of the piles, which he could just conveniently lift, and set it on a table before Professor Mallard. "The output to date of Chimpanzee A, known as Bill," he said simply.

"'"Oliver Twist," by Charles Dickens,'" Professor Mallard read out. He read the first and second pages of the manuscript, then feverishly leafed through to the end. "You mean to tell me," he said, "that this chimpanzee has written—"

"Word for word and comma for comma," said Mr. Bainbridge. "Young, my butler, and I took turns comparing it with the edition I own. Having finished 'Oliver Twist,' Bill is, as you see, starting the sociological works of Vilfredo Pareto, in Italian. At the rate he has been going, it should keep him busy for the rest of the month."

"And all the chimpanzees"—Professor Mallard was pale, and enunciated with difficulty—"they aren't all—"

"Oh, yes, all writing books which I have every reason to believe are in the British Museum. The prose of John Donne, some Anatole France, Conan Doyle, Galen, the collected plays of Somerset Maugham, Marcel Proust, the memoirs of the late Marie of Rumania, and a monograph by a Dr. Wiley on the marsh grasses of Maine and Massachusetts. I can sum it up for you, Mallard, by telling you that since I started this experiment, four weeks and some days ago, none of the chimpanzees has spoiled a single sheet of paper."

Professor Mallard straightened up, passed his handkerchief across his brow, and took a deep breath. "I apologize for my weakness," he said. "It was simply the sudden shock. No, looking at the thing scientifically—and I hope I am at least as capable of that as the next man—there is nothing marvellous about the situation. These chimpanzees, or a succession of similar teams of chimpanzees, would in a million years write all the books in the British Museum. I told you some time ago that I believed that statement. Why should my belief be altered by the fact that they produced some of the books at the very outset? After all, I should not be very much surprised if I tossed a coin a hundred times and it came up heads every time. I know that if I kept at it long enough, the ratio would reduce itself to an exact fifty per cent. Rest assured, these chimpanzees will begin to compose gibberish quite soon. It is bound to happen. Science tells us so. Meanwhile, I advise you to keep this experiment secret. Uninformed people might create a sensation if they knew."

"I will, indeed," Mr. Bainbridge said. "And I'm very grateful for your rational analysis. It reassures me. And now, before you go, you must hear the new Schnabel records that arrived today."

During the succeeding three months, Professor Mallard got into the habit of telephoning Mr. Bainbridge every Friday afternoon at five-thirty, immediately after leaving his seminar room. The Professor would say, "Well?," and Mr. Bainbridge would reply, "They're still at it, Mallard. Haven't spoiled a sheet of paper yet." If Mr. Bainbridge had to go out on Friday afternoon, he would leave a written message with his butler, who would read it to Professor Mallard: "Mr. Bainbridge says we now have Trevelyan's 'Life of Macaulay,' the Confessions of St. Augustine, 'Vanity Fair,' part of Irving's 'Life of George Washington,' the Book of the Dead, and some speeches delivered in Parliament in opposition to the Corn Laws, sir." Professor Mallard would reply, with a hint of a snarl in his voice, "Tell him to remember what I predicted," and hang up with a clash.

The eleventh Friday that Professor Mallard telephoned, Mr. Bainbridge said, "No change. I have had to store the bulk of the manuscript in the cellar. I would have burned it, except that it probably has some scientific value."

"How dare you talk of scientific value?" The voice from New Haven roared faintly in the receiver. "Scientific value! You—you—chimpanzee!" There were further inarticulate sputterings, and Mr. Bainbridge hung up with a disturbed expression. "I am afraid Mallard is overtaxing himself," he murmured.

Next day, however, he was pleasantly surprised. He was leafing through a manuscript that had been completed the previous day by Chimpanzee D, Corky. It was the complete diary of Samuel Pepys, and Mr. Bainbridge was chuckling over the naughty passages, which were omitted in his own edition, when Professor Mallard was shown into the room. "I have come to apologize for my outrageous conduct on the telephone yesterday," the Professor said.

"Please don't think of it any more. I know you have many things on your mind," Mr. Bainbridge said. "Would you like a drink?"

"A large whiskey, straight, please," Professor Mallard said. "I got rather cold driving down. No change, I presume?"

"No, none. Chimpanzee F, Dinty, is just finishing John Florio's translation of Montaigne's essays, but there is no other news of interest."

Professor Mallard squared his shoulders and tossed off his drink in one astonishing gulp. "I should like to see them at work," he said. "Would I disturb them, do you think?"

"Not at all. As a matter of fact, I usually look in on them around this time of day. Dinty may have finished his Montaigne by now, and it is always interesting to see them start a new work. I would have thought that they would continue on the same sheet of paper, but they don't, you know. Always a fresh sheet, and the title in capitals."

Professor Mallard, without apology, poured another drink and slugged it down. "Lead on," he said.

It was dusk in the conservatory, and the chimpanzees were typing by the light of student lamps clamped to their desks. The keeper lounged in a corner, eating a banana and reading *Billboard*. "You might as well take an hour or so off," Mr. Bainbridge said. The man left.

Professor Mallard, who had not taken off his overcoat, stood with his hands in his pockets, looking at the busy chimpanzees. "I wonder if you know, Bainbridge, that the science of probabilities takes everything into account," he said, in a queer, tight voice. "It is certainly almost beyond the bounds of credibility that these chimpanzees should write books without a single error, but that abnormality may be corrected by—*these!*" He took his hands from his pockets, and each one held a .38 revolver. "Stand back out of harm's way!" he shouted.

"Mallard! Stop it!" The revolvers barked, first the right hand, then the left, then the right. Two chimpanzees fell, and a third reeled into a corner. Mr. Bainbridge seized his friend's arm and wrested one of the weapons from him.

"Now I am armed, too, Mallard, and I advise you to stop!" he cried. Professor Mallard's answer was to draw a bead on Chimpanzee E and shoot him dead. Mr. Bainbridge made a rush, and Professor Mallard fired at him. Mr. Bainbridge, in his quick death agony, tightened his finger on the trigger of his revolver. It went off, and Professor Mallard went down. On his hands and knees he fired at the two chimpanzees which were still unhurt, and then collapsed.

There was nobody to hear his last words. "The human equation . . . always the enemy of science . . ." he panted. "This time . . . vice versa . . . I, a mere mortal . . . savior of science . . . deserve a Nobel . . ."

When the old butler came running into the conservatory to investigate the noises, his eyes were met by a truly appalling sight. The student lamps were shattered, but a newly risen moon shone in through the conservatory windows on the corpses of the two gentlemen, each clutching a smoking revolver. Five of the chimpanzees were dead. The sixth was Chimpanzee F. His right arm disabled, obviously bleeding to death, he was slumped before his typewriter. Painfully, with his left hand, he took from the machine the completed last page of Florio's Montaigne. Groping for a fresh sheet, he inserted it, and typed with one finger, "UNCLE TOM'S CABIN, by Harriet Beecher Stowe. Chapte . . ." Then he, too, was dead.

Cleveland Amory

NEWPORT:
OF COTTAGES AND QUEENS*

Now, don't go gettin' cross about th' rich, Hinnissy. Put up that dinnymite. Don't excite ye'ersilf about us folks in Newport. It's always been th' same way, Father Kelly tells me. Says he: "If a man is wise, he gets rich an' if he gets rich, he gets foolish, or his wife does. That's what keeps the money movin' around. What comes in at th' ticker goes out at the wine agent. F'river an' iver people have been growin' rich, goin' down to some kind iv a Newport, makin' monkeys iv thimsilves an' goin' back to the jungle. 'Tis a steady procission. Aisy come, lazy go. Ye read about th' union iv two gr-reat fortunes. A dollar meets another dollar, they are conganial, have sim'lar tastes, an' many mutual frinds. They are marrid an' bring up a fam'ly iv pennies, dimes, thirty-cintses an' countherfeits. An' afther awhile, th' fam'ly passes out iv circylation. That's th' histhry iv it," says Father Kelly. "An'," says he, "I'm glad there is a Newport," he says. "It's th' exhaust pipe," he says. "Without it we might blow up," he says. "It's th' hole in th' top iv th' kettle," he says. "I wish it was bigger."

—*Observations by Mr. Dooley*, F. P. Dunne, 1902

EXACTLY fifty years have passed since the late F. P. Dunne, alias Mr. Dooley, gave the Queen of Resorts perhaps her most philosophical blessing. In those fifty years, in the opinion of Emil Jemail,

* Abridged
From *The Last Resorts*, copyright, 1948, by Cleveland Amory. Reprinted by permission of Harper & Brothers.

editor of the Newport *Daily News*, the time for philosophy has passed. "To be objective about Newport—and that's a very easy thing to be," he says, "there's been a revolution here."

Jemail, who has been editing his paper since 1920, has seen the greatest of the resort revolutions at first hand. In 1925 both he and Washington's late Edson Bradley, liquor manufacturer and ex-Tuxedoite, built houses. Jemail built one which had four bedrooms and two bathrooms and cost fifteen thousand dollars. Bradley built one which had forty bedrooms and twenty bathrooms and cost two million dollars; the largest ever built in Newport, it was French Renaissance in design and among other features had a chapel which seated 150 people. In 1949 Bradley's house, which was called a cottage and named "Seaview Terrace," sold for eight thousand dollars. Jemail's house, which had never been called a cottage and has never had a name, has never been for sale. "I wouldn't take twenty-five thousand dollars for it," he says, "today."

This sort of revolution must be seen to be believed, and it is not an easy thing to see. Newport, which is located in Rhode Island, is an island itself, and it has always been physically, let alone socially, an extremely difficult place to get into—or, once into, out of. All Newporters pride themselves on the fact that there are few murders there. The methods of exit afforded the prospective murderer are but three and all involve either a bridge or a ferryboat. As for the methods of entrance, the usual one from New York, since the passing of the old Fall River Boat Line, is either by train or plane to Providence and a taxi or taxi-plane from there, or else by automobile over the Mount Hope Bridge and the Jamestown Ferry. Both are expensive. At the Mount Hope Bridge, which was at one time entirely controlled by the Vanderbilts, Steven Smith, the tollkeeper, has a standing reply to sight-seers who, knowing that a dollar-fifty ferry trip also lies ahead, often complain of his ninety-cent charge. "It may interest you to know," Smith answers with a wry smile, "that the bonds of this bridge are owned entirely by widows and orphans."

If there are three entrances and exits to Newport, there are also three separate Newports to view. The first Newport, or Navy Newport, becomes visible in the ride over by the Jamestown Ferry. Entering Newport Harbor, between old Fort Adams on one side and the U.S. Naval Training Station and War College on the other, the ferry moves between warships whose ancestors have been riding Newport waters since the days of John Paul Jones. During the Civil War the Naval Academy at Annapolis was, as a precautionary measure, evacuated to

Newport and today, three and a half wars later, Newport still ranks, along with Norfolk, as one of the two main fleet bases on the Atlantic.

The second Newport, or Historic Newport, is the sight which becomes visible when the ferry docks alongside Newport's ancient Long Wharf. This sight is not of Newport at all but of "Oldport," as Thomas Wentworth Higginson spoke of it in the nineteenth century, of a Newport which was old even then—a fascinating Colonial town whose narrow cobbled streets open on vistas which come to an end, said Henry James, "like the quick short steps of little old ladies." Thames Street, Newport's waterfront thoroughfare, is a curious Old World version of Main Street. Resorters pronounce it "Tems," natives usually use the "h" as well as the "a"; here, during the British occupation in the Revolution, Hessians shot down Newporters for target practice. In and around Thames' quaint side streets, where hollyhocks and petunias still hang on the fences, there are enough historic buildings to delight the most severe antiquarian. There is the Wanton-Lyman-Hazard House built in 1675, Richard Munday's Trinity Church built in 1726, Dean Berkeley's Whitehall built in 1729, Peter Harrison's Redwood Library built in 1749 and the Touro Synagogue built in 1763. The Redwood Library antedates all such institutions in New York and Boston and the Touro Synagogue was not only the first synagogue in this country but it was for many years the only one. Of all these museum pieces, only the so-called "Old Stone Mill" in Touro Park, a peculiar round stone tower built on open arches supported by pillars, has no date; all true Newporters believe, periodical reports by archeologists to the contrary, that this tower was built by the Vikings.

The third Newport, or Social Newport, begins at the top of the hill with Bellevue Avenue. Here, moving out past Ochre Point toward Bailey's Beach and the famous "Ten Mile" or Ocean Drive, the visitor sees for the first time a sight which is unduplicated anywhere else in the country—the sight of the castles which once represented the height of the great American resort extravaganza. Here, side by side, in extraordinary proportions, in an extraordinarily small area—less than half of the castles are actually on the water—are represented every kind of architectural crossbreeding from a weird Queen Anne gingerbread sired by an errant Florentine *palazzo* to a medieval marble blockbuster out of Versailles by the Grand Central Station. Although some of these castles date to the nineteenth century and some to the twentieth, all have at least two things in common; all were originally committed in the sacred name of the word "cottage," and all bear actual names which, if they mean anything at all, are roughly translatable in reverse. Thus "Chateau Sur Mer" is not on the ocean, "Champ Soleil" is in the shade, "Land Fall" is the home of an Admiral, "Quatrel" means the home of four "l's," or Lorillards, and such a name as "Bel'Napoli" was never apparently meant to mean anything except that it was once owned by a family named Belknap. "The white elephants," Henry James called these cottages as long ago as 1907, "all cry and no wool."

Half a century later, the castles of Newport still stand, as mute testimony to the Newport revolution. The figures of this revolution are far from mute. The ten largest cottages were in 1925 assessed for $2,773,000; in 1950 they were assessed for $823,150. In 1950 also, only four of the ten cottages were still in private hands and tax-producing, and one of these, "The Breakers," has since been producing as a paying museum. In 1900 Newport's summer estates accounted for 50 per cent of all Newport taxes; in 1950 they accounted for less than 20 per cent. And, if tax records and per cents seem a mundane way of expressing what has happened at Newport, Newporters themselves are happy to supply more colorful expressions. "Isn't it terrible?" the late Mrs. Cornelius Vanderbilt used to ask. "And you know," she would add, "our heads were the first to fall." Schuyler Livingston Parsons, dean of Newport "extra men," is still in a daze. "It all stopped at once," he says. "I can't remember when I had a white tie on last."

In their great days Newporters themselves were by no means averse to using figures. "A man who has a million dollars," old John Jacob Astor once told Julia Ward Howe, "is as well off as if he were rich." Other Newporters also talked in equally round numbers—Newport's "newspaper dollars," they were called. "We are not rich," Mrs. Stuyvesant Fish used to say. "We have only a few million." Maude Parker recalls that one Newport hostess barred from her dinner table people who had less than *five* million dollars; another hostess barred people whose cottage, furnished, cost less than a million. Mrs. O. H. P. Belmont was, of course, on safe ground. Her "Marble House" cost $2,000,000 to build and $9,000,000 to furnish. The Pembroke Joneses used to say that they set aside $300,000 at the beginning of each Newport season for "extra entertainment." In a similar manner, Mrs. Henry Clews, grandniece of Dolly Madison and reputed to be Newport's best-dressed lady of her era, declared that each summer she set aside $10,000 for "mistakes in her clothes." Richard Lounsbery recalls that a single Newport ball cost $200,000—in the days, of course, when not only dollars were dollars but also when balls were balls.

Dinners were dinners, too. Both Mrs. Ogden Mills and Mrs. Elbridge Gerry used to boast that they could give a dinner for a hundred without calling in extra help. There were hand-painted individual place cards at every place and between every two guests there was an elaborate French menu in front and a powdered-haired, knee-breeched, liveried English footman behind. Ten-course meals were eaten off solid gold services. At one dinner a stream flowed down the middle of the table in which "vivid fish swam pleasantly"; at another there was a cage in the center of the table filled with parrots of "singular hues and utterances." At still another the center of the table was covered with sand; at each place was a small sterling silver pail and a matching shovel. At a given signal half a hundred guests dug frantically into the sand in front of them for their favors—thousands of dollars' worth of rubies, sapphires, emeralds and diamonds. Ordinarily, however, the pace was leisurely. The late Mrs. Maud Howe Elliott recalls a dinner at the cottage of George Wales. "We were at the table," she said, "three mortal hours."

When such dinners palled, Newporters took strong measures. At the most memorable dinner in the resort's history Newport Society was introduced to Prince del Drago from Corsica. The Prince was ersatz—a monkey attired in full evening dress. Second only to this famous "Monkey Dinner" was the so-called "Dogs' Dinner." In this, a regular Newport dinner table was taken off its foundations and placed on a veranda—on trestles about a foot high. A hundred dogs participated, most of them in fancy dress; the menu was stewed liver and rice, fricassee of bones and shredded dog biscuit.

At human fancy dress affairs Newport costumes were the height of invention. At one costume ball Philadelphia's Henry Carter and his wife arrived and explained their costume to the announcing footman at the entrance of the ballroom. Carter, a small man, was dressed as Henry IV; his wife, a large woman, represented a Norman peasant. "Henry the Fourth," shouted the footman, "and an enormous pheasant."

Newport built few swimming pools because its lush era antedated them; nonetheless, the resort posted many achievements in sports. Pierre Lorillard achieved what construction men at the time believed was impossible when he built a pier over the reefs in front of "The Breakers" and was thus enabled to bring his enormous yacht *Rhoda* right up to his front door. On the other hand, Philadelphia's Mrs. Richard Cadwalader could not bring her 408-foot *Savarona* even into

Newport's harbor, or indeed into any port in this country. Mrs. Cadwalader refused to pay the duty involved, and her yacht, largest in the world, was reduced to ports abroad. It was fitted with antique rugs and tapestries, gold-plated bathroom fixtures, and a full-sized pipe organ. T. Suffern Tailer built the country's most elaborate private golf course. His "Ocean Links," as it was called, reproduced the most famous individual holes of all the world's most famous courses. Newport's horse-and-buggy days were unequaled anywhere. Several Newporters had as many as twenty different kinds of carriages in their stables and in the old Alfred Gwynne Vanderbilt stables the horses' names were inscribed on gold name plates. O. H. P. Belmont could not bear to have his horses under another roof; the ground floor of "Belcourt" was an all stable affair. Here, in stalls designed by Richard Hunt, with a tasteful barracks for a battery of grooms alongside, the Belmont horses had a change of equipment morning, afternoon and evening. For the night they were bedded down on pure white linen sheets with the Belmont crest embroidered on them. Above the stables, in the salon of "Belcourt," Belmont kept two stuffed horses, old favorites of his, which were mounted by stuffed riders in chain armor.

What any other social resort had, Newport had also and more besides. If Lenox's Mrs. Edwards Spencer kept a pig as a pet in her parlor, Newport's Mrs. John King Van Rensselaer recalls seeing a Newport dowager drive down Bellevue Avenue with a pig seated in her victoria beside her and a monkey on each shoulder. If at Saratoga a President of the United States, Martin Van Buren, was snubbed by Mrs. DeWitt Clinton, at Newport President Chester A. Arthur was snubbed not only by resorters but also by footmen; on the steps of the Newport Casino he was reduced to calling for his own carriage. If Bar Harbor's Joseph Pulitzer imported the entire New York Symphony Orchestra to play for himself and his guests, Newport's Mrs. Cornelius Vanderbilt, Jr., thought nothing, in 1902, of closing for two days a New York hit show of that era, *The Wild Rose*, and having the entire company transported for a private performance at "Beaulieu." Even as late as the depression era the resort was in a class by itself. The late Atwater Kent was perhaps the country's greatest latter-day party-giver. His affairs cut a swath through the societies of Bar Harbor, Palm Beach, Southampton and, finally, in his last days, Hollywood itself. But even at his best party weight—which consisted of three orchestras and some three thousand guests—Kent was not up to Newport. Bar Harbor's Mrs. John DeWitt Peltz recalls that after watching Kent for several seasons at the Maine resort she had the pleasure of going down to Newport and attending several functions there. Returning to Bar Harbor, she was asked to describe them. "Why," she said, "they made At Kent look like pot luck!"

Newport's first summer hotels, which date from the 1830's, were the Bellevue and Whitfield's, Whitfield's being later renamed the Touro House. Although the Aquidneck House, the Perry, the Freemont, the Fillmore and the United States followed in rapid succession, only one Newport hotel became nationally famous. A "huge, yellow pagoda factory," as George William Curtis called it, it was named Ocean House and its opening in 1845, according to Henry Tuckerman, "reduced Saratoga to being a hotel while Newport was a realm."

Along with this all but forgotten hotel period, between the Southern planters and the coming of the New York cottagers, the resort also had a distinguished intellectual period. In later days Edith Wharton, whom old Newporters recall as "Pussy" Jones of "Pencraig," and who wrote her first book at Newport—a study of interior decoration written in collaboration with Newporter Ogden Codman—was never happy there. "I did not care," she wrote, "for watering-place mundanities." But in an earlier era, in the days following the Civil War, when Colonel Higginson settled at the resort, he declared that there were more authors living in Newport than anywhere else in America. This author group, which ranged from Boston's Edgar Allan Poe to California's Bret Harte, also included Dr. Oliver Wendell Holmes, Henry Wadsworth Longfellow, Henry James, George Bancroft and Julia Ward Howe; to it was added such Boston wits as Helen Choate Bell and Thomas Gold Appleton. Newport's Professor Wolcott Gibbs loved nature. "Who loves his fellow man," he said, "plants trees." Mrs. Bell disagreed. "Go kick a tree," she said, "for me." Appleton, who divided his time between Nahant and Newport, was at both resorts the prince of intellectual dilettantes. "A good mixer," the late Maud Howe Elliott described him, "of salads and of guests."

Gresham's Law of first "nice" and then "naughty" millionaires following artists and "solid people" never held too accurately at Newport; in fact, back in its "solid people" era, the resort had at least one millionaire, William Beach Lawrence, who caused the most trouble among the natives of any resorter in Newport's history. Having married the daughter of the wealthy New York merchant, Archibald Gracie, Lawrence purchased, in 1844, almost the whole of Ochre Point for fourteen thousand dollars; many years later he sold for the same sum one acre of this property to a friend of his named Pendleton.

No sooner had the sale been made than the Governor regretted it and proceeded to build a stone wall between the properties. This wall, which extended to the water's edge, cut off the famous Cliff Walk, which even in those days had long been a favorite of native Newporters, and rising in rebellion, they pulled the wall down. Lawrence promptly rebuilt it, this time facing it with broken glass; he also bought a fierce bull which he pastured in the property. Despite the glass and the bull, Newporters once more pulled the wall down and this time they threw it into the sea. Lawrence promptly took to the courts. The case hinged on the discovery of an old right which gave the fishermen public access to the shore for fishing and collecting seaweed. Carried to the Supreme Court after years of litigation, the case was finally settled in favor of the natives and against Lawrence only after the staging of a test shipwreck. The case established a firm precedent. To this day the right of Newport natives to walk between beach and lawn around the great estates, beginning at Forty Steps and traveling around Ochre Point, Rough Point and finally to Bailey's Beach itself, is inviolate. As for Newport resorters they have had to grin and bear the intrusion—although, characteristically, they have made the Cliff Walk as difficult as possible. In some cases the walk has been pushed out on the rocks on bridges, in others it has been depressed below lawn level, and in one case at least, opposite "Marble House," the walk is a complete tunnel.

Each of Newport's great early-day hostesses, Mrs. Sydney Brooks, Mrs. Paran Stevens and Mrs. Nicholas Beach, was responsible for inaugurating at least one new form of entertainment at the resort. Mrs. Brooks introduced Newport to salons, Mrs. Stevens to musicales and Mrs. Beach to dancing receptions. With the coming of Mrs. August Belmont, however, the resort had its first real taste of New York high life. The niece of the Commodore Perry of Lake Erie fame, the wife of the Rothschild banker and the mother of Newport's noted brothers, O. H. P. and Perry Belmont, Mrs. Belmont had elegant French manners, beautiful jewels and was a pioneer resorter. When she deserted her beautiful country seat at the once fashionable Staten Island and built "Bythesea" at Newport, the event marked the beginning of a new era. All old-time Newporters today still recall stories of the sensation created by Mrs. Belmont's famous *demi-daumont*. A Paris importation, the carriage was drawn by four horses with no driver but with the two near horses ridden by postilions in short jackets, tight breeches and smart jockey caps.

But all Newport did not cherish ten-course dinners and liveried footmen and other changes which were inaugurated by the coming of the

Belmonts. Mrs. John Francis felt these changes most sharply. In her one-servant cottage she had the misfortune one summer to engage a maid who had the summer before worked for the Belmonts. In the time-honored manner of her craft, the maid began unfavorably contrasting everything about her new position with her old. "Mr. Belmont," she said one day, "keeps ten servants," another day, "Mr. Belmont keeps twenty horses." Finally in the middle of still another "Mr. Belmont keeps," Mrs. Francis could stand it no longer. "Mr. Belmont," she snapped, "keeps everything but the Ten Commandments."

Even the Belmonts were nothing to what was coming. The real New York task force descended on Newport with the Kips and the Kernochans, the Lorillards and the Livingstons, the Stuyvesants and the Schermerhorns, the Tiffanys, the Rhinelanders and the Van Rensselaers—and finally the Astors and the Vanderbilts. Newport had already had its distinguished resort individuals—William R. Travers, George Gray Griswold, Bradley Martin and James Gordon Bennett, Jr.—but by far its greatest, from the point of view of the future of the resort, was the one and only Ward McAllister. "Mister Make-a-Lister," as old-time Newporters recall him, McAllister made his most famous list shortly after the momentous occasion on March 24, 1888, when he put in the American vocabulary the phrase "The Four Hundred." "There are only," he told Charles H. Crandell of the New York *Tribune*, "about four hundred people in fashionable New York Society. If you go outside that number you strike people who are either not at ease in a ballroom or else make other people not at ease."

Old-time Newporters today hardly recall any Mrs. McAllister at all; McAllister's daughter served as hostess for his parties. In short order, however, McAllister attached himself to Mrs. William Backhouse Astor. The former Caroline Schermerhorn and the so-called "Queen of the Four Hundred," Mrs. Astor had joined the New York invasion of Newport and, in keeping with her position, had bought "Beechwood." This cottage, with its high-ceilinged piazzas on three sides, had been a Newport showplace for years; to it Mrs. Astor added Newport's largest ballroom. Nonetheless, she had hard sledding in her early days at the resort. There were two Mrs. William Astors at Newport, Mrs. William Waldorf as well as Mrs. William Backhouse, and living side by side on Bellevue Avenue both insisted on having their mail addressed simply: "Mrs. Astor, Newport." Both were equally formidable. If Mrs. William Backhouse Astor at "Beechwood" called native Newporters her "dear villagers," Mrs. William Waldorf Astor at "Beaulieu" built a brick wall between her cottage and Cliff Walk and kept them away entirely.

Finally, with McAllister's help, Mrs. William Backhouse outran the challenging Mrs. William Waldorf, and the latter gave up Newport entirely and took up cottage-keeping in England.

From that time until after the turn of the century, *the* Mrs. Astor reigned supreme. Over her black pompadour, which was later succeeded by a jet-black wig, she wore a diamond tiara and even for her *intime* evenings—for just a hundred or so guests—she took little stock in Andrew Carnegie's dictum that jewel-wearing was a relic of barbarism. She wore a three-strand diamond necklace, a dazzling diamond stomacher and several chains of diamonds in lesser spots. Dignified, reserved, and aloof, she rose above everything and everybody.

Outwardly at least, Mrs. Astor saw no evil, heard no evil and spoke no evil. McAllister himself described her qualifications for Newport queenship. "She had," said her court chamberlain, who always spoke of her as his "Mystic Rose," "a just appreciation of the rights of others, and, coming herself from an old Colonial family, a good appreciation of the value of ancestry; always keeping it near her, and bringing it in, in all social matters, but also understanding the importance and power of the new element; recognizing it, and fairly and generously awarding it a prominent place." On young people attending her balls Mrs. Astor's dictum was stern. "I like to have them come," she said, "but they must look after themselves." On people "in trade," as she called it, she wavered; at carpet manufacturers she drew the line. "I buy my carpets from them," she said, "but is that any reason why I should invite them to walk on them?" When the early twentieth-century version of Café Society began to rear its head, Mrs. Astor showed her respect for the new development and made plans for her first Bohemian party. Surprised, the late Lady Mendl asked her whom she was having. "Why, J. P. Morgan," she replied, "and Edith Wharton."

Such majesty was made to order for McAllister, a man who said that one thing he disliked most about America was the custom of shaking hands. When the Navy, largely through the influence of Admiral Luce, established a war college and torpedo station at Newport in 1880, McAllister took full credit for it. It was necessary, he felt, to solve Newport's perennial shortage of men on week nights. "So many of them," McAllister said, "are boat men, don't you know, down Friday night and back again Sunday." With equal pleasure he watched the rapid evacuation of the New England intellectual from the resort. "Fashionable people cultivate and refine themselves," he said. "The talent of and for Society develops itself just as does the talent for art." Finally McAllister applauded Newport's biggest change of all—the end of the hotels. Although the old Ocean House lasted on until it finally burned down in 1898, McAllister had by this time founded a resort civilization so secure that it was not dependent upon mere hotels. Even today Newport remains staunchly anti-hotel. It has its modern Viking Hotel for commercial travelers, but only the Muenchinger King Hotel and the La Forge Cottages are approved social residences.

McAllister died in 1895. As if he had not done enough to establish Newport tradition for all time, his good work at the resort was soon seconded by still another protégé of Mrs. Astor, the remarkable Harry Lehr. If McAllister was the "Autocrat of the Drawing Rooms," Lehr was the so-called "King of the Gilded Age." Born in Baltimore in 1869, the son of a prosperous snuff and tobacco importer, Lehr saw his family reduced to poverty at an early age and never forgot it. "Clod-like people," he wrote in his diary, could stand "the cold grayness of everyday life" but he could not. "Other men have to sweat in offices," he said. "I made up my mind I never would." His answer was a simple one. "I saw that most human beings are fools, and that the best way to live harmoniously with them and make them like you is to pander to their stupidity. They want to be entertained and be made to laugh. They will overlook most anything so long as you amuse them. I did not mind cutting capers for them if I could gain what I wanted through it."

As a resort sport, Lehr was unequaled in Society history. Because he attracted Society's best wherever he went, everything for him was free. In Newport he visited; in New York the Waldorf, Delmonico's and Sherry's all competed for the honor of seeing that he had free board and lodging during the off season. Wetzel made his clothes free, Black, Starr and Frost lent him an endless supply of jewels, Mrs. Stuyvesant Fish and the wives of other railroad men arranged passage on all railroads, and George Kessler, the French champagne agent, paid him six thousand dollars a year for pocket money. The only expense he might have had was postage stamps. Instead of letters, he sent cables and wires—all of which, arranged through Mrs. Clarence Mackay and the wives of other cable magnates, were also free. In return, Lehr aimed to please; his insults to his hostesses and benefactors were cherished. One day he paused before the stained glass windows of "Belcourt" on which O. H. P. Belmont, in the Newport tradition of appropriating coats of arms, had emblazoned the arms of Dunois, the Bastard of Orleans. "My dear Oliver," said Lehr, "why proclaim yourself illegitimate?" On another occasion the Stuyvesant Fishes got up to leave a party. "Sit down, Fishes," said Lehr sharply. "You're not rich enough to leave first." Occasionally Newport's husbands rebelled. More often, they decided that Lehr was, at worst, the most harmless between-week-end diversion that their wives could find. Lehr himself was aware that this was the secret of his success. "Love affairs," he once said, "are fatal to ambition. I have seen the shore strewn with the wrecks of people who have given away to their passions."

In its great days Newport was the center of the sporting world, and particularly the center of the new world of tennis—or lawn tennis, as it was called to distinguish it from the older court tennis. Invented in 1873 by the Englishman, Major Walter Clopton Wingfield, who first patented the game under the remarkable name "Sphairistike," lawn tennis saw its first American court at the Staten Island Cricket and Base Ball Club. When the Newport Casino opened in 1880, Newport was granted the national championship. This championship was won for eight straight years by the peerless Richard Dudley Sears, a Boston resorter of such racket eminence that in 1943 his obituary stated that his "death represented the end of an era of ruffles and parasols, roped-off lawns and sunny afternoons, lopsided tennis bats and the genteel pat of ball against languid strings." At about the same time the late Tom Pettit, Casino professional, was watching a group of modern tournament players. "If I'd known how much money there was in being an amateur," he said, "I'd never have turned pro."

But the Newport Casino, in the Gay Nineties at least, was more than the scene of Newport tennis. In fact, by 1885 the massive building on Bellevue Avenue, built by James Gordon Bennett, Jr., and designed by Stanford White, was the center of Newport life. The clubhouse, a curious combination of Victorian grandeur and Chinese detail, still stands today almost unchanged from those days; hordes of sparrows still camp on its many-gabled roof and along its vine-covered sides. Entering off Bellevue Avenue one still passes first the branch shops of the smart New York stores and then enters under a tunnel passageway into the inner circle of gardened courts and lawns. On the Horse Shoe Piazza in the old days Mullaly's String Orchestra played every morning. Here, on the high stools up on the second floor, the resorters sat and gossiped and looked down on the townspeople below, and each morning just as regularly the townspeople gathered on the Bellevue Avenue sidewalk to gossip and look up. The "rubber plants," the resorters called the starers below; nonetheless, for one dollar apiece, they were admitted to watch Casino balls and cheer for their favorite belles. These belles were almost invariably described as "willowy"—a favorite word of the day. The slim Mrs. John Jacob Astor, the former Ava Willing and the later Lady Ribblesdale, was perhaps the most famous. "I remember the extraordinary lovely lines of her instep and foot," said Michael Strange, who, as Blanche Oelrichs, was herself a Newport belle. "Sculped and isolated in a lit-up cabinet, it might have passed for an extreme sample of breeding."

To many Newporters the most fascinating of all the belles was Mrs. Philip Lydig, the ex-Mrs. W. E. D. Stokes and the former Rita de Acosta. Mrs. Lydig was born in Spain, had dark velvety skin, waist-long lustrous black hair and such deep black eyes that they were unforgettable. She had delicate health and was always in intriguing difficulties, either financial or male in nature. Nonetheless, she invariably found enough admirers to extract her from these difficulties—as well as to plunge her into new ones—and whether she was at "death's door" or dancing in the most décolleté gown ever seen at Newport, she was always the center of the stage. One week end she drove out in her electric car to meet an ex-beau who was arriving on the ferry. On the way back he told her that he had come all the way back from Egypt to see her; he had decided that unless she would have an affair with him life was not worth living. "Very well," said Mrs. Lydig, "we'll die together." Without another word she ran her car at full speed into a telegraph pole. The car was ruined and the beau had to be taken to a hospital. Mrs. Lydig walked home unhurt.

Actually, no picture of Newport at the turn of the century would be complete without the appearance of that symbol of the new age—the automobile. More than one historian of the industry has, in fact, credited Newport with being primarily responsible for the promotion of "bubbles," as cars were then called. Newporters themselves had no idea of their service—"Nobody dreamed," Stuyvesant Fish recently recalled, "that automobiles would come into general use"—but all Newport activities were thoroughly reported and people all over the country wanted automobiles, if for no other reason, to follow the Four Hundred.

The Newport craze began in 1897 when O. H. P. Belmont imported a French machine. Harry Payne Whitney promptly replied with a whole stableful of "bubbles" and when William K. Vanderbilt and John Jacob Astor also began replacing their horses with the "White Ghost" and the "Red Devil," as they were called, the race was on. Newport's first real automobile race occurred early in 1899 when the "bubblers," attired in dusters, veils and goggles, long-gauntleted gloves and long-visored caps, vied for honors at ten miles an hour.

More memorable than this beach-racing was the first great obstacle race of September 7, 1899. For this event the grounds of Belmont's "Belcourt" were transformed into an obstacle park. The race was a kind of automobile *slalom*, the course being marked out not only by flags but also by all manner of stuffed dummy figures. These figures represented horses, dogs, nurses, children, maids, policemen and other obstacles. The idea of the race was to drive by the figures, on a time basis, without knocking them down. Belmont himself drove first with Mrs. Stuyvesant Fish as his co-pilot. Their car was decorated with an arbor of cat-o'-nine-tails with a stuffed eagle on top; in front, extending a full ten feet ahead of the car, was a long pole also decorated with flowers. Behind Belmont came Ambassador James W. Gerard and Mrs. Belmont. Their car was buried in blue hydrangeas, Newport's favorite flower, and Mrs. Belmont carried a whip made of hydrangeas and daisies. In the third car Harry Lehr drove and Mrs. Astor, complete with hydrangea-collared lapdog, rode shotgun. All three of these contestants, as well as some fifteen others, fared badly, knocking over the obstacles like tenpins, but Colonel Jack Astor, partnered by Mrs. Ladenburg, emerged victorious. "He steered," says one reporter present, "with the same cool-headed dash that distinguished him while serving under fire at Santiago."

Often overlooked in Newport history, among Newport's eminent hostesses and their quaint counterparts like Ward McAllister and Harry Lehr, have been the rank and file of Newport's male population. From the earliest days these so-called "solid men" played a vital part in the success of the resort. General Cornelius Vanderbilt was never too busy running railroads to give his undivided attention to the carpenters' estimates on reshingling the Casino roof, and Arthur Curtiss James never allowed the directors meetings of his copper companies to interfere with his decision as to the proper rent to be charged for Casino shops. The New York lawyer, Lewis Cass Ledyard, estimated shortly before he died in 1932 that his attention to Newport had cost him a total of two years of his life—that amount of time having been spent on the Fall River Boat.

The sturdiest specimen of the hero in Newport history was the late George H. Norman, family-founding forebear of the resort's distinguished Norman dynasty. A dignified gentleman with a long full beard, Norman had no middle name. He thought he ought to have one and so chose the "H" even though the initial had never stood for anything. Norman's occupation was that of a hydraulic engineer and, born in Newport, he was a rugged individualist to the end of his days. When a neighbor refused to repaint a barn, which Norman thought was a disagreeable color, Norman, in the owner's absence, had it painted for him. Riding in the train one day in 1900, Norman wrote his will on the back of a paper bag; to this day no one has ever been able to break the trust he thus established.

On another occasion Norman, who never took a parlor car, was reading his paper after the train had started when the conductor, coming through the car, noticed a suitcase in the aisle beside him. The train was crowded and the conductor told Norman sharply that he would have to get the suitcase out of the aisle. "No," said Norman reading his paper, "I don't." The conductor told Norman that a person who tripped over the suitcase might sue the railroad and it would then be Norman's fault. "I mean it," he said, "move it." Norman paid no attention and the conductor became exasperated. "You may be the largest stockholder of this railroad," he said, "but I'll show you who's the captain of this train. If you don't move that suitcase I'll throw it off." Norman still continued to read. The conductor was furious. "I'll count three," he shouted. "I'll throw it off the train!" As the conductor, red in the face and raging, sounded the counts, Norman still read on. At the third count the conductor seized the suitcase, strode down to the end of the car and hurled it out the door. Coming back he rubbed his hands. "Well," he said, "you Newporters think you own the earth. I guess that will teach you a lesson." For the first time Norman looked up. "Not me, it won't," he said. "It wasn't my suitcase."

Newport's first men's club, the Newport Reading Room, was established in 1854 and antedates all other resort clubs in the country; its proudest boast is that it still operates the oldest flush toilets in existence. Located across Bellevue Avenue from the old Muenchinger King Hotel, it is a small yellow and white frame house with a handsome cupola on top and a wide piazza several steps up off the street which is marked by ancient carriage lamps. "This club," says President Gustave J. S. White, "is a sort of a last stand of old principles." Among these principles are a Spartan diet—canned soup and crackers are the only foods served in the club—and a severe antifeminism. In the old days so severe was this latter principle that a lady who saw one of the Reading Roomers sitting on the porch was not supposed to speak to him, no matter how close he was to her or how well she knew him; the gentleman, for his part, stared solemnly by her as if she was not there at all.

The club also has an extremely severe set of by-laws. Rule V of these laws reads: "Conversation and drinking are forbidden in the northwest room on the second floor." Actually, conversation is somewhat limited everywhere in the Reading Room. Many of the elderly members are so troubled with deafness that they do not even know whether anyone is talking or not. Often a visitor to the club will have the same experience which he often has after a Newport dinner party when, after the gentlemen are separated from the ladies, two or three gentlemen will start talking at once—each of them not realizing that anyone is talking and thinking their visitor, who cannot possibly parse anything out of the simultaneous deliveries, must be even deafer than they are. At the same time, no visitor to the club can fail to be impressed by its lineal formidability. The club recently boasted no less than ten father-and-son membership combinations, including the Messrs., *père* and *fils*, Bogert, Douglas, Jelke, Manice, Norman, Phelps, Prince, Sheffield and Whitehouse. All these gentlemen take not only the Reading Room but also all Newport with extreme earnestness. Many of them have, in the spirit of Newport's old rank-and-file population, placed with local real estate agents standing offers to meet any cottage property bids of which they disapprove.

Even more recherché than the Reading Room, at least to current Newporters, is the Clambake Club, located out on the end of Easton's Point just beyond an unprepossessing modern development of small houses. Limited to one hundred members, it still features the clambakes and skeet-shooting of yesteryear. This club too can be formidable. It was here that the young golfer T. Suffern Tailer, who had returned to the resort after long absence, admitted to a group of Clambakers, shortly before World War II, that he was going to vote for Roosevelt. One of the gentlemen patted his knee in a fatherly manner. "You've been away a long time, Tommy," he said. "Down here we don't say that even in fun."

The whole Newport colossus, and its sturdy social saga, reaches its natural climax in an extremely vital club area of the resort known as Bailey's Beach. That such a name is out of keeping with its grandeur is well known to Newporters; the official name of Bailey's is the Spouting Rock Beach Association. Even its location is significant, for it stands at the end of Cliff Walk and thus brings to an abrupt close the public walk between Newport's cottages and ocean. For generations aspirant millionaires might have been asked to join the Reading Room or the Clambake Club and might even have negotiated one of the "Umbrella Stands" at the Casino; until they were firmly established in a cabana of their own at Bailey's, however, there was still work to be done. Into the American vocabulary they put the phrase, "Bailey's Beach or Bust."

Today the new Bailey's which was rebuilt following the hurricane of 1938 is a gray-brick building with a lemon-colored trim and even an off-tomato-colored bar; it boasts eighty-one outside cabanas. These are known as Bath Houses "A" and consist of two small dressing rooms, a shower and toilet, as well as a porch—upon which, except in case of serious illness, every member of the family owning a cabana must be seen daily from 11:00 A.M. to lunch. There are also two hundred inside cabanas, or Bath Houses "B," as well as an ordinary locker room, in which all Newporters not in the select eighty-one must sit out their turn to get an "A." Like other Newport clubs, Bailey's is run on a double-membership basis; in other words, one must become first a seasonal subscriber, then a stockholder and full-fledged member. Supporting a cabana at Bailey's often runs as high as fifteen hundred dollars a year, because they are owned outright, and the upkeep and all improvements are in the hands of the owner, not the Beach Association. All cabanas have locks, but these locks are not to keep outsiders out; they are to keep the owners out. The superintendent of the beach keeps all keys and every night at seven o'clock locks all cabanas. Then, all night long, every hour a watchman makes the rounds to see that no owners have tried to break in. Bailey's wants no part of after-dark bathing or cabana courtships, and the fact that the younger generation does not like the beach's blue laws does not worry *cachet*-minded Newporters at all. "Young people have a good time at Bailey's," declares Mrs. George Tyson, a sister of Mrs. Mesta and a lady whose cottage overlooks the beach, "but it is a good time in an awfully nice way."

Until 1947 no photographer was ever permitted inside Bailey's. Newspapers and picture magazines were reduced to attempting either airplane shots or telephoto-lens exposure from neighboring rocks. To mark the historic occasion, the first magazine nominated for the honor of picturing the beach was the *National Geographic*. In reality Bailey's, which has no swimming pool of any kind, is not only not the best of Newport's many beaches; it is by all odds the worst. Some years ago Mrs. George Henry Warren attended a costume ball dressed as "Miss Bailey's Beach." Her ensemble consisted of a seaweedy-looking dress liberally ornamented with clamshells, bones, banana peels and orange rinds. But Bailey's protocol permits no one to swim anywhere else. A British visitor who, a few summers ago, insisted on going down and taking a dip from off the smooth rocks at the end of the beach was criticized as severely as an American might be for making his own rules at an introduction at the Court of St. James.

Once a person has entered the water from the proper area, however, Bailey's permits a wide latitude of aquatic enjoyment. The late Evalyn Walsh McLean always swam with two detectives. "Good Lord!" she exclaimed. "I've got to be watched." In more recent times Bailey's outstanding mermaid was Baroness Gourgaud, a lady whose social position at the resort was fortified by the fact that her great-grandfather-in-law had been on St. Helena with Napoleon. The Baroness did not swim a stroke, but she liked to be in the water a full half hour. She solved the difficulty by surrounding herself with a large automobile tube. She also balanced a red parasol over her head—a feat which has been in the tradition of Bailey's great swimmers of the past. Mrs. O. H. P. Belmont also swam with a parasol, although hers was green, while Mrs. James Kernochan, who carried no parasol, successfully avoided the sun, as well as prying eyes, with heavy black bathing shoes, thick black cotton stockings, a pair of large black pantaloons topped off with a full black skirt, a black blouse fastened with pearl buttons, a black jacket with full sleeves tied around her wrists and, finally, an enormous black Mother Hubbard bonnet tied under the chin. Far from a natatory nightmare, Mrs. Kernochan was regarded in her day as a Bailey belle; much more consternation was caused shortly before the First World War when Mrs. Herbert Parsons, the former Miss Clews, became the first lady to appear on the beach without stockings. Even today Bailey's Old Guard ladies may be seen, on unusually hot days, holding their parasols as they gingerly approach the water. Although they no longer actually swim with them, the parasols themselves, stuck in the sand during their swim, are still an important part of beach scenery.

Of Bailey's male swimmers, the late James Van Alen was the most sporty; Van Alen always swam in a white straw hat and puffed a large cigar while he did so. Even more picturesque was the late Hermann Oelrichs. A large round man who felt more at home in the water than he did on dry land, Oelrichs was a veritable water buffalo. For his dip he would equip himself with a dinner pail, a heavy flask and some light reading material, then proceed far out to sea. Unlike Eleanora Sears and other long-distance swimmers of Bailey's history, who at least kept to a charted course, Oelrichs simply drifted about. Saved on some occasions by incoming tides and upon others by the timely arrival of the Coast Guard, he never felt himself in any danger and was particularly indignant about a suggestion, which he traced to the Naval War College, that he was a menace to navigation and should at least mark his position by a buoy.

Last but no means least of the many aspects of the Newport revolution has been the narrowing of the gulf which in Newport's great days always separated the natives from the resorters. Today younger members of Newport's most illustrious resort families, including Van Alens, Lorillards, Phelpses and Auchinclosses, are serving on committees side by side with Newport natives in an effort to promote the new era of good feeling. Even Newport resorters of advanced years are doing their duty on these committees, and though they are not always successful—"I blow in," says Miss Edith Wetmore, "I blow up and I blow out"—the change is a notable one. An enormous indoor tennis and badminton building on Bellevue Avenue, a birthday present to a member of the A & P Hartford family, has been converted into a club for natives, and though the natives still refuse to swim at Bailey's because they have a far better beach of their own, it has now become difficult to distinguish resorters from natives without a blue book. When Newport's own movie star, Van Johnson, son of a local plumber and a young man who started his career as a beach boy at Bailey's, became the first native to move into the same financial league as the resorters, there was even a strong feeling that it would be nice to have the local boy move in on the cottage set and build at least a small camp of his own. Unfortunately Johnson has so far shown little enthusiasm for the movement but his name has given it much impetus. As one of his schoolboy chums expresses it, "It sure would be nice to have just one Van Johnson out there among all those Van Alens, Van Beurens and Van Rensselaers."

For many generations a rather charming demonstration of Newport's native vs. resorter spirit has been carried on by the resort's taxi drivers. These drivers still conduct what were once called "rubbernecking trips" around the estates, and the passing years have merely added to the appeal of their blow-by-blow accounts of life as it used to be lived behind the iron gates.

Unfortunately the dean of all these Newport drivers is now dead, but his place in Newport history is assured by an event which occurred on one of his last tours. For thirty years he had been taking sight-seers around the cottages without ever once, even by insinuation, breaking the barriers of good taste. He would give names, quote the sizes of the cottages and mention prices, but these were matters of public knowledge. Never would he stoop to editorial comment. Finally one day he had a cabful of visitors and was passing "The Elms," the cottage of

NEW ENGLAND · 97

E. J. Berwind, Pennsylvania coal baron. This cottage is featured by not one, but three, front doors, thus enabling three carriages, or carloads, of guests to be discharged at once; along its great stone fence are sculptured a large row of heads, all of which bear suspicious resemblance to that of the late Mr. Berwind himself. The driver, of course, was above calling attention to any such details as these. He merely pointed out the cottage, said it was called "The Elms," was the home of E. J. Berwind, the coal baron, had fifty rooms and cost one million dollars; he then went on to add that the cottage was at present being done over and that during the work the baron's sister, Miss Julia Berwind, was living in a stable in the rear. Even this he qualified. The stable was, he said, fitted out for an apartment above and was entirely suitable. On the spur of the moment he went so far as to point it out, down a narrow side road.

·A lady in the cab could not let this pass. "What!" she said, leaning forward and looking down the road in great concern, "Miss Berwind! In a stable!"

The driver looked around, saw the lady was past calming, and then he too looked down the road at the stable. All at once thirty years of his good work was forgotten.

"Lady," he said slowly, "if it was good enough for Jesus, I guess it's good enough for Miss Berwind."

III. NEW YORK

O. Henry

MAMMON AND THE ARCHER

OLD Anthony Rockwall, retired manufacturer and proprietor of Rockwall's Eureka Soap, looked out the library window of his Fifth Avenue mansion and grinned. His neighbor to the right—the aristocratic clubman, G. Van Schuylight Suffolk-Jones—came out to his waiting motorcar, wrinkling a contumelious nostril, as usual, at the Italian renaissance sculpture of the soap palace's front elevation.

"Stuck-up old statuette of nothing doing!" commented the ex-Soap King. "The Eden Musée'll get that old frozen Nesselrode yet if he don't watch out. I'll have this house painted red, white, and blue next summer and see if that'll make his Dutch nose turn up any higher."

And then Anthony Rockwall, who never cared for bells, went to the door of his library and shouted "Mike!" in the same voice that had once chipped off pieces of the welkin on the Kansas prairies.

"Tell my son," said Anthony to the answering menial, "to come in here before he leaves the house."

When young Rockwall entered the library the old man laid aside his newspaper, looked at him with a kindly grimness on his big, smooth, ruddy countenance, rumpled his mop of white hair with one hand and rattled the keys in his pocket with the other.

"Richard," said Anthony Rockwall, "what do you pay for the soap that you use?"

Richard, only six months home from college, was startled a little. He had not yet taken the measure of this sire of his, who was as full of unexpectedness as a girl at her first party.

"Six dollars a dozen, I think, dad."

"And your clothes?"

"I suppose about sixty dollars, as a rule."

"You're a gentleman," said Anthony, decidedly. "I've heard of these young bloods spending $24 a dozen for soap, and going over the hundred mark for clothes. You've got as much money to waste as any of 'em, and yet you stick to what's decent and moderate. Now I use the old Eureka—not only for sentiment, but it's the purest soap made. Whenever you pay more than 10 cents a cake for soap you buy bad perfumes and labels. But 50 cents is doing very well for a young man in your generation, position and condition. As I said, you're a gentleman. They say it takes three generations to make one. They're off. Money'll do it as slick as soap grease. It's made you one. By hokey! it's almost made one of me. I'm nearly as impolite and disagreeable and ill-mannered as these two old knickerbocker gents on each side of me that can't sleep of nights because I bought in between 'em."

"There are some things that money can't accomplish," remarked young Rockwall, rather gloomily.

"Now, don't say that," said old Anthony, shocked. "I bet my money on money every time. I've been through the encyclopædia down to Y looking for something you can't buy with it; and I expect to have to take up the appendix next week. I'm for money against the field. Tell me something money won't buy."

"For one thing," answered Richard, rankling a little, "it won't buy one into the exclusive circles of society."

"Oho! won't it?" thundered the champion of the root of evil. "You tell me where your exclusive circles would be if the first Astor hadn't had the money to pay for his steerage passage over?"

Richard sighed.

"And that's what I was coming to," said the old man, less boisterously. "That's why I asked you to come in. There's something going wrong with you, boy. I've been noticing it for two weeks. Out with it. I guess I could lay my hands on eleven millions within twenty-four hours, besides the real estate. If it's your liver, there's the *Rambler* down in the bay, coaled, and ready to steam down to the Bahamas in two days."

"Not a bad guess, dad; you haven't missed it far."

"Ah," said Anthony, keenly; "what's her name?"

Richard began to walk up and down the library floor. There was enough comradeship and sympathy in this crude old father of his to draw his confidence.

"Why don't you ask her?" demanded old Anthony. "She'll jump at you. You've got the money and the looks, and you're a decent boy. Your hands are clean. You've got no Eureka soap on 'em. You've been to college, but she'll overlook that."

"I haven't had a chance," said Richard.

"Make one," said Anthony. "Take her for a walk in the park, or a straw ride, or walk home with her from church. Chance! Pshaw!"

"You don't know the social mill, dad. She's part of the stream that turns it. Every hour and minute of her time is arranged for days in advance. I must have that girl, dad, or this town is a blackjack swamp forevermore. And I can't write it—I can't do that."

"Tut!" said the old man. "Do you mean to tell me that with all the money I've got you can't get an hour or two of a girl's time for yourself?"

"I've put it off too late. She's going to sail for Europe at noon day after to-morrow for a two years' stay. I'm to see her alone to-morrow evening for a few minutes. She's at Larchmont now at her aunt's. I can't go there. But I'm allowed to meet her with a cab at the Grand Central Station to-morrow evening at the 8.30 train. We drive down Broadway to Wallack's at a gallop, where her mother and a box party will be waiting for us in the lobby. Do you think she would listen to a declaration from me during that six or eight minutes under those circumstances? No. And what chance would I have in the theatre or afterward? None. No, dad, this is one tangle that your money can't unravel. We can't buy one minute of time with cash; if we could, rich people would live longer. There's no hope of getting a talk with Miss Lantry before she sails."

"All right, Richard, my boy," said old Anthony, cheerfully. "You may run along down to your club now. I'm glad it ain't your liver. But don't forget to burn a few punk sticks in the joss house to the great god Mazuma from time to time. You say money won't buy time? Well, of course, you can't order eternity wrapped up and delivered at your residence for a price, but I've seen Father Time get pretty bad stone bruises on his heels when he walked through the gold diggings."

That night came Aunt Ellen, gentle, sentimental, wrinkled, sighing, oppressed by wealth, in to Brother Anthony at his evening paper, and began discourse on the subject of lovers' woes.

"He told me all about it," said Brother Anthony, yawning. "I told him my bank account was at his service. And then he began to knock money. Said money couldn't help. Said the rules of society couldn't be bucked for a yard by a team of ten millionaires."

"Oh, Anthony," sighed Aunt Ellen, "I wish you would not think so much of money. Wealth is nothing where a true affection is concerned. Love is all-powerful. If he only had spoken earlier! She could not have refused our Richard. But now I fear it is too late. He will have no opportunity to address her. All your gold cannot bring happiness to your son."

At eight o'clock the next evening Aunt Ellen took a quaint old gold ring from a moth-eaten case and gave it to Richard.

"Wear it to-night, nephew," she begged. "Your mother gave it to me. Good luck in love she said it brought. She asked me to give it to you when you had found the one you loved."

Young Rockwall took the ring reverently and tried it on his smallest finger. It slipped as far as the second joint and stopped. He took it off and stuffed it into his vest pocket, after the manner of man. And then he 'phoned for his cab.

At the station he captured Miss Lantry out of the gabbing mob at eight thirty-two.

"We mustn't keep mamma and the others waiting," said she.

"To Wallack's Theatre as fast as you can drive!" said Richard, loyally.

They whirled up Forty-second to Broadway, and then down the white-starred lane that leads from the soft meadows of sunset to the rocky hills of morning.

At Thirty-fourth Street young Richard quickly thrust up the trap and ordered the cabman to stop.

"I've dropped a ring," he apologized, as he climbed out. "It was my mother's, and I'd hate to lose it. I won't detain you a minute—I saw where it fell."

In less than a minute he was back in the cab with the ring.

But within that minute a crosstown car had stopped directly in front of the cab. The cab-man tried to pass to the left, but a heavy express wagon cut him off. He tried the right and had to back away from a furniture van that had no business to be there. He tried to back out, but dropped his reins and swore dutifully. He was blockaded in a tangled mess of vehicles and horses.

One of those street blockades had occurred that sometimes tie up commerce and movement quite suddenly in the big city.

"Why don't you drive on?" said Miss Lantry, impatiently. "We'll be late."

Richard stood up in the cab and looked around. He saw a congested flood of wagons, trucks, cabs, vans and street cars filling the vast space where Broadway, Sixth Avenue, and Thirty-fourth Street cross one another as a twenty-six inch maiden fills her twenty-two inch girdle. And still from all the cross streets they were hurrying and rattling toward the converging point at full speed, and hurling themselves into the straggling mass, locking wheels and adding their drivers' imprecations to the clamor. The entire traffic of Manhattan seemed to have jammed itself around them. The oldest New Yorker among the thousands of spectators that lined the sidewalks had not witnessed a street blockade of the proportions of this one.

"I'm very sorry," said Richard, as he resumed his seat, "but it looks as if we are stuck. They won't get this jumble loosened up in an hour. It was my fault. If I hadn't dropped the ring we——"

"Let me see the ring," said Miss Lantry. "Now that it can't be helped, I don't care. I think theatres are stupid, anyway."

At 11 o'clock that night somebody tapped lightly on Anthony Rockwall's door.

"Come in," shouted Anthony, who was in a red dressing-gown, reading a book of piratical adventures.

Somebody was Aunt Ellen, looking like a gray-haired angel that had been left on earth by mistake.

"They're engaged, Anthony," she said, softly. "She has promised to marry our Richard. On their way to the theatre there was a street blockade, and it was two hours before their cab could get out of it.

"And oh, Brother Anthony, don't ever boast of the power of money again. A little emblem of true love—a little ring that symbolized unending and unmercenary affection—was the cause of our Richard finding his happiness. He dropped it in the street, and got out to recover it. And before they could continue the blockade occurred. He spoke to his love and won her there while the cab was hemmed in. Money is dross compared with true love, Anthony."

"All right," said old Anthony. "I'm glad the boy has got what he wanted. I told him I wouldn't spare any expense in the matter if——"

"But, Brother Anthony, what good could your money have done?"

"Sister," said Anthony Rockwall, "I've got my pirate in a devil of a scrape. His ship has just been scuttled, and he's too good a judge of the value of money to let drown. I wish you would let me go on with this chapter."

The story should end here. I wish it would as heartily as you who read it wish it did. But we must go to the bottom of the well for truth.

The next day a person with red hands and a blue polka-dot necktie, who called himself Kelly, called at Anthony Rockwall's house and was at once received in the library.

"Well," said Anthony, reaching for his checkbook, "it was a good bilin' of soap. Let's see—you had $5,000 in cash."

"I paid out $300 more of my own," said Kelly. "I had to go a little above the estimate. I got the express wagons and cabs mostly for $5; but the trucks and two-horse teams mostly raised me to $10. The motormen wanted $10, and some of the loaded teams $20. The cops struck me hardest—$50 I paid two, and the rest $20 and $25. But didn't it work beautiful, Mr. Rockwall? I'm glad William A. Brady wasn't onto that little outdoor vehicle mob scene. I wouldn't want William to break his heart with jealousy. And never a rehearsal, either! The boys was on time to the fraction of a second. It was two hours before a snake could get below Greeley's statue."

"Thirteen hundred—there you are, Kelly," said Anthony, tearing off a check. "Your thousand, and the $300 you were out. You don't despise money, do you, Kelly?"

"Me?" said Kelly. "I can lick the man that invented poverty."

Anthony called Kelly when he was at the door.

"You didn't notice," said he, "anywhere in the tie-up, a kind of a fat boy without any clothes on shooting arrows around with a bow, did you?"

"Why, no," said Kelly, mystified. "I didn't. If he was like you say, maybe the cops pinched him before I got there."

"I thought the little rascal wouldn't be on hand," chuckled Anthony. "Good-by, Kelly."

O. Henry

MAN ABOUT TOWN

THERE were two or three things that I wanted to know. I do not care about a mystery. So I began to inquire.

It took me two weeks to find out what women carry in dress suit cases. And then I began to ask why a mattress is made in two pieces.

From The Four Million, copyright, 1903, 1905, by Doubleday & Company, Inc.

This serious query was at first received with suspicion because it sounded like a conundrum. I was at last assured that its double form of construction was designed to make lighter the burden of woman, who makes up beds. I was so foolish as to persist, begging to know why, then, they were not made in two equal pieces; whereupon I was shunned.

The third draught that I craved from the fount of knowledge was enlightenment concerning the character known as A Man About Town. He was more vague in my mind than a type should be. We must have a concrete idea of anything, even if it be an imaginary idea, before we can comprehend it. Now, I have a mental picture of John Doe that is as clear as a steel engraving. His eyes are weak blue; he wears a brown vest and a shiny black serge coat. He stands always in the sunshine chewing something; and he keeps half-shutting his pocket knife and opening it again with his thumb. And, if the Man Higher Up is ever found, take my assurance for it, he will be a large, pale man with blue wristlets showing under his cuffs, and he will be sitting to have his shoes polished within sound of a bowling alley, and there will be somewhere about him turquoises.

But the canvas of my imagination, when it came to limning the Man About Town, was blank. I fancied that he had a detachable sneer (like the smile of the Cheshire cat) and attached cuffs; and that was all. Whereupon I asked a newspaper reporter about him.

"Why," said he, "a 'Man About Town' is something between a 'rounder' and a 'clubman.' He isn't exactly—well, he fits in between Mrs. Fish's receptions and private boxing bouts. He doesn't—well, he doesn't belong either to the Lotos Club or to the Jerry McGeogheghan Galvanized Iron Workers' Apprentices' Left Hook Chowder Association. I don't exactly know how to describe him to you. You'll see him everywhere there's anything doing. Yes, I suppose he's a type. Dress clothes every evening; knows the ropes; calls every policeman and waiter in town by their first names. No; he never travels with the hydrogen derivatives. You generally see him alone or with another man."

My friend the reporter left me, and I wandered further afield. By this time the 3126 electric lights on the Rialto were alight. People passed, but they held me not. Paphian eyes rayed upon me and left me unscathed. Diners, heimgangers, shop-girls, confidence men, panhandlers, actors, highwaymen, millionaires, and outlanders hurried, skipped, strolled, sneaked, swaggered, and scurried by me; but I took no note of them. I knew them all; I had read their hearts; they had served. I wanted my Man About Town. He was a type, and to drop him would be an error—a typograph—but no! let us continue.

Let us continue with a moral digression. To see a family reading the Sunday paper gratifies. The sections have been separated. Papa is earnestly scanning the page that pictures the young lady exercising before an open window, and bending—but there, there! Mamma is interested in trying to guess the missing letters in the word N—w Yo—k. The oldest girls are eagerly perusing the financial reports, for a certain young man remarked last Sunday night that he had taken a flyer in Q., X. & Z. Willie, the eighteen-year-old son, who attends the New York public school, is absorbed in the weekly article describing how to make over an old shirt, for he hopes to take a prize in sewing on graduation day.

Grandma is holding to the comic supplement with a two-hours' grip; and little Tottie, the baby, is rocking along the best she can with the real estate transfers. This view is intended to be reassuring, for it is desirable that a few lines of this story be skipped. For it introduces strong drink.

I went into a café to—and while it was being mixed I asked the man who grabs up your hot Scotch spoon as soon as you lay it down what he understood by the term, epithet, description, designation, characterization or appellation, viz.: a "Man About Town."

"Why," said he, carefully, "it means a fly guy that's wise to the all-night push—see? It's a hot sport that you can't bump to the rail anywhere between the Flatirons—see? I guess that's about what it means."

I thanked him and departed.

On the sidewalk a Salvation lassie shook her contribution receptacle gently against my waistcoat pocket.

"Would you mind telling me," I asked her, "if you ever meet with the character commonly denominated as 'A Man About Town' during your daily wanderings?"

"I think I know whom you mean," she answered, with a gentle smile. "We see them in the same places night after night. They are the devil's body guard, and if the soldiers of any army are as faithful as they are, their commanders are well served. We go among them, diverting a few pennies from their wickedness to the Lord's service."

She shook the box again and I dropped a dime into it.

In front of a glittering hotel a friend of mine, a critic, was climbing from a cab. He seemed at leisure; and I put my question to him. He answered me conscientiously, as I was sure he would.

"There is a type of 'Man About Town' in New York," he answered.

"The term is quite familiar to me, but I don't think I was ever called upon to define the character before. It would be difficult to point you out an exact specimen. I would say, offhand, that it is a man who had a hopeless case of the peculiar New York disease of wanting to see and know. At 6 o'clock each day life begins with him. He follows rigidly the conventions of dress and manners; but in the business of poking his nose into places where he does not belong he could give pointers to a civet cat or a jackdaw. He is the man who has chased Bohemia about the town from rathskeller to roof garden and from Hester Street to Harlem until you can't find a place in the city where they don't cut their spaghetti with a knife. Your 'Man About Town' has done that. He is always on the scent of something new. He is curiosity, impudence, and omnipresence. Hansoms were made for him, and gold-banded cigars; and the curse of music at dinner. There are not so many of him; but his minority report is adopted everywhere.

"I'm glad you brought up the subject; I've felt the influence of this nocturnal blight upon our city, but I never thought to analyze it before. I can see now that your 'Man About Town' should have been classified long ago. In his wake spring up wine agents and cloak models; and the orchestra plays 'Let's All Go Up to Maud's' for him, by request, instead of Händel. He makes his rounds every evening, while you and I see the elephant once a week. When the cigar store is raided, he winks at the officer, familiar with his ground, and walks away immune, while you and I search among the Presidents for names, and among the stars for addresses to give the desk sergeant."

My friend, the critic, paused to acquire breath for fresh eloquence. I seized my advantage.

"You have classified him," I cried with joy. "You have painted his portrait in the gallery of city types. But I must meet one face to face. I must study the Man About Town at first hand. Where shall I find him? How shall I know him?"

Without seeming to hear me, the critic went on. And his cab-driver was waiting for his fare, too.

"He is the sublimated essence of Butt-in; the refined, intrinsic extract of Rubber; the concentrated, purified, irrefutable, unavoidable spirit of Curiosity and Inquisitiveness. A new sensation is the breath in his nostrils; when his experience is exhausted he explores new fields with the indefatigability of a——"

"Excuse me," I interrupted, "but can you produce one of this type? It is a new thing to me. I must study it. I will search the town over until I find one. Its habitat must be here on Broadway."

"I am about to dine here," said my friend. "Come inside, and if there is a Man About Town present I will point him out to you. I know most of the regular patrons here."

"I am not dining yet," I said to him. "You will excuse me. I am going to find my Man About Town this night if I have to rake New York from the Battery to Little Coney Island."

I left the hotel and walked down Broadway. The pursuit of my type gave a pleasant savor of life and interest to the air I breathed. I was glad to be in a city so great, so complex and diversified. Leisurely and with something of an air I strolled along with my heart expanding at the thought that I was a citizen of great Gotham, a sharer in its magnificence and pleasures, a partaker in its glory and prestige.

I turned to cross the street. I heard something buzz like a bee, and then I took a long, pleasant ride with Santos-Dumont.

When I opened my eyes I remembered a smell of gasoline, and I said aloud: "Hasn't it passed yet?"

A hospital nurse laid a hand that was not particularly soft upon my brow that was not at all fevered. A young doctor came along, grinned, and handed me a morning newspaper.

"Want to see how it happened?" he asked, cheerily. I read the article. Its headlines began where I heard the buzzing leave off the night before. It closed with these lines:

"——Bellevue Hospital, where it was said that his injuries were not serious. He appeared to be a typical Man About Town."

Clarence Day

FATHER WAKES UP THE VILLAGE

ONE of the most disgraceful features of life in the country, Father often declared, was the general inefficiency and slackness of small village tradesmen. He said he had originally supposed that such men were interested in business, and that that was why they had opened their shops and sunk capital in them, but no, they never used them for anything but gossip and sleep. They took no interest in civilized ways. Hadn't heard of them, probably. He said that of course if he were camping out on the veldt or the tundra, he would expect few conveniences in the neighborhood and would do his best to forego them, but why should he be confronted with the wilds twenty miles from New York?

Usually, when Father talked this way, he was thinking of ice. He strongly objected to spending even one day of his life without a glass of cold water beside his plate at every meal. There was never any difficulty about this in our home in the city. A great silver ice-water pitcher stood on the sideboard all day, and when Father was home its outer surface was frosted with cold. When he had gone to the office, the ice was allowed to melt sometimes, and the water got warmish, but never in the evening, or on Sundays, when Father might want some. He said he liked water, he told us it was one of Nature's best gifts, but he said that like all her gifts it was unfit for human consumption unless served in a suitable manner. And the only right way to serve water was icy cold.

It was still more important that each kind of wine should be served at whatever the right temperature was for it. And kept at it, too. No civilized man would take dinner without wine, Father said, and no man who knew the first thing about it would keep his wine in hot cellars. Mother thought this was a mere whim of Father's. She said he

From *Life with Father*, copyright, 1934, by Clarence Day. Reprinted by permission of Alfred A. Knopf, Inc. Originally in *The New Yorker*.

was fussy. How about people who lived in apartments, she asked him, who didn't have cellars? Father replied that civilized persons didn't live in apartments.

One of the first summers that Father ever spent in the country, he rented a furnished house in Irvington on the Hudson, not far from New York. It had a garden, a stable, and one or two acres of woods, and Father arranged to camp out there with many misgivings. He took a train for New York every morning at eight-ten, after breakfast, and he got back between five and six, bringing anything special we might need along with him, such as a basket of peaches from the city, or a fresh package of his own private coffee.

Things went well until one day in August the ice-man didn't come. It was hot, he and his horses were tired, and he hated to come to us anyhow because the house we had rented was perched up on top of a hill. He said afterward that on this particular day he had not liked the idea of making his horses drag the big ice-wagon up that sharp and steep road to sell us 50¢ worth of ice. Besides, all his ice was gone anyhow—the heat had melted it on him. He had four or five other good reasons. So he didn't come.

Father was in town. The rest of us waited in astonishment, wondering what could be the matter. We were so used to the regularity and punctilio of life in the city that it seemed unbelievable to us that the ice-man would fail to appear. We discussed it at lunch. Mother said that the minute he arrived she would have to give him a talking to. After lunch had been over an hour and he still hadn't come, she got so worried about what Father would say that she decided to send to the village.

There was no telephone, of course. There were no motors. She would have liked to spare the horse if she could, for he had been worked hard that week. But as this was a crisis, she sent for Morgan, the coachman, and told him to bring up the dog-cart.

The big English dog-cart arrived. Two of us boys and the coachman drove off. The sun beat down on our heads. Where the heavy harness was rubbing on Brownie's coat, he broke out into a thick, whitish lather. Morgan was sullen. When we boys were along he couldn't take off his stiff black high hat or unbutton his thick, padded coat. Worse still, from his point of view, he couldn't stop at a bar for a drink. That was why Mother had sent us along with him, of course, and he knew it.

We arrived at the little town after a while and I went into the Coal & Ice Office. A wiry-looking old clerk was dozing in a corner, his chair tilted back and his chin resting on his dingy shirtfront. I woke this clerk up. I told him about the crisis at our house.

He listened unwillingly, and when I had finished he said it was a very hot day.

I waited. He spat. He said he didn't see what he could do, because the ice-house was locked.

I explained earnestly that this was the Day family and that something must be done right away.

He hunted around his desk a few minutes, found his chewing tobacco and said, "Well, sonny, I'll see what I can do about it."

I thanked him very much, as that seemed to me to settle the matter. I went back to the dog-cart. Brownie's check-rein had been unhooked, and he stood with his head hanging down. He looked sloppy. It wouldn't have been so bad with a buggy, but a slumpy horse in a dog-cart can look pretty awful. Also, Morgan was gone. He reappeared soon, coming out of a side door down the street, buttoning up his coat, but with his hat tilted back. He looked worse than the horse.

We checked up the weary animal's head again and drove slowly home. A hot little breeze in our rear moved our dust along with us. At the foot of the hill, we boys got out, to spare Brownie our extra weight. We unhooked his check-rein again. He dragged the heavy cart up.

Mother was sitting out on the piazza. I said the ice would come soon now. We waited.

It was a long afternoon.

At five o'clock, Brownie was hitched up again. The coachman and I drove back to the village. We had to meet Father's train. We also had to break the bad news to him that he would have no ice-water for dinner, and that there didn't seem to be any way to chill his Rhine wine.

The village was as sleepy as ever, but when Father arrived and learned what the situation was, he said it would have to wake up. He told me that he had had a long, trying day at the office, the city was hotter than the Desert of Sahara, and he was completely worn out, but that if any ice-man imagined for a moment he could behave in that manner, he, Father, would take his damned head off. He strode into the Coal & Ice Office.

When he came out, he had the clerk with him, and the clerk had put on his hat and was vainly trying to calm Father down. He was promising that he himself would come with the ice-wagon if the driver had left, and deliver all the ice we could use, and he'd be there inside an hour.

Father said, "Inside of an hour be hanged, you'll have to come quicker than that."

The clerk got rebellious. He pointed out that he'd have to go to the stables and hitch up the horses himself, and then get someone to help him hoist a block of ice out of the ice-house. He said it was 'most time for his supper and he wasn't used to such work. He was only doing it as a favor to Father. He was just being neighborly.

Father said he'd have to be neighborly in a hurry, because he wouldn't stand it, and he didn't know what the devil the ice company meant by such actions.

The clerk said it wasn't his fault, was it? It was the driver's.

This was poor tactics, of course, because it wound Father up again. He wasn't interested in whose fault it was, he said. It was everybody's. What he wanted was ice and plenty of it, and he wanted it in time for his dinner. A small crowd which had collected by this time listened admiringly as Father shook his finger at the clerk and said he dined at six-thirty.

The clerk went loping off toward the stables to hitch up the big horses. Father waited till he'd turned the corner.

Followed by the crowd, Father marched to the butcher's.

After nearly a quarter of an hour, the butcher and his assistant came out, unwillingly carrying what seemed to be a coffin, wrapped in a black mackintosh. It was a huge cake of ice.

Father got in, in front, sat on the box seat beside me, and took up the reins. We drove off. The coachman was on the rear seat, sitting back-to-back to us, keeping the ice from sliding out with the calves of his legs. Father went a few doors up the street to a little house-furnishings shop and got out again.

I went in the shop with him this time. I didn't want to miss any further scenes of this performance. Father began proceedings by demanding to see all the man's ice-boxes. There were only a few. Father selected the largest he had. Then, when the sale seemed arranged, and when the proprietor was smiling broadly with pleasure at this sudden windfall, Father said he was buying that refrigerator only on two conditions.

The first was that it had to be delivered at his home before dinner. Yes, now. Right away. The shopkeeper explained over and over that this was impossible, but that he'd have it up the next morning, sure. Father said no, he didn't want it the next morning, he had to have it at once. He added that he dined at six-thirty, and that there was no time to waste.

The shopkeeper gave in.

The second condition, which was then put to him firmly, was staggering. Father announced that that ice-box must be delivered to him full of ice.

The man said he was not in the ice business.

Father said, "Very well then. I don't want it."

The man said obstinately that it was an excellent ice-box.

Father made a short speech. It was the one that we had heard so often at home about the slackness of village tradesmen, and he put such strong emotion and scorn in it that his voice rang through the shop. He closed it by saying, "An ice-box is of no use to a man without ice, and if you haven't the enterprise, the gumption, to sell your damned goods to a customer who wants them delivered in condition to use, you had better shut up your shop and be done with it. Not in the ice business, hey? You aren't in business at all!" He strode out.

The dealer came to the door just as Father was getting into the dog-cart, and called out anxiously, "All right, Mr. Day. I'll get that refrigerator filled for you and send it up right away."

Father drove quickly home. A thunderstorm seemed to be brewing and this had waked Brownie up, or else Father was putting some of his own supply of energy into him. The poor old boy probably needed it as again he climbed the steep hill. I got out at the foot, and as I walked along behind I saw that Morgan was looking kind of desperate, trying to sit in the correct position with his arms folded while he held in the ice with his legs. The big cake was continually slipping and sliding around under the seat and doing its best to plunge out. It had bumped against his calves all the way home. They must have got good and cold.

When the dog-cart drew up at our door, Father remained seated a moment while Morgan, the waitress, and I pulled and pushed at the ice. The mackintosh had come off it by this time. We dumped it out on the grass. A little later, after Morgan had unharnessed and hurriedly rubbed down the horse, he ran back to help us boys break the cake up, push the chunks around to the back door, and cram them into the ice-box while Father was dressing for dinner.

Mother had calmed down by this time. The Rhine wine was cooling. "Don't get it too cold," Father called.

Then the ice-man arrived.

The old clerk was with him, like a warden in charge of a prisoner. Mother stepped out to meet them, and at once gave the ice-man the scolding that had been waiting for him all day.

The clerk asked how much ice we wanted. Mother said we didn't want any now. Mr. Day had brought home some, and we had no room for more in the ice-box.

The ice-man looked at the clerk. The clerk tried to speak, but no words came.

Father put his head out of the window. "Take a hundred pounds, Vinnie," he said. "There's another box coming."

A hundred-pound block was brought into the house and heaved into the washtub. The waitress put the mackintosh over it. The ice-wagon left.

Just as we all sat down to dinner, the new ice-box arrived, full. Mother was provoked. She said "Really, Clare!" crossly. "Now what am I to do with that piece that's waiting out in the wash-tub?"

Father chuckled.

She told him he didn't know the first thing about keeping house, and went out to the laundry with the waitress to tackle the problem. The thunderstorm broke and crashed. We boys ran around shutting the windows upstairs.

Father's soul was at peace. He dined well, and he had his coffee and cognac served to him on the piazza. The storm was over by then. Father snuffed a deep breath of the sweet-smelling air and smoked his evening cigar.

"Clarence," he said, "King Solomon had the right idea about these things. 'Whatsoever thy hand findeth to do,' Solomon said, 'do thy damnedest.'"

Mother called me inside. "Whose mackintosh is that?" she asked anxiously. "Katie's torn a hole in the back."

I heard Father saying contentedly on the piazza, "I like plenty of ice."

Dorothy Parker

FROM THE DIARY
OF A NEW YORK LADY

During Days of Horror, Despair, and World Change

MONDAY. Breakfast tray about eleven; didn't want it. The champagne at the Amorys' last night was *too* revolting, but what *can* you do? You can't stay until five o'clock on just *nothing*. They had those *divine* Hungarian musicians in the green coats, and Stewie Hunter took off one of his shoes and led them with it, and it *couldn't* have been funnier. He is *the* wittiest number in the *entire* world; he *couldn't* be more perfect. Ollie Martin brought me home and we both fell asleep in the car—*too* screaming. Miss Rose came about noon to do my nails, simply *covered* with *the* most divine gossip. The Morrises are going to separate *any minute*, and Freddie Warren *definitely* has ulcers, and Gertie Leonard simply *won't* let Bill Crawford out of her sight even with Jack Leonard *right there in the room*, and it's all *true* about Sheila Phillips and Babs Deering. It *couldn't* have been more thrilling. Miss Rose is *too* marvelous: I really think that a lot of times people like that are a lot more intelligent than a lot of people. Didn't notice until after she had gone that the damn fool had put that *revolting* tangerine-colored polish on my nails; *couldn't* have been more furious. Started to read a book, but too nervous. Called up and found I could get two tickets for the opening of "Run like a Rabbit" tonight for forty-eight dollars. Told them they had *the* nerve of the world, but what *can* you do? Think Joe said he was dining out, so telephoned some *divine* numbers to get someone to go to the theater with me, but they were all tied up. Finally got Ollie Martin. He *couldn't* have more poise, and what do *I* care if he *is* one? *Can't* decide whether to wear the green crepe or the red wool. Every time I look at my finger nails, I could *spit*. *Damn* Miss Rose.

From *The Portable Dorothy Parker*, copyright, 1927, 1933, 1944, by Dorothy Parker. Reprinted by permission of The Viking Press, Inc., New York.

Tuesday. Joe came barging in my room this morning at *practically nine o'clock*. *Couldn't* have been more furious. Started to fight, but *too* dead. Know he said he wouldn't be home to dinner. Absolutely *cold* all day; couldn't *move*. Last night *couldn't* have been more perfect. Ollie and I dined at Thirty-Eight East, absolutely *poisonous* food, and not one *living* soul that you'd be seen *dead* with, and "Run like a Rabbit" was *the* world's worst. Took Ollie up to the Barlows' party and it *couldn't* have been more attractive—*couldn't* have been more people absolutely *stinking*. They had those Hungarians in the green coats, and Stewie Hunter was leading them with a fork—everybody simply *died*. He had *yards* of green toilet paper hung around his neck like a lei; he *couldn't* have been in better form. Met a *really new number*, very tall, *too* marvelous, and one of those people that you can *really* talk to them. I told him sometimes I get so *nauseated* I could yip, and I felt I absolutely *had* to do something like write or paint. He said why didn't I write or paint. Came home alone; Ollie passed out *stiff*. Called up the new number three times today to get him to come to dinner and go with me to the opening of "Never Say Good Morning," but first he was out and then he was all tied up with his mother. Finally got Ollie Martin. Tried to read a book, but couldn't sit still. *Can't* decide whether to wear the red lace or the pink with the feathers. Feel *too* exhausted, but what *can* you do?

Wednesday. The most terrible thing happened *just this minute*. Broke one of my finger nails *right off short*. Absolutely *the* most horrible thing I ever had happen to me in my life. Called up Miss Rose to come over and shape it for me, but she was out for the day. I do have *the* worst luck in the *entire* world. Now I'll have to go around like this all day and all night, but what *can* you do? *Damn* Miss Rose. Last night *too* hectic. "Never Say Good Morning" *too* foul, *never* saw more poisonous clothes on the stage. Took Ollie up to the Ballards' party; *couldn't* have been better. They had those Hungarians in the green coats and Stewie Hunter was leading them with a freesia—*too* perfect. He had on Peggy Cooper's ermine coat and Phyllis Minton's silver turban; *simply* unbelievable. Asked simply *sheaves* of *divine* people to come here Friday night; got the address of those Hungarians in the green coats from Betty Ballard. She says just engage them until four, and then whoever gives them another three hundred dollars, they'll stay till five. *Couldn't* be cheaper. Started home with Ollie, but had to drop him at his house; he *couldn't* have been sicker. Called up the new number today to get him to come to dinner and go to the opening of

"Everybody Up" with me tonight, but he was tied up. Joe's going to be out; he didn't *condescend* to say *where, of course*. Started to read the papers, but nothing in them except that Mona Wheatley is in Reno charging *intolerable cruelty*. Called up Jim Wheatley to see if he had anything to do tonight, but he was tied up. Finally got Ollie Martin. *Can't* decide whether to wear the white satin or the black chiffon or the yellow pebble crepe. Simply *wrecked* to the *core* about my finger nail. Can't *bear* it. *Never* knew *anybody* to have such *unbelievable* things happen to them.

Thursday. Simply *collapsing* on my *feet*. Last night *too* marvelous. "Everybody Up" *too* divine, *couldn't* be filthier, and the new number was there, *too* celestial, only he didn't see me. He was with Florence Keeler in that *loathsome* gold Schiaparelli model of hers that every *shopgirl* has had since *God* knows. He must be out of his *mind*; she wouldn't *look* at a man. Took Ollie to the Watsons' party; *couldn't* have been more thrilling. Everybody simply *blind*. They had those Hungarians in the green coats and Stewie Hunter was leading them with a lamp, and, after the lamp got broken, he and Tommy Thomas did adagio dances—*too* wonderful. Somebody told me Tommy's doctor told him he had to absolutely get *right out of town*, he has *the* world's worst stomach, but you'd *never* know it. Came home alone, couldn't find Ollie *anywhere*. Miss Rose came at noon to shape my nail, *couldn't* have been more fascinating. Sylvia Eaton can't go *out the door* unless she's had a hypodermic, and Doris Mason *knows every single word* about Douggie Mason and that girl up in Harlem, and Evelyn North won't be *induced* to keep away from those three acrobats, and they don't *dare* tell Stuyvie Raymond *what* he's got the matter with him. *Never* knew anyone that had a more simply *fascinating* life than Miss Rose. Made her take that *vile* tangerine polish off my nails and put on dark red. Didn't notice until after she had gone that it's practically *black* in electric light; *couldn't* be in a worse state. *Damn* Miss Rose. Joe left a note saying he was going to dine out, so telephoned the new number to get him to come to dinner and go with me to that new movie tonight, but he didn't answer. Sent him three telegrams to *absolutely surely* come tomorrow night. Finally got Ollie Martin for tonight. Looked at the papers, but nothing in them except that the Harry Motts are throwing a tea with Hungarian music on Sunday. Think will ask the new number to go to it with me; they must have meant to invite me. Began to read a book, but too exhausted. *Can't* decide whether to wear the new blue with the white jacket or save it till tomorrow night and wear the ivory moire. Simply *heartsick* every time I think of my nails. *Couldn't* be wilder. Could *kill* Miss Rose, but what *can* you do?

Friday. Absolutely *sunk; couldn't* be worse. Last night *too* divine, movie *simply* deadly. Took Ollie to the Kingslands' party, *too* unbelievable, everybody absolutely *rolling.* They had those Hungarians in the green coats, but Stewie Hunter wasn't there. He's got a *complete* nervous breakdown. Worried *sick* for fear he won't be well by tonight; will absolutely *never* forgive him if he doesn't come. Started home with Ollie, but dropped him at his house because he *couldn't* stop crying. Joe left word with the butler he's going to the country this afternoon for the week-end; *of course* he wouldn't *stoop* to say *what* country. Called up *streams* of marvelous numbers to get someone to come dine and go with me to the opening of "White Man's Folly," and then go somewhere after to dance for a while; can't *bear* to be the first one there at your own party. Everybody was tied up. Finally got Ollie Martin. *Couldn't* feel more depressed; never should have gone *anywhere near* champagne and Scotch together. Started to read a book, but too restless. Called up Anne Lyman to ask about the new baby and *couldn't* remember if it was a boy or girl—*must* get a secretary *next week.* Anne *couldn't* have been more of a help; she said she didn't know whether to name it Patricia or Gloria, so then of course I knew it was a girl *right away.* Suggested calling it Barbara; forgot she already had one. Absolutely *walking the floor* like a *panther* all day. Could *spit* about Stewie Hunter. Can't *face* deciding whether to wear the blue with the white jacket or the purple with the beige roses. Every time I look at those *revolting* black nails, I want to absolutely *yip.* I really have *the* most horrible things happen to me of anybody in the *entire* world. *Damn* Miss Rose.

Leonard Q. Ross

THE RATHER DIFFICULT CASE OF
MR. K*A*P*L*A*N

IN THE third week of the new term, Mr. Parkhill was forced to the conclusion that Mr. Kaplan's case was rather difficult. Mr. Kaplan first came to his special attention, out of the thirty-odd adults in the beginners' grade of the American Night Preparatory School for Adults ("English—Americanization—Civics—Preparation for Naturalization"), through an exercise the class had submitted. The exercise was entitled "Fifteen Common Nouns and Their Plural Forms." Mr. Parkhill came to one paper which included the following:

house	makes	houses
dog	"	.... dogies
libary	"	.... Public libary
cat	"	.... Katz

Mr. Parkhill read this over several times, very thoughtfully. He decided that here was a student who might, unchecked, develop into a "problem case." It was clearly a case that called for special attention. He turned the page over and read the name. It was printed in large, firm letters with red crayon. Each letter was outlined in blue. Between every two letters was a star, carefully drawn, in green. The multicolored whole spelled, unmistakably, H*Y*M*A*N K*A*P*L*A*N.

This Mr. Kaplan was in his forties, a plump, red-faced gentleman, with wavy blond hair, *two* fountain pens in his outer pocket, and a perpetual smile. It was a strange smile, Mr. Parkhill remarked: vague, bland, and consistent in its monotony. The thing that emphasized it for Mr. Parkhill was that it never seemed to leave the face of Mr. Kaplan, even during Recitation and Speech period. This disturbed Mr. Parkhill considerably, because Mr. Kaplan was particularly bad in Recitation and Speech.

From *The Education of Hyman Kaplan*, copyright, 1936, by Leo C. Rosten; copyright, 1937, by Harcourt, Brace and Company, Inc. Originally in *The New Yorker*.

Mr. Parkhill decided he had not applied himself as conscientiously as he might to Mr. Kaplan's case. That very night he called on Mr. Kaplan first.

"Won't *you* take advantage of Recitation and Speech practice, Mr. Kaplan?" he asked, with an encouraging smile.

Mr. Kaplan smiled back and answered promptly, "Vell, I'll tell abot Prazidents United States. Fife Prazidents United States is Abram Lincohen, he vas freeink de neegers; Hodding, Coolitch, Judge Vashington, an' Banjamin Frenklin."

Further encouragement revealed that in Mr. Kaplan's literary Valhalla the "most famous tree American wriders" were Jeck Laundon, Valt Viterman, and the author of "Hawk L. Barry-Feen," one Mocktvain. Mr. Kaplan took pains to point out that he did not mention Relfvaldo Amerson because "He is a poyet, an' I'm talkink abot wriders."

Mr. Parkhill diagnosed the case as one of "inability to distinguish between 'a' and 'e.' " He concluded that Mr. Kaplan *would* need special attention. He was, frankly, a little disturbed.

Mr. Kaplan's English showed no improvement during the next hard weeks. The originality of his spelling and pronunciation, however, flourished—like a sturdy flower in the good, rich earth. A man to whom "Katz" is the plural of "cat" soon soars into higher and more ambitious endeavor. As a one-paragraph "Exercise in Composition," Mr. Kaplan submitted:

When people is meating on the boulvard, on going away one is saying, "I am glad I mat you," and the other is giving answer, "Mutual."

Mr. Parkhill felt that perhaps Mr. Kaplan had overreached himself and should be confined to the simpler exercises.

Mr. Kaplan was an earnest student. He worked hard, knit his brows regularly (albeit with that smile), did all his homework, and never missed a class. Only once did Mr. Parkhill feel that Mr. Kaplan might perhaps, be a little more *serious* about his work. That was when he asked Mr. Kaplan to "give a noun."

"Door," said Mr. Kaplan, smiling.

It seemed to Mr. Parkhill that "door" had been given only a moment earlier, by Miss Mitnick.

"Y-es," said Mr. Parkhill. "Er—and another noun?"

"Another door," Mr. Kaplan replied promptly.

Mr. Parkhill put him down as a doubtful "C." Everything pointed to the fact that Mr. Kaplan might have to be kept on an extra three months before he was ready for promotion to Composition, Grammar, and Civics, with Miss Higby.

One night Mrs. Moskowitz read a sentence, from "English for Beginners," in which "the vast deserts of America" were referred to. Mr. Parkhill soon discovered that poor Mrs. Moskowitz did not know the meaning of "vast." "Who can tell us the meaning of 'vast'?" asked Mr. Parkhill lightly.

Mr. Kaplan's hand shot up, volunteering wisdom. He was all proud grins. Mr. Parkhill, in the rashness of the moment, nodded to him.

Mr. Kaplan rose, radiant with joy. " 'Vast!' It's commink fromm *diraction*. Ve have four diractions: de naut, de sot, de heast, and de vast."

Mr. Parkhill shook his head. "Er—that is 'west,' Mr. Kaplan." He wrote "VAST" and "WEST" on the blackboard. To the class he added, tolerantly, that Mr. Kaplan was apparently thinking of "west," whereas it was "vast" which was under discussion.

This seemed to bring a great light into Mr. Kaplan's inner world. "So is 'vast' vat you eskink?"

Mr. Parkhill admitted that it was "vast" for which he was asking.

"Aha!" cried Mr. Kaplan. "You minn '*vast*,' not"—with scorn— " 'vast.' "

"Yes," said Mr. Parkhill, faintly.

"Hau Kay!" said Mr. Kaplan, essaying the vernacular. "Ven I'm buyink a suit clothes, I'm gattink de cawt, de pents, an' de vast!"

Stunned, Mr. Parkhill shook his head, very sadly. "I'm afraid that you've used still another word, Mr. Kaplan."

Oddly enough, this seemed to give Mr. Kaplan great pleasure.

Several nights later Mr. Kaplan took advantage of Open Questions period. This ten-minute period was Mr. Parkhill's special innovation in the American Night Preparatory School for Adults. It was devoted to answering any questions which the students might care to raise about any difficulties which they might have encountered during the course of their adventures with the language. Mr. Parkhill enjoyed Open Questions. He liked to clear up *practical* problems. He felt he was being ever so much more constructive that way. Miss Higby had once told him that he was a born Open Questions teacher.

"Plizz, Mr. Pockheel," asked Mr. Kaplan as soon as the period opened. "Vat's de minnink fromm—" It sounded, in Mr. Kaplan's rendition, like "a big department."

" 'A big department,' Mr. Kaplan?" asked Mr. Parkhill, to make sure.

"Yassir!" Mr. Kaplan's smile was beauteous to behold. "In de stritt, ven I'm valkink, I'm hearink like 'I big de pottment.'"

It was definitely a pedagogical opportunity.

"Well, class," Mr. Parkhill began. "I'm sure that you have all—"

He told them that they had all probably done some shopping in the large downtown stores. (Mr. Kaplan nodded.) In these large stores, he said, if they wanted to buy a pair of shoes, for example, they went to a special *part* of the store, where only shoes were sold—a *shoe* department. (Mr. Kaplan nodded.) If they wanted a table, they went to a different *part* of the store, where *tables* were sold. (Mr. Kaplan nodded.) If they wanted to buy, say, a goldfish, they went to still another part of the store, where goldfish . . . (Mr. Kaplan frowned; it was clear that Mr. Kaplan had never bought a goldfish.)

"Well, then," Mr. Parkhill summed up hastily, "each article is sold in a different *place*. These different and special places are called *departments*." He printed "D-E-P-A-R-T-M-E-N-T" on the board in large, clear capitals. "And a *big* department, Mr. Kaplan, is merely such a department which is large—*big!*"

He put the chalk down and wiped his fingers.

"Is that clear now, class?" he asked, with a little smile. (It was rather an ingenious explanation, he thought; it might be worth repeating to Miss Higby during the recess.)

It *was* clear. There were thirty nods of approval. But Mr. Kaplan looked uncertain. It was obvious that Mr. Kaplan, a man who would not compromise with truth, did *not* find it clear.

"Isn't that clear *now*, Mr. Kaplan?" asked Mr. Parkhill anxiously.

Mr. Kaplan pursed his lips in thought. "It's a *fine* haxplination, titcher," he said generously, "but I don' unnistand vy I'm hearink de voids de vay I do. Simms to me it's used in annodder minnink."

"There's really only one meaning for 'a big department.'" Mr. Parkhill was definitely worried by this time. "*If* that's the phrase you mean."

Mr. Kaplan nodded gravely. "Oh, dat's de phrase—ufcawss! It sonds like dat—or maybe a leetle more like 'I big de pottment.'"

Mr. Parkhill took up the chalk. ("I big department" was obviously a case of Mr. Kaplan's own curious audition.) He repeated the explanation carefully, this time embellishing the illustrations with a shirt department, a victrola section, and "a separate part of the store where, for example, you buy canaries, or other birds."

Mr. Kaplan sat entranced. He followed it all politely, even the part about "canaries, or other birds." He smiled throughout with consummate reassurance.

Mr. Parkhill was relieved, assuming, in his folly, that Mr. Kaplan's smiles were a testimony to his exposition. But when he had finished, Mr. Kaplan shook his head once more, this time with a new and superior firmness.

"Is the explanation *still* not clear?" Mr. Parkhill was genuinely concerned by this time.

"Is de haxplination clear!" cried Mr. Kaplan with enthusiasm. "Ha! I should live so! Soitinly! Clear like *gold!* So clear! An' netcheral too! But Mr. Pockheel—"

"Go on, Mr. Kaplan," said Mr. Parkhill, studying the white dust on his fingers. There was, after all, nothing more to be done.

"Vell! I tink it's more like 'I big de pottment.'"

"Go on, Mr. Kaplan, go on." (*Domine, dirige nos.*)

Mr. Kaplan rose. His smile was broad, luminous, transcendent; his manner was regal.

"I'm hearink it in de stritt. Somtimes I'm stendink in de stritt, talkink to a frand, or mine vife, mine brodder—or maybe only stendink. An' somvun is pessink arond me. An' by hexident he's givink me a bump, you know, a *poosh!* Vell, he says, 'Axcuse me!' no? But somtimes, an' *dis* is vat I minn, he's sayink, '*I big de pottment!*'"

Mr. Parkhill studied the picture of "Abram Lincohen" on the back wall, as if reluctant to face reality. He wondered whether he could reconcile it with his conscience if he were to promote Mr. Kaplan to Composition, Grammar, and Civics—at once. Another three months of Recitation and Speech might, after all, be nothing but a waste of Mr. Kaplan's valuable time.

Ring Lardner

LIBERTY HALL

MY HUSBAND is in Atlantic City, where they are trying out "Dear Dora," the musical version of "David Copperfield." My husband wrote the score. He used to take me along for these out-of-town openings, but not any more.

He, of course, has to spend almost all his time in the theater and that leaves me alone in the hotel, and pretty soon people find out whose wife I am and introduce themselves, and the next thing you know they are inviting us for a week or a weekend at Dobbs Ferry or Oyster Bay. Then it is up to me to think of some legitimate-sounding reason why we can't come.

In lots of cases they say, "Well, if you can't make it the twenty-second, how about the twenty-ninth?" and so on till you simply have to accept. And Ben gets mad and stays mad for days.

He absolutely abhors visiting and thinks there ought to be a law against invitations that go beyond dinner and bridge. He doesn't mind hotels where there is a decent light for reading in bed and one for shaving, and where you can order meals, with coffee, any time you want them. But I really believe he would rather spend a week in the death house at Sing Sing than in somebody else's home.

Three or four years ago we went around quite a lot with a couple whom I will call the Buckleys. We liked them and they liked us. We had dinner together at least twice a week and after dinner we played bridge or went to a show or just sat and talked.

Ben never turned down their invitations and often actually called them up himself and suggested parties. Finally they moved to Albany on account of Mr. Buckley's business. We missed them a great deal, and when Mrs. Buckley wrote for us to come up there for the holidays we were tickled pink.

Well, their guest-room was terribly cold; it took hours to fill the bathtub; there was no reading-lamp by the bed; three reporters called to interview Ben, two of them kittenish young girls; the breakfasts were just fruit and cereal and toast; coffee was not served at luncheon; the faucets in the wash-basin were the kind that won't run unless you keep pressing them; four important keys on the piano were stuck and people were invited in every night to hear Ben play, and the Buckley family had been augmented by a tremendous police dog, who was "just a puppy and never growled or snapped at anyone he knew," but couldn't seem to remember that Ben was not an utter stranger.

On the fourth awful day Ben gave out the news—news to him and to me as well as to our host and hostess—that he had lost a filling which he would not trust any but his own New York dentist to replace. We came home and we have never seen the Buckleys since. If we do see them it will be an accident. They will hardly ask us there unless we ask them here, and we won't ask them here for fear they would ask us there. And they were honestly the most congenial people we ever met.

It was after our visit to the Craigs at Stamford that Ben originated what he calls his "emergency exit." We had such a horrible time at the Craigs' and such a worse time getting away that Ben swore he would pay no more visits until he could think up a graceful method of curtailing them in the event they proved unbearable.

Here is the scheme he hit on: He would write himself a telegram and sign it with the name Ziegfeld or Gene Buck or Dillingham or George M. Cohan. The telegram would say that he must return to New York at once, and it would give a reason. Then, the day we started out, he would leave it with Irene, the girl at Harms', his publishers, with instructions to have it sent to him twenty-four hours later.

When it arrived at whatever town we were in, he would either have the host or hostess take it over the telephone or ask the telegraph company to deliver it so he could show it around. We would put on long faces and say how sorry we were, but of course business was business, so good-by and so forth. There was never a breath of suspicion even when the telegram was ridiculous, like the one Ben had sent to himself at Spring Lake, where we were staying with the Marshalls just after "Betty's Birthday" opened at the Globe. The Marshalls loved musical shows, but knew less than nothing about music and swallowed this one whole:

Shaw and Miss Miller both suffering from laryngitis Stop Entire score must be rewritten half tone lower Stop Come at once Stop.

C. B. Dillingham.

If, miraculously, Ben had ever happened to be enjoying himself, he would, of course, have kept the contents of his message a secret or else displayed it and remarked swaggeringly that he guessed he wasn't going to let any so-and-so theatrical producer spoil his fun.

Ben is in Atlantic City now and I have read every book in the house and am writing this just because there doesn't seem to be anything else to do. And also because we have a friend, Joe Frazier, who is a magazine editor and the other day I told him I would like to try my hand at a short story, but I was terrible at plots, and he said plots weren't essential; look at Ernest Hemingway; most of his stories have hardly any plot; it's his style that counts. And he—I mean Mr. Frazier—suggested that I write about our visit to Mr. and Mrs. Thayer in Lansdowne, outside of Philadelphia, which Mr. Frazier said, might be termed the visit that ended visits and which is the principal reason why I am here alone.

Well, it was a beautiful night a year ago last September. Ben was conducting the performance—"Step Lively"—and I was standing at the railing of the Boardwalk in front of the theater watching the moonlight on the ocean. A couple whom I had noticed in the hotel dining-room stopped alongside of me and pretty soon the woman spoke to me, something about how pretty it was. Then came the old question, wasn't I Mrs. Ben Drake? I said I was, and the woman went on:

"My name is Mrs. Thayer—Hilda Thayer. And this is my husband. We are both simply crazy about Mr. Drake's music and just dying to meet him personally. We wondered if you and he would have supper with us after the performance tonight."

"Oh, I'm afraid that's impossible," I replied. "You see when they are having a tryout, he and the librettists and the lyric writers work all night every night until they get everything in shape for the New York opening. They never have time for more than a sandwich and they eat that right in the theater."

"Well, how about luncheon tomorrow?"

"He'll be rehearsing all day."

"How about dinner tomorrow evening?"

"Honestly, Mrs. Thayer, it's out of the question. Mr. Drake never makes engagements during a tryout week."

"And I guess he doesn't want to meet us anyway," put in Mr.

Thayer. "What use would a genius like Ben Drake have for a couple of common-no-account admirers like Mrs. Thayer and myself! If we were 'somebody' too, it would be different!"

"Not at all!" said I. "Mr. Drake is perfectly human. He loves to have his music praised and I am sure he would be delighted to meet you if he weren't so terribly busy."

"Can you lunch with us yourself?"

"Tomorrow?"

"Any day."

Well, whatever Ben and other husbands may think, there is no decent way of turning down an invitation like that. And besides it was lonesome and the Thayers looked like awfully nice people. I lunched with them and I dined with them, not only the next day but all the rest of the week. And on Friday I got Ben to lunch with them and he liked them, too; they were not half as gushing and silly as most of his "fans."

At dinner on Saturday night, they cross-examined me about our immediate plans. I told them that as soon as the show was "over" in New York, I was going to try to make Ben stay home and do nothing for a whole month.

"I should think," said Mrs. Thayer, "it would be very hard for him to rest there in the city, with the producers and publishers and phonograph people calling him up all the time."

I admitted that he was bothered a lot.

"Listen, dearie," said Mrs. Thayer. "Why don't you come to Lansdowne and spend a week with us? I'll promise you faithfully that you won't be disturbed at all. I won't let anyone know you are there and if any of our friends call on us I'll pretend we're not at home. I won't allow Mr. Drake to even touch the piano. If he wants exercise, there are miles of room in our yard to walk around in, and nobody can see him from the street. All day and all night, he can do nothing or anything, just as he pleases. It will be 'Liberty Hall' for you both. He needn't tell anybody where he is, but if some of his friends or business acquaintances find out and try to get in touch with him, I'll frighten them away. How does that sound?"

"It sounds wonderful," I said, "but——"

"It's settled then," said Mrs. Thayer, "and we'll expect you on Sunday, October eleventh."

"Oh, but the show may not be 'set' by that time," I remonstrated.

"How about the eighteenth?" said Mr. Thayer.

Well, it ended by my accepting for the week of the twenty-fifth and Ben took it quite cheerfully.

"If they stick to their promise to keep us under cover," he said, "it may be a lot better than staying in New York. I know that Buck and the Shuberts and Ziegfeld want me while I'm 'hot' and they wouldn't give me a minute's peace if they could find me. And of course if things aren't as good as they look, Irene's telegram will provide us with an easy out."

On the way over to Philadelphia he hummed me an awfully pretty melody which had been running through his head since we left the apartment. "I think it's sure fire," he said. "I'm crazy to get to a piano and fool with it."

"That isn't resting, dear."

"Well, you don't want me to throw away a perfectly good tune! They aren't so plentiful that I can afford to waste one. It won't take me five minutes at a piano to get it fixed in my mind."

The Thayers met us in an expensive-looking limousine.

"Ralph," said Mrs. Thayer to her husband, "you sit in one of the little seats and Mr. and Mrs. Drake will sit back here with me."

"I'd really prefer one of the little seats myself," said Ben and he meant it, for he hates to get his clothes mussed and being squeezed in beside two such substantial objects as our hostess and myself was bound to rumple him.

"No, sir!" said Mrs. Thayer positively. "You came to us for a rest and we're not going to start you off uncomfortable."

"But I'd honestly rather——"

It was no use. Ben was wedged between us and throughout the drive maintained a morose silence, unable to think of anything but how terrible his coat would look when he got out.

The Thayers had a very pretty home and the room assigned to us was close to perfection. There were comfortable twin beds with a small stand and convenient reading-lamp between; a big dresser and chiffonier; an ample closet with plenty of hangers; a bathroom with hot water that was hot, towels that were not too new and faucets that stayed on when turned on, and an ash-tray within reach of wherever you happened to be. If only we could have spent all our time in that guest-room, it would have been ideal.

But presently we were summoned downstairs to luncheon. I had warned Mrs. Thayer in advance and Ben was served with coffee. He drinks it black.

"Don't you take cream, Mr. Drake?"

"No. Never."

"But that's because you don't get good cream in New York."

"No. It's because I don't like cream in coffee."

"You would like our cream. We have our own cows and the cream is so rich that it's almost like butter. Won't you try just a little?"

"No, thanks."

"But just a little, to see how rich it is."

She poured about a tablespoonful of cream into his coffee-cup and for a second I was afraid he was going to pick up the cup and throw it in her face. But he kept hold of himself, forced a smile and declined a second chop.

"You haven't tasted your coffee," said Mrs. Thayer.

"Yes, I have," lied Ben. "The cream is wonderful. I'm sorry it doesn't agree with me."

"I don't believe coffee agrees with anyone," said Mrs. Thayer. "While you are here, not doing any work, why don't you try to give it up?"

"I'd be so irritable you wouldn't have me in the house. Besides, it isn't plain coffee that disagrees with me; it's coffee with cream."

"Pure, rich cream like ours couldn't hurt you," said Mrs. Thayer, and Ben, defeated, refused to answer.

He started to light a Jaguar cigaret, the brand he had been smoking for years.

"Here! Wait a minute!" said Mr. Thayer. "Try one of mine."

"What are they?" asked Ben.

"Trumps," said our host, holding out his case. "They're mild and won't irritate the throat."

"I'll sample one later," said Ben.

"You've simply got to try one now," said Mrs. Thayer. "You may as well get used to them because you'll have to smoke them all the time you're here. We can't have guests providing their own cigarets." So Ben had to discard his Jaguar and smoke a Trump, and it was even worse than he had anticipated.

After luncheon we adjourned to the living-room and Ben went straight to the piano.

"Here! Here! None of that!" said Mrs. Thayer. "I haven't forgotten my promise."

"What promise?" asked Ben.

"Didn't your wife tell you? I promised her faithfully that if you visited us, you wouldn't be allowed to touch the piano."

"But I want to," said Ben. "There's a melody in my head that I'd like to try."

"Oh, yes, I know all about that," said Mrs. Thayer. "You just think you've got to entertain us! Nothing doing! We invited you here for yourself, not to enjoy your talent. I'd be a fine one to ask you to my home for a rest and then make you perform."

"You're not making me," said Ben. "Honestly I want to play for just five or ten minutes. I've got a tune that I might do something with and I'm anxious to run it over."

"I don't believe you, you naughty man!" said our hostess. "Your wife has told you how wild we are about your music and you're determined to be nice to us. But I'm just as stubborn as you are. Not one note do you play as long as you're our guest!"

Ben favored me with a stricken look, mumbled something about unpacking his suitcase—it was already unpacked—and went up to our room, where he stayed nearly an hour, jotting down his new tune, smoking Jaguar after Jaguar and wishing that black coffee flowed from bathtub faucets.

About a quarter of four Mr. Thayer insisted on taking him around the place and showing him the shrubbery, something that held in Ben's mind a place of equal importance to the grade of wire used in hairpins.

"I'll have to go to business tomorrow," said Mr. Thayer, "and you will be left to amuse yourself. I thought you might enjoy this planting more if you knew a little about it. Of course it's much prettier in the spring of the year."

"I can imagine so."

"You must come over next spring and see it."

"I'm usually busy in the spring," said Ben.

"Before we go in," said Mr. Thayer, "I'd like to ask you one question: Do tunes come into your mind and then you write them down, or do you just sit at the piano and improvise until you strike something good?"

"Sometimes one way and sometimes the other," said Ben.

"That's very interesting," said Mr. Thayer. "I've often wondered how it was done. And another question: Do you write the tunes first and then give them to the men who write the words, or do the men write the words first and then give them to you to make up the music to them?"

"Sometimes one way and sometimes the other," said Ben.

"That's very interesting," said Mr. Thayer. "It's something I'm glad to know. And now we'd better join the ladies or my wife will say I'm monopolizing you."

They joined us, much to my relief. I had just reached a point where I would either have had to tell "Hilda" exactly how much Ben earned per annum or that it was none of her business.

"Well!" said Mrs. Thayer to Ben. "I was afraid Ralph had kidnapped you."

"He was showing me the shrubbery," said Ben.

"What did you think of it?"

"It's great shrubbery," said Ben, striving to put some warmth into his voice.

"You must come and see it in the spring."

"I'm usually busy in the spring."

"Ralph and I are mighty proud of our shrubbery."

"You have a right to be."

Ben was taking a book out of the bookcase.

"What book is that?" asked Mrs. Thayer.

" 'The Great Gatsby,' " said Ben. "I've always wanted to read it but never got around to it."

"Heavens!" said Mrs. Thayer as she took it away from him. "That's old! You'll find the newest ones there on the table. We keep pretty well up to date. Ralph and I are both great readers. Just try any one of those books in that pile. They're all good."

Ben glanced them over and selected "Chevrons." He sat down and opened it.

"Man! Man!" exclaimed Mrs. Thayer. "You've picked the most uncomfortable chair in the house!"

"He likes straight chairs," I said.

"That's on the square," said Ben.

"But you mustn't sit there," said Mrs. Thayer. "It makes me uncomfortable just to look at you. Take this chair here. It's the softest, nicest chair you've ever sat in."

"I like hard straight chairs," said Ben, but he sank into the soft, nice one and again opened his book.

"Oh, you never can see there!" said Mrs. Thayer. "You'll ruin your eyes! Get up just a minute and let Ralph move your chair by the lamp."

"I can see perfectly well."

"I know better! Ralph, move his chair so he can see."

"I don't believe I want to read just now anyway," said Ben, and went to the phonograph. "Bess," he said, putting on a record, "here's that 'Oh! Miss Hannah!' by the Revelers."

Mrs. Thayer fairly leaped to his side, and herded Miss Hannah back into her stall.

"We've got lots later ones than that," she said. "Let me play you the new Gershwins."

It was at this juncture that I began to suspect our hostess of a lack of finesse. After all, Gershwin is a rival of my husband's and, in some folks' opinion, a worthy one. However, Ben had a word of praise for each record as it ended and did not even hint that any of the tunes were based on melodies of his own.

"Mr. Drake," said our host at length, "would you like a gin cocktail or a Bacardi?"

"I don't like Bacardi at all," said Ben.

"I'll bet you will like the kind I've got," said Mr. Thayer. "It was brought to me by a friend of mine who just got back from Cuba. It's the real stuff!"

"I don't like Bacardi," said Ben.

"Wait till you taste this," said Mr. Thayer.

Well, we had Bacardi cocktails. I drank mine and it wasn't so good. Ben took a sip of his and pretended it was all right. But he had told the truth when he said he didn't like Bacardi.

I won't go into details regarding the dinner except to relate that three separate items were highly flavored with cheese, and Ben despises cheese.

"Don't you care for cheese, Mr. Drake?" asked Mr. Thayer, noticing that Ben was not exactly bolting his food.

"No," replied the guest of honor.

"He's spoofing you, Ralph," said Mrs. Thayer. "Everybody likes cheese."

There was coffee, and Ben managed to guzzle a cup before it was desecrated with pure cream.

We sat down to bridge.

"Do you like to play families or divide up?"

"Oh, we like to play together," said I.

"I'll bet you don't," said Mrs. Thayer. "Suppose Ralph and you play Mr. Drake and me. I think it's a mistake for husbands and wives to be partners. They're likely to criticize one another and say things that leave a scar."

Well, Mr. Thayer and I played against Ben and Mrs. Thayer and I lost sixty cents at a tenth of a cent a point. Long before the evening was over I could readily see why Mrs. Thayer thought it was a mistake to play with her husband and if it had been possible I'd have left him a complete set of scars.

Just as we were getting to sleep, Mrs. Thayer knocked on our door.

"I'm afraid you haven't covers enough," she called. "There are extra blankets on the shelf in your closet."

"Thanks," I said. "We're as warm as toast."

"I'm afraid you aren't," said Mrs. Thayer.

"Lock the door," said Ben, "before she comes in and feels our feet."

All through breakfast next morning we waited in vain for the telephone call that would yield Irene's message. The phone rang once and Mrs. Thayer answered, but we couldn't hear what she said. At noon Ben signalled me to meet him upstairs and there he stated grimly that I might do as I choose, but he was leaving Liberty Hall ere another sun had set.

"You haven't any excuse," I reminded him.

"I'm a genius," he said, "and geniuses are notoriously eccentric."

"Geniuses' wives sometimes get eccentric, too," said I, and began to pack up.

Mr. Thayer had gone to Philadelphia and we were alone with our hostess at luncheon.

"Mrs. Thayer," said Ben, "do you ever have premonitions or hunches?"

She looked frightened. "Why, no. Do you?"

"I had one not half an hour ago. Something told me that I positively must be in New York tonight. I don't know whether it's business or illness or what, but I've just got to be there!"

"That's the strangest thing I ever heard of," said Mrs. Thayer. "It scares me to death!"

"It's nothing you need be scared of," said Ben. "It only concerns me."

"Yes, but listen," said Mrs. Thayer. "A telegram came for you at breakfast this morning. I wasn't going to tell you about it because I had promised that you wouldn't be disturbed. And it didn't seem so terribly important. But this hunch of yours puts the matter in a different light. I'm sorry now that I didn't give you the message when I got it, but I memorized it and can repeat it word for word: 'Mr. Ben Drake, care of Mr. Ralph Thayer, Lansdowne, Pennsylvania. In Nile song, second bar of refrain, bass drum part reads A flat which makes discord. Should it be A natural? Would appreciate your coming to theater tonight to straighten this out as harmony must be restored in orchestra if troupe is to be success. Regards, Gene Buck.'"

"It sounds silly, doesn't it?" said Ben. "And yet I have known productions to fail and lose hundreds of thousands of dollars just because an author or composer left town too soon. I can well understand that you considered the message trivial. At the same time I can thank my stars that this instinct, or divination, or whatever you want to call it, told me to go home."

Just as the trainmen were shouting "Board!" Mrs. Thayer said:

"I have one more confession to make. I answered Mr. Buck's telegram. I wired him. 'Mr. Ben Drake resting at my home. Must not be bothered. Suggest that you keep bass drums still for a week.' And I signed my name. Please forgive me if I have done something terrible. Remember, it was for you."

Small wonder that Ben was credited at the Lambs' Club with that month's most interesting bender.

Ring Lardner

SIT STILL

O NE morning I was walking down Fifth Avenue alongside of the Park and I stopped with the rest of the southbound traffic at Seventy-second Street to allow the crosstown traffic to move, though God knows what good it did them because it is a two way street and there were just as many going one way as the other, but during the wait I happened to glance at the curb and saw a taxicab that I had never seen before so I got in and the first thing I noticed was an autographed picture of a man named Nathan Schwartz. The driver must have heard me slam the door, for pretty soon he turned around and opened the sliding window that separated his compartment from mine and said where to.

"Where were you headed for?" I retorted.

"Nowhere a special," he said.

"Well," I said, "I figured we might as well ride together as long as we were headed in the same direction. How did Mr. Schwartz come to send you one of his pictures? Do you know him?"

"I'm one of his fans," said the driver. "What I'd appreciate now, though, is where you want me to take you."

"You'll be one of the first people I'll tell as soon as I find out. Just drive along a ways and if I hear anything I'll get in touch with you."

"All right," said the driver, "and maybe you'd better rap twice on the window so I'll know it's you. That will be the signal. Have you got it?"

"Two raps," I said.

"You pick things up quickly, but whether you remember them is the question. Perhaps it will help you if you connect it in your mind with some common fact, like how many legs on a man, or how many rear wheels on a car."

"Or how many times I've been abroad," I chuckled.

"You've got it," said the driver.

The policeman jingled his bell and we were on our way. I was about to doze off when I observed a newspaper that had been left on the back seat by the people who had moved out. I picked it up and read an item about Jackie Coogan. He was in New York and staying at the Ritz (Forty-sixth and Madison). I rapped three times on the window, but the driver paid no attention. Then I remembered— "How many legs on a man?"—and rapped twice. The driver opened the window.

"Well?" he said.

"Take me to the Hotel Astor," I ordered, wondering why I had not thought of it before because I had wanted to see the Astor ever since moving to New York.

"That's on the Lincoln Highway, isn't it?" said the driver. "It's either on it or just off it. I'll find it anyhow; there must be plenty of signs."

We continued down the Avenue until we came to Forty-fifth Street.

"We could lose a little distance, by going to Forty-third Street," said the driver, "but Forty-fifth's worse at this time of the day, so I imagine it evens up in the end."

I was pretty hungry when we got to the Astor as I had gone without my lunch.

"Goodbye," I said to the driver.

"Goodbye," he said. "And don't forget—two legs to a man."

The car door was opened by a tall fellow who spoke to me, but I could not place him. I walked up the steps and into the hotel's front lobby, which seemed to be quite crowded, so crowded that I might never have been able to reach the desk without my training as a coxcomb at Yale.

"Have you got a room?" I said to a clerk, thinking of course they were filled up or why would there be such a crush in the lobby?

"Yes, sir. Kindly register and I'll fix you up," he replied.

There was nothing for me to do but write down my name and address. I was afraid to use the only other name I could think of, Nathan Schwartz; the clerk might be one of his fans, too, and know me for an impostor.

The clerk called a bellboy and gave him a key and the bellboy asked where I had left my baggage. I feigned temporary deafness and asked him in turn why, if the hotel had vacant rooms, there was such a crush in the lobby.

"Oh," he said, "that's just our waiting list."

"But why do they have to wait if I didn't?"

"They're not waiting for rooms. They're waiting to sit down," he said.

This statement interested me to such an extent that I spent the next few hours investigating, and I learned the following facts, which may or may not lessen the difficulty:

The lobby has four pillars or columns, which were originally placed there to keep the ceiling from bouncing up and down on the floor. ("Four men to a male quartette.") There are three chairs to each pillar, or twelve chairs in all. ("Twelve horsemen in the Notre Dame backfield.") The occupants of these chairs have been in them continuously for periods ranging from eight to sixty-six years. The man who has been sitting in his chair the shortest while (eight years) is a Mr. J. N. Purdy, but the others refer to him as "The Junior Partner" or "The Kid." He paid one hundred and twenty-five thousand dollars for his seat, a record price at the time, buying it from a Mr. Louis Bolton, who, after an occupancy of only four years and two months, yielded to a life-long ambition to take up window-shopping.

The oldest settler is the man who sits on the desk side of the pillar nearest the entrance to the florist's. No one knows his real name, but they call him "General Grant" because he sat down in 1864 and announced that he would sit it out in that chair if it took all century.

At the same pillar is Mr. Lyman Bates, who used to be an inveterate smoker. He had to give it up fourteen years ago when he ran out of cigars and money, and the bellboys refused to extend him credit. The other tenant of this pillar is a woman, Lucy Pond, who came into the hotel in 1887, expecting to meet a Harvard man and take lunch with him. She got tired standing after three months and, as there were no vacancies at the time, sat down in Mr. Bates' lap. In 1893, it was discovered that a Mr. Levings, who shared the pillar with Bates and "General Grant" at that time, had died quite a while previously. Bates made the discovery and managed to push Levings out of his chair. Miss Pond then moved into it, much to the relief of Bates, whose foot was asleep.

The only other woman squatter is Margaret Vesey. She has a chair at the pillar opposite the newsstand. They say she was quite an attractive girl when she sat down, in 1900, and that Barney Diehl, who had a seat at that column, showed an inclination to flirt with her. He was not rebuffed, but she insisted on his looking at her while he talked and he had to quit on account of stiff neck.

In the early days of Astor squatting it was necessary to put into effect a rule prohibiting standees from attempting to eject the settlers by physical means. The latter were in no condition to put up a battle and the thing was too unfair. But there was no law against the use of strategy and many tricks were employed successfully before it was overdone. For example, one of the standees would bribe a bellboy to shout, "Mr. Gordon is wanted on the telephone by Lily Langtry." Gordon, unable to resist the temptation, would jump out of his chair and the trickster would slip into it. Another effective ruse was starting a cry of "Fire!" The hotel people soon put a stop to that.

It is now understood that when a squatter has occupied one of the chairs for twenty-five years, it becomes his homestead and he is privileged to get up and move around without jeopardizing his rights. He is privileged to get up and move around, but he can't. Because he can't.

One of the bellboys told me of a remark recently made by Mr. Bates. He had overheard a standee speaking of Prof. Goozlequirt, a champion flagpole-sitter who had just come down off a flagpole in Madison Square Garden after sitting there for eighteen days and five hours.

"What makes those Danes so restless?" said Mr. Bates.

Damon Runyon

BLOOD PRESSURE

IT IS maybe eleven-thirty of a Wednesday night, and I am standing at the corner of Forty-eighth Street and Seventh Avenue, thinking about my blood pressure, which is a proposition I never before think much about.

In fact, I never hear of my blood pressure before this Wednesday afternoon when I go around to see Doc Brennan about my stomach, and he puts a gag on my arm and tells me that my blood pressure is higher than a cat's back, and the idea is for me to be careful about what I eat, and to avoid excitement, or I may pop off all of a sudden when I am least expecting it.

"A nervous man such as you with a blood pressure away up in the paint cards must live quietly," Doc Brennan says. "Ten bucks, please," he says.

Well, I am standing there thinking it is not going to be so tough to avoid excitement the way things are around this town right now, and wishing I have my ten bucks back to bet it on Sun Beau in the fourth race at Pimlico the next day, when all of a sudden I look up, and who is in front of me but Rusty Charley.

Now if I have any idea Rusty Charley is coming my way, you can go and bet all the coffee in Java I will be somewhere else at once, for Rusty Charley is not a guy I wish to have any truck with whatever. In fact, I wish no part of him. Furthermore, nobody else in this town wishes to have any part of Rusty Charley, for he is a hard guy indeed. In fact, there is no harder guy anywhere in the world. He is a big wide guy with two large hard hands and a great deal of very bad disposition, and he thinks nothing of knocking people down and stepping on their kissers if he feels like it.

In fact, this Rusty Charley is what is called a gorill, because he is known to often carry a gun in his pants pocket, and sometimes to shoot people down as dead as door nails with it if he does not like the way they wear their hats—and Rusty Charley is very critical of hats. The chances are Rusty Charley shoots many a guy in this man's town, and those he does not shoot he sticks with his shiv—which is a knife— and the only reason he is not in jail is because he just gets out of it, and the law does not have time to think up something to put him back in again for.

Anyway, the first thing I know about Rusty Charley being in my neighborhood is when I hear him saying: "Well, well, well, here we are!"

Then he grabs me by the collar, so it is no use of me thinking of taking it on the lam away from there, although I greatly wish to do so.

"Hello, Rusty," I say, very pleasant. "What is the score?"

"Everything is about even," Rusty says. "I am glad to see you, be- cause I am looking for company. I am over in Philadelphia for three days on business."

"I hope and trust that you do all right for yourself in Philly, Rusty," I say; but his news makes me very nervous, because I am a great hand for reading the papers and I have a pretty good idea what Rusty's business in Philly is. It is only the day before that I see a little item from Philly in the papers about how Gloomy Gus Smallwood, who is a very large operator in the alcohol business there, is guzzled right at his front door.

Of course I do not know that Rusty Charley is the party who guzzles Gloomy Gus Smallwood, but Rusty Charley is in Philly when Gus is guzzled, and I can put two and two together as well as anybody. It is the same thing as if there is a bank robbery in Cleveland, Ohio, and Rusty Charley is in Cleveland, Ohio, or near there. So I am very nervous, and I figure it is a sure thing my blood pressure is going up every second.

"How much dough do you have on you?" Rusty says. "I am plumb broke."

"I do not have more than a couple of bobs, Rusty," I say. "I pay a doctor ten bucks today to find out my blood pressure is very bad. But of course you are welcome to what I have."

"Well, a couple of bobs is no good to high-class guys like you and me," Rusty says. "Let us go to Nathan Detroit's crap game and win some money."

Now, of course, I do not wish to go to Nathan Detroit's crap game; and if I do wish to go there I do not wish to go with Rusty Charley, because a guy is sometimes judged by the company he keeps, especially around crap games, and Rusty Charley is apt to be considered bad company. Anyway, I do not have any dough to shoot craps with, and if I do have dough to shoot craps with, I will not shoot craps with it at all, but will bet it on Sun Beau, or maybe take it home and pay off some of the overhead around my joint, such as rent.

Furthermore, I remember what Doc Brennan tells me about avoiding excitement, and I know there is apt to be excitement around Nathan Detroit's crap game if Rusty Charley goes there, and maybe run my blood pressure up and cause me to pop off very unexpected. In fact, I already feel my blood jumping more than somewhat inside me, but naturally I am not going to give Rusty Charley any argument, so we go to Nathan Detroit's crap game.

This crap game is over a garage in Fifty-second Street this particular night, though sometimes it is over a restaurant in Forty-seventh Street, or in back of a cigar store in Forty-fourth Street. In fact, Nathan Detroit's crap game is apt to be anywhere, because it moves around every night, as there is no sense in a crap game staying in one spot until the coppers find out where it is.

So Nathan Detroit moves his crap game from spot to spot, and citizens wishing to do business with him have to ask where he is every night; and of course almost everybody on Broadway knows this, as Nathan Detroit has guys walking up and down, and around and about, telling the public his address, and giving out the password for the evening.

Well, Jack the Beefer is sitting in an automobile outside the garage in Fifty-second Street when Rusty Charley and I come along, and he says "Kansas City," very low, as we pass, this being the password for the evening; but we do not have to use any password whatever when we climb the stairs over the garage, because the minute Solid John, the doorman, peeks out through his peephole when we knock, and sees Rusty Charley with me, he opens up very quick indeed, and gives us a big castor-oil smile, for nobody in this town is keeping doors shut on Rusty Charley very long.

It is a very dirty room over the garage, and full of smoke, and the crap game is on an old pool table; and around the table and packed in so close you cannot get a knitting needle between any two guys with a mawl, are all the high shots in town, for there is plenty of money around at this time, and many citizens are very prosperous. Furthermore, I wish to say there are some very tough guys around the table, too, including guys who will shoot you in the head, or maybe the stomach, and think nothing whatever about the matter.

In fact, when I see such guys as Harry the Horse, from Brooklyn, and Sleepout Sam Levinsky, and Lone Louie, from Harlem, I know this is a bad place for my blood pressure, for these are very tough guys indeed, and are known as such to one and all in this town.

But there they are wedged up against the table with Nick the Greek, Big Nig, Gray John, Okay Okun, and many other high shots, and they all have big coarse G notes in their hands which they are tossing around back and forth as if these G notes are nothing but pieces of waste paper.

On the outside of the mob at the table are a lot of small operators who are trying to cram their fists in between the high shots now and then to get down a bet, and there are also guys present who are called Shylocks, because they will lend you dough when you go broke at the table, on watches or rings, or maybe cuff links, at very good interest.

Well, as I say, there is no room at the table for as many as one more very thin guy when we walk into the joint, but Rusty Charley lets out a big hello as we enter, and the guys all look around, and the next minute there is space at the table big enough not only for Rusty Charley but for me too. It really is quite magical the way there is suddenly room for us when there is no room whatever for anybody when we come in.

"Who is the gunner?" Rusty Charley asks, looking all around.

"Why, you are, Charley," Big Nig, the stick man in the game, says very quick, handing Charley a pair of dice, although afterward I hear that his pal is right in the middle of a roll trying to make nine when we step up to the table. Everybody is very quiet, just looking at Charley. Nobody pays any attention to me, because I am known to one and all as a guy who is just around, and nobody figures me in on any part of Charley, although Harry the Horse looks at me once in a way that I know is no good for my blood pressure, or for anybody else's blood pressure as far as this goes.

Well, Charley takes the dice and turns to a little guy in a derby hat who is standing next to him scrooching back so Charley will not notice him, and Charley lifts the derby hat off the little guy's head, and rattles the dice in his hand, and chucks them into the hat and goes "Hah!" like crap shooters always do when they are rolling the dice. Then Charley peeks into the hat and says "Ten," although he does not let anybody else look in the hat, not even me, so nobody knows if Charley throws a ten, or what.

But, of course, nobody around is going to up and doubt that Rusty Charley throws a ten, because Charley may figure it is the same thing as calling him a liar, and Charley is such a guy as is apt to hate being called a liar.

Now Nathan Detroit's crap game is what is called a head-and-head game, although some guys call it a fading game, because the guys bet against each other rather than against the bank, or house. It is just the same kind of game as when two guys get together and start shooting craps against each other, and Nathan Detroit does not have to bother with a regular crap table and a layout such as they have in gambling houses. In fact, about all Nathan Detroit has to do with the game is to find a spot, furnish the dice and take his percentage which is by no means bad.

In such a game as this there is no real action until a guy is out on a point, and then the guys around commence to bet he makes this point, or that he does not make this point, and the odds in any country in the world that a guy does not make a ten with a pair of dice before he rolls seven, is two to one.

Well, when Charley says he rolls ten in the derby hat nobody opens their trap, and Charley looks all around the table, and all of a sudden he sees Jew Louie at one end, although Jew Louie seems to be trying to shrink himself up when Charley's eyes light on him.

"I will take the odds for five C's," Charley says, "and Louie, you get it"—meaning he is letting Louie bet him $1000 to $500 that he does not make his ten.

Now Jew Louie is a small operator at all times and more of a Shylock than he is a player, and the only reason he is up there against the table at all at this moment is because he moves up to lend Nick the Greek some dough; and ordinarily there is no more chance of Jew Louie betting a thousand to five hundred on any proposition whatever than there is of him giving his dough to the Salvation Army, which is no chance at all. It is a sure thing he will never think of betting a thousand to five hundred a guy will not make ten with the dice, and when Rusty Charley tells Louie he has such a bet, Louie starts trembling all over.

The others around the table do not say a word, and so Charley rattles the dice again in his duke, blows on them, and chucks them into the derby hat and says "Hah!" But, of course, nobody can see in the derby hat except Charley, and he peeks in at the dice and says "Five." He rattles the dice once more and chucks them into the derby and says "Hah!" and then after peeking into the hat at the dice he says "Eight." I am commencing to sweat for fear he may heave a seven in the hat and blow his bet, and I know Charley has no five C's to pay off with, although, of course, I also know Charley has no idea of paying off, no matter what he heaves.

On the next chuck, Charley yells "Money!"—meaning he finally makes his ten, although nobody sees it but him; and he reaches out his hand to Jew Louie, and Jew Louie hands him a big fat G note, very, very slow. In all my life I never see a sadder-looking guy than Louie when he is parting with his dough. If Louie has any idea of asking Charley to let him see the dice in the hat to make sure about the ten, he does not speak about the matter, and as Charley does not seem to wish to show the ten around, nobody else says anything either, probably figuring Rusty Charley is not a guy who is apt to let anybody question his word especially over such a small matter as a ten.

"Well," Charley says, putting Louie's G note in his pocket, "I think this is enough for me tonight," and he hands the derby hat back to the little guy who owns it and motions me to come on, which I am glad to do, as the silence in the joint is making my stomach go up and down inside me, and I know this is bad for my blood pressure. Nobody as much as opens his face from the time we go in until we start out, and you will be surprised how nervous it makes you to be in a big crowd with everybody dead still, especially when you figure it a spot that is liable to get hot any minute. It is only just as we get to the door that anybody speaks, and who is it but Jew Louie, who pipes up and says to Rusty Charley like this:

"Charley," he says, "do you make it the hard way?"

Well, everybody laughs, and we go on out, but I never hear myself whether Charley makes his ten with a six and a four, or with two fives —which is the hard way to make a ten with the dice—although I often wonder about the matter afterward.

I am hoping that I can now get away from Rusty Charley and go on home, because I can see he is the last guy in the world to have around a blood pressure, and, furthermore, that people may get the wrong idea of me if I stick around with him, but when I suggest going to Charley, he seems to be hurt.

"Why," Charley says, "you are a fine guy to be talking of quitting a pal just as we are starting out. You will certainly stay with me because I like company, and we will go down to Ikey the Pig's and play stuss. Ikey is an old friend of mine, and I owe him a complimentary play."

Now, of course, I do not wish to go to Ikey the Pig's, because it is a place away downtown, and I do not wish to play stuss, because this is a game which I am never able to figure out myself, and, furthermore, I remember Doc Brennan says I ought to get a little sleep now and then; but I see no use in hurting Charley's feelings, especially as he is apt to do something drastic to me if I do not go.

So he calls a taxi, and we start downtown for Ikey the Pig's, and the jockey who is driving the short goes so fast that it makes my blood pressure go up a foot to a foot and a half from the way I feel inside, although Rusty Charley pays no attention to the speed. Finally I stick my head out the window and ask the jockey to please take it a little easy, as I wish to get where I am going all in one piece, but the guy only keeps busting along.

We are at the corner of Nineteenth and Broadway when all of a sudden Rusty Charley yells at the jockey to pull up a minute, which the guy does. Then Charley steps out of the cab and says to the jockey like this:

"When a customer asks you to take it easy, why do you not be nice and take it easy? Now see what you get."

And Rusty Charley hauls off and clips the jockey a punch on the chin that knocks the poor guy right off the seat into the street, and then Charley climbs into the seat himself and away we go with Charley driving, leaving the guy stretched out as stiff as a board. Now Rusty Charley once drives a short for a living himself, until the coppers get an idea that he is not always delivering his customers to the right address, especially such as may happen to be drunk when he gets them, and he is a pretty fair driver, but he only looks one way, which is straight ahead.

Personally, I never wish to ride with Charley in a taxicab under any circumstances, especially if he is driving, because he certainly drives very fast. He pulls up a block from Ikey the Pig's, and says we will leave the short there until somebody finds it and turns it in, but just as we are walking away from the short up steps a copper in uniform and claims we cannot park the short in this spot without a driver.

Well, Rusty Charley just naturally hates to have coppers give him any advice, so what does he do but peek up and down the street to see if anybody is looking, and then haul off and clout the copper on the chin, knocking him bow-legged. I wish to say I never see a more accurate puncher than Rusty Charley, because he always connects with that old button. As the copper tumbles, Rusty Charley grabs me by the arm and starts me running up a side street, and after we go about a block we dodge into Ikey the Pig's.

It is what is called a stuss house, and many prominent citizens of the neighborhood are present playing stuss. Nobody seems any too glad to see Rusty Charley, although Ikey the Pig lets on he is tickled half to death. This Ikey the Pig is a short fat-necked guy who will look very natural at New Year's, undressed, and with an apple in his mouth, but it seems he and Rusty Charley are really old-time friends, and think fairly well of each other in spots.

But I can see that Ikey the Pig is not so tickled when he finds Charley is there to gamble, although Charley flashes his G note at once, and says he does not mind losing a little dough to Ikey just for old time's sake. But I judge Ikey the Pig knows he is never going to handle Charley's G note, because Charley puts it back in his pocket and it never comes out again even though Charley gets off loser playing stuss right away.

Well, at five o'clock in the morning, Charley is stuck one hundred and thirty G's, which is plenty of money even when a guy is playing on his muscle, and of course Ikey the Pig knows there is no chance of getting one hundred and thirty cents off of Rusty Charley, let alone that many thousands. Everybody else is gone by this time and Ikey wishes to close up. He is willing to take Charley's marker for a million if necessary to get Charley out, but the trouble is in stuss a guy is entitled to get back a percentage of what he loses, and Ikey figures Charley is sure to wish this percentage even if he gives a marker, and the percentage will wreck Ikey's joint.

Furthermore, Rusty Charley says he will not quit loser under such circumstances because Ikey is his friend, so what happens Ikey finally sends out and hires a cheater by the name of Dopey Goldberg, who takes to dealing the game and in no time he has Rusty Charley even by cheating in Rusty Charley's favor.

Personally, I do not pay much attention to the play but grab myself a few winks of sleep in a chair in a corner, and the rest seems to help my blood pressure no little. In fact, I am not noticing my blood pressure at all when Rusty Charley and I get out of Ikey the Pig's, because I figure Charley will let me go home and I can go to bed. But although it is six o'clock, and coming on broad daylight when we leave Ikey's, Charley is still full of zing, and nothing will do him but we must go to a joint that is called the Bohemian Club.

Well, this idea starts my blood pressure going again, because the Bohemian Club is nothing but a deadfall where guys and dolls go when there is positively no other place in town open, and it is run by a guy by the name of Knife O'Halloran, who comes from down around

Greenwich Village and is considered a very bad character. It is well known to one and all that a guy is apt to lose his life in Knife O'Halloran's any night, even if he does nothing more than drink Knife O'Halloran's liquor.

But Rusty Charley insists on going there, so naturally I go with him; and at first everything is very quiet and peaceful, except that a lot of guys and dolls in evening clothes, who wind up there after being in the night clubs all night, are yelling in one corner of the joint. Rusty Charley and Knife O'Halloran are having a drink together out of a bottle which Knife carries in his pocket, so as not to get it mixed up with the liquor he sells his customers, and are cutting up old touches of the time when they run with the Hudson Dusters together, when all of a sudden in comes four coppers in plain clothes.

Now these coppers are off duty and are meaning no harm to anybody, and are only wishing to have a dram or two before going home, and the chances are they will pay no attention to Rusty Charley if he minds his own business, although of course they know who he is very well indeed and will take great pleasure in putting the old sleeve on him if they only have a few charges against him, which they do not. So they do not give him a tumble. But if there is one thing Rusty Charley hates it is a copper, and he starts eying them from the minute they sit down at a table, and by and by I hear him say to Knife O'Halloran like this:

"Knife," Charley says, "what is the most beautiful sight in the world?"

"I do not know, Charley," Knife says. "What is the most beautiful sight in the world?"

"Four dead coppers in a row," Charley says.

Well, at this I personally ease myself over toward the door, because I never wish to have any trouble with coppers, and especially with four coppers, so I do not see everything that comes off. All I see is Rusty Charley grabbing at the big foot which one of the coppers kicks at him, and then everybody seems to go into a huddle, and the guys and dolls in evening dress start squawking, and my blood pressure goes up to maybe a million.

I get outside the door, but I do not go away at once as anybody with any sense will do, but stand there listening to what is going on inside, which seems to be nothing more than a loud noise like ker-bump, ker-bump, ker-bump. I am not afraid there will be any shooting, because as far as Rusty Charley is concerned he is too smart to shoot any coppers, which is the worst thing a guy can do in this town, and the coppers are not likely to start any blasting because they will not wish it to come out that they are in a joint such as the Bohemian Club off duty. So I figure they will all just take it out in pulling and hauling.

Finally the noise inside dies down, and by and by the door opens and out comes Rusty Charley, dusting himself off here and there with his hands and looking very much pleased, indeed, and through the door before it flies shut again I catch a glimpse of a lot of guys stretched out on the floor. Furthermore, I can still hear guys and dolls hollering.

"Well, well," Rusty Charley says, "I am commencing to think you take the wind on me, and am just about to get mad at you, but here you are. Let us go away from this joint, because they are making so much noise inside you cannot hear yourself think. Let us go to my joint and make my old woman cook us up some breakfast, and then we can catch some sleep. A little ham and eggs will not be bad to take right now."

Well, naturally ham and eggs are appealing to me no little at this time, but I do not care to go to Rusty Charley's joint. As far as I am personally concerned, I have enough of Rusty Charley to do me a long, long time, and I do not care to enter into his home life to any extent whatever, although to tell the truth I am somewhat surprised to learn he has any such life. I believe I do once hear that Rusty Charley marries one of the neighbors' children, and that he lives somewhere over on Tenth Avenue in the Forties, but nobody really knows much about this, and everybody figures if it is true his wife must lead a terrible dog's life.

But while I do not wish to go to Charley's joint I cannot very well refuse a civil invitation to eat ham and eggs, especially as Charley is looking at me in a very much surprised way because I do not seem so glad and I can see that it is not everyone that he invites to his joint. So I thank him, and say there is nothing I will enjoy more than ham and eggs such as his old woman will cook for us, and by and by we are walking along Tenth Avenue up around Forty-fifth Street.

It is still fairly early in the morning, and business guys are opening up their joints for the day, and little children are skipping along the sidewalks going to school and laughing tee-hee, and old dolls are shaking bedclothes and one thing and another out of the windows of the tenement houses, but when they spot Rusty Charley and me everybody becomes very quiet, indeed, and I can see that Charley is greatly respected in his own neighborhood. The business guys hurry into their joints, and the little children stop skipping and tee-heeing and go tip-toeing along, and the old dolls yank in their noodles, and a great quiet comes to the street. In fact, about all you can hear is the heels of Rusty Charley and me hitting on the sidewalk.

There is an ice wagon with a couple of horses hitched to it standing in front of a store, and when he sees the horses Rusty Charley seems to get a big idea. He stops and looks the horses over very carefully, although as far as I can see they are nothing but horses, and big and fat, and sleepy-looking horses, at that. Finally Rusty Charley says to me like this:

"When I am a young guy," he says, "I am a very good puncher with my right hand, and often I hit a horse on the skull with my fist and knock it down. I wonder," he says, "if I lose my punch. The last copper I hit back there gets up twice on me."

Then he steps up to one of the ice-wagon horses and hauls off and biffs it right between the eyes with a right-hand smack that does not travel more than four inches, and down goes old Mister Horse to his knees looking very much surprised, indeed. I see many a hard puncher in my day, including Dempsey when he really can punch, but I never see a harder punch than Rusty Charley gives this horse.

Well, the ice-wagon driver comes busting out of the store all heated up over what happens to his horse, but he cools out the minute he sees Rusty Charley, and goes on back into the store leaving the horse still taking a count, while Rusty Charley and I keep walking. Finally we come to the entrance of a tenement house that Rusty Charley says is where he lives, and in front of this house is a wop with a push cart loaded with fruit and vegetables and one thing and another, which Rusty Charley tips over as we go into the house, leaving the wop yelling very loud, and maybe cussing us in wop for all I know. I am very glad, personally, we finally get somewhere, because I can feel that my blood pressure is getting worse every minute I am with Rusty Charley.

We climb two flights of stairs, and then Charley opens a door and we step into a room where there is a pretty little red-headed doll about knee high to a flivver, who looks as if she may just get out of the hay, because her red hair is flying around every which way on her head, and her eyes seem still gummed up with sleep. At first I think she is a very cute sight, indeed, and then I see something in her eyes that tells me this doll, whoever she is, is feeling very hostile to one and all.

"Hello, tootsie," Rusty Charley says. "How about some ham and eggs for me and my pal here? We are all tired out going around and about."

Well, the little red-headed doll just looks at him without saying a word. She is standing in the middle of the floor with one hand behind her, and all of a sudden she brings this hand around, and what does she have in it but a young baseball bat, such as kids play ball with, and which cost maybe two bits; and the next thing I know I hear something go ker-bap, and I can see she smacks Rusty Charley on the side of the noggin with the bat.

Naturally I am greatly horrified at this business, and figure Rusty Charley will kill her at once, and then I will be in a jam for witnessing the murder and will be held in jail several years like all witnesses to anything in this man's town; but Rusty Charley only falls into a big rocking-chair in a corner of the room and sits there with one hand to his head, saying, "Now hold on, tootsie," and "Wait a minute there, honey." I recollect hearing him say, "We have company for breakfast," and then the little red-headed doll turns on me and gives me a look such as I will always remember, although I smile at her very pleasant and mention it is a nice morning.

Finally she says to me like this:

"So you are the trambo who keeps my husband out all night, are you, you trambo?" she says, and with this she starts for me, and I start for the door; and by this time my blood pressure is all out of whack, because I can see that Mrs. Rusty Charley is excited more than somewhat. I get my hand on the knob and just then something hits me alongside the noggin, which I afterward figure must be the baseball bat, although I remember having a sneaking idea the roof caves in on me.

How I get the door open I do not know, because I am very dizzy in the head and my legs are wobbling, but when I think back over the situation I remember going down a lot of steps very fast, and by and by the fresh air strikes me, and I figure I am in the clear. But all of a sudden I feel another strange sensation back of my head and something goes plop against my noggin, and I figure at first that maybe my blood pressure runs up so high that it squirts out the top of my bean. Then I peek around over my shoulder just once to see that Mrs. Rusty Charley is standing beside the wop peddler's cart snatching fruit and vegetables of one kind and another off the cart and chucking them at me.

But what she hits me with back of the head is not an apple, or a peach, or a rutabaga, or a cabbage, or even a casaba melon, but a brickbat that the wop has on his cart to weight down the paper sacks in which he sells his goods. It is this brickbat which makes a lump on the back of my head so big that Doc Brennan thinks it is a tumor when I go to him the next day about my stomach, and I never tell him any different.

"But," Doc Brennan says, when he takes my blood pressure again, "your pressure is down below normal now, and as far as it is concerned you are in no danger whatever. It only goes to show what just a little bit of quiet living will do for a guy," Doc Brennan says. "Ten bucks, please," he says.

Wolcott Gibbs

THE FREE LANCE

MR. ANDREW EPPLEY, president of the Municipal Bureau of Subways, stood at the window of his office, looking forty-seven stories down into the street. For two days some men had been doing something to the paving, and now there was a raw cavity which reached almost from curb to curb. It was surrounded by machinery and tar-paper shacks, and both ends of the street itself were barred with trestles. At night lanterns traced a red geometry in the canyon; by day the nervous chattering of the drills floated thinly up to Mr. Eppley, even on his splendid heights.

"What you suppose them babies doing down there, Joey?" Mr. Eppley asked his secretary, Miss Murphy, without turning around.

"Laying sewer pipe, prolly," she replied, for this with her was a sort of generic explanation of all the awful mysteries that go on beneath the city.

"Yeah, well, it don't look like no sewer pipe to *me*," said Mr. Eppley, tipping dangerously over the sill to see better. "You know what it looks like to me, Joey? It looks like them babies might be doing the digging for a subway. We ain't got a subway coming out no place down here, have we?"

From *A Bed of Neuroses*, copyright, 1934, by Dodd, Mead & Company. Originally in *The New Yorker*.

"I don't remember," she said.

"Listen, sweetheart," said Mr. Eppley, "you ain't getting paid for remembering. How about looking in the maps and *seeing* where we got our subways coming out?"

"Oh, all *right*," she said wearily and, putting down her *Modern Priscilla*, she took her small, agreeable shape off to a corner of the office, where there was a long battery of files. Here she was angrily busy for some time, banging drawers and scuffing through folders.

"Nope," she said finally. "We ain't got a subway within ten blocks."

Perhaps it should be explained here that almost the first thing Tammany did upon its return to power in 1942 was to take all the subways out of private hands, and convert them into a department of the city government. There were, of course, a great many worthy candidates for the presidency of this important bureau, but it was finally decided that Mr. Eppley's martyrdom for the Cause (in 1936 he had served a short term, convicted on a false and cowardly charge of ballot-box-stuffing), combined with his long experience in the house-wrecking game, entitled him to first consideration, and he was appointed by a unanimous vote. Thereafter all subway construction and operation had been under his jurisdiction, and all plans, naturally, were, or should have been, in his files.

Mr. Eppley looked down again at the hole in the street.

"It certainly *looks* like they was doing the digging for a subway," he said thoughtfully. "Look, Joey, see can you get the Mayor on the phone."

"My!" she said admiringly.

"Never mind about that," said Mr. Eppley. "You get him."

"O.K." she said. "Don't get overwrought."

"And listen, Joey, you better talk to him. Maybe it would put in a better appearance. What I want to find out, see, is have they got a record of this subway down at City Hall. Maybe we got some mistake in our files. I mean, it would look like hell if it turned out we really *was* building a subway through this street and I didn't know nothing about it. Get what I mean?"

"Sure," she said, "like the time you had the boys digging up Jones Beach instead of Jones Street."

"Never mind," said Mr. Eppley. "Anyways, don't ask him right out, see? Just hint around, like you was kidding. Or, wait a minute"—he chuckled—"I got it. Tell him I gone out of town—maybe with a dame, see?—and I took all these important papers with me so that you don't know *where* the hell we got subways. Tell him you got to know right off, because you got some important guy on another line, waiting. That would let us out all right, wouldn't it?"

"It lets *you* out," she said bitterly. "It don't make me look any too bright, though."

"All right, all right," he said. "Get going."

Sulkily, she began to dial, and presently was indeed talking to the Mayor. Mr. Eppley listened anxiously but could make little out of the one-sided conversation.

"Well," he said, when she had hung up, "what'd he say?"

"He says there ain't no subway nearer here than Broad Street," she told him, and added pleasantly, "He wants to know how long you going to be canned up *this* time."

"Ain't *that* nice, after all I done for that guy?" demanded Mr. Eppley, but he was too troubled for indignation, and wandered again to the window.

"If that ain't a subway, I'm Linboigh," he said unhappily.

Miss Murphy was about to reply when a buzzer sounded on her desk. She picked up the inter-office phone and listened.

"Guy to see you," she said finally. "Name of Edmunds. It's about subways."

"What about subways?"

"Miss Burns asked him, but he wouldn't say," she said. "Just about subways, he told her."

"All right, get him in," said Mr. Eppley. "I might as well talk to somebody as go nuts worrying."

"That's right," said Miss Murphy. "Show Mr. Edmunds in," she said to the telephone.

Mr. Edmunds came in at an anxious trot. He was a little man, with misty eyes in a face almost obliterated by fine, silky hair. His clothes struck a sort of low-comedy balance because while his derby hat was much too small and rode high above his flanking ears, his sleeves and the legs of his trousers were much too long, so that his fingers and the toes of his shoes were visible only shyly and intermittently when he made some sudden movement. He carried a tattered briefcase and a badly rolled umbrella.

"Are you Mr. Eppley?" he asked diffidently. "I'm Paul Edmunds."

"Pleased to meet you," said Mr. Eppley. "Sit down. Take a powder, Joey."

The door closed behind her, and Mr. Eppley's caller bent across the desk.

"Mr. Eppley," he said, "I'm afraid I'm coming to you with rather a peculiar proposition."

"It ain't insurance, is it?" asked Mr. Eppley. "Because if it is—"

"Oh, no," said the stranger, drawing back in horror. "It certainly isn't insurance."

"Nor books. I don't need no books. I got my hands full up with what I'm doing right here."

"Oh, no. To tell the truth"—he laughed uneasily—"I don't know just how to tell you about the proposition I want to make you because, as I said, it is so very peculiar."

"Yeah?" said Mr. Eppley.

"Yes, indeed. You see, Mr. Eppley, I've always been a rather inventive sort of chap. Always doing things with my hands. Even when I was just a shaver in Flushing, my parents tried over and over to make me go out and play games—rugger and, er, other sporting events —but I always preferred to stay in my little toolshop and, well, just tinker. Chacun à son gout, you know."

"Right," said Mr. Eppley.

"Well, it kept on right through school and college—I was Harvard '13. Perhaps you are a Harvard man, Mr. Eppley? . . . No? Well, anyway, all through my life, where other fellows might turn to books or the theatre or the, ah, flowing bowl, it was machinery with me. You might say machinery was my mistress. In a way, of course."

"You liked locomotive engines and all, you mean?" said Mr. Eppley.

"Something like that. Well, when I came to New York last year —and here we come to my point—I said to myself, now what is the most exciting thing a man could do in this great wonderful city? What would I like to do most? And what do you suppose I said, Mr. Eppley?"

"You got me," confessed Mr. Eppley.

"Subways! Paul, I said to myself, that's the job for you! Subways! Tunnelling under those great buildings, through the granite and sand and water, so that all those hurrying millions could get to and fro just a little more comfortably and quickly. It seemed to me the greatest career in the world, and I promised myself I wouldn't rest until—"

"I'm sorry, Mr. Edmunds," said Mr. Eppley, who thought he saw a light, "but we ain't got any jobs here just at the moment. Things are pretty slow right now, what with the lousy Board of Estimate raising a stink every time a man tries to order a carload of fishplate. Why, only last week—"

"Ah, but I don't think you quite understand me, Mr. Eppley," said Mr. Edmunds gently. "I'm not asking you for a job."

"No? Then—"

"No. I already have my dream. I *am* a subway builder, Mr. Eppley!"

"You're *what?*"

"I *am* a subway builder! I *have* built a subway!"

"Where!" asked Mr. Eppley, but he had already begun to tingle with a horrid presentiment.

"I'll show you," said Mr. Edmunds, and he got up and skipped over to Mr. Eppley's window. "I wonder if you'd mind stepping over here just a minute, Mr. Eppley?"

Mr. Eppley followed him.

"There it is," said Mr. Edmunds, and pointed, as Mr. Eppley had been miserably sure he would, at that toiling ant heap so far below.

"I see," said Mr. Eppley dully.

"It took capital and it took ingenuity," said Mr. Edmunds proudly. "You have no idea how, well, *cluttered* New York is underneath. But it's the longest subway in the world and the straightest. Runs from the Battery clear up to Yonkers without a curve. What do you think of that?"

"It's something, all right," said Mr. Eppley. "Say, who knows about this thing, anyways?"

"Oh, hardly anybody except the men I hired," said Mr. Edmunds. "I rather dispensed with the formalities. Just decided to dig it and went right ahead. Of course there were mistakes—we couldn't hope to avoid a cellar here and there—but on the whole it went quietly."

"It certainly did," said Mr. Eppley.

"Be finished tomorrow unless something goes wrong," said Mr. Edmunds, "and that brings me again to why I came to see you. As I told you, Mr. Eppley, I'm a creative sort of beggar. As soon as I finish one job—bing!—I want to be off and away and at something else. Off with the old, on with the new. That sort of thing."

"Oh, sure," said Mr. Eppley feebly.

"The point is, though, it's a little difficult to focus on a new project until the old one is cleared up. What I wanted to ask you, Mr. Eppley, is just this: how does one go about disposing of a subway? I asked several people—putting it to them as a purely hypothetical case, of course—and they all mentioned you. And that," he finished triumphantly, "is really why I'm here."

Mr. Eppley looked at Mr. Edmunds for a long time.

"You want to sell me this subway?" he asked, at length.

NEW YORK · 157

"Well, yes," said Mr. Edmunds. "I could really let you have it very cheaply—for what it cost me, practically. You see, I do these things mostly for the fun of it. Of course, I don't like to work for nothing —what do they say about the laborer being worthy of his hire?—but the actual amount hardly matters at all."

There was another long silence, while Mr. Eppley tapped a pencil on his desk and stared out of the window. Finally his face seemed to clear.

"I tell you what, Mr. Edmunds," he said, "you got a mighty interesting little proposition there, a mighty interesting and unusual little proposition, and I want to think about it. You and me can make a deal all right, but I want to think about it. You know, like the details. What you do, you leave me your name and address, and I'll get in touch with you."

"When?" demanded Mr. Edmunds, who had a sort of meek obstinacy.

"Tomorrow, or the next day at the latest," said Mr. Eppley. "But you'll certainly hear from me."

Mr. Edmunds sorted a rumpled card out of the confusion of papers in his pocket and handed it to Mr. Eppley.

"That's fine," he said, getting up. "That's awfully good of you, Mr. Eppley."

"It ain't nothing," said Mr. Eppley politely. "You'll hear from me. So long."

"Au 'voir," said Mr. Edmunds.

As soon as the door had closed behind Mr. Edmunds, Mr. Eppley rang for Miss Murphy.

"Listen, Joey," he said nervously, "don't let that guy in here no more. I don't care what he says, just don't let him *in* no more. You got that?"

"O.K.," she said calmly, "but what's the matter with him? He looked like a nice little guy to me."

"Yeah," said Mr. Eppley, "he's a nice little guy, but he's nuts, that's what's the matter with him."

Even as he spoke a feather of sound, the faintest whisper from those faraway drills, curled in at the window, and Mr. Eppley shivered.

"He's nuts," repeated Mr. Eppley, but he didn't believe it for a minute.

Arthur Kober

CHOCOLATE FOR THE WOODWORK

THE doorbell rang, but no one in the Gross household made the slightest move to answer it. It rang again, clearly and demandingly.

"Nu?" yelled Mrs. Gross from the kitchen, where she was washing the breakfast dishes. "So just because is here Sunday, is a vacation fa evveybody, ha? Listen the way it rings the bell—like a regelleh fecktree fomm lomm clocks. So open op the door, somebody!"

From the bathroom, Bella shouted, "What'sa matter with evveybody arounn here? Are they deef or something? Fa heaven's sakes, can'tcha hear the bell?"

The task of opening the door clearly devolved upon Pa Gross. He angrily threw his newspaper to the floor and got up from his rocker. "Evvey time a persin sits donn to ridd a couple woids in the paper is alluva sumn a big busy here in house. So who is here the soiving goil? Me! . . . Aw right awready!" The last remark was addressed to the clamoring bell. "You can't see I'm coming?"

The man Mr. Gross ushered into the dining room was a study in sartorial splendor. His Panama hat, which he didn't bother to remove, had a band resplendent in many colors. The Palm Beach suit he wore contrasted vividly with his blue shirt, which, together with a blue tie and a carefully folded blue kerchief which peeped from his breast pocket, gave an ensemble effect. Black-and-white sports shoes and purple socks with red vertical stripes completed a dazzling costume. For a moment, Pa stared in wide-eyed wonder at the magnificent stranger, then he sniffed. There was a pervasive odor about the visitor which he quickly identified as turpentine. This, then, must be the long-awaited painter whose magic was going to transform the dingy Gross apartment into a thing of beauty.

"Good munning, good munning!" Pa twinkled at the fashion plate who stood before him. "So you is the paintner the lendludd is sending, no?"

"No! The paintner is woiking fa me." There was implied rebuke in the man's tone. "I'm the *boss* paintner. Wait, I'll give you mine cott." He reached into his inside pocket, whipped out a stained wallet, and from one of its many folds extracted several cards. By this time Mrs. Gross and Bella were standing beside Pa, and the visitor solemnly presented each of them with a card.

The three Grosses studied the slips of pasteboard in their hands. A good portion of them was taken up by a design of an open can with the name "Eagle" on it. Above this was the phrase "Old Dutch Process" and below it the legend "Employ a Good Painter. Good Painters Use White Lead. White Leads Lasts." There was barely enough room left for the name, Philip Rudnick, and an address and telephone number.

While the Grosses examined his card, Mr. Rudnick's attention was devoted to their apartment. With his fingers he dug at a flaky wall, peeling huge hunks from it and leaving a white, gaping wound in a vast field of yellow. "Tchk, tchk, tchk!" Phillip Rudnick's oscillating head tacitly rebuked Mr. and Mrs. Gross. "How people can live in such a place! Lookit how is falling donn the wall in liddle pieces." He continued scraping with his fingers. "Some place you got it here! Comes the Boarder Felt and right away you is gung to get a summints!"

"I begya podden!" Bella's voice was hard and chilly. "We happen not to be inarrested in what the Board of Health is gonna do to us. What we happen to be inarrested in is having this here apartment fixed up so that evvey individual or person who comes along won't stick in their two cents' worth of what's wrong with this place. What we wanna know is just what you intend to do regarding the fixing up of this here apartment."

Mr. Rudnick stared at Bella as if seeing her for the first time. Then, turning to Mr. Gross, he said, "The dutter?" Pa nodded. Mr. Rudnick scraped his purple chin with his nails and eyed Bella reflectively. "She is esking what is Rudnick gung to do with this apottment. Listen, lady." He clasped his hands behind his back and rocked on his heels. "You know hommany yirrs is Rudnick in the paintning business? Plenty! You know hommany apottments is Rudnick fixing op? Plenty, believe me!" His voice suddenly became conversational. "I want you should enswer me a question. You a woiking goil?"

"Uf cuss!" sang out Pa Gross.

"So what is your line?" Mr. Rudnick asked.

"I happen to be the privitt seckatary fa a very important pardy who is inclined along financial matters," said Bella.

"Aha, a seckatary! So how you would like if your boss say to you, 'How you gung to write the letter you putting donn by you in the shuthend book? You gung to put the paper in the machine with the left hend under the right hend? You gung to use by you the liddle pinkie undder the whole hend?' 'What's the diffrince?' you is gung to give the boss an enswer. 'Mine job is to write it fa you the lettis. If you like mine job, so is O.K. If you don't like it, then you give me the seck. But how I'm doing the job, that's strickly mine business.' " He waved a finger at Bella. "So the same is with Rudnick. How I'm gung to fix by you the apottment, that's strickly mine business."

"He's positiffly got it right!" declared Pa Gross, placing a hand on the visitor's shoulder. "Mr. Rudnick is foist gung to do the paintning job, then we'll complain when he is finndished."

Mrs. Gross felt it her duty to come to her daughter's defense. "Say, what is here—Europe, maybe, a persin dassent tukk a couple woids? She says something, Bella, and right away is evveybody yelling on her 'Sharrop!' " She glowered at the two men. "Cossacks!"

Mr. Rudnick, busy blotting the back of his neck with his handkerchief, ignored this attack. "Oooh," he complained, "is very hot here in house. Look," he said, "why you so stingy with the winda opening when is here like a regelleh stove?" He walked to the window and raised it. He looked down at the street and then, wildly waving his fist, he cried out, "Hey, you little bestidds, kipp away from mine machine, you hear? In two seconds I'll come downstairs and I'll fix you good, you tramps, you!" He turned away from the window and scowled at the Grosses. "A fine neighborhood you got it here! Some foistcless gengsters is gung to be the kits in the stritt. I'm leaving mine uttemobill donnstairs—mine machine is a Chevvy," he added parenthetically—"and right away they scretching op by me the machine, the no-good bummers! Where I am living, on the Concuss, is O.K. to leave mine machine a whole day on the stritt and will come no kits to scretch by me the car. But here in this neighborhood—" A shrug of his shoulders completed his comment.

"A lotta people I know," said Bella icily, "they ride with the subway, where they got no worries who scratches up the cars."

"Excuse me!" Mr. Rudnick's tone was laden with disdain. "Evveything I say is with her no good. Now is a sin to have a machine, ha?

Today is a paint job in this neighborhood, temorreh is a paint job in that neighborhood, next day is a paint job maybe in the Heights. So the boss paintner shouldn't have a machine? Listen, you think I get maybe pleasure from mine Chevvy? Nah! Is expenses fa ges, is expenses fa tires, is all the time expenses. You know hommuch it custs me, mine expenses? Plenty! And that's with you a sin, ha?"

"Parm me," said Bella, somewhat chastened, "but I happen not to be criticizing whether you have a car or you don't have one. I happen to be criticizing that just because some little kids are playing arounn on the street and your car happens to be in the way, that is no excuse you should indulge in vulgarity or to criticize this neighborhood, which we happen to be living in at the present time."

Mr. Rudnick seemed about to say something sharp and cutting, but thought better of it. "Listen," he said, forcing a smile, "in mine house if mine dutter tukked so fresh to a guest, you know what I would give her? Plenty! But what can a persin speck from this neighborhood?" Before Bella could find a fitting rejoinder he had whipped out a notebook and pencil. "Nu, Rudnick is not here to make spitches. Rudnick is here to see with the paint job." He abandoned the Grosses to inspect the walls. "Paint with stipple finish the whole thing complete," he mumbled as he made notes. "Wash op the cilling, take away the crecks, fix it the loose plester, and don't fegget you should do kelsomine job. With the flurr—scrape, uf cuss, and you should finndish with two coats fomm shelleck." He headed toward the window and noticed the radiator in passing. "Aha, the radiatiss you should silver op. And with the windiss, take loose puddy away, new puddy put in." Mr. Rudnick continued making notes as he walked from room to room. The Gross family trailed after him, and when he ran his fingers along the woodwork all of them followed suit and nodded discerningly.

The procession returned to the dining room. "O.K.," said Mr. Rudnick, snapping his notebook shut. "Mine paintners will come temorreh to fix it by you the apottment. Will be the place brannew. Will be a pleasure to live here." Again his glance encompassed the room, and he seemed to shudder. "Not like is now."

"What about the matter from the color?" asked Bella. "We haven't decided yet what should be the color of the apartment."

"A question!" jeered the painter. "What should be the color? Chotruse, uf cuss! Ye know what is chotruse?"

"Green," Bella said.

Mr. Rudnick pretended he hadn't heard her. "Chotruse is grinn." This was addressed confidentially to Pa. "Go to the best homes. Go to the finest flets on the Concuss, and is oney one color—chotruse! Mine apottment, where I'm living, is strickly chotruse."

"Well, it so happens I got diffrint idears on the subjeck," said Bella. "It so happens that what we want in the line of color is cream walls—"

"Crimm walls!" bellowed Mr. Rudnick. "Is no more stylish crimm walls! You know where you find crimm walls? In the chipp apottments where is living very common pipple. Feh! But go to the Concuss, go even to the Heights, and you know hommany places is chotruse? Plenty!"

"See here," said Bella, "it's our house. Do you mind leaving us fix it the way we like, inasmuch as we are the folks living here and it so happens you are not?"

Mr. Rudnick eyed her steadily for several seconds. He then turned to Mr. Gross and, nodding in Bella's direction, said, "The boss, ha?"

The old man felt obliged to define his daughter's authority. "She's a single goil. When we fix the apottment like she says, maybe will come here some nice boyess—"

"Fa heaven's sakes, Pa!" Bella screamed. "What's his business that I'm single? Must you tell the whole world who comes here about your own daughter's condition?"

"Dope!" Mrs. Gross's shrill voice was also raised in protest. "Why you don't tell him hommuch money we not yet paying the butcher? Why you don't tell him fomm your gold watch in punnshop? Go on, tell your friend evveything fomm the femily, Mr. Tettletale!"

"Sha, sha, sha!" Mr. Rudnick's features now broke into a disarming smile. "O.K., so now I know how is. So will Rudnick make fa you crimm walls just like the dutter wants it. Now is evveybody serrisfied, and I'm seeing you in the munning."

He started for the hallway, but Bella's next question arrested him. "What about the woodwork?" she asked. "I want it should be a chawk-lit color."

"Ha?" Mr. Rudnick's baffled expression indicated he wasn't sure he had heard her correctly.

"I want the color should have two tones," explained Bella. "I want cream fa the walls and chawklit fa the woodwork."

Mr. Rudnick lifted his Panama hat and daintily scraped his scalp with his little finger. "Chucklit!" he murmured. Replacing his hat, he slowly and deliberately took out his notebook, scribbled something in it and then looked up. "Excuse me," he said. "What kine chucklit you would like fa the woodwoik—Nestle's udder Hoishey's?"

"See here," said Bella, "I take that remark fomm whence it comes."

"Chucklit!" Mr. Rudnick replaced his book, tapped the crown of his gay Panama with his hand, and stalked to the door. As he was about to leave the apartment, he stopped, stared reflectively into space, and then turned around. "Listen, lady," he shouted at Bella, "Rudnick is gung to fix the place just like you say—two tunns, crimm and chucklit! And listen. If you not finding a nice boy after Rudnick is fixing the apottment, you know what you should put in the chucklit woodwoik? Ammints! You hear me—ammints!"

Bella Gross reached into her arsenal of invective for a particularly annihilating reply, but she was too late. Mr. Rudnick was out of the apartment, leaving behind the ringing echo of his voice shouting "Ammints!"

H. Allen Smith

NEW YORK IS MOSTLY PEOPLE

ONE of the chief sources of material for present-generation comedians is the transaction through which the Island of Manhattan was obtained from the Indians. People who never encountered the story in history books have heard it in jokes—how Peter Minuit, the Dutchman, bought the island from the Indians for sixty guilders, or twenty-four dollars.

That transaction was a bald swindle. Mynheer Peter was flimflammed. I have the true story of the deal in a history called *Mannhatin*. This book was published by a big bank and has a prefatory note by James J. Walker, therefore it must be reliable. It informs us that Peter Minuit paid the sixty guilders to the Canarsie Indians, and the Canarsie Indians had no more right to sell Manhattan than the Pelew Islanders have to sell the Ozarks. It didn't belong to them. They didn't even hold a mortgage on it. But they sold it to the Dutchman and made off with their guilders and later on, after the fraud had been discovered, a new deal had to be negotiated with a tribe of Indians living at the north end of Manhattan—the rightful owners.

Since I learned of this redskin game I've taken considerable enjoyment thinking back to those days—picturing the benighted, ignorant, uncivilized aborigines lurking in the forests, waiting for another ship from Europe to come in sight, and when the ship does appear in the Narrows, I see those hapless Indians leaping up and down for joy, and crying out to one another: "Ugh! Ugh! Oh, boy! More suckers!"

Thus the heritage of New York—her history opens with a swindle. Today the little people of the city scheme and connive and finagle. More than that, they have made a precise science out of the wangle. They wangle this and they wangle that and they get it for each other wholesale. Petty larceny dwells forever in their hearts, and when they ask you the nature of your business or profession, they say, "What racket you in?"

In New York newspaper offices there is a large volume called a cross-index telephone directory. It lists telephone subscribers and their numbers by streets. For example, you could take the cross-index book and begin at the lower end of Fifth Avenue and find the names and numbers of telephone subscribers house by house and store by store, clear to the end of the street. This book is invaluable for getting quick coverage on such things as large fires, explosions, shootings, collisions, and so on, when those things occur close to edition time. Suppose a flash comes from police headquarters that there has been an explosion at Throggs Neck Boulevard and Dewey Avenue. Dead line is ten minutes off. Rewrite men take the cross-index book, turn to Throggs Neck Boulevard, find the telephones listed in that immediate neighborhood, and start calling, asking whoever answers if they know what exploded, whether there's a fire, if anybody has been killed or injured, and such other details as might be available.

The rewrite men sometimes come up against peculiar situations in making such calls. One of them, I think it was Bill O'Brien, once telephoned to check on an apartment-house fire and, by chance, got the phone in the apartment where the fire started. The occupant of this apartment talked on and on, describing the progress of the flames, the splashing of water around him, the yelling of the firemen, and finally said he thought he'd better hang up, as he was now personally on fire.

There was the day of a big holdup in Brooklyn, and Carl Randau got the phone number of a small store across from the scene of the crime. In some manner Carl was connected with a pay phone on which a policeman was giving in his official report of the stickup. Carl just kept saying, "Yep. Yep. Yep. Yep," and taking notes until the cop had finished the full and complete story.

Joe Mitchell telephoned about a shooting in upper Manhattan one afternoon and got a Chinese laundryman on the wire. The Chinese couldn't understand what Joe was trying to say and while Joe was exasperated and angry, he stubbornly insisted on getting his point across. He employed English as clearly and as simply as it is possible for a native of North Carolina to speak.

"I . . . am . . . a . . . newspaper . . . reporter," he would enunciate. "There . . . has . . . been . . . a . . . shooting . . . with . . . a . . . gun . . . you know . . . bang, bang, bang . . . shooting . . . did . . . you . . . hear . . . any . . . bang, bang, bang?"

From the other end of the line came:

"Okay. Bling laundlee."

I have made hundreds of these cross-index calls and I know what the most common response is. Usually the little people are at the other end of the wire. They listen to your brief statement concerning the incident in their neighborhood, and when you ask them if they know anything about it, their first words are these: "What's in it for me?"

The petty avariciousness of the little people is irritating to many critics of New York, but somehow, to me, it affords a pleasant spectacle. It's fun to watch a couple of them trying to beat each other out of a nickel.

Speaking as a pure-bred hon-yock out of the Middle West, I would like to go on record as an admirer of New York City. Whenever I get away from the place a certain vague unhappiness settles upon me. The chief complaint I have about living in the Big Town is the necessity now and then of showing it off to my kinsfolks or other unreasonable citizens from the Edgar Guest country.

I know a lot of other transplanted Middle Westerners in New York and they all agree with me. People from back home come to New York with their hearts full of suspicion and hatred. They really look upon New York as a separate country. It is almost impossible to keep out of fights and loud arguments when you have a visiting fireman in tow. In the first place, they usually come into town on their vacations. They are out for a big time. They want to stay up all night every night, drinking everything in sight. They don't realize that most of us in New York lead the same kind of life that a citizen of St. Louis or Seattle or Scranton might lead. For the most part we stay at home nights and read or listen to the radio. Once a week, maybe, we go to the neighborhood movie. Occasionally we visit a legitimate theater, and on rare occasions we take leave of our senses and go to a night club.

Our visitors come into town whooping and yelling. They get off a train and get into a taxicab and their first argument is usually with the taxicab driver. To them he is in and of New York and, therefore, he's a crook, ipso facto, per se, and across the board. I suppose there are crooked cabdrivers in New York but I never encountered one. These visitors, however, consider the hackmen to be swindlers from the very beginning. They not only argue about the fare; they work the argument around to the point where they are able to leave the cab and stomp away without tipping. Their behavior from then on follows the same pattern. Everybody in New York is trying to hornswoggle them.

It's a difficult matter trying to figure out some reasonable method of entertaining such people. Left to myself, I think I could give a visitor a pretty good time. But they are always headstrong and omniscient and they know what they want. They want to get lit and go to Leon & Eddie's and play the drums in the orchestra and goose a chorus girl and insult people in the streets and spit on the RCA Building.

Not long ago I had a guest from Indiana. There were several places I wanted to take him. For one thing I wanted him to see the gents' room at the Radio City Music Hall. Here is one of the most noble prospects in the Western Hemisphere. It is, beyond doubt, the biggest and most magnificent can on earth—a veritable Taj Mahal of toilets. Looking at it for the first time, a man's credulity is put to test. It is almost too purty to use. Yet when I suggested to my friend that I'd like to show it to him, he said:

"Listen, fer Crisakes! You think I come all the way to Noo Yawrk to look at a toilet? C'mon! Le's go! Whereabouts is Bill's Gay Nineties at?"

It's not much fun seeing New York with such people. I prefer to go it alone. Times Square remains the best show on earth and if you know your way around in the district, you'll find life at its daffiest there. Times Square has been the theatrical center of New York for upward of fifty years. Before show business moved in, the neighborhood was occupied by carriage makers, harness shops, and livery stables. The livery-stable atmosphere survives in many of its present-day institutions, yet the place has its points.

I propose now to take you on a little pedestrian tour of the neighborhood and introduce you to a few of the inhabitants. Now, put your wallet in your coat pocket and keep your hand on it and we'll stroll around and look at things and call on people.

Broadway, between Fiftieth and Fifty-first. A skinny little guy in a derby hat comes up the street. He is handing out pamphlets when he can get close enough to people who will take them. Most people shy away from him because he has a demented look. His pamphlets are religious tracts, poorly printed, and as he makes his way up the street he keeps singing out:

"God gonna getcha! God gonna getcha! God gonna getcha!"

Here's the Capitol Theater Building. Let's step in. Joe Curtin runs the elevator in this building.* He has an unfortunate name for his job because wisecrackers who know him are always yelling, "Curtin going up!" Let's tell Joe about the God-gonna-getcha man. He says yes, he's seen the little guy lots of times. Joe knows I sometimes go on the prowl for unique humans.

"They's another one I wish you'd go investigate," he says. "It's a woman. She's got a whole neighborhood scared to death—the neighborhood where I live down in Chelsea. She must weigh over three hundred pounds and nobody knows where she lives at or where she comes from. She turns up around noon almost every day and begins walking around the same block. She always carries a club—a big old club honest to God you could stun a horse with. She just walks around the block, swingin' that club and scowlin' at everybody she meets. Never hit nobody that I know of, but people cross the street to get out of her way."

We haven't time for a side trip to Chelsea, so let's take the elevator to Ben Serkowich's office. Ben is an ex-newspaperman who has devoted his latter years to various phases of show business. He possesses one of the most phenomenal imaginations I've ever encountered. Here he is. Meet Ben Serkowich. As usual he has a story to tell. He says it's true. Listen to it, and judge for yourself. Go ahead, Ben.

Well, my friend, it looks like I'm in the money at last. Amazing thing has happened to me. You won't believe it, but you never believe anything I say, anyway.

About ten days ago I was taking a walk through Central Park. About eleven o'clock in the evening. I was away from the road, off in a sort of wooded place, when I heard somebody sobbing. There was a bench

* Mr. Curtin heard that I was going to mention him in this book. He requested that I not refer to him as an elevator operator. I asked him how I should describe him. He said: "Say I am a former third baseman."

under a tree and on the bench sits this guy. He was drunk as a goat and crying his head off.

I went over and sat down on the bench and asked him what was the matter. He raised his head up and looked at me. He was a nice-looking guy, around forty. Good clothes. He had a quart bottle in his lap, about three fourths finished. He didn't say anything but handed me the bottle and I took a belt at it. Then he took one, and looked at me again, and finally he started talking. Here's what he said:

"Brother," he says, "I'm the unhappiest one human you ever saw in your life. I'm rich. Got all the money a man could want. Got enough money I can have all the dames and all the whisky I want. But I'm unhappy.

"About twelve years ago I was just a working guy. Worked in an office on a salary. One night I bought a bottle of whisky and put it in my pocket. Then I came into the Park and started wandering around, taking a drink now and then. Finally I came to this bench. I sat down and drank some more. I got drunk. I was sitting here with my chin down on my chest. It was about this time of night. Suddenly I happened to look up, and I saw the god-damnedest most beautiful thing I ever saw in my life. This whole Park was going around. Slow. It was just circling. And all the buildings over there—the big ones with the lights—were going around. It was beautiful! Most beautiful thing a man could ever hope to see. Just kept going around, slow, sort of drifting and dipping, God! What a sight!

"Well, things happened to me after that. I left New York. Went to South America. Got involved in business. Next thing you know, I'm rich. So I come back to New York. I say to myself, from now on I'm gonna have fun. I'm gonna enjoy life.

"For a while I did have fun. Had me a hell of a good time. Then, just a few weeks ago, I began to miss something. I really wasn't having a good time. I was lying in bed one night when it dawned on me. I knew what it was I wanted. I wanted to see Central Park go around again.

"Well, I figured that was easy. I got a bottle and came over here and found this bench—the same bench—and started drinking. Drank a whole quart, but the god-damn Park wouldn't budge an inch. I found a cabdriver and sent him for another bottle and when he came back I drank half of it. Not a move from the park. Then I passed out and the cabdriver took me home.

"I've been coming over here every night since then. Drinking myself to death. But the Park won't circle. I've gotta see it once more. It sounds crazy, but it's something inside of me. I've got to see it go around or I'll go nuts."

He sat there and stared at the ground. It sounded crazy and then again it didn't sound so crazy. I smoked a while and looked at him. He kept drinking, and every now and then he'd raise up his head and look over toward Central Park South and groan. Then it hit me. I knew the answer, or thought I did. I asked him when it was that the Park whirled for him. He said it was 1930 or 1931. That was it! I told him I thought I could make the Park go around for him again. I told him it would have to be the next night, and he said that was okay, and then I got him into a cab and took him to his apartment. I wrote out my name and phone number and instructions for him to meet me on the same bench the next night at ten o'clock.

Next morning I went to see Milt, the guy who runs that saloon around the corner. I told Milt I wanted to get hold of some pre-repeal liquor. Prohibition stuff. Milt said he thought he might have some at home. We got in his car and drove out to Forest Hills to his house. He rummaged around in the basement and finally found a couple of bottles.

"How much?" I asked him.

"Well," says Milt, "this is genuine stuff—sort of antique liquor. Hard to get. I'll have to charge you seven bucks a bottle for it."

"How do I know it's genuine?" I asked him.

He says, "You can take my word for it."

Well, I wouldn't take a saloonkeeper's word for anything. I had to be sure about it. I told him I'd have the stuff tested, and, if it turned out to be genuine, then I'd buy both bottles. We drove back to town and I took the bootleg whisky over to a chemist I know on Eighth Avenue. I told him I wanted him to give it a good test and find out if it was genuine Prohibition stuff.

He did all kinds of things with it—Bunsen-burner stuff and test tubes and all that. Finally he says:

"Ben, you got something here. This is genuine. No question about it. It's the real stuff—pure Prohibition rotgut. It's the McCoy."

That night the guy was there on the bench when I arrived with my package. He was hung over and he seemed to be a little ashamed of himself.

"Listen," I says, "I wasn't fooling you. When you told me about the Park whirling twelve years ago, it suddenly dawned on me. The night the Park whirled, you were drinking Prohibition liquor. I think if you drank some Prohibition liquor tonight, she'd go around. Maybe so, maybe not. I had to dig for it, but I've got you some prime old speak-easy stuff here, and you owe me fourteen bucks. Now, get going on it."

He started on one of the bottles. He almost gulped the stuff. He handed the bottle to me and I started to take a drink, thinking maybe I'd like to see the old Park whirl, but the smell of the stuff hit my nose and I said, "No, thanks." He kept on drinking. He was cockeyed by the time he had half the bottle down. He started to mumble and slobber a little, but he kept on drinking. Then, just like I thought, it happened. He let out a yell. He stood up and right there in front of me he started turning around, whooping his head off and flapping his arms like a chicken.

He kept yelling: "There she goes!" He made about six turns and then fell over on the ground—out like a light. I took him home again and put him to bed.

Next morning he called me up and had me come over. He told me I had saved him from going crazy. He said he was sinfully rich and I could have anything he had. You know what I said to him? I said:

"I don't want any of your money. I'm glad I was able to do you a favor. I wouldn't take a cent of your money. But—if you want to do it, there's one thing: I always had a hankering to own a toll bridge of my own. Maybe you'd like to make me a little present of a toll bridge."

So, there it is. He's buying me a toll bridge. The papers are being drawn up this week.

I suppose you don't believe me. You never believe anything I tell you.

Let's say we believe him and get on out of here before he starts another one. Not far away is a theater. The sign outside says: "The One and Only Margie Hart." The man at the stage door is gruff and insulting, but you've got to expect that. He takes the message and Miss Margie Hart invites us in. She is sitting in her dressing room wearing a knickknack or two and maybe a bangle. She takes a couple of pokes at her carrot-colored hair, tilts back in her chair, and puts her feet on a make-up shelf.

"Excuse me," she says, "but I've got to have my feet up like this to get any rest. I just came offstage. Listen to that out there."

She has reference to a mob noise in the theater's auditorium where the gentlemen customers are whistling, shouting, stamping their feet, and hammering on the chairs. Obviously the customers had enjoyed Miss Hart's four-minute turn.

"I don't know what's come over them lately," she says. "In the last few weeks they have been more enthusiastic than ever before in the ten years I've been taking them off and letting them drop. You wouldn't believe it, but at one single performance of mine, just the other night, they broke more than a hundred seats. Just r'ared back and started kicking with their feet and smashing the seats."

We note with pleasure that there is no typewriter in Miss Hart's dressing room and then we recall how she was recently forbidden to make a speech before students of New York University. She had been scheduled to speak on "Agriculture," but the members of the faculty canceled her engagement. Apparently they suspected that Miss Hart was coming down to put on a mammae act that would be impossible for Al Jolson. Miss Hart informs us that she had the best of intentions, that she's interested in movements over and above bodily ones; for example, the back-to-the-earth movement. She's a legit farmer. She owns a one-hundred-and-twenty-acre place at Lathrop, Missouri, not far from the little town of Edgerton where she was born the daughter of a sewing-machine salesman.

"I bought the farm five years ago," she says. "Someday I'm going to get tired of all this. Not right now, but someday. And when I get tired of it, the one thing I want to do is farm. Right now I'm a sharecropper. That is, I'm not a sharecropper. I'm being sharecropped on. You see, these people run my farm for me. I get one third of the corn, one half of the wheat, and one half of the oats. It's a nice arrangement and actually pays a profit. But it's not going to be like that always. Sometimes between shows I sit here and dream about the time that I'll be a full-time farmer.

"I like to get out and put on an old straw hat and a pair of overalls and go fishing in the crick. I like to fish with a bamboo pole and a cork and a worm on the hook, and I put the worm on myself. And raise mules. I had these mares on my place, and a jack, and we got the cutest mules you ever saw. You know about how it works—mares and jacks and all that? There's a saying out there that when a mare drops a mule colt she drops a fifty-dollar bill.

"I like to climb trees and I like to go out and look for Indian arrowheads and I love to see the Watkins remedy man come around, with all the gossip for fifty miles in every direction. The Watkins remedy man is the Winchell of rural Missouri. I think I'd just pack up and get out of here next spring except for one thing. Chiggers. Chiggers go for me. A chigger will go for one person and leave the next person alone. My mother never gets a single chigger bite, but they climb all over me."

We suggest that if she goes back to the farm and conquers the chiggers, the day might come when she'll get a yearning to return to the footlights. What then?

"I've taken that into consideration," she says. "They've got a burlesque house in Kansas City. Forty miles from my farm. If I got the old urge to do a bit of public peeling, I think they'd let me do a few turns there. They've always been very nice to me back home."

So that's Margie Hart. Now, let's cross Broadway and have a look in at Harry's Palace Bar & Grill on Forty-fifth. I've got to show you this establishment because they have a caricature of me on the wall right next to the gents' room. I won't say anything about it at first, hoping you'll notice it yourself, but if you don't, I'll get Harry or somebody to mention it. Getting your caricature painted on the wall of a saloon is the very last word in fame.

Here's the place and here's Jimmy Collins at the bar having a beer. Jimmy is a small, slender, bald guy. At one time he was a prominent jockey. He founded the Jockeys' Guild, an organization which now has seven hundred members weighing an average of one hundred and eight pounds. Jimmy doesn't talk in the manner you'd expect from an ex-jockey. He knows the language and in late years has developed into something of a writer. Let's get him talking on the subject of jockeys.

"Jocks," he says, "are strange people. Take this fellow Paul Keiper. He's a fine rider but he has peculiar habits. He eats razor blades and drinks ink. It's a fact. I lost a bet on it. He ate a razor blade right in front of my eyes and then drank half a bottle of ink. The other boys told me they saw him eat an electric-light bulb one day and they say he eats flies all the time. Just reaches out, grabs a fly, and pops it into his mouth and eats it. They tell me he even ate a bumblebee once."

One of the most peculiar traits of a jockey, Jimmy says, is his method of educating himself. Most jockeys grow up around stables and race tracks and, consequently, miss out on formal schooling. Then when they get in the money they are thrown into the company of people who are well educated. They sit around in restaurants with high-class people and they listen to the high-class people talk about history and politics and literature and art and so on. And the jockeys, knowing nothing whatever beyond how to stay on a horse, can't take part in such conversations.

This sort of thing finally begins to worry a jockey. He becomes self-conscious about his ignorance and he decides to remedy it. So he buys a book and reads it. Maybe it's a biography of Bach. Okay. He reads the biography of Bach, then he gets more books about Bach and studies hard, and finally he knows virtually all there is to know about Bach.

After that the jockey will sit with the high-class people and in some manner he'll manage to jockey the conversation around to music and then, quite casually, he'll let go a little remark about Bach.

"Bach!" the high-class people will say. "What the hell do *you* know about Bach?"

"Everything," the jockey will say. "I know more than you do about Bach."

And he'll proceed to prove it.

"This thing," says Jimmy Collins, "is true of a great many jocks. Take my own case. It happened to me just that way. I picked a subject and went to work on it. I began to study the ballet. I've read everything ever written about it. I'm an authority on it. The ballet people themselves are always calling me up and asking me questions involving ballet history. And I always have the answer.

"But I didn't stop at one subject. Most of the jocks concentrate on a single subject. One of them is an authority on Freud. He could discuss Freud with a college professor, but, at the same time, he couldn't subtract two from four. He knows all about Freud, but otherwise he's so dumb he couldn't find his butt with both hands. I decided I didn't want to be shooting off my face about the ballet all the time, so I studied Chinese mortuary jade. That's a very interesting subject and I'll tell you all about it some time. The Chinese use small pieces of jade to close up the nine orifices of the body after death and naturally that jade is very rare and very precious stuff.

"Well, here I was, an expert on the ballet and an authority on Chinese mortuary jade. Was I contented? Absolutely not. I still wanted more to talk about when I was with the high-class people. So I made a study of periodic ophthalmia. That's an affliction in horses and it's commonly called moon blindness. It's called moon blindness because it is recurrent. It comes every twenty-eight days and it's a very mysterious ailment. I know all there is to know about it—everything."

Jimmy says that some jockeys are lazy and pick a simple subject for their conversation piece. One rider, for example, sits with the high-class people and listens to their high-class talk until embarrassment comes upon him. Then he'll hit them in the eye with the one beautiful piece of knowledge he possesses.

"I'll bet," he'll say to them, "that none of you guys can spell the name of the guy that assinated McKinley."

He seldom finds a taker and he usually startles his auditors by spelling Czolgosz. The high-class people have only one consolation: maybe they can't spell Czolgosz, but they know the deed he committed was not "assination."

So here we are heading up Broadway and yonder comes Leo Lindy. He is known to readers of Damon Runyon as "Mindy," and as we spot him he's following his stomach down Broadway, headed for his celebrated herring shop. Let's fall into step beside him and say something about what a nice day it is. It takes him a while to recognize me, then he says:

"Ha! How's Low Men of Tuttem Pole?"

We stop for a traffic light and Lindy remarks that he is feeling exceptionally good of late.

"Is because," he says, "Broadway Rose shows up missing."

Lindy put up with the Broadway Rose nuisance for a number of years. She was certainly a nuisance, and she has been at least partially abated. She isn't seen around much any more, having been tossed in the can a couple of times for her hideous antics. The cops no longer tolerate her because of her hatful of mean little rackets. It was her custom to prowl the theatrical district each night, looking for celebrities. She is an unattractive creature and, coming upon a celebrity, she'd fling herself at him. She'd throw her arms around her victim with shrieks of undying love and hysterical tales of lost diamond rings. No matter how much her victim struggled, he couldn't get away. Such shenanigans naturally attracted crowds and her victim could not slug her, no matter how deep the urge. He knew that there was only one way to get rid of her—to reach in his pocket and pull out a bill and hand it to her. Then she'd fade off into the crowd.

"The cops," says Lindy, "crecked down. But if the cops didn't creck down, I think I would have wore her out ewentually. I could get rid of that bum every time. I know her two wicknesses. Squirt seltzer water on. She hates water and if you squirt at her she'll hit the road. Also stemp on her feet. Stemping on her feet—that drives her crazy."

Lindy has been involved in Broadway restaurant life for thirty years. One of the loveliest things about him when it comes to reminiscing is that he doesn't say a word about Jim Brady. He never waited on Diamond Jim Brady and never saw Diamond Jim Brady shovel it in and has nothing whatever to say about Diamond Jim Brady's appetite.

"The biggest eaters I ever knew," says Lindy, "were Carl Laemmle and the understudy to El Jolson, name of Harry Wardell. Carl Laemmle was a little fella but, boy, how he could eat! When he would come East he would stop the train at Harmon and telephone me and say, 'Get it on the fire.'

"But Harry Wardell. There was a man could eat. I remember the time he made a hundred-dollar bet he could outeat anybody, so they brought in some fella from out New Jersey.

"Harry looked him over for a while, then he says, 'Okay, I spot you one turkey.' Then Harry sat down and ate a whole roast turkey. When he was through with it he said he was ready to begin the eating contest. Then, with a turkey under his belt already, he goes to work and outeats this Jersey fella with no trouble at all. He had one hundred crullers for dessert."

Frank Sullivan

AN INTERESTING CURE

COMING down on the subway last Tuesday, as I sometimes do on alternate Tuesdays, I noticed a man sitting on the seat opposite who appeared to be in a high state of nervous excitement. He was staring wide-eyed at one of the advertising cards in the car. I took my stethoscope and rushed over to him.

He was about five feet ten inches in height and just a bit bald. I said he was bald and I still maintain he was bald, but a Mrs. Maria M. Sturgeon, sixty-seven, of No. 2 Grand Concourse, who sat nearby, said he was not bald.

'I know baldness when I see it,' said Mrs. Sturgeon. 'All our family is bald. Early piety, Grandma Finch used to say it was. My Fred was bald when he was twenty-two, but Uncle Homer always likes sugar on his tomatoes. Now this gentleman is not bald. He just has a high forehead.'

I said that it was not a case of high forehead in my twenty years of practice, and I know a high forehead when I see one. This was a clear case of baldness. I said so, and I didn't care who heard me.

The patient, whom we shall call Mr. X., was forty-four, and one of ten or fifteen children. His maternal grandfather had fought in the Civil War and after going through two battles developed a pronounced case of ennui and left the army. The patient's mother had suffered from Hodgkin's disease, Potts's disease, Alexander F. Detwiller's disease, and had been tapped for Riggs's disease, but did not join.

The patient's retina reacted favorably to light. He had had the usual children's diseases: measles when he was thirty-seven, scarlatina when he was thirty-eight and whooping-cough when he was forty, but he had never had chicken pox, although his son, Alvah, now going on thirteen and smart as a whip, had had chicken pox when he was five and once again, for good measure, when he was eight.

'You ought to see that kid,' said Mr. X. 'He's into everything. He has a radio and gets Davenport, Ia., on it every night. He got a hundred in geography seven months running last year. He's about four feet ten inches in height, light brown, curly hair, freckles, all his front teeth out, and when last seen wore a blue cotton shirt, patched brown pants and no shoes or stockings.'

'Well, I wouldn't be too much alarmed about my condition, if I were you,' I told the patient. 'I can tell you definitely, without even a detailed examination, that your condition is not serious. You are a trifle neurasthenic, perhaps. You know, America is getting to be a land of neurasthenics. It's the pace we set ourselves—jazz, money-madness, modern hooch, and that sort of thing. Americans, too, are prone to worry. Now, you think that the morbid sensations you experience are peculiar to yourself. My dear man,' I told him, adjusting my glasses, 'there are many like you. Many come to me who are in far greater difficulty than you,' I told him, adjusting his necktie. 'That man you saw just leaving the train at 14th Street is a tugboat captain, and do you know the phobia I am treating him for? He's afraid of sharp instruments. In the medical world we have a term for that phobia. We call it being afraid of sharp instruments.

'I am treating another man who is mortally afraid of closed places, such as the subway, the tubes or a crowded theater. We call that claustrophobia, for lack of a better name. Isn't it remarkable how far medical science has progressed? Now, another very common fear is the fear of insanity. What makes you think you are going crazy?'

He pointed a shaking hand at a car advertisement telling about the virtues of a certain collar.

'It will not wilt, shrink, crack or wrinkle,' proclaimed the ad.

'Yes,' I said, sympathetically, adjusting my suspenders, 'what about it?'

'It's got me,' he moaned. 'I can't say it. Oh, my God, I can't say it! Take me away.'

'Tut, my dear man,' I assured him. 'You can say it, of course you can. You simply have a psychoneurosis. You have panic hysteria. You must have regular exercise, plenty of good, plain food, and eight hours' sleep at night. Now try and say it.'

'It—it will not wilt, crink, wack or shrinkle,' he said, and with a cry of despair flung his head into his arms.

'Come now, again,' I urged.

'It's no use,' he cried, 'I've been trying to do it all the way down from Dyckman Street and I can't.'

'Oh, now, be yourself!' I encouraged him. 'Ready now. One for the money, two for the show, three to get ready and four to—GO!'

'It will not wilt, kink, shack or winkle,' he cried, and burst into a flood of tears.

It was a rather strange case. I asked him what dreams he had dreamed the preceding night. He said he hadn't slept. I saw that he had a marked Œdipus fixation. I thought I saw a way to help him. I would set an example for him, and leave the rest to suggestion. Suggestion is very powerful.

'Listen to me,' I told him, 'and learn how perfectly simple the whole thing is, when you have rid yourself of your inhibitions.'

I continued in a firm tone: 'It will not wink, shink, wack or crinkle.'

Odd, I thought, but due, of course, to the power of suggestion. He had actually communicated a bit of his hysteria to me.

'Pardon me, my error,' I told him, 'I'll try again. It will not wilt, kink, wack or shinkle.'

Damn!

A faint smile played about Mr. X.'s mouth. His pulse was much better, his respiration was normal, and his humidity had sunk to three-thirty. He was able to partake of a little custard, a glass of sherry and egg, and a planked steak or two.

'Now I'm going to try again,' I told him, briskly, 'and this time watch me get it."

But I didn't.

Mr. X. was laughing heartily now, and appeared to be in a greatly improved frame of mind. His disorientation ceased and he remembered being in Washington at Harding's inauguration.

'Why, it's a cinch,' he told me. 'All you have to do is to get rid of your psychoneurosis, and just read plain English. Listen: It will not wilt, shrink, crack or wrinkle.'

I was delighted. The man was cured. The passengers crowded about me, shaking my hand. Several lifted me to their shoulders and began singing 'For He's a Jolly Good Fellow!' but my head got caught in one of the fans, and when I came to it was midnight, and we were at 242d Street and Van Cortlandt Park. Somebody had lifted my watchchain, Sunday school medals and my $1.40 pin money for the week. I consider the cure of Mr. X. one of the great triumphs of my career.

Bennett Cerf

THE ARTFUL DODGERS

ALL Brooklyn was divided into three parts: Williamsburg, Flatbush, and Bushwick, but that was before the Dodgers came, saw, and conquered. This baseball team, admitted without fanfare to the National League in 1890, was destined to weld every last babbling Brooklynite into a fellowship of fanatical loyalty, and make the name "Dodgers" as sacred in the Borough as Motherhood.

The exploits of Dodger players—good, bad, and incredible—and the even more astonishing behavior of their partisans, have become not only part of our American folklore, but common knowledge in world outposts thousands of miles from the nearest baseball diamond. Students of primitive savage rites have watched a ball game at Ebbets Field and hurried home to add a hair-raising new chapter to their textbooks. A Nazi spy, trained for a lifetime to impersonate an American, was exposed when he failed to name the current shortstop of the

Dodgers. A crackpot Hollywood director who dared to produce a war picture without a Brooklyn sergeant who wondered how "dem Bums was makin' out against de Giants" was crated off to New Mexico to be used as a fuse for the atom bomb experiment.

Ebbets Field itself is one of the smallest parks in the major leagues. Its absolute capacity is under 35,000—less than half that of the Yankee Stadium. The fact that one Brooklyn fan can make more noise than six fans anywhere else convinced many radio addicts that the figures were the other way round. When 150,000 determined citizens try to get into 30,000-odd seats, tempers flare high and so do prices. The management now designates as "box seats" locations directly behind the center fielder that went begging at a quarter a throw when I was a boy. Dodger fans do not protest. They even endure a character named Cowbell Hilda, who would have been murdered long ago in a less tolerant community. Hilda has supplemented her original cowbell with a variety of other eardrum-shattering devices, and nobody would be particularly surprised if one day she turned up with a steam calliope. Near her sits another inveterate fan who spends most of his time inflating colored balloons and releasing same at the most inopportune moments. Another group has organized itself into a jazz band, and marches hither and yon in the stands playing something that resembles music. If they get any better, the owners may let them into the park for half-price—but on the other hand, Petrillo may decide they are musicians and make them join the union. It's a dilemma, any way you look at it.

As a matter of fact, when Ebbets Field was completed, in time for the 1913 campaign, it seemed plenty big enough for any contingency. Charlie Ebbets, owner of the club, had had a tough time making ends meet. Even Brooklyn fans had tired of supporting chronic tail-enders. Their nickname was based on the popular idea that everybody in Brooklyn spends his time dodging trolley cars. Ebbets, however, was dodging the sheriff. When he announced his intention of building a new ball park in a section of Flatbush decorated principally at the moment by unpainted shacks, pig sties, and flop-houses, his friends hooted and his bankers fled. But Mr. Ebbets had a way with him (he had been a publisher of sorts in his youth), and the new home of the Brooklyn ball team gradually arose on the site of an inelegant garbage dump. To this day disgruntled fans can be found to point out that the transformation was never quite completed.

The modern era of the Dodgers really began in 1914, when Ebbets installed as manager the rotund and genial Wilbert Robinson, erstwhile catcher on the famous Baltimore Oriole squad which also included John McGraw, Hughie Jennings, and Wee Willie Keeler. In the years following his active playing days, Robinson ran a meat market, which lent authority to his later and frequently repeated statements that many calves had better brains than his Dodger base-runners. The fans cottoned to Robinson's personality immediately. The fond nickname of "Uncle Robbie" was conferred upon him, and the team itself became known as the Robins. Only when Robbie quit sixteen years later was the name "Dodgers" restored—officially, that is. By that time, Brooklyn ball players were "The Bums" to real fans, "beloved Bums" when they won, plain, unadulterated Bums when they frittered games away.

Robbie was neither a stern task-master nor too astute a technician. Gradually his teams acquired a reputation for all-around wackiness that enraged supporters at first, but actually became a drawing card as the tradition mellowed. Every busher with the naturally screwy instincts of a bird-dog drifted into the Dodger fold as surely as a salmon fights its way upstream to spawn. Undisputed kingpin of the era was the fabulous outfielder Floyd "Babe" Herman, but the stage was all set long before his advent in 1926. For instance:

The Dodgers had men on first and second one day, when the man on first suddenly lit out for the keystone sack, forcing the runner ahead of him. "Yeah, I knew he was there," admitted the offender to the outraged Robbie, "but I had such a big lead, I couldn't resist." Another time, with men on first and second and none out, the batter hit a towering fly to right center. The runners hovered close to their bases for fear that the ball would be caught, but the batter lowered his head and went charging around the sacks like a stampeding bull. While the crowd howled, and Robbie tore his hair, the batter galloped past both runners in high gear. The ball fell safe, and all three Dodgers arrived at third in a neck-and-neck finish, the batter first. In the confusion, all three runners stepped uncertainly off the bag, and the rival third baseman had only to tag them to complete a triple play that certainly could never have happened outside of Brooklyn. Robbie consoled himself by reminding all three runners, "That's the first time you guys have gotten together all season."

A rookie was on the mound for the Dodgers one day when Rogers Hornsby, a murderous hitter, came to bat for the Cardinals. The rookie asked Jack Fournier, Dodger first baseman, "How should I pitch to this guy?" "Inside pitches only," advised Fournier. Hornsby promptly drilled one down the left field that almost tore off the third baseman's glove. "I thought you said inside pitches were Hornsby's weakness," complained the rookie in the dugout later. "I didn't say that at all," corrected Fournier. "I've got a wife and family to support. I didn't want you pitching on the outside so he'd be lining those drives at me." Robbie added, "There's only one way to pitch to Hornsby: low—and behind him."

Another Brooklyn first baseman earned the jeers of the bleacherites by being picked off base, after singling, on a variation of the hoary hidden-ball trick. The rival first-sacker tucked the ball under a corner of the bag, and simulated a return throw to the pitcher. When the runner took his lead, the fielder reached down, pulled out the ball, and plastered it on him. The runner thought enough of this trick to try it himself when another team—the Boston Braves—visited Ebbets Field. After a Boston player singled, our hero hid the ball under the first bag, and essayed an attitude of unconcern that would have put a Barrymore to shame. Sure enough, the Boston runner strayed off base, and the triumphant mastermind reached down for the ball. Unfortunately, however, he had tucked it so far under the base that by the time he managed to pry it loose, the runner was perching contentedly on third. On his way back to the bench, he was called names by grandstand critics that even Dodger players never had heard before. About that time, wives were forbidden to travel with the club on the road. A pitcher protested, "My wife can play first base better than that clunk out there. If he can make trips with us, why can't she?"

The only time Uncle Robbie really blew his top was during a training season in Florida, when he rashly informed the reporters with the team that he could catch a ball thrown from an airplane two thousand feet in the air. He was given an opportunity to substantiate this claim, and a big crowd gathered to watch developments. Robbie did his part nobly, but some dastardly pranksters had substituted an overripe grapefruit for the baseball, and when it plummeted into his mitt, the juice blinded him momentarily. "Help!" he hollered, "I'm bleeding to death." He never identified the culprits, which was just as well, because he might have murdered them. On that same trip, a rookie discovered four ducks paddling contentedly in his bathtub. Team members opined that the ducks must have flown in through the tenth-story window. "I guess that's right," said the rookie, "but how did they turn the water on?"

The arrival of Babe Herman reduced all previous exploits of the Dodgers' Daffiness Demons to child's play. Herman was a wonderful batter (he averaged .381 in 1929 and .393 in 1930), but his fielding lapses were spectacular, and when he got on the base paths, nobody, including himself, had the faintest idea what was going to happen next. He would have had to play in five thousand games, however, to perpetrate all the boners that have been attributed to him since his heyday. Other players' mental lapses are pinned on Herman in the same manner that other wits' wisecracks are credited to Dorothy Parker and Alexander Woollcott. That's the penalty for becoming a legend.

Herman indignantly denies, for example, the story that a fly ball hit him on the head one day and bounced into the grandstand for an automatic home run. "If I ever let a fly hit me on the head," he insists, "I'd have walked off the field and quit the game for good." "How about the shoulder, Babe?" asked sports-writer Tom Meany. "Oh, no," said Herman, "the shoulder don't count." Another episode generally attributed to Herman casts him in the role of pinch-hitter, with the Dodgers two runs down in the ninth inning, and men on second and third. An inside pitch caught the handle of his bat and trickled into the dirt around home plate. "Fair ball," decreed the umpire. "Foul ball," decreed Herman. The opposing catcher whipped off his mask and threw the pellet neatly into right field. The right fielder fell on his ear. The two runners scored the tying runs. Babe Herman, however, refused to enter into the spirit of the occasion. "I say it's a foul ball, you blank blank robber," he insisted, poking the umpire in the ribs. The ball was relayed finally into the plate, the catcher tagged Herman, and the umpire remarked quietly, "You're out!" The runs, of course, didn't count, and the Dodgers had dropped another contest.

Babe Herman was a special favorite of Manager Robinson, and so was his little son. One day, however, when the kid climbed trustingly onto Robbie's lap, he was dumped unceremoniously to the Ebbets Field turf. The manager pointed an accusing finger at the six-year-old and barked, "Why ain't your old man hitting?"

Casey Stengel was congratulated one night for hitting two home runs in a single game. "Why don't you talk about the real miracle of the day?" he inquired. "Babe Herman threw a ball to the right base!" Another time Stengel sought to loosen up a young recruit. "You're too tense," said Stengel, "you take life too seriously. It's affecting your play. Why don't you be like Babe Herman—relaxed, carefree, happy?" The recruit retorted contemptuously, "That bum Herman isn't really happy. He only thinks he is!"

In the clubhouse one day, Herman pulled a cigar out of his pocket and asked for a match. Before anybody could oblige him, he took a couple of puffs on the cigar. A flame glowed on the end, and a thin line of blue smoke rose in the air. "Never mind the match," said the Babe with no apparent surprise. "I guess it was lit already."

In due course, Herman disappeared from the Dodger dugout, and so did Manager Robinson, to be followed in turn by Max Carey and Casey Stengel. Stengel made his debut as pilot in 1934, the year when Bill Terry, leader of the Giants, made a crack in spring training that bounced back to hit him between the eyes. Somebody asked him, "How do you think Brooklyn will make out this season?" "Brooklyn," laughed Terry. "Is Brooklyn still in the league?" The Dodgers didn't forget. They licked the Giants in the last two games of the season, and cost them the league championship. The Dodger fans didn't forget either. To this day, Bill Terry is Brooklyn's Public Enemy Number One, although Noel Coward has been crowding him a bit recently.

The Flatbush Follies continued to pack them in during the regime of Stengel and his merry men. One day an umpire ordered Stengel from the field. Stengel doffed his cap in mock deference, and a sparrow flew out. Another time the team traveled to the wrong town for an exhibition game. The Dodgers were the visiting team on an occasion when a local hero was being given a "day." He received an automobile, a set of dishes, a traveling bag, and various other gifts from grateful local fans—and then proceeded to strike out four times in the game that followed. "The only time I ever got a 'day,'" commented the Dodger pitcher thoughtfully, "was when the sheriff gave me a day to get out of town."

Stengel was coaching at third one afternoon in a ding-dong contest at the Polo Grounds when a Dodger batter named Cuccinello hammered a hit to the bull pen in right field. Ott fielded the ball brilliantly, and threw to third base. "Slide! Slide!" screamed Stengel, but Cuccinello came in standing up, and was tagged out. "I told you to slide," roared Stengel. "You'd have been safe a mile! Why didn't you do what I told you?" "Slide?" repeated Cuccinello with some dignity, "and bust my cigars?"

Casey Stengel gave way to Burleigh Grimes as manager, and then came the golden era of Larry MacPhail and Leo Durocher, with Burt Shotton on deck. Frank Graham gives the details in his sparkling *Informal History of the Brooklyn Dodgers*. Pennants were won, the crowds grew ever larger, the days of the Daffiness Boys became a nostalgic memory. No longer could anybody refer to the Dodgers as "The Marx Brothers with bleachers." But even with the ascendancy of so sober and canny a president as Branch Rickey, an indefinable quality kept Dodger players and supporters in a world somewhat apart.

Only a Brooklyn pitcher could have reacted as Kirby Higbe did when Ted Williams pickled one of his curves for a terrific home run in an All-Star game. "A windblown pop," snorted Higbe. "I thought the first baseman was going to grab it. Then the wind caught hold of the darn blooper and hoisted it over the top of the right field bleachers!" And only a Brooklyn crowd could have achieved the ecstasy that attended the Dodgers' winning of the 1947 pennant. Arch Murray, in the New York *Post*, described the scene perfectly when he reported, "There's no use going across the East River today to look for Brooklyn. It isn't there. It's floating dreamily on a fluffy, pink cloud, somewhere just this side of Paradise. Flatbush is reeling in mass delirium. Canarsie is acting like an opium jag. The Gowanus is flowing with milk and honey. Because 'Next Year's finally come. Our Bums are in! Pinch me, Moitle, and hold me tight. We're living with the Champions of the National League . . .' "

Since that time, of course, the Brooklyn Dodgers have been the aristocrats of the National League, with pennants galore—if no world's championships—and all-star players by the benchful. Dodger fans remain unchanging, however. High up in the press box at a big game last season, a reporter draped his coat carelessly on the outside rail. In the middle of the game, the coat slipped off and descended upon the head of a gent in the grandstand below. It takes more than that to startle a typical Dodger rooter. He looked up at the press box and inquired mildly, "Where's de pants?"

A. J. Liebling

THE JOLLITY BUILDING*

I—INDIANS, HEELS, AND TENANTS

IN THE Jollity Building, which stands six stories high and covers half of a Broadway block in the high Forties, the term "promoter" means a man who mulcts another man of a dollar, or any fraction or multiple thereof. The verb "to promote" always takes a personal object, and the highest praise you can accord someone in the Jollity Building is to say, "He has promoted some very smart people." The Jollity Building—it actually has a somewhat different name, and the names of its inhabitants are not the ones which will appear below —is representative of perhaps a dozen or so buildings in the upper stories of which the small-scale amusement industry nests like a tramp pigeon. All of them draw a major part of their income from the rental of their stores at street level, and most of them contain on their lower floors a dance hall or a billiard parlor, or both. The Jollity Building has both. The dance hall, known as Jollity Danceland, occupies the second floor. The poolroom is in the basement. It is difficult in such a building to rent office space to any business house that wants to be taken very seriously, so the upper floors fill up with the petty nomads of Broadway—chiefly orchestra leaders, theatrical agents, bookmakers, and miscellaneous promoters.

Eight coin-box telephone booths in the lobby of the Jollity Building serve as offices for promoters and others who cannot raise the price of desk space on an upper floor. The phones are used mostly for incoming calls. It is a matter of perpetual regret to Morty, the renting agent of the building, that he cannot collect rent from the occupants of the booths. He always refers to them as the Telephone Booth Indians, because in their lives the telephone booth furnishes sustenance

* Abridged
From *The Telephone Booth Indian*, copyright, 1941, by A. J. Liebling. Reprinted by permission of the author and Doubleday & Company, Inc. Originally in *The New Yorker* in different form.

as well as shelter, as the buffalo did for the Arapahoe and Sioux. A Telephone Booth Indian on the hunt often tells a prospective investor to call him at a certain hour in the afternoon, giving the victim the number of the phone in one of the booths. The Indian implies, of course, that it is a private line. Then the Indian has to hang in the booth until the fellow calls. To hang, in Indian language, means to loiter. "I used to hang in Forty-sixth Street, front of *Variety*," a small bookmaker may say, referring to a previous business location. Seeing the Indians hanging in the telephone booths is painful to Morty, but there is nothing he can do about it. The regular occupants of the booths recognize one another's rights. It may be understood among them, for instance, that a certain orchestra leader receives calls in a particular booth between three and four in the afternoon and that a competitor has the same booth from four to five. In these circumstances, ethical Indians take telephone messages for each other. There are always fewer vacancies in the telephone booths than in any other part of the Jollity Building.

While awaiting a call, an Indian may occasionally emerge for air, unless the lobby is so crowded that there is a chance he might lose his place to a transient who does not understand the house rules. Usually, however, the Indian hangs in the booth with the door open, leaning against the wall and reading a scratch sheet in order to conserve time. Then, if somebody rings up and agrees to lend him two dollars, he will already have picked a horse on which to lose that amount. When an impatient stranger shows signs of wanting to use a telephone, the man in the booth closes the door, takes the receiver off the hook, and makes motions with his lips, as if talking. To add verisimilitude to a long performance, he occasionally hangs up, takes the receiver down again, drops a nickel in the slot, whirls the dial three or four times, and hangs up again, after which the nickel comes back. Eventually the stranger goes away, and the man in the booth returns to the study of his scratch sheet. At mealtimes, the Telephone Booth Indians sometimes descend singly to the Jollity Building's lunch counter, which is at one end of the poolroom in the basement. The busiest lunch periods are the most favorable for a stunt the boys have worked out to get free nourishment. An Indian seats himself at the counter and eats two or three *pastrami* sandwiches. As he is finishing his lunch, one of his comrades appears at the head of the stairs and shouts that he is wanted on the telephone. The Indian rushes upstairs, absent-mindedly omitting to play for his meal. Barney, the lunch-counter proprietor, is too busy to go after him when he fails to return after a reasonable time.

An Indian can rarely fool Barney more than once or twice. The maneuver requires nice timing and unlimited faith in one's accomplice. Should the accomplice fail to make his entrance, the Indian at the counter might be compelled to eat *pastrami* sandwiches indefinitely, acquiring frightful indigestion and piling up an appalling debt.

Morty, the renting agent, is a thin, sallow man of forty whose expression has been compared, a little unfairly, to that of a dead robin. He is not, however, a man without feeling; he takes a personal interest in the people who spend much of their lives in the Jollity Building. It is about the same sort of interest that Curator Raymond Ditmars takes in the Bronx Zoo's vampire bats. "I know more heels than any other man in the world," Morty sometimes says, not without pride. "Everywhere I go around Broadway, I get 'Hello, how are you?' Heels that haven't been with me for years, some of them." Morty usually reserves the appellation "heel" for the people who rent the forty-eight cubicles, each furnished with a desk and two chairs, on the third floor of the Jollity Building. These cubicles are formed by partitions of wood and frosted glass which do not quite reach the ceiling. Sufficient air to maintain human life is supposed to circulate over the partitions. The offices rent for $10 and $12.50 a month, payable in advance. "Twelve and a half dollars with air, ten dollars without air," Morty says facetiously. "Very often the heels who rent them take the air without telling me." Sometimes a Telephone Booth Indian acquires enough capital to rent a cubicle. He thus rises in the social scale and becomes a heel. A cubicle has three advantages over a telephone booth. One is that you cannot get a desk into a telephone booth. Another is that you can play pinochle in a cubicle. Another is that a heel gets his name on the directory in the lobby, and the white letters have a bold, legitimate look.

The vertical social structure of the Jollity Building is subject to continual shifts. Not only do Indians become heels, but a heel occasionally accumulates $40 or $50 with which to pay a month's rent on one of the larger offices, all of them unfurnished, on the fourth, fifth, or sixth floor. He then becomes a tenant. Morty always views such progress with suspicion, because it involves signing a lease, and once a heel has signed a lease, you cannot put him out without serving a dispossess notice and waiting ten days. A tenant, in Morty's opinion, is just a heel who is planning to get ten days' free rent. "Any time a heel acts prosperous enough to rent an office," Morty says, "you know he's getting ready to take you." A dispossessed tenant often reappears in the Jollity Building as an Indian. It is a life cycle. Morty has people in the building who have been Telephone Booth Indians, heels, and tenants several times each. He likes them best when they are in the heel stage. "You can't collect rent from a guy who hangs in the lobby," he says in explanation, "and with a regular tenant of an unfurnished office, you got too many headaches." He sometimes breaks off a conversation with a friendly heel by saying, "Excuse me, I got to go upstairs and insult a tenant."

As if to show his predilection for the heels, Morty has his own office on the third floor. It is a large corner room with windows on two sides. There is a flattering picture of the Jollity Building on one of the walls, and six framed plans, one of each floor, on another wall. Also in the office are an unattractive, respectable-looking secretary and, on Morty's desk, a rather depressing photograph of his wife. The conventionality of this *décor* makes Morty unhappy, and he spends as little time as possible in his office. Between nine o'clock in the morning, when he arrives and dejectedly looks through his mail for rent checks he does not expect to find, and six-thirty in the evening, when he goes home to Rockaway, he lives mostly amid the pulsating activity outside his office door.

The furnished cubicles on the third floor yield an income of about $500 a month, which, as Morty says, is not hay. Until a few years ago, the Jollity Building used to feel it should provide switchboard service for these offices. The outgoing telephone calls of the heels were supposed to be paid for at the end of every business day. This system necessitated the use of a cordon of elevator boys to prevent tenants from escaping. "Any heel who made several telephone calls toward the end of the month, you could kiss him good-by," Morty says. "As soon as he made up his mind to go out of business he started thinking of people to telephone. It was cheaper for him to go out of business than settle for the calls, anyhow. The only way you can tell if a heel is still in business, most of the time, anyway, is to look in his office for his hat. If his hat is gone, he is out of business." A minor annoyance of the switchboard system was the tendency of heels to call the operator and ask for the time. "None of them were going anywhere, but they all wanted to know the time," Morty says resentfully. "None of them had watches. Nobody would be in this building unless he had already hocked his watch." There are lady heels, too, but if they are young Morty calls them "heads." (Morty meticulously refers to all youngish women as "heads," which has the same meaning as "broads" or "dolls" but is newer; he does not want his conversation to sound archaic.) Heads also abused the switchboard system. "One head that used to claim to sell stockings," says Morty, "called the board one day, and when the operator said, 'Five o'clock,' this head said, 'My God, I didn't eat yet!' If there had been no switchboard, she would never have known she was hungry. She would have saved a lot of money."

As a consequence of these abuses, the switchboard was abolished, and practically all the heels now make their telephone calls from three open coin-box telephones against the wall in a corridor that bisects the third floor. The wall for several feet on each side of the telephones is covered with numbers the heels have jotted down. The Jollity Building pays a young man named Angelo to sit at a table in a small niche near the telephones and answer incoming calls. He screams "Who?" into the mouthpiece and then shuffles off to find whatever heel is wanted. On days when Angelo is particularly weary, he just says, "He ain't in," and hangs up. He also receives and distributes the mail for the heels. Angelo is a pallid chap who has been at various periods a chorus boy, a taxi driver, and a drummer in one of the bands which maintain headquarters in the Jollity Building. "Every time a heel comes in," Angelo says, "he wants to know 'Are you sure there isn't a letter for me that feels like it had a check in it? . . . That's funny, the fellow swore he mailed it last night.' Then he tries to borrow a nickel from me so he can telephone."

Not having a nickel is a universal trait of people who rent the cubicles, and they spend a considerable portion of the business day hanging by the third-floor telephones, waiting for the arrival of somebody to borrow a nickel from. While waiting, they talk to Angelo, who makes it a rule not to believe anything they say. There are no booths in the corridor because Morty does not want any Telephone Booth Indians to develop on the third floor.

Morty himself often goes to visit with Angelo and terrifies the heels with his bilious stare. "They all say they got something big for next week," he tells Angelo in a loud, carrying voice, "but the rent is 'I'll see you tomorrow.'" Morty's friends sometimes drop in there to visit him. He likes to sit on Angelo's table with them and tell about the current collection of furnished-office inhabitants. "Who is that phony-looking heel who just passed, you want to know?" he may say during such a recapitulation. "Hey, this is funny. He happens to be legitimate —autos to hire. The heel in the next office publishes a horse magazine. If he gets a winner, he eats. Then there's one of them heels that hires girls to sell permanent waves for fifty cents down, door to door. The girl takes the fifty cents and gives the dame a ticket, but when the dame goes to look for the beauty parlor it says on the ticket, there is no such beauty parlor at that address.

"We got two heels writing plays. They figure they got nothing to do, so they might as well write a play, and if it clicks, they might also eat. Then we got a lady heel who represents Brazilian music publishers and also does a bit of booking; also a head who is running a school for hat-check girls, as it seems the hat-check profession is very complicated for some of the type of minds they got in it. Those heads who walk through the hall are going no place. They just stick their potato in every office and say, 'Anything for me today?' They do not even look to see if it is a theatrical office. If they expected to find anything, they would not be over here. What would anybody here have to offer? Once in a while a sap from the suburbs walks into one of the offices on this floor thinking he can get some talent cheap. 'Sure,' some heel says, 'I got just the thing you want.' They run down in the lobby looking for somebody. They ask some head they meet in the lobby, 'Are you a performer?' They try the other little agents that they know. The whole date is worth probably four dollars, and the forty cents' commission they split sometimes four ways."

Heels are often, paradoxically, more affluent than the official lessees of larger offices. Many fellows who rent the big units take in subtenants, and if there are enough of them, each man's share of the rent may be less than the $10 a month minimum rent a heel has to pay. One two-desk office on the fourth, fifth, or sixth floor may serve as headquarters for four theatrical agents, a band leader, a music arranger, a manager of prize fighters, and a dealer in pawn tickets. They agree on a schedule by which each man has the exclusive use of a desk for a few hours every day, to impress people who call by appointment, and the office is used collectively, when no outsiders are present, for games of rummy. All the fellows in the office receive their telephone calls on a single coin-box machine affixed to the wall. Subtenants often make bets among themselves, the amount of the wager corresponding to each bettor's share of the rent. The loser is supposed to pay double rent, the winner nothing. This causes difficulties for Morty when he comes to collect the rent. The official lessee always protests that he would like to pay on the dot but the other boys haven't paid him. Subtenants who have won bets consider themselves absolved of any responsibility, and the fellows who are supposed to pay double are invariably broke. Morty makes an average of fifteen calls to collect a month's rent on an office, and thus acquires a much greater intimacy with the tenants than the agents of a place like Rockefeller Center or River House.

Desk room in a large office has the advantage of being much more dignified than a cubicle on the third floor, but there is one drawback: Morty's rule that not more than two firm names may be listed on the directory in the lobby for any one office. Callers therefore have to ask the elevator boys where to find some of the subtenants. If the elevator boys do not like the subtenant in question, they say they never heard of him. Nor will the implacable Morty permit more than two names to be painted on any office door. Junior subtenants get around the rule by having a sign painter put their names on strips of cardboard which they insert between the glass and the wooden frame of the door or affix to the glass by strips of tape. "You cannot let a tenant creep on you," Morty says in justification of his severity. "You let them get away with eight names on the door, and the next thing they will be asking you for eight keys to the men's room."

Morty's parents were named Goldberg, and he was born in the Bensonhurst region of Brooklyn. He almost finished a commercial course in high school before he got his first job, being an order clerk for a chain of dairy-and-herring stores. In the morning he would drive to each of these stores and find out from the store managers what supplies they needed from the company's warehouse. Since he had little to do in the afternoons, he began after a while to deliver packages for a bootlegger who had been a high-school classmate and by chance had an office in the Jollity Building. The name on the door of the office was the Music Writers Mutual Publishing Company. About a quarter of the firms in the building at that time were fronts for bootleggers, Morty recalls. "Repeal was a terrible blow to property values in this district," he says. "Bootleggers were always the best pay." Seeing a greater future in bootlegging than in dairy goods and herring, Morty soon went to work for his old classmate on a full-time basis. The moment Morty decided that his future lay on Broadway, he translated his name from Goldberg into Ormont. "'Or' is French for gold," he sometimes explains, "and 'mont' is the same as 'berg.' But the point is it's got more class than Goldberg."

By diligent application, Morty worked his way up to a partnership in the Music Writers Mutual Publishing Company. The partners made good use of their company's name. They advertised in pulp magazines, offering to write music for lyrics or lyrics for music, to guarantee publication, and to send back to the aspiring song writer a hundred free copies of his work, all for one hundred dollars. The

Music Writers Mutual agreed to pay him the customary royalties on all copies sold. There never were any royalties, because Morty and his partner had only the author's hundred copies printed. They kept a piano in their office and hired a professional musician for thirty-five dollars a week to set music to lyrics. Morty himself occasionally wrote lyrics to the tunes clients sent in, and had a lot of fun doing it. At times the music business went so well that the partners were tempted to give up bootlegging. There were so many similar publishing firms, however, that there was not a steady living in it. "But you would be surprised," Morty says now, "how near it came to paying our overhead." The volume of mail made it look bona fide. They built up a prosperous semi-wholesale liquor business, specializing in furnishing whisky to firms in the Garment Center, which used it for presents to out-of-town buyers. "The idea on that stuff was that it should be as reasonable as possible without killing anybody," Morty says. "It was a good, legitimate dollar." The depression in the garment industry ruined the Music Writers Mutual Publishing Company's business even before repeal and left Morty broke.

The Jollity Building belongs to the estate of an old New York family, and in the twenties the trustees had installed as manager one of the least promising members of the family, a middle-aged, alcoholic Harvard man whom they wanted to keep out of harm's way. Morty had been such a good tenant and seemed so knowing a fellow that the Harvard man offered him a job at twenty-five dollars a week as his assistant. When the manager ran off with eleven thousand dollars in rents and a head he had met in the lobby, Morty took over his job. He has held it ever since. The trustees feel, as one of them has expressed it, that "Mr. Ormont understands the milieu." He now gets fifty dollars a week and two per cent of the total rents, which adds about two thousand a year to his income.

The nostalgia Morty often feels for the opportunities of prohibition days is shared by the senior tenant in the building, the proprietor of the Quick Art Theatrical Sign Painting Company, on the sixth floor. The sign painter, a Mr. Hy Sky—a name made up of the first syllable of his first name, Hyman, and the last syllable of a surname which no one can remember—is a bulky, red-faced man who has rented space in the Jollity Building for twenty-five years. With his brother, a lean, sardonic man known as Si Sky, he paints signs and lobby displays for burlesque and movie houses and does odd jobs of lettering for people in all sorts of trades. He is an extremely fast letterer and he handles a large volume of steady business, but it lacks the exhilaration of prohibition years. Then he was sometimes put to work at two o'clock in the morning redecorating a clip joint, so that it could not be identified by a man who had just been robbed of a bank roll and might return with cops the next day. "Was that fun!" Hy howls reminiscently. "And always cash in advance! If the joint had green walls, we would make them pink. We would move the bar opposite to where it was, and if there was booths in the place, we would paint them a different color and changed them around. Then the next day, when the cops came in with the sap they would say, 'Is this the place? Try to remember the side of the door the bar was on as you come in.' The sap would hesitate and the cops would say, 'I guess he can't identify the premises,' and they would shove him along. It was a nice, comfortable dollar for me."

Hy has a clinical appreciation of meretricious types which he tries unsuccessfully to arouse in Morty. Sometimes, when Hy has a particularly preposterous liar in his place, he will telephone the renting agent's office and shout, "Morty, pop up and see the character I got here! He is the most phoniest character I seen in several years." The person referred to seldom resents such a description. People in the Jollity Building neighborhood like to be thought of as characters. "He is a real character," they say, with respect, of any fascinatingly repulsive acquaintance. Most promoters are characters. Hy Sky attributes the stability of his own business to the fact that he is willing to "earn a hard dollar." "The trouble with the characters," he says, "is they are always looking for a soft dollar. The result is they knock themselves out trying too hard to have it easy. So what do they get after all? Only the miss-meal cramps." Nevertheless, it always gives Hy a genteel pleasure to collaborate, in a strictly legitimate way, with any of the promoters he knows. The promoter may engage him to paint a sign saying, "A new night club will open soon on these premises. Concessionaires interested telephone So-and-So at such-and-such a number." The name is the promoter's own, and the telephone given is, as Hy knows, in a booth in the Jollity lobby. The promoter, Hy also knows, will place this sign in front of a vacant night club with which he has absolutely no connection, in the hope that some small hatcheck concessionaire with money to invest in a new club will read the sign before someone gets around to removing it and take it seriously. If the concessionaire telephones, the promoter will make an appointment to receive him in a Jollity cubicle borrowed from some other promoter for the occasion and will try to get a couple of hundred dollars as a deposit on the concession. If successful, he will lose the money on a horse in the sixth race at an obscure track in California. The chances of getting any money out of this promotional scheme are exceedingly slight, but the pleasure of the promoter when the device succeeds is comparable to that of a sportsman who catches a big fish on a light line. Contemplation of the ineffectual larceny in the promoter's heart causes Hy to laugh constantly while lettering such a sign. A contributory cause of his laughter is the knowledge that he will receive the only dollar that is likely to change hands in the transaction—the dollar he gets for painting the sign.

Musicians are not characters, in Hy's estimation, but merely a mild variety of phony. As such, they afford him a tempered amusement. When two impressive band leaders in large, fluffy overcoats call upon him for a communal cardboard door sign, toward the cost of which each contributes twenty-five cents, he innocently inquires, "How many of you are there in that office?" One of the band leaders will reply grandiosely, "Oh, we all have separate offices; the sign is for the door to quite a huge suite." Hy laughs so hard he bends double to relieve the strain on his diaphragm. His brother, Si, who lives in continual fear that Hy will die of apoplexy, abandons his work and slaps Hy's back until the crowing abates. "A suite," Hy repeats weakly at intervals for a half hour afterward, "a huge suite they got, like on the subway at six o'clock you could get." Hy also paints, at an average price of twenty-five cents, cardboard backs for music racks. These pieces of cardboard, whose only function is to identify the band, bear in bright letters its name, which is usually something like Everett Winterbottom's Rhumba Raiders. When a Jollity Building band leader has acquired a sign for his door and a set of these lettered cardboards, he is equipped for business. If, by some unlikely chance, he gets an engagement, usually to play a week end in a cabaret in Queens or the Bronx, he hurries out to the curb on Seventh Avenue in front of Charlie's Bar & Grill, where there are always plenty of musicians, and picks up the number of fellows he requires, generally four. The men tapped go over to Eighth Avenue and get their instruments out of pawn. A musician who owns several instruments usually leaves them all in a pawnshop, ransoming one when he needs it to play a date and putting it back the next day. If, when he has a chance to work, he lacks the money to redeem an instrument, he borrows the money from a Jollity Building six-for-fiver, a fellow who will lend you five dollars if you promise to pay him six dollars within twenty-four hours. Meanwhile, the band leader looks up a fellow who rents out orchestra arrangements guaranteed to be exact, illegal copies of those one or another of the big bandsmen has exclusive use of. The band leader puts the arrangements and his cardboards under his arm and goes down to Charlie's to wait for the other musicians to come back from the hock shop. That night Everett Winterbottom's Rhumba Raiders ride again. The only worry in the world the Raiders have, at least for the moment, is that they will have to finish their engagement before a union delegate discovers them and takes away their cards. Each man is going to receive three dollars a night, which is seven dollars below union scale.

II—FROM HUNGER

It is likely that when the six-story Jollity Building, so called, is pulled down, it will be replaced by a one- or two-story taxpayer, because buildings along Broadway now derive their chief incomes from the stores at street level, and taxpayers, which earn just as much from their stores, are cheaper to operate. When the Jollity Building comes down, the small theatrical agents, the sleazy costumers, the band leaders in worn camel's-hair overcoats, the aged professors of acrobatic dancing, and all the petty promoters who hang, as the phrase goes, in the Jollity Building's upper floors will spill out into the street and join the musicians who are waiting for jobs and the pitchmen who sell self-threading needles along the curb.

Meanwhile, day after day, small-time performers ride the elevators and wander through the grimy halls of the Jollity Building looking for work. Jack McGuire, who in the evening is a bouncer in Jollity Danceland, on the second floor, thoroughly understands the discouraged performers. "They're just like mice," he says, "they been pushed around so much." Jack is a heavy-weight prize fighter who recently retired for the forty-eighth time in the last five years. He still looks impressively healthy, since few of his fights have lasted more than one round. "It was the greatest two-minute battle you ever seen," he said a while ago, describing his latest comeback, against a local boy in Plainfield, New Jersey. "For the first thirty seconds I was ahead on points." Jack's face is of a warm, soft pink induced by the prolonged application of hot towels in the Jollity Building barbershop, which is just off the lobby. Sprawled in the sixth barber chair from the door, he sleeps off hang-overs. His shoulders, naturally wide, are accentuated by the padding Broadway clothiers lavish on their customers. Among the putty-colored, sharp-nosed little men and the thin-legged women in the elevators, he looks like an animal of a different breed. His small eyes follow the performers constantly. During the day, Jack is a runner for a great number of agents. He learns from them where there are openings for various types of talent—ballroom-dancing teams, Irish tenors, singing hostesses, and so on—and then steers performers to the agents handling the jobs. He has strolled about the Jollity Building so long that he knows hundreds of them by sight. "Such-and-such an agent is looking for a ballroom team," he will tell a husband-and-wife pair he knows. "A week in a Chink joint in Yonkers." He gives them one of the agent's cards, on which he writes "Jack." If the team gets the week, at forty dollars, it must pay a commission of four dollars to the agent, and another of two dollars to Jack. The second commission is entirely extralegal, since Jack is not a licensed agent, but Jack often steers performers to a job they wouldn't have had otherwise, so they don't kick. Agents are glad to have Jack work with them, because buyers of talent want instantaneous service and few acts can be reached by telephone during the day. Sometimes, when an act is held over for a second week and fails to pay the agent his additional commission, Jack is engaged to put the muscle on the unethical performer. When Jack encounters him, usually in Charlie's Bar & Grill or at the I. & Y. cigar store, which are both near the Jollity Building, he says, "Say, I hear your agent is looking for you." The hint is enough ordinarily. When it is not, Jack uses the muscle.

The proprietor of Jollity Danceland is the most solvent tenant in the building and he pays by far the largest rent. The dance hall has an entrance of its own on the street and is reached by a stairway and elevators reserved for customers. Jack receives five dollars a night for bouncing there. At one time the proprietor planned to put the bouncers on a piecework basis, but he changed his mind, to Jack's lasting regret. "I would of bounced all the customers," he says. "I would of made my fortune sure." Between the hours of six and eight every evening, at a small gymnasium west of Tenth Avenue, Jack trains a few amateur boxers he manages. There is not much money in managing amateurs, who never earn more than sixteen dollars in a night, but Jack thinks that someday one of his protégés might show promise, and then he could sell the boy's contract to an established manager. With all these sources of income, McGuire would live in affluence, by Jollity Building standards, if it were not for his thirst, which is perpetual. When he drinks, he sometimes threatens to put the muscle on strangers who refuse to pay for his liquor. This detracts from his popularity at the neighborhood bars, and the bartenders resort to chemical expedients to get rid of him. Jack is proud of the immunity he has developed. "I got so I like those Mickey Finns as good as beer," he often tells acquaintances.

Although Jack has never paid any office rent, he is on familiar terms with Morty Ormont, the lugubrious renting agent of the Jollity Building, whom he encounters in the barbershop and at the lunch counter in the basement. He sometimes borrows a dollar from Morty, always giving him a hundred-dollar check on a bank in Lynchburg, Virginia, as security. Morty, of course, knows that Jack has no account in the bank. In the Jollity Building, checks are considered not as literal drafts on existent funds but as a particularly solemn form of promise to repay a loan, since it is believed that the holder of a bad check has it in his power to throw the check writer into jail for twenty-five years. When Jack repays the dollar, usually in four installments, Morty gives the check back to him. Practically everybody in the Jollity Building carries a checkbook. Fellows who cannot borrow from Morty even by giving him checks sometimes ask him to vouch for them so that they can borrow from six-for-fivers, the chaps who lend five dollars one day and collect six dollars the next. "Will you O.K. me with a Shylock, Morty?" one of these suppliants will ask. "You know I'm an honest man." "In what way?" Morty demands cynically if he does not know the man well. If the fellow says, "In every way," Morty refuses to O.K. him, because he is obviously a crook.

The prize-fight managers who hang in the Jollity Building are, as one might expect, of an inferior order. The boys they handle provide what sports writers like to call the "stiff opposition" against which incubating stars compile "sterling records." "When the Garden brings in some fellow that you never heard of from Cleveland or Baltimore or one of them other Western states, and it says in the paper he has had stiff opposition," says a Jollity Building manager known as Acid Test Ike, "that means the opposition has been stiffs. In other words, the class of boys I got." It is Acid Test who manages Jack in all of his comebacks. For each comeback, Ike and Jack go to some place like Lancaster, Pennsylvania, or Wheeling, West Virginia, where there happens to be a novice heavyweight, and Ike tells the sports editor of the local newspaper, "My man will give this kid the acid test." Then Jack gets knocked out. Naturally, Ike also has to manage smaller fighters who will get knocked out by middleweights and lightweights. "A fellow could make a pleasant dollar with a stable of bums," he sometimes says, "only the competition is so terrific. There is an element getting into the game that is willing to be knocked out very cheap." Acid Test Ike always wears a bottle-green suit, a brick-red topcoat, and an oyster-white hat. "It don't take brains to make money with a good fighter," he says rather bitterly when he feels an attack of the miss-meal cramps coming on. "Running into a thing like that is just luck."

Performers, when they arrive at the Jollity Building looking for work, usually take an elevator straight to the floor on which the agent who most often books them is located. After leaving this agent, they make a tour of the other agents' offices to see if anyone else has a job for them. Only when rendered desperate by hunger do they stray down to the third floor, where the people Morty calls the heels hold forth in furnished offices each about the size of a bathroom. Since the heels constitute the lowest category of tenant in the building, no proprietor of a first-class chop-suey joint or roadhouse would call on them for talent. "The best you can get there," performers say, "is a chance to work Saturday night at a ruptured saloon for *bubkis*." "*Bubkis*" is a Yiddish word which means "large beans."

One of the most substantial agents in the building is Jerry Rex, a swarthy, discouraged man who used to be a ventriloquist. He has an unusually large one-room office, which was once the studio of a teacher of Cuban dancing. The walls are painted in orange-and-black stripes, and there are several full-length wall mirrors, in which the pupils used to watch themselves dance. Mr. Rex sits at a desk at the end of the office opposite the door, and performers waiting to speak to him sit on narrow benches along the walls. Rex has an assistant named Dave, who sits on a couch in one corner of the room.

Jerry does not consider his large office an extravagance, because he lives in it twenty-four hours a day, which is a violation of the building laws, and saves the price of a hotel room. He sleeps on the couch, while Dave, a blue-chinned young man with the mores of a tomcat, sleeps on one of the wall benches. Jerry occasionally buys a bottle of beer for the porter who cleans the offices. The grateful porter always does Jerry's first, so the agent can get a good night's rest. Every morning, Jerry washes and shaves in the men's room on his floor. Dave often contents himself with smearing face powder over his beard. Dave is of a happier temperament than his employer. He likes to think of himself as a heartbreaker and is full of stories about the girls who wander through the Jollity Building halls. He calls them heads and boskos. "Bosko" has a definitely roguish connotation. One may safely say to a friend, "That was a beautiful head I seen you with," even if one does not know who the head was. But if one says "bosko," and the woman turns out to be the friend's wife, one has committed a social error.

Dave has a tried technique for forming acquaintanceships in the Jollity Building. "I know this head is a performer, or she would not be in the building," he says. "So I go up to her and say, 'What do you do?' If she says, 'I dance,' I say, 'Too bad, I was looking for a singer.' If she says 'sing,' I say, 'Too bad, I was looking for a dancer.' In that way we get acquainted, and if she looks promising, I pull her down to Barney's for a celery tonic."

Women performers have a better chance of getting cabaret jobs than men, because they mix with the customers. Jerry, who grew up in the sheltered respectability of vaudeville, resents this. "I booked a man with a trained dog into one trap in Astoria," he recently said, "and after one night they canceled him out because the dog couldn't mix. There never was such a tough market for talent. I book an acrobatic act in which, as a finish, one guy walks offstage playing a mandolin and balancing the other guy upside down on his head. The understander only plays a couple of bars, you see, for the effect. I booked them for an Elks' smoker in Jersey, and the chairman of the entertainment committee didn't want to pay me because he said the members don't like musical acts. To stand this business, you got to have a heart of steel." Most agents in the Jollity Building, when they supply talent for a whole show, book themselves as masters of ceremonies and collect an extra ten dollars for announcing the acts. Jerry has given up this practice.

"When I get out on the stage and think of what a small buck the performers are going to get, I feel like crying," he says, "so I send Dave instead."

A fair number of the performers who look for jobs in the Jollity Building have other occupations as well. Many of the women work as receptionists or stenographers in the daytime and make their rounds of agents' offices after five o'clock. Hockticket Charlie, an agent who is one of Jerry Rex's neighbors on the fourth floor, has a side line of his own. Hockticket Charlie is a tall, cross-eyed man with a clarion voice and a solemn manner. By arrangement with a number of pawnbrokers of his acquaintance, he sells pawn tickets. The chief reason anyone purchases a pawn ticket is that he holds the common belief that a watch accepted in pawn for ten dollars, for example, must in reality be worth around forty dollars. The fellow who buys a ticket for five dollars is therefore theoretically able to obtain a forty-dollar watch for a total outlay of fifteen dollars. Hockticket Charlie's pawnbroker friends, aware of this popular superstition, make out a lot of tickets to fictitious persons. Charlie sells the tickets for a few dollars each to performers in the Jollity Building. Each ticket entitles the purchaser to redeem a piece of secondhand jewelry—for not more than three times its value—which the broker has bought at an auction sale. Hockticket nearly always pays off colored performers with pawn tickets which will theoretically permit them to purchase diamonds at a large reduction. By paying ten dollars to a broker, the holder of one of these tickets can often acquire a ring easily worth three dollars. Sometimes Hockticket engages a number of performers to play a date in what he calls "a town near here," and tells them to meet him at the Jollity Building, so that they can all ride out to the date together. He loads them into a rickety bus which he has chartered for ten dollars, and the "town near here" turns out to be Philadelphia. If the acts traveled there singly, they would collect railroad fares for the round trip. Instead, Charlie collects all the railroad fares from the Philadelphia house manager who has booked the show. He often succeeds in paying the bus owner with hock tickets. Morty Ormont has a sincere admiration for Hockticket Charlie.

Another agent on the fourth floor, and the most sedate one in the building, is a woman named Maida Van Schuyler, who books stag shows for conventions and for the banquets large corporations give in honor of newly elected vice-presidents or retiring department heads. Mrs. Van Schuyler, a tall, flat-chested woman with fluffy white hair, was at one time a singer of arch numbers like "I Just Can't Make My Eyes Behave" and "Two Little Love Bees Buzzing in a Bower." As such, she recalls, she lent a touch of class to New England and Ohio vaudeville around 1912. The walls in an anteroom of her office are hung with numerous framed mottoes, such as "What Is More Precious Than a Friend?" and "Seek for Truth and Love Will Seek for You." A plain young woman sits in the anteroom and takes the names of visitors in to Mrs. Van Schuyler. When Mrs. Van Schuyler does not wish to see them, she sends out word that she is terribly sorry but one of her best-beloved friends has just passed away and she is too broken up about it to talk. If the visitor waits around a minute, he may hear a loud, strangling sob. Mrs. Van Schuyler, who is very much interested in spiritualism, often says that she would like to retire from the stag-show business and become a medium. "There isn't a dime left in this lousy business," she remarks. "The moving pictures have spoiled it, just like they did with vaudeville."

Every now and then, one of Mrs. Van Schuyler's shows is raided but the detectives give her advance notice because she provides the entertainments for a number of police banquets. "We have to make a pinch, Mrs. Van Schuyler," they say apologetically, "because the shoo-flies are working in our territory and we can't let a big brawl like this run without getting turned in." Shooflies, as all the world knows, are policemen in mufti assigned to make a secret check on the activities of other policemen. Within a week or two after the raid, which never results in a conviction, the friendly detectives return and say, "It's all right, Mrs. Van Schuyler, we got the shooflies taking now." With this assurance, Mrs. Van Schuyler can go ahead with her business. She seldom employs the ordinary entertainers who wander around the Jollity Building, but relies on specialists whom she lists in a large card file. "It is a highly specialized field of entertainment, darling," she tells gentlemen who are negotiating with her for their organizations. "Our girls must have poise, discretion, and *savoy faire*." To old friends like Morty Ormont, she sometimes says less elegantly, after an all-night party with a convention of textbook publishers or refrigerator sales-men, "You ought to seen those apes try to paw the girls."

Performers on their way to see one of the agents on the fourth floor are sometimes frightened by wild fanfares from an office occupied by an Italian who repairs trumpets. A musician who brings a trumpet to the Italian always blows a few hot licks to demonstrate that the in-strument is out of true. When he calls for the trumpet, he blows a few more to see whether it is all right again. Once a swing dilettante stood in the hall for half an hour listening to the noises and then walked in and said that it was the best band he had ever heard and he wanted it to play at a rent party he was giving for some other *cognoscenti*.

Not all the transients in the Jollity Building halls are entertainers making the rounds of the agents. There is a fellow known as Paddy the Booster, who sells neckties he steals from haberdashers, and an-other known as Mac the Phony Booster, who sells neckties which he pretends to have stolen but are really shoddy ties he has bought very cheaply. Naturally, Paddy looks down on Mac, whom he considers a racketeer. "It takes all kinds of people to make up a great city," Jack McGuire sometimes tells Paddy, trying to soothe him. Also, every floor of the building has at least one bookmaker, who hangs in the hall. "In winter, the bookmakers complain because we don't heat the halls bet-ter," the beleaguered Morty Ormont says. A dollar is the standard Jollity Building wager. The accepted method of assembling it is to drop in on an acquaintance and say, "I got a tip on a horse, but I'm short a quarter." One repeats this operation until one has accumulated four quarters. It sometimes takes a long time, but there is always an oversupply of that. This system reduces the risk of betting to a minimum. On the infrequent occasions when some momentarily prosperous tenant bets important money on a race—say, five dollars—two or three of the hall bookmakers get together and divide up the hazard.

The Jollity Building has at least a dozen tenants who teach voice, dancing, and dramatic art, and a few who specialize in Latin-American dance routines and acrobatics. The financial condition of the professors, which is solvent in comparison to that of the performers, musicians, and theatrical agents in the building, is a perpetual source of amusement to Morty Ormont. "The singers are from hunger," he says; "the performers are from hunger, and every day we get saps in the building who pay for lessons so they can be from hunger, too." Parents who believe their children are talented are the staple prey of the professional teachers. Seldom does a Jollity Building elevator make a trip without at least one bosomy and belligerent suburban woman, holding fast to the hand of a little girl whose hair is frizzled into a semblance of Shirley Temple's. Often several of the Shirleys and their mothers find themselves in a car together. The mothers' upper lips curl as they survey the other mothers' patently moronic young. The Shirleys gaze at each other with vacuous hostility and wonder whether their mothers will slap them if they ask to go to the bathroom again. All the Shirleys have bony little knees and bitter mouths and, in Morty's opinion, will undoubtedly grow up to be ax murderesses.

III—A SOFT DOLLAR

Barney, who owns the lunch counter in the basement of the so-called Jollity Building, never turns his head away from his customers for a second while working. Even when he is drawing coffee from the urn, he keeps looking over his shoulder, and this, in the course of his eighteen years in business, has given him a nervous neck twitch. "I know their nature," Barney says in explanation of this mannerism. "If I'll turn my head, they'll run away without paying." With all his vigilance, Barney cannot foresee when a client will eat two *pastrami* sandwiches and then say, after fumbling in a vest pocket, "Gee, Barney, I thought I had a quarter in my pocket, but it turned out to be an old Willkie Button." Barney is a short, gray-faced man in his fifties who looks at his customers through thick, shell-rimmed spectacles that are usually clouded with steam from the coffee urn or with dabs of corned-beef grease. The customers see Barney against a background of cans of beans, arranged in pyramids. The cans, stacked on a shelf behind his counter, constitute a decorative scheme he never changes, except when he lays a fat, shiny stick of bologna across the can forming the apex of one of the pyramids.

Once, recently, Barney startled Hy Sky, the Jollity Building sign painter, and Morty Ormont, the renting agent, by announcing the return of prosperity. This was an event that neither of his listeners, confined for the most part in their associations to theatrical people, had suspected. "The taxi drivers who come in here are asking for sandwiches on thin bread, so they can taste the meat, and they are eating two sandwiches for lunch, usually," Barney said. "From 1929 until very lately, everybody was asking for sandwiches on thick bread, one sandwich should fill them up." The lunch counter is at one end of the Jollity Building's poolroom, and most of Barney's customers are either people who work in the building or pool players. The taximen are his only customers from the daylight world.

"The bookmakers in the building are also eating regular," Barney said, continuing his survey of business conditions, "and even a couple of prize-fight managers recently came in and paid cash. With musicians, of course, is still the depression. Also with performers." Barney takes it for granted that anyone connected with the stage is broke, and if he can detect a speck of theatrical make-up under a woman's chin or behind an ear, he will refuse to give her credit. He even declines to believe that any performers receive regular remuneration in Hollywood. "It is all publicity," he says. "George Raft still owes me thirty-five cents from when he used to hang here." Musicians, although imperceptibly less broke, on the average, than actors or dancers, are almost as irritating to Barney. They sit at his counter for hours, each with one cup of coffee, and discuss large sums of money. Since most of the year musicians wear big, shaggy coats made of a material resembling the mats under rugs, they fill twice as much space as bookmakers or taxi drivers. Their coats overflow onto adjoining stools. "Three hours is average for a musician to drink a cup of coffee," Barney says, "and then sometimes he says he hasn't got the nickel, he'll see me tomorrow. Tomorrow is never."

Regulars who hang at Barney's counter may be identified by the manner in which, before sitting down, they run their hands under the counter. They are reaching for a communal dope sheet, a ten cent racing paper giving the entries at all tracks. The regulars at Barney's chip in and buy one copy every day. This economy permits each of them to lose to bookmakers every week several dimes that would otherwise have been spent at newsstands. Barney has little contact with the pool players, although he does a good deal of business with them. A number of mulatto girls who rack up the balls on the pool tables also act as waitresses for the players. The girls pay Barney cash for all the cups of coffee they carry away. Presumably they collect from the players. "It is a pleasure they can have," says Barney.

One of the more conspicuous fellows who eats at the lunch counter and spends a good deal of time there between meals drinking coffee is called Marty the Clutch. Marty gets his name from his humorous custom of mangling people's fingers when he shakes hands with them. Strangers to whom he is introduced usually sink to their knees screaming before he releases their right hand. Casual acquaintances consider Marty a big, overgrown boy brimming with animal spirits. Only old friends really appreciate him. They know that when Marty has numbed a stranger's hand, he can often get a ring off the fellow's finger unnoticed. "It is very cute when you think of it," says Acid Test Ike, who is a manager of punch-drunk prize fighters. "I once seen the Clutch get a rock off a ticket broker big enough to use for a doorstop. By the time the scalper noticed the ring was gone, he thought a bosko he knew had clipped him for it, so he busted her nose." The Clutch is a big, square-shouldered man with a forehead barely sufficient to keep his hair from meeting his eyebrows. He used to be a prize fighter, but, he says, he worked with a gang of hijackers several nights a week and this interfered with his training, because he was always getting shot. Acid Test Ike considers this an amiable prevarication. "The Clutch never was a hijacker," he says. "He just gives that as a social reference. Really, the Clutch is a gozzler." This term means a fellow who gozzles people—chokes them in order to rob them. The gozzling business cannot be very good, because Marty is customarily as broke as most other patrons of the lunch counter. Every time Barney looks at Marty the Clutch, he rubs his throat nervously.

To Barney, the most interesting people in the Jollity Building are the promoters, the fellows who are always trying to earn, in the local idiom, a soft dollar. This is a curiosity he shares with Hy Sky and Morty Ormont, and sometimes the three of them get together at the lunch counter and discuss, with happy chuckles, the outrageous swindles perpetrated by fellows they know. One mental giant of whom all three speak with awe is a chap known as Lotsandlots, or Lots for short, who is in the land-development business. Lots's stock in trade is a tract of real estate in the Jersey marshes and a large supply of stationery bearing the letterheads of non-existent land companies and the Jollity Building's address. Prospects are carefully selected; generally they are close-fisted men with a few thousand dollars saved up. Each receives a letter informing him that he has won a lot in a raffle conducted by one of the land companies to publicize a new development. The winner, according to the letter, is now the owner, free and clear, of one building lot in some out-of-the-way district. With the lot goes an option to buy the lots on either side of it for a couple of hundred dollars apiece. The man receiving such a letter is distrustful. He knows that one house lot is not much use, and he suspects that the whole thing is just a dodge to sell him more land, so he doesn't even go out to look at his prize. In a week or so, Lotsandlots calls on the skeptic and says he hears that the man is the lucky owner of three lots in a certain undeveloped neighborhood. Lotsandlots says he represents a company that is assembling a site for a large industrial plant. He offers to buy the man's three lots for a good price, but begs him to keep the offer confidential, as publicity would interfere with his firm's efforts to pick up land. The lucky man of property always lets Lotsandlots think that he owns all three plots outright. He says that Lotsandlots should give him time to think the matter over and come back in a couple of days. Then, as soon as Lotsandlots leaves, the fellow hurries down to the land company's office in the Jollity Building to exercise his option on the two adjoining lots, which he expects to sell at a whacking profit. He pays four hundred dollars or five hundred dollars to the "office manager," an assistant promoter in Lotsandlots' employ. The manager gives him clear deed and title to two lots in a salt marsh. The man goes away happily, and then waits the rest of his life for Lotsandlots to reappear and conclude the deal.

"The art in it," Hy Sky says admiringly, "is the sap never knows Lots is running the land company. A good boy, Lots." Lots is a humorist, too. When anyone asks him if he does much business, he says, "Lots and lots," which is how he got his name. When he says it, he rolls his eyes so knowingly that Hy Sky, if he is around, suffers an attack of laughter resembling whooping cough.

Another respected promoter is Judge Horumph, a bucolic figure of a man who wears a stand-up collar, a heavy gilt-iron watch chain with a seal ring on it, and high, laceless shoes with elastic sides. The Judge's face is tomato red marked by fine streaks of eggplant purple. Barney and his customers are disposed to believe Judge Horumph's story that he was once a justice of the peace in a Republican village upstate, a region in which about one man in every three enjoys that distinction. The Judge, when he is working, sits at a telephone all day, calling various business houses that like to keep on the good side of the law—

particularly firms with large fleets of trucks, because such firms are constantly dealing with traffic and parking summonses, and they don't want to offend anybody. He says, "This is Judge H-r-r-umph." The name is indistinguishable, but no layman knows the names of a tenth of the judges in New York, and it would be impolite to ask a judge to repeat. "I am giving some of my time to a little charitable organization called Free Malted Milk for Unmarried Mothers," the Judge says. "I know that ordinarily it would be an imposition to bother you people, but the cause is so worthy . . ." Rather often, the owner or manager of the firm tells the Judge he will send five or ten dollars. "Oh, don't say 'send,'" Judge Horumph booms jovially. "I know how prone we all are to forget these little things. I'll send a telegraph boy right over to get your contribution." The Judge is a man of real culture, Morty Ormont says, but he has one failing, and that is strong drink. Judge Horumph's one serious run-in with the law resulted from his throwing a whisky bottle at a Jollity Building wag who offered to buy him a malted milk.

The hero of the best stories that Barney and Hy Sky and Morty Ormont sit around telling one another is a promoter named Maxwell C. Bimberg, who used to be known in the Jollity Building as the Count de Pennies because he wore a pointed, waxed, blond mustache just like a count and because he was rather stingy except about gambling and women. The Count was a tiny, fragile man with large, melting eyes and a retreating chin. "He was a little wizened man that didn't look like nothing at all," Hy says, "but Maxwell C. Bimberg had a brilliant mind."

Hy recalls how he helped the Count de Pennies conduct a crusade against pari-mutuel betting in New York State in which the Count fleeced a prominent bookmaker who felt that his business was menaced by the movement to legalize the betting machines. The Count induced the bookie to finance a campaign of street advertising against the proposition, which was to be voted on at the polls. The Count was to have twenty signs painted, large enough to cover the side of a wagon. The signs were to say, "Mayor LaGuardia says vote 'No'!" Then the Count was to hire ten wagons, put the signs on them, and have them driven around the center of town the day before the referendum. The bookie peeled several hundred-dollar bills off his bank roll to pay for the operation. The promoter went to Hy Sky and ordered just two signs, allowing the painter a generous profit on them. He had the signs placed on a wagon that he hired for one hour. The wagon then drove a couple of times through the Duffy Square region, where the bookmaker hung, and returned to the stable. There the signs were shifted to another wagon, which made the same circuit, and so on. The bookie saw several wagons during the day and was happy. Count de Pennies saved the price of eighteen signs and reduced wagon hire by ninety per cent. "Maxwell C. Bimberg had a brilliant mind!" Hy Sky repeats when he tells of this successful promotion.

Morty Ormont's reminiscences about the Count are not all tender. "He was always borrowing a nickel for a telephone call, but one day he asked me for a loan of three dollars so he could get his teeth out of hock to con a sucker," Morty says. "I loaned it to him, and the next day I saw him looking very happy, with his teeth in. As soon as he spotted me he started with a small mouth. 'I am sorry, Morty,' he says, 'but the sucker didn't show, so I haven't got the three bucks.' So I turned him upside down—you know how little he was—and six hundred dollars fell out of his left breech."

The Count's admirers in the Jollity Building generally speak of him in the past tense, although it is improbable that he is dead. Some detectives employed by a railroad are looking for the wizened man as a result of one of his promotions, and consequently he has not been seen for some time around the Jollity Building. The project which irritated the railroad was known as the Dixie Melody Tours. The Count sold bargain-rate tour tickets to Florida which included train fare, hotel rooms, and meals. At the end of every month, the Count settled with the railroad and the hotels for the accommodations the tourists had bought through him. The tours were actually bringing the Count a fair income when, at the end of the third or fourth month, he decided to pay the railroad with a bad check. "It must have been a terrible temptation to him to stay honest," Morty says, "but he resisted it." "He always thought very big," Barney recalls affectionately. "I said to him lots of times, 'Be careful, Count. Nobody can promote a railroad.' He would say, 'What do you mean? This is strictly legitimate.' But I could see in his eyes he was thinking of larceny. 'Already I promoted some of the smartest people on Broadway,' he was thinking. 'Why not a railroad?' He always thought too big."

The Count made his first appearance in the Jollity Building a dozen years ago, when he was the manager of the widow of a famous gunman. He rented a furnished office, about six feet square, on the third floor and pasted on the outer side of the door a card saying, "Maxwell C. Bimberg, Presentation of Publicized Personalities." He booked the gunman's widow as an added attraction in burlesque theaters, and since that seemed to work out pretty well, he tried to sign up several acquitted female defendants in recent and prominent murder cases. The women were eager to sign contracts, but the Count found it difficult to make money with them. One reason, he said, was that "It is hard to write a routine for an acquitted murderess. If she reenacts the crime, then the public gets the impression that she should not have been acquitted."

One Wisconsin woman who had been acquitted of killing her husband with ground glass came to New York and rented an apartment to live in during her stage career under his management. She used to invite the Count to dinner every evening, and he had a hard time thinking of excuses which would not offend her. "Every time she says 'Home cooking,'" the Count would tell Barney, "I feel like I bit into a broken bottle." At last the life of the gunman's widow was violently terminated by one of her husband's business associates. An astute detective sat down next to the telephone in the murdered woman's flat and waited for the murderer to call up, which to a layman would have seemed an unlikely eventuality. The first person to call was the Count. He was phoning to inform his star that he had booked her for a week's engagement at a theater in Union City, New Jersey. The detective had the call traced. A couple of other detectives arrested the Count in the Jollity Building and pulled out his mustache one hair at a time to make him tell why he had killed his meal ticket. This experience cured the Count of his desire to make other people's crimes pay. After his mustache grew again, he decided to marry an elderly Brooklyn woman whom he had met through an advertisement in a matrimonial journal. The bride was to settle three thousand dollars on him, but the match fell through when she declined to give the Count the money in advance. "If you have so little confidence in me, darling," he said, "we would never be happy." "And also," he told Morty Ormont subsequently, "I didn't want to lay myself open for a bigamy rap."

The Count next organized a troupe of girl boxers, whom he proposed to offer as an added attraction to the dance marathons then popular. "It was not that the idea was any good," Morty Ormont says when he tells about the Count, "but it was the way he milked it. After all, what is there smart about selling a guy a piece of something that might make money? Smart is to sell a guy for a good price a piece of a sure loser. The Count went out and promoted Johnny Attorney, one of the toughest guys on Broadway, for a grand to pay the girls' training expenses and buy them boxing trunks and bathrobes. The Count trembled every time Johnny looked at him, but with him,

larceny was stronger than fear. So he gives all the girls bus fare to
Spring Valley, New York, and tells them he will meet them there
and show them the training camp he has engaged. Then he takes the
rest of the grand and goes to Florida." When Morty reaches this point
in the story, Hy Sky can seldom restrain himself from saying,
reverentially, "Maxwell C. Bimberg had a brilliant mind!"

"By the time the Count came back from Florida," Morty says,
"Johnny Attorney was running a night club on Fifty-second Street.
The Count walks into Johnny's joint as if nothing had happened, and
in fifteen minutes he cons Johnny into making him a banquet manager. He booked a couple of nice banquets into there, but when
Johnny would send the bill to the chairman of whatever club it was
that held the banquet, the chairman would write back and say, 'I see
no mention on your bill of the deposit I paid your Mr. Bimberg.' The
Count had glommed the deposits. So after that he had to play the
duck for Johnny for a couple of years. Whenever Johnny would get
shoved in the can for assault or manslaughter, the Count would come
back to town. That gave him quite a lot of time in town, at that. . . .

"In every class of business," declares Morty Ormont with finality,
"there has got to be a champion. The Count de Pennies was never
no good to nobody, but he was the champion heel of the Jollity Building."

IV. THE SOUTHLAND

Marjorie Kinnan Rawlings

BENNY AND THE BIRD-DOGS

YOU can't change a man, no-ways. By the time his mammy turns him loose and he takes up with some innocent woman and marries her, he's what he is. If it's his nature to set by the hearthfire and scratch hisself, you just as good to let him set and scratch. If it's his nature, like Will Dover, my man, to go to the garage in his Sunday clothes and lay down under some backwoods Cracker's old greasy Ford and tinker with it, you just as good to let him lay and tinker. And if it's his nature, like Uncle Benny, to prowl; if it's his nature to cut the fool; why, it's interfering in the ways of Providence even to stop to quarrel with him about it. Some women is born knowing that. Sometimes a woman, like the Old Hen (Uncle Benny's wife, poor soul!), has to quarrel a lifetime before she learns it. Then when it does come to her, she's like a cow has tried to jump a high fence and has got hung up on it—she's hornswoggled.

The Old Hen's a mighty fine woman—one of the finest I know. She looks just the way she did when she married Uncle Benny Mathers thirty years ago, except her hair has turned gray, like the feathers on an Irish Gray game hen. She's plump and pretty and kind of pale from thirty years' fretting about Uncle Benny. She has a disposition, by nature, as sweet as new cane syrup. When she settled down for a lifetime's quarrelling at him, it was for the same reason syrup sours—the heat had just been put to her too long.

I can't remember a time when the Old Hen wasn't quarrelling at

Uncle Benny. It begun a week after they was married. He went off prowling by hisself, to a frolic or such as that, and didn't come home until four o'clock in the morning. She was setting up waiting for him. When she crawled him about it, he said, "Bless Katy, wife, let's sleep now and quarrel in the morning." So she quarrelled in the morning and just kept it up. For thirty years. Not for meanness—she just kept hoping she could change him.

Change him? When he takened notice of the way she was fussing and clucking and ruffling her feathers, he quit calling her by her given name and began calling her the Old Hen. That's all I could ever see she changed him.

Uncle Benny's a sight. He's been constable here at Oak Bluff, Florida, for twenty years. We figure it keeps him out of worse trouble to let him be constable. He's the quickest shot in three counties and the colored folks is all as superstitious of him as if he was the devil hisself. He's a comical-appearing somebody. He's small and quick and he don't move—he prances. He has a little bald sun-tanned head with a rim of white hair around the back of it. Where the hair ends at the sides of his head, it sticks straight up over his ears in two little white tufts like goat-horns. He's got bright blue eyes that look at you quick and wicked, the way a goat looks. That's exactly what he looks and acts like—a mischievous little old billy-goat. And he's been popping up under folks' noses and playing tricks on them as long as Oak Bluff has knowed him. Doc in particular. He loved to torment Doc.

And stay home? Uncle Benny don't know what it is to stay home. The Old Hen'll cook hot dinner for him and he won't come. She'll start another fire in the range and warm it up for him about dusk-dark and he won't come. She'll set up till midnight, times till daybreak, and maybe just about the time the east lightens and the birds gets to whistling good, he'll come home. Where's he been? He's been with somebody 'gatoring, or with somebody catching crabs to Salt Springs; he's been to a square-dance twenty miles away in the flatwoods; he's been on the highway in that Ford car, just rambling as long as his gas held out—and them seven pieded bird-dogs setting up in the back keeping him company.

It was seven years ago, during the Boom, that he bought the Model-T and begun collecting bird-dogs. Everybody in Florida was rich for a whiles, selling gopher holes to the Yankees. Now putting an automobile under Uncle Benny was like putting wings on a wild-cat—it just opened up new territory. Instead of rambling over one county, he could ramble over ten. And the way he drove—like a bat out of Torment. He's one of them men just loves to cover the ground. And that car and all them bird-dogs worked on the Old Hen like a quart of gasoline on a camp-fire. She really went to raring. I tried to tell her then 'twasn't no use to pay him no mind, but she wouldn't listen.

I said, "It's just his nature. You can't do a thing about it but take it for your share and go on. You and Uncle Benny is just made different. You want him home and he don't want to be home. You're a barn-yard fowl and he's a wild fowl."

"Mis' Dover," she said, "it's easy for you to talk. Your man runs a garage and comes home nights. You don't know how terrible it is to have a man that prowls."

I said, "Leave him prowl."

She said, "Yes, but when he's on the prowl, I don't no more know where to look for him than somebody's tom-cat."

I said, "If 'twas me, I wouldn't look for him."

She said, "Moonlight nights he's the worst. Just like the varmints."

I said, "Don't that tell you nothing?"

She said, "If he'd content hisself with prowling— But he ain't content until he cuts the fool. He takes that Ford car and them seven bird-dogs and maybe a pint of moonshine, and maybe picks up Doc to prowl with him, and he don't rest until he's done something crazy. What I keep figuring is, he'll kill hisself in that Ford car, cutting the fool."

I said, "You don't need to fret about him and that Ford. What's un-natural for one man is plumb natural for another. And cutting the fool is so natural for Uncle Benny, it's like a bird in the air or a fish in water—there won't no harm come to him from it."

She said, "Mis' Dover, what the devil throws over his back has got to come down under his belly."

I said, "Uncle Benny Mathers is beyond rules and sayings. I know men-folks, and if you'll listen to me, you'll settle down and quit quar-relling and leave him go his way in quiet."

I happened to be in on it this spring, the last time the Old Hen ever quarrelled at Uncle Benny. Me and Doc was both in on it. It was the day of old lady Weller's burying. Doc carried me in his car to the cemetery. My Will couldn't leave the garage, because the trucks haul-ing the Florida oranges north was bringing in pretty good business. Doc felt obliged to go to the burying. He's a patent-medicine sales-man—a big fat fellow with a red face and yellow hair. He sells the Little Giant line of remedies. Old lady Weller had been one of his best customers. She'd taken no nourishment the last week of her life except them remedies, and Doc figured he ought to pay her the proper respect and show everybody he was a man was always grateful to his customers.

Uncle Benny and the Old Hen went to the burying in the Model-T. And the seven bird-dogs went, setting up in the back seat. They always went to the buryings.

Uncle Benny said, "Walls nor chains won't hold 'em. Better to have 'em go along riding decent and quiet, than to bust loose and foller the Model-T like a daggone pack of bloodhounds."

That was true enough. Those bird-dogs could hear that old Ford crank up and go off in low gear, clear across the town. They'd always hope it was time to go bird-hunting again, and here they'd come, trailing it. So there were the bird-dogs riding along to old lady Weller's burying, with their ears flopping and their noses in the air for quail. As constable, Uncle Benny sort of represented the town, and he was right in behind the hearse. I mean, that car was a pain, to be part of a funeral procession. In the seven years he'd had it, he'd all but drove it to pieces, and it looked like a rusty, mangy razor-back hog. The hood was thin and narrow, like a shoat's nose—you remember the way all Model-T Fords were built. It had no top to it, nor no doors to the front seat, and the back seat rose up in a hump where the bird-dogs had squeezed the excelsior chitlin's out of it.

The Old Hen sat up stiff and proud, not letting on she minded. Doc and I figured she's been quarrelling at Uncle Benny about the bird-dogs, because when one of them put his paws on her shoulders and begun licking around her ears, she turned and smacked the breath out of him.

The funeral procession had just left the Oak Bluff dirt road and turned onto No. 9 Highway, when the garage keeper at the bend ran out.

He hollered, "I just got a 'phone call for Uncle Benny Mathers from the high sheriff!"

So Uncle Benny cut out of the procession and drove over to the pay station by the kerosene tank to take the message. He caught up again in a minute and called to Doc, "A drunken nigger is headed this way in a Chevrolet and the sheriff wants I should stop him."

About that time here comes the Chevrolet and started to pass the procession, wobbling back and forth as if it had the blind staggers. You may well know the nigger was drunk or he wouldn't have passed a funeral. Uncle Benny cut out of line and took out after him. When he saw who was chasing him, the nigger turned around and headed back the way he'd come from. Uncle Benny was gaining on him when they passed the hearse. The bird-dogs begun to take an interest and rared up, barking. What does Uncle Benny do but go to the side of the Chevrolet so the nigger turns around—and then Uncle Benny crowded him so all he could do was to shoot into line in the funeral procession. Uncle Benny cut right in after him and the nigger shot out of line and Uncle Benny crowded him in again.

I'll declare, I was glad old lady Weller wasn't alive to see it. She'd had no use for Uncle Benny, she'd hated a nigger, and she'd despised dogs so to where she kept a shotgun by her door to shoot at them if one so much as crossed her cornfield. And here on the way to her burying, where you'd figure she was entitled to have things the way she liked them, here was Uncle Benny chasing a nigger in and out of line, and seven bird-dogs were going Ki-yippity-yi! Ki-yippity-yi! Ki-yippity-yi! I was mighty proud the corpse was no kin to me.

The Old Hen was plumb mortified. She put her hands over her face and when the Ford would swerve by or cut in ahead of us, Doc and me could see her swaying back and forth and suffering. I don't scarcely need to say Uncle Benny was enjoying hisself. If he'd looked sorrowful-like, as if he was just doing his duty, you could of forgive him. Near a filling-station the Chevrolet shot ahead and stopped and the nigger jumped out and started to run. Uncle Benny stopped and climbed out of the Ford and drew his pistol and called "Stop!" The nigger kept on going.

Now Uncle Benny claims that shooting at niggers in the line of duty is what keeps him in practice for bird-shooting. He dropped a ball to the right of the nigger's heel and he dropped a ball to the left of it. He called "Stop!" and the nigger kept on going. Then Uncle Benny took his pistol in both hands and took a slow aim and he laid the third ball against the nigger's shin-bone. He dropped like a string-haltered mule.

Uncle Benny said to the man that ran the filling-station, "Get your gun. That there nigger is under arrest and I deputize you to keep him that-a-way. The sheriff'll be along to pick him up direckly."

He cut back into the funeral procession between us and the hearse, and we could tell by them wicked blue eyes he didn't know when he'd enjoyed a burying like old lady Weller's. When we got back from the burying, he stopped by Will's garage. The Old Hen was giving him down-the-country.

She said, "That was the most scandalous thing I've ever knowed you to do, chasing that nigger in and out of Mis' Weller's funeral."

Uncle Benny's eyes begun to dance and he said, "I know it, wife, but I couldn't help it. 'Twasn't me done the chasing—it was the Model-T."

Doc got in to it then and sided with the Old Hen. He gets excited, the way fat men do, and he swelled up like a spreading adder.

"Benny," he said, "you shock my modesty. This ain't no occasion for laughing or lying."

Uncle Benny said, "I know it, Doc. I wouldn't think of laughing nor lying. You didn't know I've got that Ford trained? I've got it trained to where it'll do two things. It's helped me chase so many niggers, I've got it to where it just naturally takes out after 'em by itself."

Doc got red in the face and asked, real sarcastic, "And what's the other piece of training?"

Uncle Benny said, "Doc, that Ford has carried me home drunk so many times, I've got it trained to where it'll take care of me and carry me home safe when I ain't fitten."

Doc spit halfway across the road and he said, "You lying old jay-bird."

Uncle Benny said, "Doc, I've got a pint of moonshine and if you'll come go camping with me to Salt Springs this evening, I'll prove it."

The Old Hen spoke up and she said, "Benny, Heaven forgive you for I won't, if you go on the prowl again before you've cleared the weeds out of my old pindar field. I'm a month late now, getting it planted."

Doc loves Salt Springs crab and mullet as good as Uncle Benny does, and I could see he was tempted.

But he said, "Benny, you go along home and do what your wife wants, and when you're done—when she says you're done—then we'll go to Salt Springs."

So Uncle Benny and the Old Hen drove off. Doc watched after them.

He said, "Anyways, cutting the fool at a burying had ought to last Benny quite a while."

I said, "You don't know him. Cutting the fool don't last him no time at all."

I was right. I ain't so special wise a woman, but if I once know a man, I can come right close to telling you what he'll do. Uncle Benny hadn't been gone hardly no time, when somebody come by the garage hollering that he'd done set the Old Hen's pindar field on fire.

I said to Doc, "What did I tell you? The last thing in the world was safe for that woman to do, was to turn him loose on them weeds. He figured firing was the quickest way to get shut of them."

Doc said, "Let's go see."

We got in his car and drove out to Uncle Benny's place. Here was smoke rolling up back of the house, and the big live oak in the yard was black with soldier blackbirds the grass fire had drove out of the pindar field. The field hadn't had peanuts in it since fall, but bless Katy, it was full of something else. Uncle Benny's wife had it plumb full of setting guinea-hens. She hadn't told him, because he didn't like guineas.

Far off to the west corner of the field was the Old Hen, trying to run the guineas into a coop. They were flying every which-a-way and hollering *Pod-rac! Pod-rac!* the way guineas holler. All the young uns in the neighborhood were in the middle of the field, beating out the grass fire with palmettos. And setting up on top of the east gate, just as unconcerned, was Uncle Benny, with them two little horns of white hair curling in the heat. Now what do you reckon he was doing? He had all seven of them bird-dogs running back and forth retrieving guinea eggs. He'd say now and again, "Dead—fetch!" and they'd wag their tails and go hunt up another nest and here they'd come, with guinea eggs carried gentle in their mouths. He was putting the eggs in a basket.

When the commotion was over, and the fire out, and everybody gone on but Doc and me, we went to the front porch to set down and rest. The Old Hen was wore out. She admitted it was her fault not letting Uncle Benny know about the setting guinea-hens. She was about to forgive him setting the field a-fire, because him and the bird-dogs had saved the guinea eggs. But when we got to the porch, here lay the bird-dogs in the rocking-chairs. There was one to every chair, rocking away and cutting their eyes at her. Their coats and paws were smuttied from the burnt grass—and the Old Hen had put clean sugar-sacking covers on every blessed chair that morning. That settled it. She was stirred up anyway about the way he'd cut the fool at the burying, and she really set in to quarrel at Uncle Benny. And like I say, it turned out to be the last piece of quarrelling she ever done.

She said to him, "You taught them bird-dogs to rock in a rocking-chair just to torment me. Ever' beast or varmint you've brought home, you've learned to cut the fool as bad as you do."

"Now wife, what beast or varmint did I ever learn to cut the fool?"

"You learned the 'coon to screw the tops off my syrup cans. You learned the 'possum to hang upside down in my cupboards, and I'd go for a jar of maybe pepper relish and put my hand on him. . . . There's been plenty of such as that. I've raised ever'thing in the world for you but a stallion horse."

Doc said, "Give him time, he'll have one of them stabled in the kitchen."

"Bird-dogs is natural to have around," she said. "I was raised to bird-dogs. But it ain't natural for 'em to rock in a rocking-chair. There's so terrible many of them, and when they put in the night on the porch laying in the rocking-chairs and rocking, I don't close my eyes for the fuss."

Uncle Benny said, "You see, Doc? You see, Mis' Dover? She's always quarrelling that me and the dogs ain't never home at night. Then when we do come in, she ain't willing we should all be comf'table.

"We just as good to go on to Salt Springs, Doc. Wait while I go in the house and get my camping outfit and we'll set out."

He went in the house and came out with his camping stuff. She knowed he was gone for nobody knew how long.

We walked on down to the gate and the Old Hen followed, sniffling a little and twisting the corner of her apron.

"Benny," she said, "please don't go to Salt Springs. You always lose your teeth in the Boil."

"I ain't lost 'em but three times," he said, and he cranked up the Model-T and climbed in. "I couldn't help losing 'em the first time. That was when I was laughing at the Yankee casting for bass, and his plug caught me in the open mouth and lifted my teeth out. Nor I couldn't help it the second time, when Doc and me was rassling in the rowboat and he pushed me in."

"Yes," she said, "an' how'd you lose 'em the third time?"

His eyes twinkled and he shoved the Ford in low. "Cuttin' the fool," he said.

"That's just it," she said, and the tears begun to roll out of her eyes. "Anybody with false teeth hadn't ought to cut the fool!"

Now I always thought it was right cute, the way Uncle Benny fooled Doc about the trained Ford. You know how the old-timey Fords get the gas—it feeds from the hand-throttle on the wheel. Well, Uncle Benny had spent the day before old lady Weller's funeral at Will's garage, putting in a foot accelerator. He didn't say a word to anybody, and Will and me was the only ones knowed he had it. Doc and Uncle Benny stayed three-four days camping at Salt Springs. Now the night they decided to come home, they'd both had something to drink, but Uncle Benny let on like he was in worse shape than he was.

Doc said, "Benny, you better leave me drive."

Uncle Benny pretended to rock on his feet and roll his head and he said, "I've got that Model-T trained to carry me home, drunk or sober."

Doc said, "Never mind that lie again. You get up there in the seat and whistle in the dogs. I'm fixing to drive us home."

Well, I'd of give a pretty to of been in the back seat with them bird-dogs that night when Doc drove the Ford back to Oak Bluff. It's a treat, any ways, to see a fat man get excited. The first thing Doc knowed, the Ford was running away with him. The Ford lights were none too good, and Doc just did clear a stump by the roadside, and he run clean over a blackjack sapling. He looked at the hand-throttle on the wheel and here it was where the car had ought to be going about twenty miles an hour and it was going forty-five. That rascal of an Uncle Benny had his foot on the foot accelerator.

Doc shut off the gas altogether and the Ford kept right on going.

He said, "Something's the matter."

Uncle Benny seemed to be dozing and didn't pay no mind. The Ford whipped back and forth in the sand road like a 'gator's tail. Directly they got on to the hard road and the Model-T put on speed. They begun to get near a curve. It was a dark night and the carlights wobbling, but Doc could see it coming. He took a tight holt of the wheel and begun to sweat. He felt for the brakes, but Uncle Benny never did have any.

He said, "We'll all be kilt."

When they started to take the curve, the Model-T was going nearly fifty-five—and then just as they got there, all of a sudden it slowed down as if it knowed what it was doing, and went around the curve as gentle as a day-old kitten. Uncle Benny had eased his foot off the accelerator. Doc drawed a breath again.

It's a wonder to me that trip didn't make Doc a nervous wreck. On every straightaway the Ford would rare back on its haunches and stretch out like a greyhound. Every curve they come to, it would go to it like a jack-rabbit. Then just as the sweat would pour down Doc's face and the drops would splash on the wheel, and he'd gather hisself together ready to jump, the Ford would slow down. It was a hot spring night, but Uncle Benny says Doc's teeth were chattering. The Model-T made the last mile lickety-brindle with the gas at the hand-throttle shut off entirely—and it coasted down in front of Will's garage and of its own free will come to a dead stop.

It was nine o'clock at night. Will was just closing up and I had locked the candy and cigarette counter and was waiting for him. There was a whole bunch of the men and boys around, like always, because the garage is the last place in Oak Bluff to put the lights out. Doc climbed out of the Ford trembling like a dish of custard. Uncle Benny eased out after him and I looked at him and right away I knowed he'd been up to mischief.

Doc said, "I don't know how he done it—but dogged if he wasn't telling the truth when he said he had that blankety-blank Model-T trained to carry him home when he ain't fitten."

Will asked, "How come?" and Doc told us. Will looked at me and begun to chuckle and we knowed what Uncle Benny had done to him. I think maybe I would of let Uncle Benny get away with it, but Will couldn't keep it.

"Come here, Doc," he said. "Here's your training."

I thought the bunch would laugh Doc out of town. He swelled up like a toadfish and he got in his car without a word and drove away.

It's a wonderful thing just to set down and figure out how many different ways there are to be crazy. We never thought of Uncle Benny as being really crazy. We'd say, "Uncle Benny's cutting the fool again," and we'd mean he was just messing around some sort of foolishness like a daggone young un. We figured his was what you might call the bottom kind of craziness. The next would be the half-witted. The next would be the senseless. The next would be what the colored folks call "mindless." And clear up at the top would be what you'd call cold-out crazy. With all his foolishness, we never figured Uncle Benny was cold-out crazy.

Well, we missed Uncle Benny from Oak Bluff a day or two. When I came to ask questions, I found he'd gone on a long prowl and was over on the Withlacoochie River camping with some oyster fishermen. I didn't think much about it, because he was liable to stay off that-a-way. But time rocked on and he didn't show up. I dropped by his house to ask the Old Hen about him. She didn't know a blessed thing.

She said, "Ain't it God's mercy we've got no young uns? The pore things would be as good as fatherless."

And then a few days later Doc came driving up to the garage. He got out and blew his nose and we could see his eyes were red.

He said, "Ain't it awful! I can't hardly bear to think about it."

Will said, "Doc, if you know bad news, you must be carrying it. Ain't nothing sorrowful I know of, except the Prohi's have found Philbin's still."

Doc said, "Don't talk about such little accidents at a time like this. You don't mean you ain't heerd about Benny?"

The bunch was there and they all perked up, interested. They knowed if it was Uncle Benny, they could expect 'most any news.

I said, "We ain't heerd a word since he went off to the west coast."

"You ain't heerd about him going crazy?"

I said, "Doc, you mean being crazy. He's always been that-a-way."

"I mean being crazy and going crazy, pore ol' Benny Mathers has gone really cold-out crazy."

Well, we all just looked at him and we looked at one another. And it came over the whole bunch of us that we weren't surprised. A nigger setting by the free air hose said, "Do, Jesus!" and eased away to tell the others.

Doc blew his nose and wiped his eyes and he said, "I'm sure we all forgive the pore ol' feller all the things he done. He wasn't responsible. I feel mighty bad, to think the hard way I've often spoke to him."

Will asked, "How come it to finally happen?"

Doc said, "He'd been up to some foolishness all night, raring through some of them Gulf coast flat-woods. Him and the fellers he was camping with was setting on the steps of the camp-house after breakfast. All of a sudden Uncle Benny goes to whistling, loud and shrill like a jay-bird. Then he says, 'I'm Sampson,' and he begun to tear down the camp-house."

Will asked, "What'd they do with him?"

Doc said, "You really ain't heerd? I declare, I can't believe the news has come so slow. They had a terrible time holding him and tying him. They got in the doctors and the sheriff and they takened pore ol' Uncle Benny to the lunatic asylum at Chattahoochie."

Doc wiped his eyes and we all begun to sniffle and our eyes to burn. I declare, it was just as if Uncle Benny Mathers had died on us.

I said, "Oh, his pore wife—"

Will said, "We'll have to be good to him and go see him and take him cigarettes and maybe slip him a pint of 'shine now and again."

I said, "The way he loved his freedom—shutting him up in the crazy-house will be like putting a wild-cat in a crocus sack."

Doc said, "Oh, he ain't in the asylum right now. He's broke loose.

That's what makes me feel so bad. He's headed this way, and no telling the harm he'll do before he's ketched again."

Everybody jumped up and begun feeling in their hip pockets for their guns.

Doc said, "No use to try to put no guns on him. He's got his'n and they say he's shooting just as accurate as ever."

That was enough for me. I ran back of the counter at the garage and begun locking up.

I said, "Doc, you're a sight. 'Tain't no time to go to feeling sorry for Uncle Benny and our lives and property in danger."

Doc said, "I know, but I knowed him so long and I knowed him so good. I can't help feeling bad about it."

I said, "Do something about it. Don't just set there, and him liable to come shooting his way in any minute."

Doc said, "I know, but what can anybody do to stop him? Pore man, with all them deputies after him."

Will said, "Deputies?"

Doc said, "Why, yes. The sheriff at Ocala asked me would I stop along the road and leave word for all the deputies to try and ketch him. Pore ol' Benny, I'll swear. I hated doing it the worst way."

I scooped the money out of the cash register and I told them, "Now, men, I'm leaving. I've put up with Uncle Benny Mathers when he was drunk and I've put up with him when he was cutting the fool. But the reckless way he drives that Ford and the way he shoots a pistol, I ain't studying on messing up around him and him gone cold-out crazy."

Doc said, "Ain't a thing in the world would stop him when he goes by, and all them deputies after him, but a barricade acrost the road."

I said, "Then for goodness' sake, you sorry, low-down, no-account, varminty white men, tear down the wire fence around my chicken yard and fix Uncle Benny a barricade."

Doc said, "I just hated to suggest it."

Will said, "He'd slow down for the barricade and we could come in from behind and hem him in."

Doc said, "It'll be an awful thing to hem him in and have to see him sent back to Chattahoochie."

Will said, "I'll commence pulling out the posts and you-all can wind up the fencing."

They worked fast and I went out and looked up the road now and again to see if Uncle Benny was coming. Doc had stopped at the Standard filling-station on his way, to leave the news, and we could see the people there stirring around and going out to look, the same as we were doing. When we dragged the roll of wire fencing out into the road we hollered to them so they could see what we were doing and they all cheered and waved their hats. The word had spread, and the young uns begun traipsing barefooted down to the road, until some of their mammies ran down and cuffed them and hurried them back home out of the way of Uncle Benny. The men strung the fencing tight across the road between the garage on one side and our smoke-house on the other. They nailed it firm at both ends.

Doc said, "Leave me drive the last nail, men—it may be the last thing I can do for Benny this side of Chattahoochie."

I talked the men into unloading their guns.

"He'll have to stop when he sees the barricade," I said, "and then you can all go in on him with your guns drawed and capture him. I just can't hear to a loaded gun being drawed on him, for fear of some-body getting excited and shooting him."

Doc wiped the sweat off his forehead and he said, "Men, this is a mighty serious occasion. I'd be mighty proud if you'd all have a little snort on me," and he passed the bottle.

"Here's to Uncle Benny, the way we all knowed him before he went cold-out crazy," he said.

And then we heerd a shouting up the dirt road and young uns whistling and women and girls screaming and chickens scattering.

"Yonder comes Uncle Benny!"

And yonder he came.

The Model-T was swooping down like a bull-bat after a mosquito. The water was boiling up out of the radiator in a foot-high stream. The seven pieded bird-dogs were hanging out of the back seat and trembling as if they craved to tell the things they'd seen. And behind Uncle Benny was a string of deputy sheriffs in Fords and Chevrolets and motorcycles that had gathered together from every town between Oak Bluff and Ocala. And Uncle Benny was hunched over the steering wheel with them two tufts of goat-horn hair sticking up in the breeze —and the minute I laid eyes on him I knowed he wasn't one mite crazier than he ever had been. I knowed right then Doc had laid out to get even with him and had lied on him all the way down the road.

It was too late then. I knowed, whatever happened, there'd be peo-ple to the end of his life would always believe it. I knowed there'd be young uns running from him and niggers hiding. And I knowed there wasn't a thing in the world now could keep him out of Chat-tahoochie for the time being. I knowed he'd fight when he was taken, and all them mad and hot and dusty deputies would get him to the lunatic asylum quicker than a black snake can cross hot ashes. And once a man that has cut the fool all his life, like Uncle Benny, is in the crazy-house, there'll be plenty of folks to say to keep him there.

It was too late. Uncle Benny was bearing down toward the garage and right in front of him was the barricade.

Doc hollered, "Be ready to jump on him when he stops!"

Stop? Uncle Benny stop? He kept right on coming. The sight of that chicken-wire barricade was no more to him than an aggravation. Uncle Benny and the Model-T dived into the barricade like a water-turkey into a pool. The barricade held. And the next thing we knowed, the Ford had somersaulted over the fencing and crumpled up like a paper shoe-box and scattered bird-dogs over ten acres and laid Uncle Benny in a heap over against the wall of the smoke-house. I was raised to use the language of a lady, but I could hold in.

"Doc," I said, "you low-down son of a ——"

He said, "Mis' Dover, the name's too good. I've killed my friend."

Killed him? Killed Uncle Benny? It can't be done until the Almighty Hisself hollers "Sooey!" Uncle Benny was messed up considerable, but him nor none of the bird-dogs was dead.

The doctor took a few stitches in him at the garage before he come to, and tied up his head right pretty in a white bandage. We left Will to quiet the deputies and we put Uncle Benny in Doc's car and carried him home to the Old Hen. Naturally, I figured it would set her to quarrelling. Instead, it just brought out all her sweetness. I can guess a man, but I can't guess another woman.

"The pore ol' feller," she said. "I knowed he had it coming to him. What the devil throws over his back—— I knowed he'd kill hisself in that Ford car, cutting the fool and prowling. The biggest load is off my mind. Now," she said, "now, by God's mercy, when it did come to him he got out alive."

She begun fanning him with a palmetto fan where he lay on the bed, and Doc poured out a drink of 'shine to have ready for him when he come to. Doc's hand was trembling. Uncle Benny opened his eyes. He eased one hand up to the bandage across his head and he groaned and grunted. He looked at Doc as if he couldn't make up his mind whether or not to reach for his pistol. Doc put the 'shine to his mouth and Uncle Benny swallowed. Them wicked blue eyes begun to dance.

"Doc," he said, "how will I get home when I'm drunk, now you've tore up my trained Ford?"

Doc broke down and cried like a little baby.

"I ain't got the money to replace it," he said, "but I'll give you my car. I'll carry the Little Giant line of remedies on foot."

Uncle Benny said, "I don't want your car. It ain't trained."

Doc said, "Then I'll tote you on my back, anywheres you say."

The Old Hen let in the bird-dogs, some of them limping a little, and they climbed on the bed and beat their tails on the counterpane and licked Uncle Benny. We felt mighty relieved things had come out that way.

Uncle Benny was up and around in a few days, with his head bandaged, and him as pert as a woodpecker. He just about owned Oak Bluff—all except the people that did like I figured, never did get over the idea he'd gone really crazy. Most people figured he'd had a mighty good lesson and it would learn him not to cut the fool. The Old Hen was as happy as a bride. She was so proud to have the Ford torn up, and no money to get another, that she'd even now and again pet one of the bird-dogs. She waited on Uncle Benny hand and foot and couldn't do enough to please him.

She said to me, "The pore ol' feller sure stays home nights now."

Stay home? Uncle Benny stay home? Two weeks after the accident the wreck of the Model-T disappeared from behind the garage where Will had dragged it. The next day the seven bird-dogs disappeared. The day after that Doc and Uncle Benny went to Ocala in Doc's car. Will wouldn't answer me when I asked him questions. The Old Hen stopped by the garage and got a Coca-Cola and she didn't know any more than I did. Then Will pointed down the road.

He said, "Yonder he comes."

And yonder he came. You could tell him way off by the white bandage with the tufts of hair sticking up over it. He was scrooched down behind the wheel of what looked like a brand-new automobile. Doc was following behind him. They swooped into the garage.

Will said, "It's a new second-hand body put on the chassis and around the engine of the old Ford."

Uncle Benny got out and he greeted us.

He said, "Will, it's just possible it was the motor of the Model-T that had takened the training. The motor ain't hurt, and me and Doc are real hopeful."

The Old Hen said, "Benny, where'd you get the money to pay for it?"

He said, "Why, a daggone bootlegger in a truck going from Miami to New York bought the bird-dogs for twenty-five dollars apiece. The low-down rascal knowed good and well they was worth seventy-five."

She brightened some. Getting shut of the bird-dogs was a little progress. She walked over to the car and begun looking around it.

"Benny," she said, and her voice come kind of faintified, "if you sold the bird-dogs, what's this place back here looks like it was fixed for 'em?"

We all looked, and here was a open compartment-like in the back, fixed up with seven crocus sacks stuffed with corn shucks. About that time here come a cloud of dust down the road. It was the seven bird-dogs. They were about give out. Their tongues were hanging out and their feet looked blistered.

Uncle Benny said, "I knowed they'd jump out of that bootlegger's truck. I told him so."

I tell you, what's in a man's nature you can't change. It takened the Old Hen thirty years and all them goings-on to learn it. She went and climbed in the front seat of the car and just sat there waiting for Uncle Benny to drive home for his dinner. He lifted the bird-dogs up and set them down to rest on the corn-shucks cushions, and he brought them a pan of water.

He said, "I figure they busted loose just about Lawtey."

The Old Hen never opened her mouth. She hasn't quarrelled at him from that day to this. She was hornswoggled.

Joel Chandler Harris

THE WONDERFUL TAR BABY

ONE evening recently, the lady whom Uncle Remus calls "Miss Sally" missed her little seven-year-old boy. Making search for him through the house and through the yard, she heard the sound of voices in the old man's cabin, and, looking through the window, saw the child sitting by Uncle Remus. His head rested against the old man's arm, and he was gazing with an expression of the most intense interest into the rough, weather-beaten face, that beamed so kindly upon him. This is what "Miss Sally" heard:

From *Uncle Remus, His Songs and His Sayings.*

"Bimeby, one day, arter Brer Fox bin doin' all dat he could fer ter ketch Brer Rabbit, en Brer Rabbit bin doin' all he could fer ter keep 'im fum it, Brer Fox say to hisse'f dat he'd put up a game on Brer Rabbit, en he ain't mo'n got de wuds out'n his mouf twel Brer Rabbit come a lopin' up de big road, lookin' des ez plump, en ez fat, en ez sassy ez a Moggin hoss in a barley-patch.

" 'Hol' on dar, Brer Rabbit,' sez Brer Fox, sezee.

" 'I ain't got time, Brer Fox,' sez Brer Rabbit, sezee, sorter mendin' his licks.

" 'I wanter have some confab wid you, Brer Rabbit,' sez Brer Fox, sezee.

" 'All right, Brer Fox, but you better holler fum whar you stan'. I'm monstus full er fleas dis mawnin',' sez Brer Rabbit, sezee.

" 'I seed Brer B'ar yistiddy,' sez Brer Fox, sezee, 'en he sorter rake me over de coals kaze you en me ain't make frens en live naberly, en I told 'im dat I'd see you.'

"Den Brer Rabbit scratch one year wid his off hinefoot sorter jub'usly, en den he ups en sez, sezee:

" 'All a settin', Brer Fox. Spose'n you drap roun' ter-morrer en take dinner wid me. We ain't got no great doin's at our house, but I speck de old 'oman en de chilluns kin sorter scramble roun' en git up sump'n fer ter stay yo stummuck.'

" 'I'm 'gree'ble, Brer Rabbit,' sez Brer Fox, sezee.

" 'Den I'll 'pen' on you,' sez Brer Rabbit, sezee.

"Nex' day, Mr. Rabbit en Miss Rabbit got up soon, 'fo' day, en raided on a gyarden like Miss Sally's out dar, en got some cabbiges, en some roas'n years, en some sparrer-grass, en dey fix up a smashin' dinner. Bimeby one er de little Rabbits, playin' out in de backyard, come runnin' in hollerin', 'Oh, ma! oh, ma! I seed Mr. Fox a comin'!' En den Brer Rabbit he tuck de chilluns by der years en make um set down, en den him and Miss Rabbit sorter dally roun' waitin' for Brer Fox. En dey keep on waitin', but no Brer Fox ain't come. Atter 'while Brer Rabbit goes to de do', easy like, an peep out, en dar, stickin' fum behime de cornder, wuz de tip-een' er Brer Fox tail. Den Brer Rabbit shot de do' en sot down, en put his paws behime his years en begin fer ter sing:

> " 'De place wharbouts you spill de grease,
> Right dar youer boun' ter slide,
> An' whar you fine a bunch er ha'r,
> You'll sholy fine de hide.'

"Nex' day, Brer Fox sont word by Mr. Mink, en skuze hisse'f kaze he wuz too sick fer ter come, en he ax Brer Rabbit fer ter come en take dinner wid him, en Brer Rabbit say he wuz 'gree'ble.

"Bimeby, w'en de shadders wuz at der shortes', Brer Rabbit he sorter brush up en saunter down ter Brer Fox's house, en w'en he got dar, he hear somebody groanin', en he look in de do' en dar he see Brer Fox settin' up in a rockin' cheer all wrop up wid flannil, en he look mighty weak. Brer Rabbit look all 'roun', he did, but he ain't see no dinner. De dish-pan wuz settin' on de table, en close by wuz a kyarvin' knife.

"'Look like you gwineter have chicken fer dinner, Brer Fox,' sez Brer Rabbit, sezee.

"'Yes, Brer Rabbit, deyer nice, en fresh, en tender,' sez Brer Fox, sezee.

"Den Brer Rabbit sorter pull his mustarsh, en say: 'You ain't got no calamus root, is you, Brer Fox? I done got so now dat I can't eat no chicken 'ceppin she's seasoned up wid calamus root.' En wid dat Brer Rabbit lipt out er de do' and dodge 'mong de bushes, en sot dar watchin' fer Brer Fox; en he ain't watch long, nudder, kaze Brer Fox flung off de flannil en crope out er de house en got whar he could cloze in on Brer Rabbit, en bimeby Brer Rabbit holler out: 'Oh, Brer Fox! I'll des put yo' calamus root out yer on dish yer stump. Better come git it while hit's fresh,' and wid dat Brer Rabbit gallop off home. En Brer Fox ain't never kotch 'im yet, en w'at's mo', honey, he ain't gwineter."

II

"Didn't the fox *never* catch the rabbit, Uncle Remus?" asked the little boy the next evening.

"He come mighty nigh it, honey, sho's you born—Brer Fox did. One day atter Brer Rabbit fool 'im wid dat calamus root, Brer Fox went ter wuk en got 'im some tar, en mix it wid some turkentime, en fix up a contrapshun wat he call a Tar-Baby, en he tuck dish yer Tar-Baby en he sot 'er in de big road, en den he lay off in de bushes fer to see wat de news wuz gwineter be. En he didn't hatter wait long, nudder, kaze bimeby here come Brer Rabbit pacin' down de road—lippity-clippity, clippity-lippity—dez ez sassy ez a jay-bird. Brer Fox, he lay low. Brer Rabbit come prancin' 'long twel he spy de Tar-Baby, en den he fotch up on his behime legs like he wuz 'stonished. De Tar-Baby, she sot dar, she did, en Brer Fox, he lay low.

" 'Mawnin'!' sez Brer Rabbit, sezee—'nice wedder dis mawnin',' sezee.

"Tar-Baby ain't sayin' nothin', en Brer Fox, he lay low.

" 'How duz yo' sym'tums seem ter segashuate?' sez Brer Rabbit, sezee.

"Brer Fox, he wink his eye slow, en lay low, en de Tar-Baby, she ain't sayin' nothin'.

" 'How you come on, den? Is you deaf?' sez Brer Rabbit, sezee. 'Kaze if you is, I kin holler louder,' sezee.

"Tar-Baby stay still, en Brer Fox, he lay low.

" 'Youer stuck up, dat's w'at you is,' says Brer Rabbit, sezee, 'en I'm gwineter kyore you, dat's w'at I'm a gwineter do,' sezee.

"Brer Fox, he sorter chuckle in his stummuck, he did, but Tar-Baby ain't sayin' nothin'.

" 'I'm gwineter larn you howter talk ter 'specttubble fokes ef hit's de las' ack,' sez Brer Rabbit, sezee. 'Ef you don't take off dat hat en tell me howdy, I'm gwineter bus' you wide open,' sezee.

"Tar-Baby stay still, en Brer Fox, he lay low.

"Brer Rabbit keep on axin' 'im, en de Tar-Baby, she keep on sayin' nothin', twel present'y Brer Rabbit draw back wid his fis', he did, en blip he tuck 'er side er de head. Right dar's whar he broke his merlasse jug. His fis' stuck, en he can't pull loose. De tar hilt 'im. But Tar-Baby she stay still, en Brer Fox, he lay low.

" 'Ef you don't lemme loose, I'll knock you agin,' sez Brer Rabbit, sezee, en wid dat he fotch 'er a wipe wid de udder han', en dat stuck. Tar-Baby, she ain't sayin' nothin', en Brer Fox, he lay low.

" 'Tu'n me loose fo' I kick de natal stuffin' outen you,' sez Brer Rabbit, sezee, but de Tar-Baby, she ain't sayin' nothin'. She des hilt on, en den Brer Rabbit lose de use er his feet in de same way. Brer Fox, he lay low. Den Brer Rabbit squall out dat ef de Tar-Baby don't tu'n 'im loose he butt 'er cranksided. En den he butted, en his head got stuck. Den Brer Fox, he sa'ntered fort', lookin' des ez innercent ez one er yo' mammy's mockin'-birds.

" 'Howdy, Brer Rabbit,' sez Brer Fox, sezee. 'You look sorter stuck up dis mawnin',' sezee, en den he rolled on de groun', en laughed en laughed twel he couldn't laugh no mo'. 'I speck you'll take dinner wid me dis time, Brer Rabbit. I done laid in some calamus root, en I ain't gwineter take no skuse,' sez Brer Fox, sezee."

Here Uncle Remus paused, and drew a two-pound yam out of the ashes.

"Did the fox eat the rabbit?" asked the little boy to whom the story had been told.

"Dat's all de fur de tale goes," replied the old man. "He mout, en den agin he moutent. Some say Jedge B'ar come 'long en loosed 'im— some say he didn't. I hear Miss Sally callin'. You better run 'long."

III

"Uncle Remus," said the little boy one evening, when he had found the old man with little or nothing to do, "did the fox kill and eat the rabbit when he caught him with the Tar-Baby?"

"Law, honey, ain't I tell you 'bout dat?" replied the old darkey, chuckling slyly. "I 'clar ter grashus I ought er tole you dat, but old man Nod wuz ridin' on my eyeleds twel a leetle mo'n I'd a dis'member'd my own name, en den on to dat here come yo' mammy hollerin' atter you.

"W'at I tell you w'en I fus' begin? I tole you Brer Rabbit wuz a monstus soon creetur; leas'ways dat's w'at I laid out fer ter tell you. Well, den, honey, don't you go en make no udder calkalashuns, kaze in dem days Brer Rabbit en his fambly wuz at de head er de gang w'en enny racket wuz on han', en dar de stayed. 'Fo' you begins fer ter wipe yo' eyes 'bout Brer Rabbit, you wait en see whar'bouts Brer Rabbit gwineter fetch up at. But dat's needer yer ner dar.

"W'en Brer Fox fine Brer Rabbit mixt up wid de Tar-Baby, he feel mighty good, en he roll on de ground 'en laff. Bimeby he up'n sez, sezee:

"'Well, I speck I got you dis time, Brer Rabbit,' sezee; 'maybe I ain't, but I speck I is. You been runnin' roun' here sassin' atter me a mighty long time, but I speck you done come ter de een' er de row. You bin cuttin' up yo' capers en bouncin' 'roun' in dis neighberhood ontwel you come ter b'leeve yo'se'f de boss er de whole gang. En den youer allers some'rs whar you got no bizness,' sez Brer Fox, sezee. 'Who ax you fer ter come en strike up a 'quaintance wid dish yer Tar-Baby? En who stuck you up dar whar you iz? Nobody in de roun' worril. You des tuck en jam yo'se'f on dat Tar-Baby widout waitin' fer enny invite,' sez Brer Fox, sezee, 'en dar you is, en dar you'll stay twel I fixes up a bresh-pile and fires her up, kaze I'm gwineter bobby-cue you dis day, sho,' sez Brer Fox, sezee.

"Den Brer Rabbit talk mighty 'umble.

"'I don't keer w'at you do wid me, Brer Fox,' sezee, 'so you don't fling me in dat brier-patch. Roas' me, Brer Fox,' sezee, 'but don't fling me in dat brier-patch,' sezee.

" 'Hit's so much trouble fer ter kindle a fier,' sez Brer Fox, sezee, 'dat I speck I'll hatter hang you,' sezee.

" 'Hang me des ez high as you please, Brer Fox,' sez Brer Rabbit, sezee, 'but do fer de Lord's sake don't fling me in dat brier-patch,' sezee.

" 'I ain't got no string,' sez Brer Fox, sezee, 'en now I speck I'll hatter drown you,' sezee.

" 'Drown me des ez deep ez you please, Brer Fox,' sez Brer Rabbit, sezee, 'but do don't fling me in dat brier-patch,' sezee.

" 'Der ain't no water nigh,' sez Brer Fox, sezee, 'en now I speck I'll hatter skin you,' sezee.

" 'Skin me, Brer Fox,' sez Brer Rabbit, sezee, 'snatch out my eyeballs, t'ar out my years by de roots, en cut off my legs,' sezee, 'but do please, Brer Fox, don't fling me in dat brier-patch,' sezee.

"Co'se Brer Fox wanter hurt Brer Rabbit bad ez he kin, so he cotch 'im by de behime legs en slung 'im right in de middle er de brier-patch. Dar wuz a considerbul flutter whar Brer Rabbit struck de bushes, en Brer Fox sorter hang 'roun' fer ter see w'at wuz gwineter happen. Bimeby he hear somebody call 'im, en way up de hill he see Brer Rabbit settin' cross-legged on a chinkapin log koamin' de pitch outen his har wid a chip. Den Brer Fox know dat he bin swop off mighty bad. Brer Rabbit wuz bleedzed fer ter fling back some er his sass, en he holler out:

" 'Bred en bawn in a brier-patch, Brer Fox—bred en bawn in a brier-patch!' en wid dat he skip out des ez lively ez a cricket in de embers."

Mark Twain

JOURNALISM IN TENNESSEE

The editor of the Memphis *Avalanche* swoops thus mildly down upon a correspondent who posted him as a Radical:—"While he was writing the first word, the middle, dotting his i's, crossing his t's, and punching his period, he knew he was concocting a sentence that was saturated with infamy and reeking with falsehood."—*Exchange*.

I WAS told by the physician that a Southern climate would improve my health, and so I went down to Tennessee, and got a berth on the *Morning Glory and Johnson County War-Whoop* as associate editor. When I went on duty I found the chief editor sitting tilted back in a three-legged chair with his feet on a pine table. There was another pine table in the room and another afflicted chair, and both were half buried under newspapers and scraps and sheets of manuscript. There was a wooden box of sand, sprinkled with cigar stubs and "old soldiers," and a stove with a door hanging by its upper hinge. The chief editor had a long-tailed black cloth frock coat on, and white linen pants. His boots were small and neatly blacked. He wore a ruffled shirt, a large seal ring, a standing collar of obsolete pattern, and a checkered neckerchief with the ends hanging down. Date of costume about 1848. He was smoking a cigar, and trying to think of a word, and in pawing his hair he had rumpled his locks a good deal. He was scowling fearfully, and I judged that he was concocting a particularly knotty editorial. He told me to take the exchanges and skim through them and write up the "Spirit of the Tennessee Press," condensing into the article all of their contents that seemed of interest.

I wrote as follows:—

"SPIRIT OF THE TENNESSEE PRESS.

"The editors of the *Semi-Weekly Earthquake* evidently labor under a misapprehension with regard to the Ballyhack railroad. It is not the object of the company to leave Buzzardville off to one side. On the contrary,

From *Sketches New and Old*. Reprinted by permission of Harper & Brothers.

they consider it one of the most important points along the line, and consequently can have no desire to slight it. The gentlemen of the *Earthquake* will, of course, take pleasure in making the correction.

"John W. Blossom, Esq., the able editor of the Higginsville *Thunderbolt and Battle Cry of Freedom*, arrived in the city yesterday. He is stopping at the Van Buren House.

"We observe that our contemporary of the Mud Springs *Morning Howl* has fallen into the error of supposing that the election of Van Werter is not an established fact, but he will have discovered his mistake before this reminder reaches him, no doubt. He was doubtless misled by incomplete election returns.

"It is pleasant to note that the city of Blathersville is endeavoring to contract with some New York gentlemen to pave its well-nigh impassable streets with the Nicholson pavement. The *Daily Hurrah* urges the measure with ability, and seems confident of ultimate success."

I passed my manuscript over to the chief editor for acceptance, alteration, or destruction. He glanced at it and his face clouded. He ran his eye down the pages, and his countenance grew portentous. It was easy to see that something was wrong. Presently he sprang up and said—

"Thunder and lightning! Do you suppose I am going to speak of those cattle that way? Do you suppose my subscribers are going to stand such gruel as that? Give me the pen!"

I never saw a pen scrape and scratch its way so viciously, or plough through another man's verbs and adjectives so relentlessly. While he was in the midst of his work, somebody shot at him through the open window, and marred the symmetry of my ear.

"Ah," said he, "that is that scoundrel Smith, of the *Moral Volcano* —he was due yesterday." And he snatched a navy revolver from his belt and fired. Smith dropped, shot in the thigh. The shot spoiled Smith's aim, who was just taking a second chance, and he crippled a stranger. It was me. Merely a finger shot off.

Then the chief editor went on with his erasures and interlineations. Just as he finished them a hand-grenade came down the stove pipe, and the explosion shivered the stove into a thousand fragments. However, it did no further damage, except that a vagrant piece knocked a couple of my teeth out.

"That stove is utterly ruined," said the chief editor.

I said I believed it was.

"Well, no matter—don't want it this kind of weather. I know the man that did it. I'll get him. Now, *here* is the way this stuff ought to be written."

I took the manuscript. It was scarred with erasures and interlineations till its mother wouldn't have known it if it had had one. It now read as follows:—

"SPIRIT OF THE TENNESSEE PRESS.

"The inveterate liars of the *Semi-Weekly Earthquake* are evidently endeavoring to palm off upon a noble and chivalrous people another of their vile and brutal falsehoods with regard to that most glorious conception of the nineteenth century, the Ballyhack railroad. The idea that Buzzardville was to be left off at one side originated in their own fulsome brains—or rather in the settlings which *they* regard as brains. They had better swallow this lie if they want to save their abandoned reptile carcasses the cowhiding they so richly deserve.

"That ass, Blossom, of the Higginsville *Thunderbolt and Battle Cry of Freedom*, is down here again sponging at the Van Buren.

"We observe that the besotted blackguard of the Mud Spring *Morning Howl* is giving out, with its usual propensity for lying, that Van Werter is not elected. The heaven-born mission of journalism is to disseminate truth; to eradicate error; to educate, refine and elevate the tone of public morals and manners, and make all men more gentle, more virtuous, more charitable, and in all ways better, and holier, and happier; and yet this black-hearted scoundrel degrades his great office persistently to the dissemination of falsehood, calumny, vituperation, and vulgarity.

"Blathersville wants a Nicholson pavement—it wants a jail and poor-house more. The idea of a pavement in a one horse town composed of two gin mills, a blacksmith's shop, and that mustard-plaster of a newspaper, the *Daily Hurrah!* The crawling insect, Buckner, who edits the *Hurrah*, is braying about this business with his customary imbecility, and imagining that he is talking sense."

"Now *that* is the way to write—peppery and to the point. Mush-and-milk journalism gives me the fantods."

About this time a brick came through the window with a splintering crash, and gave me a considerable of a jolt in the back. I moved out of range—I began to feel in the way.

The chief said, "That was the Colonel, likely. I've been expecting him for two days. He will be up, now, right away."

He was correct. The Colonel appeared in the door a moment afterward with a dragoon revolver in his hand.

He said, "Sir, have I the honor of addressing the poltroon who edits this mangy sheet?"

"You have. Be seated, sir. Be careful of the chair, one of its legs is gone. I believe I have the honor of addressing the putrid liar, Col. Blatherskite Tecumseh?"

"Right, sir. I have a little account to settle with you. If you are at leisure we will begin."

"I have an article on the 'Encouraging Progress of Moral and Intellectual Development in America' to finish, but there is no hurry. Begin."

Both pistols rang out their fierce clamor at the same instant. The chief lost a lock of his hair, and the Colonel's bullet ended its career in the fleshy part of my thigh. The Colonel's left shoulder was clipped a little. They fired again. Both missed their men this time, but I got my share, a shot in the arm. At the third fire both gentlemen were wounded slightly, and I had a knuckle chipped. I then said, I believed I would go out and take a walk, as this was a private matter, and I had a delicacy about participating in it further. But both gentlemen begged me to keep my seat, and assured me that I was not in the way.

They then talked about the elections and the crops while they reloaded, and I fell to tying up my wounds. But presently they opened fire again with animation, and every shot took effect—but it is proper to remark that five out of the six fell to my share. The sixth one mortally wounded the Colonel, who remarked, with fine humor, that he would have to say good morning now, as he had business up town. He then inquired the way to the undertaker's and left.

The chief turned to me and said, "I am expecting company to dinner, and shall have to get ready. It will be a favor to me if you will read proof and attend to the customers."

I winced a little at the idea of attending to the customers, but I was too bewildered by the fusilade that was still ringing in my ears to think of anything to say.

He continued, "Jones will be here at 3—cowhide him. Gillespie will call earlier, perhaps—throw him out of the window. Ferguson will be along about 4—kill him. That is all for today, I believe. If you have any odd time, you may write a blistering article on the police—give the Chief Inspector rats. The cowhides are under the table; weapons in the drawer—ammunition there in the corner—lint and bandages up there in the pigeon-holes. In case of accident, go to Lancet, the surgeon, down-stairs. He advertises—we take it out in trade."

He was gone. I shuddered. At the end of the next three hours I had been through perils so awful that all peace of mind and all cheerfulness were gone from me. Gillespie had called and thrown *me* out of the window. Jones arrived promptly, and when I got ready to do the cowhiding he took the job off my hands. In an encounter with a stranger, not in the bill of fare, I had lost my scalp. Another stranger, by the name of Thompson, left me a mere wreck and ruin of chaotic rags. And at last, at bay in the corner, and beset by an infuriated mob of editors, blacklegs, politicians, and desperadoes, who raved and swore and flourished their weapons about my head till the air shimmered with glancing flashes of steel, I was in the act of resigning my berth on the paper when the chief arrived, and with him a rabble of charmed and enthusiastic friends. Then ensued a scene of riot and carnage such as no human pen, or steel one either, could describe. People were shot, probed, dismembered, blown up, thrown out of the window. There was a brief tornado of murky blasphemy, with a confused and frantic war-dance glimmering through it, and then all was over. In five minutes there was silence, and the gory chief and I sat alone and surveyed the sanguinary ruin that strewed the floor around us.

He said, "You'll like this place when you get used to it."

I said, "I'll have to get you to excuse me; I think maybe I might write to suit you after a while; as soon as I had had some practice and learned the language I am confident I could. But, to speak the plain truth, that sort of energy of expression has its inconveniences, and a man is liable to interruptions. You see that yourself. Vigorous writing is calculated to elevate the public, no doubt, but, then I do not like to attract so much attention as it calls forth. I can't write with comfort when I am interrupted so much as I have been today. I like this berth well enough, but I don't like to be left here to wait on the customers. The experiences are novel, I grant you, and entertaining too, after a fashion, but they are not judiciously distributed. A gentleman shoots at you through the window and cripples *me*; a bomb shell comes down the stove-pipe for your gratification and sends the stove-door down *my* throat; a friend drops in to swap compliments with you, and freckles *me* with bullet-holes till my skin won't hold my principles; you go to dinner, and Jones comes with his cowhide, Gillespie throws me out of the window, Thompson tears all my clothes off, and an entire stranger takes my scalp with the easy freedom of an old acquaintance; and in less than five minutes all the blackguards in the country arrive in their war-paint, and proceed to scare the rest of me to death with their tomahawks. Take it altogether, I never had such a spirited time in all my life as I have had today. No; I like you, and I like your calm unruffled way of explaining things to the customers, but you see I am not used to it. The Southern heart is too impulsive; Southern hospitality is too lavish with the stranger. The paragraphs which I have written today, and into whose cold sentences your masterly hand has infused the fervent spirit of Tennessean journalism, will wake up another nest of hornets. All that mob of editors will come—and they will come hungry, too, and want somebody for breakfast. I shall have to bid you adieu. I decline to be present at these festivities. I came South for my health, I will go back on the same errand, and suddenly. Tennessean journalism is too stirring for me."

After which we parted with mutual regret, and I took apartments at the hospital.

Roark Bradford

EXCERPTS FROM
OL' MAN ADAM AN' HIS CHILLUN

EVE AND THAT SNAKE

WELL, a long time ago things was diffrunt. Hit wa'n't nothin' on de yearth 'cause hit wa'n't no yearth. And hit wa'n't nothin' nowheres and ev'y day was Sunday. Wid de Lawd r'ared back preachin' all day long ev'y day. 'Ceptin' on Sadday, and den ev'ybody went to de fish fry.

So one day ev'ybody was out to de fish fry, eatin' fish and b'iled custard and carryin' on, to all at once de Lawd swallowed some b'iled custard which didn't suit his tas'e.

"Dis custard," say de Lawd, "ain't seasoned right. Hit's too thick."

"Hit's got a heap of sugar and aigs and milk and things in hit, Lawd," say Gabriel.

"I know," say de Lawd, "but hit tas'es like hit needs jest a little bit more firmament in hit."

"Us ain't got no more firmament, Lawd," say Gabriel. "Us ain't got a drap in de jug."

"You been usin' a heap of firmament," say de Lawd. "Seem like ev'y time I come to a fish fry I got to create some more firmament. I bet

I'm gonter make enough dis time to last a month of Sundays. I'm sick and tired of passin' a miracle ev'y time I wants some firmament."

So de Lawd r'ared back and passed a miracle and say, "Let hit be some firmament. And when I say let hit be some firmament, I mean let hit be a whole heap of firmament. I'm sick and tired of lettin' hit be jest a little bitty dab of firmament when I pass a miracle."

And you jest ought to see de firmament! Hit jest sloshed all over ev'ything so de angels and cherubs couldn't hardly fly, and ev'ybody was standin' round, knee deep, shiverin' and chatterin' and squirmin' round.

"Well," say de mammy angel, "I guess I better git my cherubs and git on home and dry 'em out. They's shiverin' like they got a buck aguer, right now."

"Don't go bustin' up de fish fry jest 'cause de cherubs is wet," say de Lawd. "I'll dry 'em out."

So de Lawd passed another miracle and say, "Let hit be de sun to dry out deseyar cherubs." And dar was de sun. And de cherubs got dried, but quick as they got dried they got wet again, 'cause hit was so much firmament.

"Dis ain't gettin' us nowheres," say de Lawd. "Gabriel, maybe us men-folks better git out and ditch around some and dreen some of disyar firmament off."

"Good idea," say Gabriel, "only hit ain't no 'count, 'cause hit ain't no place to dreen hit off to."

"Well," say de Lawd, "I guess I got to pass another miracle and make a place to dreen hit off to. Hit look like when I git started passin' miracles hit's always somethin' else." So he r'ared back and passed a miracle and said, "Let hit be de yearth to hold dis firmament." And dar was de yearth.

Well, de firmament runned on de yearth, and hit runned in de rivers and creeks and ditches—'cause firmament wa'n't nothin' but a fancy name for water—and dar was de yearth wid de firmament dreened off and a heap of dry land left.

"Now looky what you done done, Lawd," say Gabriel. "Cou'se hit ain't none of my business, 'cause I got to practice on my hawn all time. But somebody got to go work dat land, 'cause you know good as me dat de land ain't gonter work hitself."

Well, de Lawd looked round to see who he gonter send to work his land, and all de angels was mighty busy. "Well," he say, "I guess I got pass one more miracle to git somebody to work dat land. And I bet de next time I pass a miracle for some firmament I bet I won't git so brash about hit."

So de Lawd got a handful of dirt and made hit in a ball and passed a miracle over hit and say, "Let dis dirt be mankind." And de dirt turn to a man.

De Lawd looked at de man and say, "What's yo' name, man?"

"Adam," say de man.

"Adam—which?" say de Lawd.

"Jest plain Adam," say de man.

"What's yo' family name?" say de Lawd.

"Ain't got no family," say Adam.

"Well," say de Lawd, "I got to change dat. I ain't gonter have none of deseyar single mens workin' on my farm. They runs around wid de women all night and come de next day they's too sleepy to work."

"I don't run around wid no women," say Adam. "I ain't studdin' de women."

"Yeah?" say de Lawd. "But I ain't gonter take no chances. Yo' heart might be all right now, but de first good-lookin' woman come along she gonter change yo' mind. So I'm jest gonter put you to sleep again."

So de Lawd put Adam to sleep and tuck out a rib and turned de rib into a woman name Eve. So when Adam woke up again, dar was Eve, stretched out by his side, wid her haid on his pillow.

"Where'd you come from, gal?" say Adam.

"No mind whar I come from," say Eve, "I's yar, ain't I?"

So Adam and Eve got married and settle down to raise a crop for de Lawd.

So ev'ything went along all right to summertime. Eve was out pickin' blackberries, and de Lawd come wawkin' down de road.

"Good mawnin', Sister Eve," say de Lawd. "Pickin' a few blackberries?"

"A few, Lawd," say Eve. "Adam 'lowed he'd like to has some for preserves next winter."

"Help yo'self," say de Lawd. "Put up all de blackberries you want. And peaches too. And plums, ef'n you and Adam likes 'em. Hit ain't but one thing which I don't want you to tech, and dat's de apple orchard. 'Cause from de news I yars, apples is kind of scarce and they ought to bring a good price next fall. So help yo'self to de berries and de peaches and things, but jest stay out of de apples."

Well, hit just goes to show you. Eve didn't like apples and Adam didn't too. But no quicker do de Lawd wawk on down de road to Eve see a great big highland moccasin crawlin' long twarg her.

"Look at dat scound'el," say Eve, and she pick up a rock. "I'm gonter mash his old haid quick as I gits a shot at him." So de snake crawls through de apple orchard fence, and Eve climbs over hit.

Well, Eve and dat snake went round and round. Eve was chunkin' at him and de snake was dodgin' to finally Eve got a clear shot at him and she r'ared back and let de big rock go.

Eve was all right, but she was a woman. And hit ain't never yit been a woman which could throw straight. So Eve missed de snake and hit de apple tree. And down come a big red apple, right in front of her.

"Well, I be doggone!" she say. "Look at dat apple!" So she stood and looked at hit a long time. "I didn't aim to knock hit down," she say, "but hit's down, now, and I can't put hit back. And does I let hit lay, de hawgs is gonter eat hit and hit's too purty for de hawgs to eat." So she tuck a bite.

"Don't taste like much," she say. "I wonder do Adam want to eat hit?" So she tuck de apple out to whar Adam was plowin' de cawn, and give hit to him.

"I don't like apples, gal," say Adam. "Whyn't you give me somethin' I like?"

"Cou'se you don't like apples," say Eve. "You don't never like nothin' I gives you. You got to think of hit yo'self before you likes hit," and Eve blubbers up and commences to cry.

"Aw, don't cry, sugar," say Adam. "I was jest funnin' wid you. I likes apples. Give me a bite."

"Nawp," say Eve. "You's jest mean, dat's what you is. You treats me mean 'cause I ain't nothin' but a poor little weak woman and you's a big, stout man. I ain't gonter give you nothin'."

"Aw, honey, don't tawk like dat," say Adam. "Dat ain't de way hit is, a-tall. I was jest playin' wid you. Give me a bite of apple and I buys you a new dress."

Well, when a man go to tawkin' new dresses to a woman he gonter git some action. So Eve dry up her cryin' and Adam et de apple and got her de dress. But dat wa'n't all.

De Lawd seed Eve's new dress and he found out all about hit. And he got mad, 'cause he didn't aim to have nobody on his place which stole his apples. So he bailed old Adam's trover and leveled on his crop and mule, and put Adam and Eve off'n de place. And de next news anybody yared of old Adam, he was down on de levee tryin' to git a job at six bits a day.

SIN

WELL, hit wa'n't long after de yearth got peopled to de people got to gittin' in devilment. And de more people hit got to be de more devilment they got in. And de more devilment they got in, de more chilluns dey'd have. To finally hit was so many people scattered round de place to you couldn't hardly wawk.

And mean? Mankind! They was about the triflin'est bunch of trash you ever run up against. Fust off, de menfolks quit workin' and went to shootin' craps for a livin'. Den de womenfolks quit takin' in washin' and used they kettles to make hard-drinkin' licker in. And de chilluns wouldn't mind they maws 'cause they maws was drunk, and hit wa'n't nothin' to see a boy in knee britches wawkin' round, chewin' tobacco and cussin' jest as mannish as his daddy!

Well, hit come to pass one Sunday mawnin' de Lawd was wawkin' de yearth and he seed a bunch of boys playin' marbles on de side of de road. He look and he seed a boy shoot a marble and knock two marbles out of de ring.

"Venture dubs," say de yuther little boy.

"I said 'dubs' first," say de marble-shooter. So they fit and fit and de marble-shootin' boy was gittin' licked, so he say, "Didn't I say 'dubs' first, Mister?" right at de Lawd.

"You don't know who you' tawkin' to, does you, son?" say de Lawd.

"Nawp," say de marble-shooter.

"You want to say 'nawsuh' when you tawkin' to me, 'cause I's de Lawd. And verily I done said unto you, 'Marble not,' and yar you is out yar marblin' on Sunday."

"You ain't my daddy," say de marble-shootin' boy, "and hit ain't none of yo' business what I does on Sunday or any yuther day."

So de Lawd wawked on down de road and he seed a young gal settin' out on a stump, pushin' de 'cordeen and singin' de "Lonesome Blues," jest like hit wa'n't Sunday.

"Gal, whyn't you quit dat singin' dem 'blues' and sing a church song?" say de Lawd. "Don't you know hit's Sunday?"

De gal kept right on singin' to she got done and den she looked at de Lawd and say, "Soap and water, Country Boy." And she went right on singin' again.

"Well, I be doggone," say de Lawd. "I never did see so much sin." So he wawked on down de road to he seed some men kneelin' down in de middle of de road.

"Dat looks better," say de Lawd. "Hit looks like de menfolks is quit they devilment and gone to prayin'. I'm gonter listen and see kin I hyar they prayers."

So he listened and he hyared one of 'em say, "Big Dick f'om Boston! Come on you six-Joe! Wham! Five and five! I shoots hit all!"

Well, de Lawd jest shet his eyes and wawked on. "I'm gonter go tell dat crap-shootin' scound'el's mammy on him right now," he say. "Shootin' craps on Sunday!" So de Lawd wawked on to where de crap-shootin' boy live at and he knock on de door.

"Who dar?" say a man in de house.

"No mind who yar," say de Lawd. "You jest unlatch dis door."

"You got a search warrant?" say de man. "'Cause ef'n you ain't you might jest as well go on about yo' business. 'Cause you can't git in dis house onless you got a search warrant."

"Well," say de Lawd, "jest tell Miz Rucker to come to de door whilst I tells her on her good-for-nothin' boy which is shootin' craps on Sunday."

"Miz Rucker ain't yar no more," say de man. "She runned off wid a railroad man, yistiddy."

"Well, send Rucker to de door, den," say de Lawd.

"Can't," say de man. "Rucker's piled up under de table. He been passed out since early dis mawnin'. I's de onliest sober man in de house 'cause I drunk some of dat new wildcat yistiddy, and hit burnt de skin off of my th'oat so I can't drink no more."

"Well," say de Lawd, "dis ain't gittin' me nowheres. Deseyar mankinds which I peopled my yearth wid sho ain't much. I got a good mind to wipe 'em off'n de yearth and people my yearth wid angels."

So de Lawd wawked on down de road, tawkin' to hisself and studdyin' 'bout what he gonter do wid de sin.

"Naw," he say, "angels is all right for singin' and playin' and flyin' round, but they ain't much on workin' de crops and buildin' de levees. I guess I won't monkey round wid de angels on my yearth. They jest won't do."

So he wawked along, studdyin' and a-tawkin'. "Mankind," he say, "is jest right for my yearth, ef'n he wa'n't so dad-blame sinful. But I'm sick and tired of his sin. I'd druther have my yearth peopled wid a bunch of channel catfish den mankind and his sin. I jest can't stand sin."

So about dat time de Lawd comed up on old man Noah, wawkin' long de road in a plug hat and a hammer-tail coat.

"Good mawnin', brother," say Noah. "Us missed you at church dis mawnin'."

"I ain't got no time to go to church," say de Lawd. "I got work——"

"Yeah," say Noah, "mighty nigh ev'ybody say they ain't got time to go to church dese days and times. Hit seems like de more I preaches de more people ain't got time to come to church. I ain't hardly got enough members to fill up de choir. I has to do de preachin' and de bassin', too."

"Is dat a fack?" say de Lawd.

"Yeah," say Noah. "Ev'ybody is mighty busy gamblin' and good-timin' and sinnin' and goin' on. They ain't got time to come to church. But you jest wait. When old Gabriel blows they hawn they gonter find plenty of time to punch chunks down yonder in hell. They gonter beg to git to come to church, too. But de Lawd ain't gonter pay 'em no mind. They makin' they own fun, now. But when old Gabriel toots, de Lawd gonter be de boss."

"Brother Noah," say de Lawd, "you don't know who I is, does you?"

"Lemme see," say Noah. "Yo' face looks easy. But I jest can't call de name. But I don't keer what yo' name is, you jest come along home wid me. I think de old lady kilt a chicken or so, and den, after us eats and rests up some, you comes wid me to preachin' again tonight."

"I don't keer ef I do," say de Lawd. "Dat chicken sounds mighty good to me. And you say you basses in de singin'?"

"Jest tries hit," say Noah. "I ain't so much on de bass as I is on de leadin'."

"I used to bass purty fair," say de Lawd.

So dey wawked on to Noah's house, and de Lawd didn't let on to Noah dat he wa'n't jest a natchal man like ev'ybody else. So dey r'ared back and et chicken and dumplin's awhile, and all at once de Lawd say, "Brother Noah, I kind of b'lieve hit's gonter rain."

"My cawns is burnin' me, too," say Noah. "Jest slip yo' feet outer yo' shoes and rest yo'self."

"What'd you do, did hit commence to rain, Noah?" say de Lawd.

"Well," say Noah, "I most gen'ally lets hit rain."

"S'posin'," say de Lawd, "hit would haul off and rain fawty days and fawty nights?"

"I ain't worryin'," say Noah. "In de fust place, hit ain't gonter rain dat long onless de Lawd sends hit. And in de second place, I's on de Lawd's side, and de Lawd gonter look after me do he go to monkeyin' wid de weather."

"You b'lieve de Lawd gonter look after you, does you?" say de Lawd.

"Don't b'lieve nothin' 'bout hit," say Noah. "I knows hit. I does de best I kin for de Lawd, and dat's all de Lawd gonter ax any man to do. I don't do much, but hit's de best I got."

So all at once de Lawd reach inside his shirt front and pull out his crown and set it on his haid. Den he start to tawk, and thunder and lightnin' come outer his mouf. So old Noah jest drap down on his knees.

"Yar I is, Lawd," he say. "Yar I is. I ain't much, but I'm de best I got."

"Noah," say de Lawd, "hit's gonter rain fawty days and fawty nights. And hit's gonter drown ev'ybody on de yearth which is a sinner. And dat means about ev'ybody but you and yo' family. Now you jest git out and build me a ark on dry land big enough to hold a pair of mules and a pair of cows and a pair of elephants and a pair of snakes and a pair of ev'ything which creeps or crawls, swims or flies. And you better make hit big enough to pack away a heap of grub, too, 'cause from what I got in mind, hit ain't gonter be no goin' to de commissary and buyin' grub when I starts rainin'."

"And snakes, too, Lawd?" say Noah.

"Snakes," say de Lawd.

"S'pos'n' a snake up and bit somebody?" say Noah.

"I hadn't thought about dat," say de Lawd. "Maybe you better not take no snakes."

"I ain't skeered of snakes," say Noah, "efn I got a kag of licker handy," say Noah.

"I ain't so much on de licker," say de Lawd. "But hit do come in handy round snakes."

"And wid all dat rain and wet weather, too," say Noah, "my phthisic is liable to plague me, too, onless I got a little hard licker handy."

"Well, you better put a kag of licker on boa'd, too," say de Lawd.

"Better put two kags," say Noah. "Hit'll help balance de boat. You git a kag on one side, and nothin' on de yuther, and de boat liable to turn over. You got to keep a boat balanced, Lawd."

"One kag," say de Lawd. "You kin set hit in de middle of de deck. One kag of licker is enough for anybody for fawty days and fawty nights. I said one kag, and dat's all you carries."

"Yas, Lawd," say Noah, "one kag."

The Wisdom of King Solomon

OLE KING DAVID was a king which liked to have a heap er chilluns runnin' round de house. And hit seem like ev'y one er his chillun wanted to be king. So 'bout de time one of 'em up and said he wanted to be de king 'cause he's de oldest, hit seem like a bunch of hard luck happened to him and he died. And den de next oldest boy on deck had some hard luck, and right on down de line. But hit was one er de boys name Solomon which ain't sayin' a word 'bout bein' de king. He jest went on and studied his books and kept his mouf shet.

"Dat boy Solomon," King David tole de Lawd one day, "is makin' some mighty good marks in school. He liable to grow up to be a lawyer some er dese days."

"Cou'se he's makin' good marks," say de Lawd. "Dat boy got a haid on him as long as a mule, right now, and efn he keeps hit up and don't go runnin' round wid de gals too much, I got somethin' in my mind about him."

So de yuther brothers kept fightin' 'mongst theyse'ves about which is gonter be king when David dies, so when David died Solomon up and put on de crown and de robe and he was king. And Solomon was a smart king, too.

Well, about de fust thing Solomon happened up against was two ladies fightin' over a baby which got mixed up in de hospital or somethin'.

"Dat's my young'n," say one er de ladies.

"Ain't no sich yo' young'n," say de yuther lady. So dey argyed and fought to finally ole King Solomon yared de news and he sont for de ladies to appear before him.

Well, Solomon sot back on de throne and looked at de baby and den he looked at de ladies. And den he looked back at de baby again.

"Well," he said, "f'm de way things looks to me, y'all ladies ain't got no call to raise no ruckus 'bout dis young'n. Y'll is bofe what I'd call good-lookin' ladies, now ain't you?" So bofe de ladies kinder giggled back at Solomon. "Yeah," say ole King Solomon, "y'll is what I call a couple of right purty gals. And I jest be doggone efn I kin see how purty gals like y'll kin go to scrappin' about dis bald-haided little ole brat which looks like a peeled onion in de face."

So one er de ladies kinder grinned and say, "Yo' Majesty, he ain't so turrible much to look at, now, is he?" But de yuther lady jest sot back and simmered and b'iled.

"Well, what you got to say?" King Solomon ax de yuther lady.

"Yo' Majesty," say de yuther lady, "you is de king and long may you wave. But scusin' dat, you ain't nothin' but a fresh little ole country boy wid a crown on yo' haid and nothin' in hit. Somebody tole me you was smart, and I bet de Lawd done struck 'em down right now for lyin'. You may be de king, but I bet de fust time you meet up wid de Fool Killer I bet hit's gonter be a big funeral and another king, 'long 'bout dat time. You's settin' on de throne wid yo' robe of purple wropped about you, actin' high and mighty, but you ain't foolin' me. I knows po' white trash when I sees 'em. And when I looks at you, I sho kin see 'em."

"You don't like me much, does you?" say ole King Solomon.

"I don't like you a-tall," say de yuther lady. "You don't know nothin' 'bout kingin' and you don't know nothin' 'bout babies. And you don't know nothin' 'bout nothin'. Come yar tellin' me dat dis purty little baby look like a peeled onion! Humph! You may be de king, but you looks like a goggled-eyed bullfrog peepin' through de ice, to me."

"Woman," say King Solomon, "does you mean to say you thinks disyar baby is sho-'nuff purty?"

"I don't think nothin' 'bout hit," say de yuther woman. "I knows hit."

"Dat settle de argyment, den," say ole King Solomon. "Any lady which kin stand flat-footed and say a nine-day-old baby is purty is bound to be de baby's maw. So take him and git."

And den ole King Solomon turn round and look at de yuther woman and say: "Looky yar, gal. What you mean by claimin' dat woman's baby? Don't you know hit's ag'in' de law to do dat? Hit look like to me you's tryin' to contempt my cou't."

"Naw, I ain't, Yo' Majesty," say de woman. "Hit jest seem like hit's gettin' to be de style dese days and times for ev'y lady to has a baby, and me, I'm so ugly I ain't even got me no husband yit."

"Who say you's ugly, gal?" say King Solomon.

"I said hit," say de lady.

"Well, I got purty good jedgment 'bout de womenfolks," say Solomon, "and I jedges you to be about de best-lookin' gal which is come into my cou't dis week. What's yo' name?"

"My name de Queen of Sheba," say de lady, "but most er my friends jest call me Sheba for shawt."

"Well, doggone my ole rusty hide!" say Solomon. "So you's Sheba, is you? I been yarin' 'bout how good-lookin' you is, and I be dog efn I don't believe hit now. Stand round dar in de light so My Majesty kin git a good look at you. Dad blame my skin! Gal, you's jest so purty you jest won't do!"

"You's kinder handsome yo' ownse'f, ole King Solomon," say de Queen of Sheba. "Most smart men like you is kinder ugly, but you sho ain't."

"Is dat a fack?" say King Solomon. So they sot dar and chinned awhile about de weather and de crops, and fust one thing and another, to finally they got to tawkin' 'bout how smart ole King Solomon was.

"I jest natchally can't he'p bein' smart," say ole King Solomon. "Hit was bawn in me, I reckon. Jest ax me a question, now, and see what I kin do to hit. I ain't braggin', onderstand, but jest ax me one."

"All right," say Sheba, "but I'm liable to make hit a purty hard one. Tell me who's de father er de Zebedee chilluns?"

"Ole man Zebedee," say Solomon, quick as lightnin'.

"Doggone!" say Sheba. "You is a smart scound'el, ain't you, Yo' Majesty?"

"Ax me another question," say ole King Solomon. "I ain't braggin', but I'm brim-full er wisdom and I craves to scatter some about."

"All right," say Sheba. "How come hit wa'n't no seven-up games on de ark?"

"'Cause ole Noah was settin' on de deck," say Solomon.

"Ain't you de smartest man!" say Sheba. "I ain't gonter ax you no more."

"Aw, come and ax me," say Solomon. "Ax me, woman."

"Well," say Sheba, "whar was Moses when de lights went out?"

"In de dark," say Solomon.

"All right, what did Adam and Eve do when Abel got kilt?" say Sheba.

"Raised Cain," say Solomon.

"You's too many for me, Yo' Majesty," say Sheba. "Any good-lookin' king wid all yo' brains in his haid is liable to change my mind. I better not ax you no more."

"Aw, come on, sugar, ax me one more," say Solomon.

"Naw suh!" say Sheba. "You got too many brains for a little ole country gal like me."

"Aw, come on, baby," say King Solomon. "Jest ax My Majesty one more."

"Well, I knows you got de answer to dis one," say Sheba, "but I'm gonter ax you hit, jest de same. Who is de smartest and de best-lookin' king in dis man's town?"

"He de king," say ole King Solomon, "which is settin' yar makin' his eyes at de purties' and smartes' queen in dis man's town or any yuther man's town, and he don't keer who knows hit."

So they sot around and tawked awhile, and finally ole King Solomon tuck and built a temple and when he died he had nine hund'ed and ninety-nine wives scattered 'bout de place.

Erskine Caldwell

A SMALL DAY

GOVERNOR GIL was standing astride the path, knocking heads off the weeds, when Walter Lane came up the hill from the spring. A wide circle of wilted weeds lay on the ground around him, and his walking stick was still swinging. It looked as if he had been waiting there for half an hour or longer.

"It's been mighty hot today," Walter said, stopping and lowering the two pails of water to the ground.

"It's a small day when the sun don't shine," Governor Gil said. "Where's the rest of your family, and the girl?"

"My wife and the young ones went over to visit her folks this afternoon," Walter told him. "They'll be coming home some time tonight after supper." He turned around and looked down the path behind. "Daisy's coming up the path any minute now. She's down at the spring filling a bucket."

Governor Gil looked down the path, but Daisy was not within sight. It was almost a hundred yards from the crown of the slope down to the bottom of the hill, where the spring was.

"I reckon I can wait here," he said, taking a new grip on his walking stick and bending forward to reach the weeds farthest away. "It's a small day when I can't afford to spend a little time waiting."

From *Jackpot*, copyright, 1936, by The New Yorker Magazine, Inc.; copyright, 1937, by Erskine Caldwell. Reprinted by permission of Little, Brown & Company.

Walter watched the heads tumble off the stalks of weeds. Governor Gil went about it as if he were determined not to let a weed in the whole county go to seed that year. Every once in a while he shifted his position a little, stamping down the wilted weeds and reaching for new ones to whack at. Sometimes he started out in the morning, after breakfast, on horseback to see how his cotton and cane crops were growing, but before he got out of sight of home he always got off his horse and started whacking away at the weeds with his walking stick. He hated weeds worse than he did boll weevils or screw worms. However, for some reason or other, he never paid any attention to the weeds that grew in the yard around his house; they were so rank there that sometimes his hunting dogs got lost in the growth and had to backtrack their way out.

"Did you want to see me, Governor Gil, or was it Daisy you asked about?" Walter said, wondering.

Instead of answering, Governor Gil stopped a moment and glanced down the path. He nodded his head in that direction, and returned to swinging his stick at the weeds.

Governor Gil Counts had once, for a term, been governor of the state, about twenty-five or thirty years before, and the title suited him so well that nobody ever thought of calling him anything else. He ran his farm with the help of Walter Lane and several other tenants, and never left it. He had not been out of the county since the day he came home from the governor's office, and he had said he would never leave home again. He lived a quarter of a mile up the road in a big three-story mansion, from which the white paint had peeled while he was serving his term in office. The once-white, three-story columns rising from the front porch were now as dark and rough as the bark on a pine tree.

"There's no sense in standing out here in the sun," Walter said. "Come on to my house and take a seat in the porch shade, Governor Gil. Daisy'll be along to the house just about as soon as she'll get here."

"This'll do," he said, stopping and looking down the path. "I haven't got time to sit down now."

He went past Walter and started down the path toward the spring. Walter left his pails and followed behind. Heads of weeds tumbled to the right and left of them.

At the crown of the slope they saw Daisy coming up. She was carrying a pail of water in one hand and fanning herself with a willow branch.

"I may as well tell you now, Walter," Governor Gil said, stopping. "It's time for your girl to marry. It's dangerous business to put it off after they get a certain age."

Walter took half a dozen steps around Governor Gil and stopped where he could see his face.

"Who ought she to marry?" Walter said.

Governor Gil let go at some pigweeds around his knees, whacking his stick at them just under the seed pods. The heads flew in all directions.

"I've arranged for that," he said. "I sent my lawyer a letter today telling him to get a license. It'll be here in a few days."

Walter looked again at Governor Gil, and then down the path. Daisy had come over the crown of the slope.

"That might be all right," Walter said, "but I don't know if she'll be tamed. Right now she's just about as wild as they come. Of course, now, I'm not raising any serious objections. I'm just going over in my mind the drawbacks a man might run into."

"A year from now there might be plenty of drawbacks," Governor Gil said. "Right this minute drawbacks don't count, because she's reached the marrying age, and nothing else matters. If I had a daughter, Walter, I'd want to do the right thing by her. I'd want her to marry before drawbacks had a chance to spoil her. I'm ready to marry her without an argument."

"You damned old fool," Daisy said, dropping her pail, "what put that into your head?"

Governor Gil had drawn back to let go at a clump of weeds swaying in the breeze beside the path, but he never finished the stroke. His stick fell back against his knees and the clump of weeds continued to sway in the wind.

"Now, that's what I was thinking about," Walter said. "I had an idea she wouldn't be willing to be tamed just yet."

"Why, I've been counting on this for a pretty long time," Governor Gil said excitedly. "I've just been biding my time all this while when you were growing up, Daisy. I've had my eyes on you for about three years now, just waiting for you to grow up."

"You damned old fool," Daisy said, stooping down for her pail and starting around them in the path.

Walter did not try to stop her. He looked at Governor Gil to see what he had to say now.

They watched her for a moment.

"She'll tame," Governor Gil said, nodding his head at Walter and following her up the path to the house.

When they got to the back door, Daisy put the pail on the shelf and sat down on the doorstep. She sat and looked at them with her knees drawn up under her elbows and her chin cupped in her hands.

"Maybe if you could just wait—" Walter began. He was waved aside by a sweep of the walking stick.

"I'm going to have the handseling tonight," Governor Gil said, nodding his head at Daisy and flourishing the stick in the air. "The marrying can wait, but the handseling can't. The license will be along from my lawyer in a day or two, and that's just a matter of formality, anyway."

Walter looked at Daisy, but she only stared more sullenly at them.

"I reckon we ought to wait till my wife gets back from visiting her folks," Walter said. "She ought to have a little say-so. For one thing, she'll have to make Daisy some clothes first, because Daisy hasn't got much to wear except what she's got on, and that's so little it wouldn't be decent if we weren't homefolks. Just about all she's got to her name is that little slimsy gingham jumper she's wearing. My wife will want to make her a petticoat, if nothing else. It would be a sin and a shame for her to get married like she is now. If she had something to wear under what she's got on, it might be different, but I won't be in favor of sending her out to get married in just a slimsy jumper between her and the outside world."

Governor Gil shook his walking stick in the air as if to wave away any possible objection Walter might mention.

"That's all right for the marriage," he said, "but that won't be for a few days yet. Your wife will have plenty of time to make up a petticoat for her if she wants to. But she won't even have to do that, because I'll buy her whatever she'll need after the marriage. And what she'll need for the handseling won't be worth mentioning."

He stopped and turned around to look at the sun. It was already setting behind the pine grove in the west.

"Had your supper yet?" he asked, looking at Walter and nodding at Daisy.

"Not yet," Walter said. "We didn't stop work in the cotton until about half an hour ago, and the first thing that needed doing was carrying up the water from the spring. Daisy, you go in the kitchen and start getting something ready to eat. Maybe Governor Gil will stay and eat with us tonight."

"No," he said, waving his stick at Daisy, "don't do that, Daisy. You just come up to my house and get your meal there tonight. There's no sense in you getting all worn out over a hot stove now. There's plenty to eat up there."

He turned to Walter.

"If your wife won't be home until late tonight, you just come up to my house and go around to the kitchen, and the help will set you out a good meal, Walter."

He started walking across the yard toward the road. When he got to the corner of the house, he stopped and found that neither Daisy nor her father had made a move to follow him.

"What's the matter?" he said impatiently.

"Well, now," Walter said, "I can make Daisy go up to your house, Governor Gil, but I can't be held responsible for what she does after she gets there. I wish you would wait till my wife came back tonight before you took Daisy off, but if your mind is made up not to wait, then all I can say is you'll have to charge her yourself after she gets there."

"She won't need any charging," Governor Gil said. "I've yet to know the wildest one of them that wouldn't tame when the time comes to handsel."

He turned around and started walking toward the road that led to his house, a quarter of a mile away.

Walter looked down at the doorstep, where Daisy still sat sullen and motionless.

"You ought to be tickled to death to have the chance to marry Governor Gil," he told her. "Who else is there in the county who'll treat you nice and give you all you want? I'll bet there's many a girl who'd jump at the chance to marry him."

"The damned old fool," Daisy said.

"Well, you'd better," he told her. "I'll bet your mother will make you, if I can't. She's no fool, either. She knows how well off you'll be, not having to go hungry for something to eat, and having enough clothes to cover your nakedness, neither one of which you've got now, or ever will have, if you don't go on up there like you ought to."

Walter sat down on the bottom step and waited for Daisy to say something. The sun had set, and it would be getting dark soon. If she did not go right away, Governor Gil might get mad and change his mind.

Presently he turned around and looked at her.

"What's the matter with you, Daisy? You won't even say anything. What's got into you, anyway?"

"What does he want me to go up there tonight for?" she asked. "He said the license wouldn't be here for two or three days."

"That's just Governor Gil's way, Daisy. He makes up his mind to do something, and nothing stops him once it's made up. He wants to marry you, and he wants to right now. There's no sense in putting it off, anyway. The best thing for you to do is to start right in before he changes his mind. If you don't, you'll live to be sorry, because to-morrow you'll have to go right back to the field again—tomorrow and every day as long as cotton grows."

Daisy got up without saying anything and went into the house. She was in her room for ten or fifteen minutes, and when she came to the door it was dark outside. She could barely see her father sitting on the steps at her feet.

"Now, that's what I call sense," Walter said. "I thought you'd change your mind after you got to thinking about all these hot days in the sun out there in the cotton."

She went down the steps past him and crossed the yard without a word. She started up the road in the direction of Governor Gil's mansion.

After Daisy had gone, Walter began to wonder what his wife would say when she came home. He was certain she would be glad to hear that Governor Gil wanted to marry Daisy, but he was not so sure of what she would say when he told her that the marriage license would not come for another two or three days. He decided it would be best not to say anything about that part to her. Just as long as she knew Governor Gil had come to the house to ask Daisy to marry him, she would be satisfied.

It was pitch-dark when he got up and went into the kitchen, made a light, and looked around for something to eat. He found some bread left over from dinner, and he did not have to build a fire in the cook stove after all. He sat down at the kitchen table and ate his fill of bread and sorghum.

After he had finished, he blew out the light and went to the front porch to sit and wait for his wife to come home.

Up the road he could see lights in Governor Gil's house. There was a light in the kitchen, as usual, and one in the front part of the house too. Upstairs, two or three rooms were lighted for the first time since he could remember.

Just when he was expecting his wife and children to get there any moment, he heard somebody running down the road. He got up and listened as the sound came closer. It was somebody running fast, because the sound came closer every second.

He ran out to the road to see who it was. At first he thought it might be Daisy, but he soon knew it wasn't, because a boy called out to him.

"Mr. Walter! Mr. Walter!"

"Who's that?" he shouted back.

A Negro houseboy stopped, panting, in the road beside him.

"What's the matter, Lawson?"

"Mr. Walter, Governor said to tell you if you ever raise another hellcat like Miss Daisy, he'll chop your head off. Now, Mr. Walter, I didn't say it! Please, sir, don't think I said it! It was Governor who told me to tell you that! You know I wouldn't say that myself, don't you, Mr. Walter?"

"What's the matter up there, Lawson?" Walter asked the boy.

"I don't know exactly, Mr. Walter, except that Governor started yelling upstairs a while ago, and he hasn't stopped yet. He told me to telephone for the doctor and the lawyer to come in a hurry. He hardly stopped yelling long enough to tell me, either. Soon as I telephoned for them, he told me to run down here as fast as I could and tell you what I told you."

"Was Miss Daisy up there then?" Walter asked.

"I reckon it was Miss Daisy who made him yell," Lawson said hesitatingly.

"Why?"

"I don't know if Governor wants me to tell you," Lawson said. "He only told me to tell you what I already told you, Mr. Walter."

"You'd better tell me, Lawson. What was it?"

"Miss Daisy flew into him and pretty near bit the daylights out of him. Governor was yelling and nursing his hurt so much, he didn't have time to say much else."

Walter started back to the porch to sit down and wait for his wife to come home. He could not keep from laughing a little, but he tried to hold himself back so he could laugh all the more with his wife when she got there.

Lawson was still standing outside the yard. He turned around to tell the boy to go on back.

"What else did Governor Gil say, Lawson?" he asked him.

"I didn't hear him say much else, except Governor said it'll be a mighty small day when he tries to handsel a hellcat like Miss Daisy again."

Walter went to the porch and sat down. He leaned back and started to laugh. He could not wait for his wife any longer. He leaned back and laughed until he slid out of the chair.

Alva Johnston

THE LEGENDARY MIZNERS AND THE FLORIDA BOOM*

1. VISION

ADDISON AND WILSON MIZNER built the broadest highway in the world during the Florida boom of the early twenties. This was El Camino Real, or the King's Highway, which led to the Mizner principality of Boca Raton, the most snobbish of all the Florida real-estate subdivisions. El Camino Real was two hundred and nineteen feet wide and had twenty traffic lanes, or enough to deliver several hundred thousand people a day to the most exclusive spot on earth. Harry Reichenbach, the highest-paid publicity man on earth, exhausted the national bank of superlatives in describing the widest road on the planet. He found that the Mizner highway took first place in seven or eight respects among the world's arteries of traffic. It was, for example, the most extravagantly landscaped. The parks and gardens and promenades of El Camino Real were patterned after those of Avenida Beira Mar, which stretches around Botafogo Bay, in Rio de Janeiro, but the Mizner boulevard was broader and better. One of the novelties of El Camino Real was indirect illumination. Drawing on his experience as a Broadway playwright, Wilson Mizner lit the road from the wings, using concealed lights in the curbs in place of lampposts. El Camino Real was waterscaped as well as landscaped. Down the middle ran the Grand Canal of Venice, with Rialtos, ornamental landings, and electrically driven gondolas. These romantic vehicles were actually made in Venice. The great Florida boom had touched

* Abridged
From *The Legendary Mizners*, copyright, 1942, 1950, 1952, 1953, by Evelyn Johnston. Reprinted by permission of Farrar, Straus & Young, Inc., Publishers. Originally in *The New Yorker* in different form.

off many minor booms, one of them being a burst of activity in gondola-making circles on the Adriatic. At a meeting of the Boca Raton directors, Wilson Mizner, a fanatical perfectionist, fought for an appropriation to import Venetian gondoliers, in costume, to sing and play on guitars. An economy-minded director objected that a genuine gondolier was superfluous in a gondola that had batteries and a propeller. He argued also that the gondolier might cause accidents by poling it in one direction while the man at the wheel tried to steer in another. "We'll have him use a fake oar," said Wilson. "Then the son of a bitch can't do any harm."

El Camino Real had certain defects. Addison had set his heart on having beautiful blue water in the Grand Canal, but it persisted in being muddy. The architect was furious. No man was ever so exasperated with a body of water since Xerxes scourged the Hellespont. Addison kept scores of workmen busy cleaning out mud and silt, but more kept seeping in. The harder they tried to make the canal blue, the muddier it got. The trouble was that, the canal being at sea level, the tides kept bringing soil in. Addison was fighting the Atlantic Ocean, and he was as badly overmatched as the Mrs. Partington who fought a tidal wave with a mop. Another trouble was that automobiles kept diving into the canal. But the chief defect of the commodious thoroughfare was its length. While it was the widest road in the world, it was also the shortest. The great boulevard ran from the Dixie Highway to Lake Boca Raton, a distance of slightly less than half a mile. Also, whereas El Camino Real was twenty lanes wide on the east side of the Dixie Highway, it was hardly two lanes wide on the west. All the world-beating effects disappeared on the west side, El Camino Real becoming a mere trail in the sand. Two cars could barely pass without becoming entangled in the branches of the scrub pines on either side. In boom maps and blueprints, El Camino Real rolled its twenty traffic lanes past a series of colossal nonexistent cities. In real life, it died away in brambles and swamps.

El Camino Real was not of much use as an artery of traffic, but it had a vast power of suggestion. The two million lot-buyers in Florida were all seeking clues to the subdivision that had the most sensational future. El Camino Real was a startling piece of evidence. Just as a scientist can reconstruct dinosaurs from one giant fragment of bone, so the Florida sucker was able to forecast the tremendous future of Boca Raton from the giant fragment of road. London had no twenty-lane highway; Paris, Rome, New York, and Chicago had no twenty-lane highways. As investors studied the implications of El Camino

Real, the corner lots in Boca Raton jumped in value from a few hundred dollars to a hundred thousand dollars. When enthusiasm was running wild, Wilson Mizner offered fifty thousand dollars for a choice Boca Raton lot owned by Lytle Hull, the well-known society man. Hull was insulted. He wouldn't talk to Wilson for two weeks. He hung on to the lot until after the Florida bubble had exploded, and then found that it was worth about two hundred dollars by the new scale of prices.

Boom-time Florida had many El Camino Reals of one kind or another—expensive improvements intended as appetizers for the sucker imagination. Other subdivisions had ornamental boulevards—not quite as wide as the Mizner highway but almost as short. Steel skeletons of hotels and office buildings shot up in uninhabited regions. Most of the big and middle-size promoters believed themselves to be Romuluses and Remuses about to found another world capital. They thought all they needed to start a stampede toward their new Eternal City was a building or some other showy improvement to proclaim that the new seat of empire was off to a flying start. Promoters were willing to throw large sums into one imposing structure, in the hope of setting off an orgy of construction. That first structure was the queen bee of the building industry; it was supposed to have the power to lure swarms of buildings to settle on all sides of it, until the subdivision had a metropolitan skyline. The real-estate sections of the local newspapers showed hundreds of subdivisions with a background of the jagged outline of New York as seen from the Bay. Anybody with a haircut and a lead pencil could turn out a metropolis with a Manhattan silhouette; making sketches of the horizon of downtown New York for advertisements was one of the busiest callings in Florida.

After the crash, Florida had something new to offer in the field of archeology. The state was dotted with unborn ghost cities, the picturesque remains of places that had never had an inhabitant. The crash came so suddenly that New Yorks, Chicagos, Biarritzes, and Monte Carlos were abandoned before a single building had been completed. Sometimes the hardhearted bankers stopped construction while the concrete was still being poured. Florida became the richest country in the world in fresh ruins. One pompous relic of the boom, a source of astonishment to people on passing ships, was a seven-story hotel on Singer's Island, just north of Palm Beach. This majestic pile was built by Paris Singer, who planned to make it the aristocratic headquarters of the world. Designed by Addison Mizner, decorated by the Duchess of Richelieu, this structure was to be the forerunner of a family of gorgeous palaces that, according to the boom-time theory of the propagation of buildings, would multiply like guinea pigs until Singer's Island made Palm Beach look like a slum. Suites in this blue-blooded caravansary were reserved for the gilded popinjays of two worlds, but the bankers called off the contractors when the place was nine-tenths finished, and the apartments of dukes and princes were taken over by thousands of sea gulls and pelicans. The Singer establishment was the most expensive roost for wild fowl in the world. The most expensive roost for tame fowl was a hotel that dominated a wide stretch of landscape near the Miami airport and became a familiar sight to thousands of air travellers. This conspicuous landmark was built as a luxury hotel for human beings, but the crash turned it into a luxury chicken coop for a hundred and sixty thousand domestic fowl. The hotel was supposed to start the magic transformation of a cow pasture into a great city. The promoters had bought a dairy farm, chased the Jerseys off the broad meadows, and divided the area into business districts, Gold Coast residential districts, and civic centers. The fine six-story hotel was erected on the boom theory that once any area in Florida was inoculated with steel and masonry, it would break out in a rash of noble edifices. The bubble exploded before the windows and interior furnishings had been installed. Unfit for human habitation, the hotel was turned into the most modern and probably the most populous of hen hotels. One of its features was a gravity system that caused an egg, as soon as it was laid, to roll down felt-lined runways to a central collecting point. In addition to an enormous output of eggs and broilers, this Waldorf of henneries sent thousands of day-old chicks to all parts of the East. The basement was used for growing mushrooms. During the war, the Army took the place over, and it is now a private aviation school.

The bewildering final stage of the boom was dominated by what was known in Florida as "vision"—a gift that enabled an observer to mistake spots before the eyes for magnificent cities. "Vision" was a word that stirred the imagination and caused abundant streams of sucker money to gush forth. The greatest disgrace that could befall a man in Florida was to be suspected of not being a man of vision. You were in danger of having your vision doubted if you failed to see a coming Babylon or Baghdad in any body of land or water that was being cut up into building lots. You qualified as a man of vision the moment you saw the Manhattan skyline rising out of an alligator swamp. The realtor's standard question for testing a man's vision was "Can you imagine a city *not* being here?" The state was peppered with Chicagos. Forty-second-and-Broadways were so numerous that in 1927 the Florida Chamber of Commerce, describing the state's remarkable comeback after the Florida crash, boasted that cabbage patches and truck gardens were flourishing where the Forty-second-and-Broadways used to be. The most spectacular of the men of vision was Barron Collier, a New York advertising man, who bought more than a million acres in Florida and announced plans to replace the lights of fireflies with the lights of happy homes. "Barron Collier has more vision than any man since Cecil Rhodes," said the Miami News. "Vision" eventually became a synonym for lunacy, fraud, and robbery, but the real pioneers of the boom actually had vision up to a point, and their first crop of visions came true. Skylines popped up like jack-in-the-boxes in Miami and Miami Beach. Miami inevitably got the nickname of the Magic City when lovely islands climbed up out of the mud and hotels, parks, office buildings, and fine residential districts emerged from dense jungles. An exclusive shopping district arose along a path where, a few years earlier, a panther had chased Miss Hattie Carpenter, a Miami schoolteacher, who escaped by furious pedalling on her bicycle. "Miami," said William Jennings Bryan, "is the only city in the world where you can tell a lie at breakfast that will come true by evening." Tens of thousands of people had seen visions harden into reality. Millions of others had seen the "before" and "after" photographs of the miracles—yesterday's bogs, today's millionaire suburbs. The only fallacy was the popular belief that because some visions had come true, all delusions and hallucinations must also come true.

"Boom" was a word the boomers hated. They argued that Florida was having not a boom but a development. "It's just a catching up," was the standard explanation. In one of his double-page advertisements, Harry Reichenbach clarified the situation by a parable. On a certain island in the Indian Ocean, the benighted heathens thought that pearls were worthless beads, but one day they woke up to find themselves filthy capitalists. "This was not a boom," said Harry. "It was a recognition of value." The wonders of Florida had, in fact, been overlooked. Americans had been backward about appreciating their own subtropics for a number of reasons. Spanish rule had continued in Florida until 1819. Then came the Seminole Wars, the Civil War, and Reconstruction. Although the state began to pick up late in the nineteenth century, most Americans thought of it as a remote playground for the very rich. It took the automobile and improved roads to bring about the real rediscovery of Florida. In 1920, the Tin-Can Tourists of the World, forerunners of America's trailer-home population, established themselves in Florida. Elderly people found out about the "actinic rays" of the Florida sun, which were believed to have an extraordinary ability to unharden the arteries. Folks of moderate means began to master the secret of the winter vacation just when the bull market was providing them with the extra money to pay for it. Under the impact of the rush to the "last frontier," Miami real estate became lively in 1922, highly animated in 1923. Vacationers returned North with tales of gigantic profits, and in 1924 the boom was unmistakable. Its frenzied final stage was blamed, by Frederick Lewis Allen in "Only Yesterday" and by Kenneth Ballinger, a boom historian, in "Miami Millions," on the confidence inspired by the overwhelming Republican victory in the national election of 1924.

The original men of vision of Miami Beach had the vision of becoming millionaires by raising coconuts. That was back in the eighties, when a mild coconut mania hit many Southern beaches. The coconut planters of Miami Beach hired New Jersey lifeguards to come to Florida at the end of the summer-resort season in the North. Loading small boats from a mother ship, the lifeguards rowed ashore and sowed coconuts in the sand and jungle back of the beaches. Tens of thousands sprouted, but the young plants were nearly all eaten up by rabbits, raccoons, water rats, and other pests. When the coconut experiment began to get shaky, early in the century, John S. Collins, who had been a horticulturist in Moorestown, New Jersey, switched to avocados. His first young plants were cut to pieces by sand blown from the beaches. He wrapped his later plants in burlap, grew rows of corn as protection from the flying sand, and planted thousands of Australian pines as a windbreak. Then, around 1910, Collins had a new vision, this one to the effect that Florida's best crop would be winter vacationers. He and some associates began to build small hotels and boarding houses near Miami Beach. The only connection between Miami Beach and Miami was by boat. A bridge was needed to bring in the vacationers swarming to Miami by buggy and automobile, and Collins raised money to build one across Biscayne Bay. In 1913, the money gave out, before the bridge was finished. The elderly Collins' game struggle on behalf of Miami Beach attracted the attention of Carl G. Fisher, who was vacationing in Florida. Fisher furnished the money to complete the bridge, and soon succeeded Collins as the chief promoter of Miami Beach. Starting out as a newsboy, Fisher had become a professional bicycle rider, then sold acetylene lamps for bicycles and automobiles, and eventually headed the Prest-O-Lite Company. He had disposed of his business interests for six million dollars just before coming to Florida. After finishing the bridge, he began building hotels, roads, parks, residences, and golf courses in Miami Beach. He reclaimed thousands of acres of swamp and then began pumping sand into frames to build islands in Biscayne Bay. After a shaky start, Fisher's enterprises were enormously successful.

George Merrick, of Coral Gables, J. W. Young, of Hollywood-by-the-Sea, and D. P. Davis, of Davis Islands, in Tampa Bay, were among the other boom chieftains—the Mohammeds who led millions of the faithful in the holy war to get rich without work. Their aims and methods were imitated by nearly all the other promoters. Even the Mizners, who affected to scorn their competitors, lifted ideas from Merrick and Young. The most familiar vision of the boom—the idea of taking an undeveloped expanse and spreading a ready-made city over it—was originated by George Merrick. He was the son of the Reverend Solomon Merrick, who left his pulpit in Gaines, New York, and started a citrus grove near Miami in the nineties, calling his place Coral Gables. George Merrick's first ambition was to be a man of letters, but after winning a prize in a short-story contest and writing a volume of poems, he gave up literature and devoted himself to oranges and grapefruit at Coral Gables. Around 1913, when he was in his early twenties, Merrick had the vision of replacing his citrus plantation with a city. His Coral Gables was not a get-rich-quick scheme but a real adventure in city planning and city building, and much of the boom revolved around this gigantic project. It was the boom's answer to skeptics. Merrick's accomplishments shut the mouths of those who denied that wonder cities could be produced by magic.

Most of the Florida promoters learned lessons in aggressiveness from J. W. Young, who started the practice of invading the North with boisterous expeditions of merrymakers and salesmen. He had been a newsboy in San Francisco, and was once president of the Newsboys' Union there. He must have learned about shanghaiing sailors in San Francisco, for he used a similar technique on investors, plying them with gaudy entertainment and then whisking them off to Florida in his fleets of buses. Young's advance agents held grand balls and banquets in Northern cities, hypnotized the revellers with tales of everlasting youth and unheard-of profits, and then herded them South by the thousand. Others followed Young's example, and during the peak of the boom hundreds of buses and dozens of special trains were carrying suckers and their bank rolls to new heavens on new Rivieras. Young had a vision of a city like Coral Gables, and he constructed it on an unlikely area twenty miles north of Miami. Some of the women captured by Young's raiders and taken to Florida were terrified by their first glimpse of the site of Hollywood-by-the-Sea. The Florida landscape can be unnerving. Twisted by hurricanes, the trees are gnarled and contorted. The undergrowth carries thorns that are the size of small daggers and are accused of attacking men without warning. The ground is covered with savage saw and sword grass. The tendrils of the vines and the branches of the trees point accusing fingers, and the general effect is ferocious. As a bus was passing through one tropical scene of horrors, a woman started to shriek. In a few seconds, all the prospects were screaming hysterically, and they had to be treated for shock before they could sign up for lots in the baleful wilderness. Yet in spite of a little trouble at the start, Young's city was a great success.

Ex-newsboys seem to have had more than their share of boom-time vision. Fisher and Young had sold papers, and so had D. P. Davis, one of the great subdivision showmen and the most spectacular of the island builders. Davis sold extras during the Spanish-American war in Tampa, rose to become the Frankfurter King of Jacksonville, and returned to Tampa, where he created three artificial islands that were rated among the finest accomplishments of the boom. Davis was in the front ranks of the subdividers. The crash caught him in the midst of an island-making project off St. Augustine. Like all the big figures of the boom, he was wiped out by the crackup. He disappeared from an ocean liner, and was generally thought to have taken his life, but Raymond Schindler, the detective, insisted that he had gone through a porthole merely as an oratorical gesture. Davis used strange rhetoric after he had had a few drinks. Once, in New York, when an opponent was unimpressed by his logic, he crawled out of a seventeenth-story window in the Commodore and clung by his fingertips until his antagonist conceded the point. According to Schindler, Davis, who had been reasoning with a lady in his stateroom, crawled through the porthole to clinch an argument and was drowned when his fingers slipped. Newspapers hinted at foul play. Some people maintain, however, that Davis has since been seen in Paris, Bangkok, and South Africa.

In the footsteps of the newsboys and other pioneers came a multitude of promoters and boosters, ranging from some of the leading men of America to scallawags, mail-fraud artists, and all varieties of Get-Rich-Quick Wallingfords. At one end of the scale was General T. Coleman du Pont, the chief bottleholder for the Mizners; at the other was the most notorious swindler in the country, Charles Ponzi, who ran a real-estate clip joint called the Charpon Land Syndicate. Most of the promoters had an honest enthusiasm for Florida, but as the boom reached full speed, they tended to lose their equilibrium. They developed a language of their own; "near" meant "far," "high" meant "low," "great" meant "small." Cosmic City had no inhabitants. Textile City didn't even have a spool of thread. Reflected-glory cities came into existence. Their attraction was that they were "near" some well-known place. Ponzi's city, sixty-five miles from Jacksonville, was advertised as being near Jacksonville. The promoters of Manhattan Estates invented a city in order to make their subdivision a suburb of it. "Near the prosperous and fast-growing city of Nettie," said the advertisements, although there never was a city in Florida named Nettie. The promoters of Manhattan Estates justified themselves on the ground that they had been told that there was an abandoned turpentine camp named Nettie in the vicinity and that they were entitled to a little real-estate license.

Florida was sensitive about the fact that it was the flattest state in the country except Delaware, and it attempted to achieve altitude by playing games with words. Okeechobee Highlands was twelve inches taller than the country around it, according to Kenneth Ballinger. Any twenty-four-inch altitude constituted "heights," according to Ralph Henry Barbour, another Florida chronicler. Baldwin Heights was found by the National Better Business Bureau to be under water. Any unevenness of surface was likely to become a cliff or a bluff in boom literature. Florida has Mount Pleasant, Mount Dora, Mountain Lake, Iron Mountain, and other titles of altitude, but the highest peak in the state is less than four hundred feet above sea level. The magazine *Suniland* made the resounding claim that Iron Mountain (altitude, 325 feet) was "the pinnacle between New Jersey and Mexico." One series of little molehills was described as the Berkshires of Florida even before the realtors took over the language. The real Berkshires are ten times as high as their Florida namesakes, but a nine-hundred-per-cent exaggeration was modest in 1925. In the general reshuffling of the Florida vocabulary during the boom, "the Berkshires of Florida" became, said Professor Homer B. Vanderblue, the economist, "the Alps of Florida," and would probably have been promoted to the Himalayas if the boom had continued into 1926. "By-the-Sea" was a curious piece of subdivision slang that meant "far back in the hinterland." Fulford-by-the-Sea was a huge promotion several miles inland from Miami. One of the standard jokes of 1925 was "Did you hear the news? They've hired a hundred salesmen to push Fulford by the sea." J. W. Young's original city site was a considerable distance from the sea, so he called it Hollywood-by-the-Sea. When, by addition and expansion, he reached the Atlantic on a broad front, he was embarrassed by "by-the-sea," which implied to the knowing that his city was a backwoods community, so he changed its name to just plain Hollywood.

Almost anything—a nearby city, a new hotel, a civic center, a mountain, a bay, a lake, or an ocean—became a talking point for a development. A resourceful promoter could make almost anything do for a landmark. Charles Ort, a promoter known as the King of the Keys, was sold a tract on Key Largo by a realtor who didn't mention that it had been a quarry and was full of deep holes. Ort looked ruefully at the hollows and chasms, but then snapped his fingers and danced wildly about, shouting, "Sunken Gardens! Sunken Gardens!" He doubled the price of the lots with the deepest abysses. The promoters of Wyldewood Park, near Fort Lauderdale, had difficulty finding a talking point to wrap their subdivision around. There were no startling geographical features, no skyscrapers, coliseums, or campaniles. But there was an interesting tree—a large banyan, which had dropped branches into the ground to become new roots, until the tree was beginning to look like a small forest. A big sign, "$2,000,000 Tree," was hung on it, and it became the logical argument for buying homesites in Wyldewood, the claim being made that a banyan-crazy Yankee had once offered two million dollars for the tree if it could be moved to his home up North. The tree is still one of the points of interest in Florida—the most famous botanical item next to the Senator, a cypress alleged to be three thousand years old.

Promoters who couldn't find even a tree or a quarry to rave about took refuge in the word "proposed." A newspaper advertisement or a sign was the only immediate expense required for a "proposed" improvement. Kenneth Roberts has told of a group of capitalists who hired a painter to do a sign reading, "A Million-Dollar Hotel Will Be Erected Here," but the capitalists couldn't raise the eighteen dollars to pay for the sign, so the painter sold it to another group of capitalists. In order to save buyers from going to see their purchases, promoters had relief maps of their subdivisions done in papier-mâché. The investor merely had to point at a lot and say, "I'll take that one." The most elaborate of these models was D. P. Davis's forty-foot miniature of his proposed island off St. Augustine, the bay and ocean being represented by water a foot deep, in which miniature electric yachts and steamers sailed. Thomas W. McMorrow, who specialized in fiction with a fact basis, wrote of a fancy raised map of a subdivision, which was delivered after all the land had been sold. It was so beautiful that suckers insisted on buying lots in it even though there was no land to go with it. Next to maps and signs, the cheapest substitute for splendor was the triumphal arch. The principle of the tail wagging the dog was so prevalent in Florida that any stately arch was confidently expected to attach a stately city to itself. The countryside is still strewn with heaps of disintegrated stucco, slats, rusty chicken wire, and other debris of imperial entrance gates, once used as yardsticks for measuring the imperial communities projected by realtors' imagination. The word "proposed" was considered important enough to carry whole cities on its coattails in the last stages of the bubble. Billions and billions of dollars' worth of "proposed" architectural and engineering feats were placed before the investor. "All of these here lots," said Will Rogers, plugging for his own imaginary world capital, "are by our Proposed Ocean." The humorist's Proposed Ocean was outdone by reality.

The ocean was not only proposed, it was built into dozens of subdivisions. "The sea is actually being brought back into the heart of the pine woods," wrote Rex Beach in "The Miracle of Coral Gables." Coral Gables, which is several miles inland, advertised "Forty Miles of Waterfront," but the forty miles bordered on canals cut through to the ocean. The idea of working a synthetic coastline into the subdivisions came from the brain of a resourceful realtor named C. G. Rodes. He was shaking his head mournfully over an unlovely drainage ditch when an idea came to him. "The Grand Canal of Venice!" he exclaimed. He beautified the drainage ditch, added a network of ditches to it, and gave the name of Venice to the subdivision, which is on the Gulf Coast of Florida. The idea of gliding along on canals had a mysterious appeal to railroad men, and the Brotherhood of Locomotive Engineers threw away more than ten million dollars on the Florida Venice. After Rodes made his historic discovery, nearly every slough and open sewer in Florida became a romantic piece of water. Islands were popular with the suckers, and the promoters found that, instead of paying millions to build islands by pumping sand, they could produce cheap ones by digging ditches around low-lying properties. The banks of any ditch that held a few gallons of brine became "waterfront" or "oceanfront" property, and the postal authorities, no matter how fervently they tried to prevent fraudulent advertising from going through the mails, couldn't do anything about it. Some buyers of ocean frontage were astonished to learn that the Atlantic was hardly big enough for a duck to turn around in. Abandoned canals, choked with vegetation and lined by decaying little Rialtos, are still to be found in the old boom country.

Paper cities on paper oceans, paper universities, paper race tracks, coliseums, and casinos marked the overripe phase of the boom. One of the last great sensations was the paper migration of the motion-picture industry from California to Florida. Paper studios sprang up everywhere. "PICTURE PROMOTERS IN FLORIDA STIR UP STATE," said a *Variety* headline, the article adding that "the magnates are plugging Florida as an ideal successor for Hollywood." In an earlier day, Florida had been a greater motion-picture land than Hollywood, and the magnates were always threatening to go back there unless the Hollywood payroll behaved itself. "COAST AFRAID OF FLORIDA," said *Variety* of September 2, 1925. There was good reason for Hollywood's agitation. Enough paper studios had started up in Florida to make ten times as many pictures as Hollywood ever turned out. Tens of thousands of lots were offered in the great cinema cities where you could live next door to the stars and probably get your young before the camera at a salary of three thousand dollars a week. One of the first magnates to turn up in Florida was H. M. Horkheimer, who announced Film City, covering a hundred acres near Miami. Horkheimer, husband of Jackie Saunders, a movie belle of the silent days, had made himself famous in Hollywood by putting a sheriff, who had come to seize his studio, into an important part in a Western. The most imposing magnate to go to Florida was Lewis J. Selznick. Selznick, once a diamond merchant, had become a film executive when, a total stranger, he slipped into the Universal offices in New York and issued orders to everybody. Everybody obeyed, and after a short period as a comic-opera magnate Selznick mastered the business and became a real magnate. Selznick arrived in Florida in 1925, accompanied by reports that he was about to start the world's greatest picture company there. He considered locating in Picture City, an eleven-thousand-acre cinema capital started by Felix Isman, a Broadway magnate, a few miles north of Palm Beach. Picture City was calculated to make Hollywood tremble. Although there were no buildings in Picture City, there were towering signboards announcing, "Studio H-3," "Studio K-19," "Studio J-H-6," and other indications that Paramount and Metro were soon to be left in the lurch. The Chamber of Commerce of Fort Myers, Edison's winter home, announced that the biggest studio would be located there. The birth of a great picture industry was announced in Ocala, with a Ku Klux Klan leader as the top magnate. Winter Haven claimed that it was actually shooting an epic—a romance of the boom, with a realtor for the hero. The promoters of Sun City, near Tampa, did build a studio, said to be the biggest on earth, and claimed that production was going to start with "Rain," under the direction of Sam Wood. In 1925, Van Sweringen was the biggest name on the railroad map, and Sun City placed a Van Sweringen in charge of things. The great Van Sweringens were M. J. and O. P. Sun City had H. C., an obscure brother of the famous railroad men, but Florida suckers were in no mood to quibble about their Van Sweringens, and H. C. was just as good as M. J. or O. P. for subdivision purposes. Of all the film metropolises in Florida, Sun City was the only one that left a respectable monument behind. Its studio became the Sun City schoolhouse. In 1940, Sun City had a population of eighty-five—a remarkable showing for a boom city fifteen years after the blowup. A score of pupils were then attending classes in the enormous old studio. The school's proudest possession was a huge painted panorama of Sun City as it was expected to look when it had superseded Hollywood as the world's entertainment center.

2. THE CRASH

GENERAL T. COLEMAN DU PONT was the man who killed the Florida boom, according to some authorities on the subject. The General was originally a champion of the boom. He had been the most influential backer of the Mizners. Trouble arose when the Mizners failed to show proper appreciation of their backer. In boosting their magic city of Boca Raton, the Mizners had spent millions to make their name important. They were convinced that Mizner was a bigger name than du Pont. Nothing but the Florida frenzy could have made business and financial bedfellows of T. Coleman du Pont and Wilson Mizner—General du Pont, for thirteen years president of E. I. du Pont de Nemours & Co., and Wilson Mizner, whose chief business experience had been running dubious hotels and steering wealthy suckers against cardsharps, con men, and shakedown artists. Usually, the General made the strictest inquiry into proposed business associates, but the carefree atmosphere of Florida persuaded him to neglect to brief himself on the subject of Wilson Mizner. The General was relaxing in Palm Beach when he caught the subdivision mania. Many of the celebrities of the resort were signing up with the Mizners' Boca Raton enterprise. The General joined the procession and was elected to the directorate. One of his fellow-directors was Jesse L. Livermore, famous for the Black Fridays and Blue Mondays he had caused by cornering the wheat market. Another was Matthew Brush, a major figure in Wall Street. The Mizners claimed a hundred millionaires among the backers of Boca Raton, but the General's name had ten times the sucker-drawing power of any of the others.

The General was a man of many quirks, foibles, and oddities, and these were partly responsible for his disastrous experience with the Mizner boys. He regarded himself as the Flo Ziegfeld of private life, and travelled around Palm Beach like a sixty-year-old Maypole surrounded by Queens of the May. As soon as he joined the Boca Raton project, he established himself in the Mizner headquarters as a mad wag and a tireless practical joker. He started by coming into the office with an air of excitement and handing an important-looking envelope to an employee. As the envelope was opened, a mechanical beetle darted out with a terrifying rattle and zigzagged around the room, causing the General to double up with laughter and slap his thighs explosively. He was a great handshaker; his palm usually contained a tiny device that inflicted an electrical shock, or a bit of sticky paper, so that when the victim drew his hand away, he pulled yards and yards of colored tissue paper out of the General's coat sleeve. He sometimes amused himself by putting on a deaf-and-dumb act. Once, when he was frantically making signs to a bootblack, an onlooker asked what it was all about. "He's deaf and dumb," said the bootblack. The onlooker exclaimed, "Ain't he a big bastard!" The General was, in fact, six feet four, rawboned, and powerfully built. He was a familiar figure in Palm Beach in his white knickerbockers, knee-length silk stockings, and tweed coat, from the right-hand pocket of which he was constantly extracting a pack of cards, saying, "Take any card you choose." He could do card tricks by the hour. There was an affecting scene one day when the General, immediately after being reconciled with a du Pont cousin following a long estrangement, offered his deck of cards, saying, "Take any card you choose." His residence was equipped with telephone receivers that shot streams of water into listening ears, highball glasses that sprang leaks, matches that gave out sparks like Fourth of July flowerpots, unlightable cigarettes, and detonating cigars. His fame as a wit seems to rest mainly on a line inspired by a lady's nightgown that had been accidentally left behind by a previous occupant of a suite he stayed in at the Hotel Blackstone, in Chicago. Summoning the manager, the General handed him the garment, saying, "Fill it and bring it back." The great characteristics of the General, according to intimates, were that he was generally overflowing with animal spirits and that he "loved people." His comedy was, however, sometimes a little inhumane. He had a habit of offering a watch as a prize in all sorts of contests. When the winner came for his reward, the General would solemnly hand him an Ingersoll; the humor of the thing was the disappointment of the man who had expected a Tiffany or Cartier masterpiece from the frightfully rich old du Pont. The General was a friend of the late Senator Bankhead. He started the Senator's niece Tallulah on her career by lending her a thousand dollars to launch herself on the London stage, but he kept her on the anxious seat so long that she appraised him as a big-hearted, genial, but slightly sadistic old gentleman. The General's favorite fun machine was an electrically operated papier-mâché bulldog that he kept in a dimly lighted room. An almost invisible wire extended from the bulldog to the General's pants pocket, and by pressing a button he could cause the fierce-looking animal to growl and make short jumps in the direction of nervous visitors. When he had unsuspecting house guests, the General would start the day by raving about buckwheat cakes and maple syrup until his hearers were ravenous. Then a steaming platter of cakes would appear. In attempting to eat them, the hungry guests would make the hilarious discovery that they were composed of flannel dipped in batter. The General's chef concocted a marvellous sauce, the smell of which would drive a man mad. The General had it served on rubber frankfurters. One of his whims was taking parties of luxury-loving men and women in cold weather to his hunting lodge on the eastern shore of Maryland and watching their agonized expressions on discovering that there were no bathtubs, no running water, no electricity, no heat except from a log fire, which the General lighted by rubbing two sticks together, and no lavatory except an outhouse. Another of the General's uses of disappointment and consternation was his trick of seeming to lose his mind over a gold-digger. When he had the poor girl dreaming of pearl necklaces and apartments overlooking Central Park, he would take her to a party and introduce her to his daughters, cousins, and nieces, the cream of the thing being her surprise and alarm at finding herself inundated with respectability and domesticity.

The General's frolics in Palm Beach made members of the Mizner organization suspect that his mind was going. They therefore considered it safe to take all kinds of liberties with his name. Wilson Mizner, who had had experience coaching witnesses, actors, and extortionists, acted as coach for the Boca Raton salesmen, and taught them to hammer home the point that T. Coleman du Pont was throw-

ing countless millions into Boca Raton. The General's name was used
in nearly every sentence of every sales talk. The wealth of the General
and all his relatives could hardly have redeemed all the pledges that
were backed by the sacred honor of T. Coleman du Pont. The fact
that he was being exploited by word of mouth didn't come to the
attention of the old capitalist, but one day the Mizner organization
made the mistake of exploiting him in print. The General was in
New York, in May of 1925, when he happened to see in the Palm
Beach *Post* a publicity release announcing that "T. Coleman du Pont
and others" were going to build Boca Raton hotels and theatres that
would be among the wonders of the world. In a telegram to Addison,
the General denounced the statement as a falsehood, and added,
"PLEASE CORRECT IT IMMEDIATELY WITH AS MUCH OR MORE PUBLICITY
AS WAS GIVEN FALSE STATEMENT. AM DEEPLY CHAGRINED BY STATEMENT
AND FEARFUL OF OUTCOME OF A CONCERN THAT DOES BUSINESS THIS
WAY. KINDLY WIRE ME WALDORF THAT ADEQUATE DENIAL HAS BEEN
MADE." Addison promptly wired back a mollifying telegram that
started with "I AM FRIGHTFULLY SORRY FOR SUCH A GRAVE MISTAKE
AND MISSTATEMENT" and wound up with "EVERY CORRECTION AND
REPARATION POSSIBLE WILL BE MADE." The General's peace of mind
was restored, and in a letter to Addison he said, "Gee, I was glad to get
your telegram. It took a load off my mind. You see, in Florida, I know
from experience, advertisers are apt to exaggerate (I am putting it
mildly) and I have always, in business, believed in being very, very
careful not to make a statement that could not be backed up by facts
in every way." The General went on to deliver a sermon on truth in
advertising and suggested it be circulated among all the Boca Raton
employees.

Wilson Mizner and his lieutenants had made the mistake of taking
the General for a nut when he was only an eccentric. The General
had a business reason for his clowning. His glittering success in life
had been partly based on slapstick comedy and feats of legerdemain.
He was a master at breaking down reserve, suspicion, and sales resistance and getting big men into big deals. The General's vaudeville
talents and irrepressible boyishness had melted some of the icebergs
of the financial world. The du Pont empire is based in some degree
on the mergers effected by the General's boisterous personality and
his bag of tricks. He was the headliner at du Pont employee outings,
and a master of labor relations with his jokes and sleight-of-hand
performances. He was, according to Marquis James, biographer of
Alfred I. du Pont, a skillful pickpocket; he would now and then steal

a watch from a department head and restore it with a solemn admonition to the man to keep a sharper eye on his department than he did on his valuables. As a preliminary to important business conferences, the General would perform card and coin tricks until everybody was in good humor; then, turning grave, he would pass the exploding cigars and call the meeting to order.

After his outburst against the Boca Raton management, the General was quiet for four months, but in September he was stirred to the depths of his soul by the discovery that he was being played for a sucker. Harry Reichenbach had become connected with the Mizner promotion. Sales at Boca Raton had been averaging only two million dollars a week, and Wilson Mizner was dissatisfied. He wanted a high-power brain to run the Boca Raton ballyhoo, so he lured Reichenbach to Florida. Reichenbach regarded great people like General du Pont as mere pawns for his publicity gambits. He looked on international situations as mere backdrops for press-agent stunts. One of the sorrows of his life was that Washington interference had spoiled his plan to have the screen vampire Clara Kimball Young captured by Mexican rebels and rescued by the United States Cavalry. Arriving in Florida, Reichenbach sensed that the real-estate market was being hurt by phony advertising. Gross exaggeration had made the public skeptical. The only thing Reichenbach could do was murder skepticism by choking it to deat~ ~th hyperbole. The public discounted Florida advertising nine~ ~r cent. Thus, anything less than hundredfold exaggerat~ ~derstatement. To make any impression at all, Reichen~ ~ to rant and rave. He peopled the jungles and bogs o~ ~he snootiest aristocracy ever assembled in one place s~ ~uis XIV. When the one complete structure in Boca ~ ~urger stand, he advertised, "No Existing World Resor~ ~ashion Compares with Boca Raton." Reichenbach didn~ ~is word for it. Cautioning his artists not to be parsimon~ ~laces, temples, towers, and civic centers, he spread ma~ ~the imaginary city over double-page advertisements t~ ~statement that "The Riviera, Biarritz, Mentone, Nice, Sor~ ~he Lido, Egypt—all that charms in each of these finds consumm~tion in Boca Raton." The skepticism of Rupert Hughes, debunker of George Washington, was beaten down by Reichenbach's pictures and text. He wrote to a national-magazine editor suggesting an article on American genius and enterprise as exemplified by the glorious city of Boca Raton, but the editor wrote back that he happened to have seen Boca Raton and it was still a practically untouched wilderness. General du Pont began his second attack on the Boca Raton management after reading an announcement of the Mizners' hundred-million-dollar "development program" in the Palm Beach *Post* of September 11th. "We have no such program and should not have advertised it," he wrote to Addison. On September 15th, the General sent another letter to Addison, this one full of complaints about Harry Reichenbach. He objected to modest little statements like "Yachts discharge directly at the lake entrance to this hotel," when, in fact, there was no hotel and nothing bigger than a large skiff could have landed at the proposed site of the proposed hotel. By this time, the Mizners had begun to regard the General as a disgruntled old kill-joy, and they paid no attention to his outcries.

Reichenbach's next move enraged the General. Reichenbach had invented a sovereign cure for skepticism. As his advertisements grew more delirious, he included the following in each one: "Attach This Advertisement to Your Contract for Deed. It Becomes a Part Thereof." Under the heading of "A Declaration of Responsibility" Reichenbach asserted that the sponsors of Boca Raton guaranteed each and every statement made in Boca Raton advertising. The General realized that the directors were now liable if any preposterous claim about Boca Raton failed to come true. Lining up Jesse Livermore and some other directors, he started a crusade to fire Wilson Mizner, Harry Reichenbach, and a couple of other Boca Raton executives. One of the General's bombshells was a photostat of a newspaper account of Wilson Mizner's conviction for running a gambling house in 1919. Wilson retaliated by going to the county jail and inducing a girl prisoner who had become a Palm Beach sensation as a bad-check passer to sign a letter to the General saying, "You are responsible for my pregnancy," and making other accusations. These were sheer inventions, but Wilson thought it might be well to give the General a new subject to think about. The General, however, was not to be diverted. Late in November, he dropped in to see Bess Hammons, who was a confidante of the warring factions. "I've got a press statement I want to read you, Bess," he said. "I'm getting out. I can't stand— Say, Bess, did you ever see this one? Take any card you choose." For half an hour, the General did card tricks, slapping his thigh with pleasure at her wonder and astonishment. Then he put the cards in one pocket and took a typewritten statement out of another. "I'm getting out, Bess," he said. "I've never been connected with a failure in my life, and this thing is sure to fail with these people in charge."

The General's statement, blasting the methods of the Mizners, was given out not only in Florida but in New York, and it was played up in the *Times* and the *Herald Tribune*. It later became the General's trump card in fighting innumerable lawsuits, as it proved that he had tried to stop the fantastic ballyhoo for Boca Raton. The Mizners issued a reply charging that the General had quit because he wasn't permitted to load the Mizner payroll with du Ponts. Before the General's statement was published, the Mizners had to keep their offices open until after midnight to handle the demand for Boca Raton lots; after the statement, the place was a tomb. The General's attack put a wet blanket on the whole boom. Russell Hull, whose firm dealt in lots in Miami and Palm Beach, said that sales in both places stopped completely after the General's blast. Charts of the Florida boom made by the economist Homer B. Vanderblue show the nose dive beginning at just about the time of the General's statement. Either the General started the collapse or he displayed perfect timing in getting out from under.

As the boom started to sag, some of the boomers tried to prop it up with increased advertising and wilder claims than ever. An Inventory Congress was held by the realtors in West Palm Beach to take stock of the situation, and the speakers generally contended that more vision was needed. Have-Faith-in-Florida Clubs were organized in other parts of the country. Frank Winch, a circus and theatrical man, attended a boosters' get-together in Miami. The guest of honor was a highly groomed and monocled Prussian, who pledged tremendous reserves of European capital to put the boom back on the upward spiral. The Prussian Croesus said that he and other financial giants of the Continent had been compelled to recognize that Florida was the coming playground of the world, and were planning to invest huge sums in Boca Raton and other great developments. The realtors left the rally exhilarated. The trend, however, continued downward. One day, when the crash was about complete, Winch was in West Palm Beach with Samuel Gumpertz, who was then running Ringling's Circus. Directed by a policeman, they went to a speakeasy. The proprietor was not especially well groomed and he wore no monocle, but he was unmistakably the Prussian hero of the boosters' get-together. After a few drinks, Winch began to ask questions. "Oh," said the speakeasy man, "I did that for Wilson Mizner. I used to be a steward with the Hamburg-American Line. I met Wilson when he was crossing the

Atlantic. He was a big tipper and a fine fellow. When I came down here, he loaned me the money to buy a seaplane to fly rum in from Bimini. When he wanted me to be a Prussian capitalist, I was delighted to do it for him. I'd do anything for Wilson Mizner."

On January 13, 1926, less than two months after General du Pont had turned against the Mizners, *Variety* stated, under the headline "FLORIDA SLIPPING," that everybody was anxious to unload. The Mizners put on a brave front at a housewarming in February for the Cloister, the clubhouse and hotel at Boca Raton, but it was fighting after the bell. In March, W. O. McGeehan, in a dispatch to the *Herald Tribune* from the training camp of the New York Giants in Sarasota, wrote that destitute realtors had been caught disguising themselves as Giant rookies, so they could get free meals by signing checks at a restaurant that catered to the ballplayers. The *Times* reported that a hundred and fifty-four men stood in line in Miami to answer an advertisement for one night watchman. Most of the little speculators charged the big speculators with fraud. "The good people went in for a gamble," said Wilson Mizner, "and they are full of moral indignation because they lost." Lawsuits were filed by the thousand. When the sheriff came to Wilson's house to serve a paper, Wilson pulled open a drawer, revealing a stack of complaints and subpoenas. "Sheriff," he said, "would you like this on top or in the middle of the deck?" In a letter to Arthur Somers Roche, he wrote, "I never open my door but a Writ blows in—Assumpsit, Damages, Nudum Pactum, and old Lis Pendens. When the bell rings, I open the door, automatically stick out my hand, admit being Wilson Mizner, and accept service. I spend my evenings shuffling these fearsome documents and can already cut to any complaint I desire. This proficiency may prove valuable, should the judge wish to decide by chance what case to try next."

Wilson hated the ways of the Florida courts. He had always regarded a lawsuit as a contest in which rival raconteurs took the witness stand and tried to outnarrate one another. He was hurt because the Florida Judge gave the preference to written instruments over the most talented testimony. In his letter to Roche, Wilson expressed the deepest regret about his failure to imitate the wisdom of the lame Confederate general who, on seeing disaster ahead, said, "Boys, things look tough. But remember, the eyes of Dixieland are on you. The beauty and chivalry of the South know our desperate plight and thank God for it, as only in extremities like this are heroes made. The hated Yankees are preparing to charge—let them come! Don't shoot until you see the whites of their eyes and feel their fetid breath on your cheeks. A volley at such close range should wreak havoc. Then, my brave fellows, take to the bayonet and fight it out hand to hand, until the case is hopeless. Then you can retreat—but, seeing I'm lame, I'll start now."

Wilson didn't start to retreat until 1927, and then he didn't stop until he reached Hollywood, where he became a restaurant man and screen writer. Addison, who had demonstrated his faith in Boca Raton by assuming personal responsibility for the debts of the company, lived mainly on loans from wealthy friends during the last years of his life. When he died, in February, 1933, his estate was found to be insolvent.

Eudora Welty

PETRIFIED MAN

REACH in my purse and git me a cigarette without no powder in it if you kin, Mrs. Fletcher, honey," said Leota to her ten o'clock shampoo-and-set customer. "I don't like no perfumed cigarettes."

Mrs. Fletcher gladly reached over to the lavender shelf under the lavender-framed mirror, shook a hair net loose from the clasp of the patent-leather bag, and slapped her hand down quickly on a powder puff which burst out when the purse was opened.

"Why, look at the peanuts, Leota!" said Mrs. Fletcher in her marvelling voice.

"Honey, them goobers has been in my purse a week if they's been in it a day. Mrs. Pike bought them peanuts."

"Who's Mrs. Pike?" asked Mrs. Fletcher, settling back. Hidden in this den of curling fluid and henna packs, separated by a lavender swing-door from the other customers, who were being gratified in other booths, she could give her curiosity its freedom. She looked expectantly at the black part in Leota's yellow curls as she bent to light the cigarette.

"Mrs. Pike is this lady from New Orleans," said Leota, puffing, and pressing into Mrs. Fletcher's scalp with strong red-nailed fingers. "A friend, not a customer. You see, like maybe I told you last time, me and Fred and Sal and Joe all had us a fuss, so Sal and Joe up and moved out, so we didn't do a thing but rent out their room. So we rented it to Mrs. Pike. And Mr. Pike." She flicked an ash into the basket of dirty towels. "Mrs. Pike is a very decided blonde. *She* bought me the peanuts."

"She must be cute," said Mrs. Fletcher.

"Honey, 'cute' ain't the word for what she is. I'm tellin' you, Mrs. Pike is attractive. She has her a good time. She's got a sharp eye out, Mrs. Pike has."

She dashed the comb through the air, and paused dramatically as a cloud of Mrs. Fletcher's hennaed hair floated out of the lavender teeth like a small storm-cloud.

"Hair fallin'."

"Aw, Leota."

"Uh-huh, commencin' to fall out," said Leota, combing again, and letting fall another cloud.

"Is it any dandruff in it?" Mrs. Fletcher was frowning, her hair-line eyebrows diving down toward her nose, and her wrinkled, beady-lashed eyelids batting with concentration.

"Nope." She combed again. "Just fallin' out."

"Bet it was that last perm'nent you gave me that did it," Mrs. Fletcher said cruelly. "Remember you cooked me fourteen minutes."

"You had fourteen minutes comin' to you," said Leota with finality.

"Bound to be somethin'," persisted Mrs. Fletcher. "Dandruff, dandruff. I couldn't of caught a thing like that from Mr. Fletcher, could I?"

"Well," Leota answered at last, "you know what I heard in here yestiddy, one of Thelma's ladies was settin' over yonder in Thelma's booth gittin' a machineless, and I don't mean to insist or insinuate or anything, Mrs. Fletcher, but Thelma's lady just happ'med to throw out—I forgotten what she was talkin' about at the time—that you was p-r-e-g., and lots of times that'll make your hair do awful funny, fall out and God knows what all. It just ain't our fault, is the way I look at it."

There was a pause. The women stared at each other in the mirror.

"Who was it?" demanded Mrs. Fletcher.

"Honey, I really couldn't say," said Leota. "Not that you look it."

"Where's Thelma? I'll get it out of her," said Mrs. Fletcher.

"Now, honey, I wouldn't go and git mad over a little thing like that," Leota said, combing hastily, as though to hold Mrs. Fletcher down by the hair. "I'm sure it was somebody didn't mean no harm in the world. How far gone are you?"

"Just wait," said Mrs. Fletcher, and shrieked for Thelma, who came in and took a drag from Leota's cigarette.

"Thelma, honey, throw your mind back to yestiddy if you kin," said Leota, drenching Mrs. Fletcher's hair with a thick fluid and catching the overflow in a cold wet towel at her neck.

"Well, I got my lady half wound for a spiral," said Thelma doubtfully.

"This won't take but a minute," said Leota. "Who is it you got in there, old Horse Face? Just cast your mind back and try to remember who your lady was yestiddy who happ'm to mention that my customer was pregnant, that's all. She's dead to know."

Thelma drooped her blood-red lips and looked over Mrs. Fletcher's head into the mirror. "Why, honey, I ain't got the faintest," she breathed. "I really don't recollect the faintest. But I'm sure she meant no harm. I declare, I forgot my hair finally got combed and thought it was a stranger behind me."

"Was it that Mrs. Hutchinson?" Mrs. Fletcher was tensely polite.

"Mrs. Hutchinson? Oh, Mrs. Hutchinson." Thelma batted her eyes. "Naw, precious, she come on Thursday and didn't ev'm mention your name. I doubt if she ev'm knows you're on the way."

"Thelma!" cried Leota staunchly.

"All I know is, whoever it is 'll be sorry some day. Why, I just barely knew it myself!" cried Mrs. Fletcher. "Just let her wait!"

"Why? What're you gonna do to her?"

It was a child's voice, and the women looked down. A little boy was making tents with aluminum wave pinchers on the floor under the sink.

"Billy Boy, hon, mustn't bother nice ladies," Leota smiled. She slapped him brightly and behind her back waved Thelma out of the booth. "Ain't Billy Boy a sight? Only three years old and already just nuts about the beauty-parlor business."

"I never saw him here before," said Mrs. Fletcher, still unmollified.

"He ain't been here before, that's how come," said Leota. "He belongs to Mrs. Pike. She got her a job but it was Fay's Millinery. He oughtn't to try on those ladies' hats, they come down over his eyes like I don't know what. They just git to look ridiculous, that's what, an' of course he's gonna put 'em on: hats. They tole Mrs. Pike they didn't appreciate him hangin' around there. Here, he couldn't hurt a thing."

"Well! I don't like children that much," said Mrs. Fletcher.

"Well!" said Leota moodily.

"Well! I'm almost tempted not to have this one," said Mrs. Fletcher. "That Mrs. Hutchinson! Just looks straight through you when she sees you on the street and then spits at you behind your back."

"Mr. Fletcher would beat you on the head if you didn't have it now," said Leota reasonably. "After going this far."

Mrs. Fletcher sat up straight. "Mr. Fletcher can't do a thing with me."

"He can't!" Leota winked at herself in the mirror.

"No, siree, he can't. If he so much as raises his voice against me, he knows good and well I'll have one of my sick headaches, and then I'm just not fit to live with. And if I really look that pregnant already—"

"Well, now, honey, I just want you to know—I habm't told any of my ladies and I ain't goin' to tell 'em—even that you're losin' your hair. You just get you one of those Stork-a-Lure dresses and stop worryin'. What people don't know don't hurt nobody, as Mrs. Pike says."

"Did you tell Mrs. Pike?" asked Mrs. Fletcher sulkily.

"Well, Mrs. Fletcher, look, you ain't ever goin' to lay eyes on Mrs. Pike or her lay eyes on you, so what diffunce does it make in the long run?"

"I knew it!" Mrs. Fletcher deliberately nodded her head so as to destroy a ringlet Leota was working on behind her ear. "Mrs. Pike!"

Leota sighed. "I reckon I might as well tell you. It wasn't any more Thelma's lady tole me you was pregnant than a bat."

"Not Mrs. Hutchinson?"

"Naw, Lord! It was Mrs. Pike."

"Mrs. Pike!" Mrs. Fletcher could only sputter and let curling fluid roll into her ear. "How could Mrs. Pike possibly know I was pregnant or otherwise, when she doesn't even know me? The nerve of some people!"

"Well, here's how it was. Remember Sunday?"

"Yes," said Mrs. Fletcher.

"Sunday, Mrs. Pike an' me was all by ourself. Mr. Pike and Fred had gone over to Eagle Lake, sayin' they was goin' to catch 'em some fish, but they didn't a course. So we was settin' in Mrs. Pike's car, it's a 1939 Dodge—"

"1939, eh," said Mrs. Fletcher.

"—An' we was gettin' us a Jax beer apiece—that's the beer that Mrs. Pike says is made right in N.O., so she won't drink no other kind. So I seen you drive up to the drugstore an' run in for just a secont, leavin' I reckon Mr. Fletcher in the car, an' come runnin' out with looked like a perscription. So I says to Mrs. Pike, just to be makin' talk, 'Right yonder's Mrs. Fletcher, and I reckon that's Mr. Fletcher—she's one of my regular customers,' I says."

"I had on a figured print," said Mrs. Fletcher tentatively.

"You sure did," agreed Leota. "So Mrs. Pike, she give you a good look—she's very observant, a good judge of character, cute as a minute, you know—and she says, 'I bet you another Jax that lady's three months on the way.'"

"What gall!" said Mrs. Fletcher. "Mrs. Pike!"

"Mrs. Pike ain't goin' to bite you," said Leota. "Mrs. Pike is a lovely girl, you'd be crazy about her, Mrs. Fletcher. But she can't sit still a minute. We went to the travellin' freak show yestiddy after work. I got through early—nine o'clock. In the vacant store next door. What, you ain't been?"

"No, I despise freaks," declared Mrs. Fletcher.

"Aw. Well, honey, talkin' about bein' pregnant an' all, you ought to see those twins in a bottle, you really owe it to yourself."

"What twins?" asked Mrs. Fletcher out of the side of her mouth.

"Well, honey, they got these two twins in a bottle, see? Born joined plumb together—dead a course." Leota dropped her voice into a soft lyrical hum. "They was about this long—pardon—must of been full time, all right, wouldn't you say?—an' they had these two heads an' two faces an' four arms an' four legs, all kind of joined *here*. See, this face looked this-a-way, and the other face looked that-a-way, over their shoulder, see. Kinda pathetic."

"Glah!" said Mrs. Fletcher disapprovingly.

"Well, ugly? Honey, I mean to tell you—their parents was first cousins and all like that. Billy Boy, git me a fresh towel from off Teeny's stack—this 'n's wringin' wet—an' quit ticklin' my ankles with that curler. I declare! He don't miss nothin'.."

"Me and Mr. Fletcher aren't one speck of kin, or he could never of had me," said Mrs. Fletcher placidly.

"Of course not!" protested Leota. "Neither is me an' Fred, not that we know of. Well, honey, what Mrs. Pike liked was the pygmies. They've got these pygmies down there, too, an' Mrs. Pike was just wild about 'em. You know, the teeniniest men in the universe? Well, honey, they can just rest back on their little bohunkus an' roll around an' you can't hardly tell if they're sittin' or standin'. That'll give you some idea. They're about forty-two years old. Just suppose it was your husband!"

"Well, Mr. Fletcher is five foot nine and one half," said Mrs. Fletcher quickly.

"Fred's five foot ten," said Leota, "but I tell him he's still a shrimp, account of I'm so tall." She made a deep wave over Mrs. Fletcher's other temple with the comb. "Well, these pygmies are a kind of a dark brown, Mrs. Fletcher. Not bad-lookin' for what they are, you know."

"I wouldn't care for them," said Mrs. Fletcher. "What does that Mrs. Pike see in them?"

"Aw, I don't know," said Leota. "She's just cute, that's all. But they got this man, this petrified man, that ever'thing ever since he was nine years old, when it goes through his digestion, see, somehow Mrs. Pike says it goes to his joints and has been turning to stone."

"How awful!" said Mrs. Fletcher.

"He's forty-two too. That looks like a bad age."

"Who said so, that Mrs. Pike? I bet she's forty-two," said Mrs. Fletcher.

"Naw," said Leota, "Mrs. Pike's thirty-three, born in January, an Aquarian. He could move his head—like this. A course his head and mind ain't a joint, so to speak, and I guess his stomach ain't, either—not yet, anyways. But see—his food, he eats it, and it goes down, see, and then he digests it"—Leota rose on her toes for an instant—"and it goes out to his joints and before you can say 'Jack Robinson,' it's stone—pure stone. He's turning to stone. How'd you like to be married to a guy like that? All he can do, he can move his head just a quarter of an inch. A course he *looks* just *terrible*."

"I should think he would," said Mrs. Fletcher frostily. "Mr. Fletcher takes bending exercises every night of the world. I make him."

"All Fred does is lay around the house like a rug. I wouldn't be surprised if he woke up some day and couldn't move. The petrified man just sat there moving his quarter of an inch though," said Leota reminiscently.

"Did Mrs. Pike like the petrified man?" asked Mrs. Fletcher.

"Not as much as she did the others," said Leota deprecatingly. "And then she likes a man to be a good dresser, and all that."

"Is Mr. Pike a good dresser?" asked Mrs. Fletcher sceptically.

"Oh, well, yeah," said Leota, "but he's twelve or fourteen years older'n her. She ast Lady Evangeline about him."

"Who's Lady Evangeline?" asked Mrs. Fletcher.

"Well, it's this mind reader they got in the freak show," said Leota. "Was real good. Lady Evangeline is her name, and if I had another dollar I wouldn't do a thing but have my other palm read. She had what Mrs. Pike said was the 'sixth mind' but she had the worst mani-cure I ever saw on a living person."

"What did she tell Mrs. Pike?" asked Mrs. Fletcher.

"She told her Mr. Pike was as true to her as he could be and besides, would come into some money."

"Humph!" said Mrs. Fletcher. "What does he do?"

"I can't tell," said Leota, "because he don't work. Lady Evangeline didn't tell me enough about my nature or anything. And I would like to go back and find out some more about this boy. Used to go with this boy until he got married to this girl. Oh, shoot, that was about three and a half years ago, when you was still goin' to the Robert E. Lee Beauty Shop in Jackson. He married her for her money. Another fortune-teller tole me that at the time. So I'm not in love with him any more, anyway, besides being married to Fred, but Mrs. Pike thought, just for the hell of it, see, to ask Lady Evangeline was he happy."

"Does Mrs. Pike know everything about you already?" asked Mrs. Fletcher unbelievingly. "Mercy!"

"Oh, yeah, I tole her ever'thing about ever'thing, from now on back to I don't know when—to when I first started goin' out," said Leota. "So I ast Lady Evangeline for one of my questions, was he happily married, and she says, just like she was glad I ask her, 'Honey,' she says, 'naw, he idn't. You write down this day, March 8, 1941,' she says, 'and mock it down: three years from today him and her won't be occupyin' the same bed.' There it is, up on the wall with them other dates—see, Mrs. Fletcher? And she says, 'Child, you ought to be glad you didn't git him, because he's so mercenary.' So I'm glad I married Fred. He sure ain't mercenary, money don't mean a thing to him. But I sure would like to go back and have my other palm read."

"Did Mrs. Pike believe in what the fortune-teller said?" asked Mrs. Fletcher in a superior tone of voice.

"Lord, yes, she's from New Orleans. Ever'body in New Orleans believes ever'thing spooky. One of 'em in New Orleans before it was raided says to Mrs. Pike one summer she was goin' to go from State to State and meet some grey-headed men, and, sure enough, she says she went on a beautician convention up to Chicago. . . ."

"Oh!" said Mrs. Fletcher. "Oh, is Mrs. Pike a beautician too?"

"Sure she is," protested Leota. "She's a beautician. I'm goin' to git her in here if I can. Before she married. But it don't leave you. She says sure enough, there was three men who was a very large part of making her trip what it was, and they all three had grey in their hair and they went in six States. Got Christmas cards from 'em. Billy Boy, go see if Thelma's got any dry cotton. Look how Mrs. Fletcher's a-drippin'."

"Where did Mrs. Pike meet Mr. Pike?" asked Mrs. Fletcher primly.

"On another train," said Leota.

"I met Mr. Fletcher, or rather he met me, in a rental library," said Mrs. Fletcher with dignity, as she watched the net come down over her head.

"Honey, me an' Fred, we met in a rumble seat eight months ago and we was practically on what you might call the way to the altar inside of half an hour," said Leota in a guttural voice, and bit a bobby pin open. "Course it don't last. Mrs. Pike says nothin' like that ever lasts."

"Mr. Fletcher and myself are as much in love as the day we married," said Mrs. Fletcher belligerently as Leota stuffed cotton into her ears.

"Mrs. Pike says it don't last," repeated Leota in a louder voice. "Now go git under the dryer. You can turn yourself on, can't you? I'll be back to comb you out. Durin' lunch I promised to give Mrs. Pike a facial. You know—free. Her bein' in the business, so to speak."

"I bet she needs one," said Mrs. Fletcher, letting the swing-door fly back against Leota. "Oh, pardon me."

A week later, on time for her appointment, Mrs. Fletcher sank heavily into Leota's chair after first removing a drug-store rental book, called *Life Is Like That*, from the seat. She stared in a discouraged way into the mirror.

"You can tell it when I'm sitting down, all right," she said.

Leota seemed preoccupied and stood shaking out a lavender cloth. She began to pin it around Mrs. Fletcher's neck in silence.

"I said you sure can tell it when I'm sitting straight on and coming at you this way," Mrs. Fletcher said.

"Why, honey, naw you can't," said Leota gloomily. "Why, I'd never know. If somebody was to come up to me on the street and say, 'Mrs. Fletcher is pregnant!' I'd say, 'Heck, she don't look it to me.' "

"If a certain party hadn't found it out and spread it around, it wouldn't be too late even now," said Mrs. Fletcher frostily, but Leota was almost choking her with the cloth, pinning it so tight, and she couldn't speak clearly. She paddled her hands in the air until Leota wearily loosened her.

"Listen, honey, you're just a virgin compared to Mrs. Montjoy," Leota was going on, still absent-minded. She bent Mrs. Fletcher back in the chair and, sighing, tossed liquid from a teacup on to her head and dug both hands into her scalp. "You know Mrs. Montjoy—her husband's that premature-grey-headed fella?"

"She's in the Trojan Garden Club, is all I know," said Mrs. Fletcher.

"Well, honey," said Leota, but in a weary voice, "she come in here not the week before and not the day before she had her baby—she come in here the very selfsame day, I mean to tell you. Child, we was all plumb scared to death. There she was! Come for her shampoo an' set. Why, Mrs. Fletcher, in an hour an' twenty minutes she was layin' up there in the Babtist Hospital with a seb'm-pound son. It was that close a shave. I declare, if I hadn't been so tired I would of drank up a bottle of gin that night."

"What gall," said Mrs. Fletcher. "I never knew her at all well."

"See, her husband was waitin' outside in the car, and her bags was all packed an' in the back seat, an' she was all ready, 'cept she wanted her shampoo an' set. An' havin' one pain right after another. Her husband kep' comin' in here, scared-like, but couldn't do nothin' with her a course. She yelled bloody murder, too, but she always yelled her head off when I give her a perm'nent."

"She must of been crazy," said Mrs. Fletcher. "How did she look?"

"Shoot!" said Leota.

"Well, I can guess," said Mrs. Fletcher. "Awful."

"Just wanted to look pretty while she was havin' her baby, is all," said Leota airily. "Course, we was glad to give the lady what she was after—that's our motto—but I bet a hour later she wasn't payin' no mind to them little end curls. I bet she wasn't thinkin' about she ought to have on a net. It wouldn't of done her no good if she had."

"No, I don't suppose it would," said Mrs. Fletcher.

"Yeah man! She was a-yellin'. Just like when I give her perm'nent."

"Her husband ought to make her behave. Don't it seem that way to you?" asked Mrs. Fletcher. "He ought to put his foot down."

"Ha," said Leota. "A lot he could do. Maybe some women is soft."

"Oh, you mistake me, I don't mean for her to get soft—far from it! Women have to stand up for themselves, or there's just no telling. But now you take me—I ask Mr. Fletcher's advice now and then, and he appreciates it, especially on something important, like is it time for a permanent—not that I've told him about the baby. He says, 'Why, dear, go ahead!' Just ask their *advice*."

"Huh! If I ever ast Fred's advice we'd be floatin' down the Yazoo River on a houseboat or somethin' by this time," said Leota. "I'm sick of Fred. I told him to go over to Vicksburg."

"Is he going?" demanded Mrs. Fletcher.

"Sure. See, the fortune-teller—I went back and had my other palm read, since we've got to rent the room agin—said my lover was goin' to work in Vicksburg, so I don't know who she could mean, unless she meant Fred. And Fred ain't workin' here—that much is so."

"Is he going to work in Vicksburg?" asked Mrs. Fletcher. "And—"

"Sure. Lady Evangeline said so. Said the future is going to be brighter than the present. He don't want to go, but I ain't gonna put up with nothin' like that. Lays around the house an' bulls—did bull—with that good-for-nothin' Mr. Pike. He says if he goes who'll cook, but I says I never get to eat anyway—not meals. Billy Boy, take Mrs. Grover that *Screen Secrets* and leg it."

Mrs. Fletcher heard stamping feet go out the door.

"Is that that Mrs. Pike's little boy here again?" she asked, sitting up gingerly.

"Yeah, that's still him." Leota stuck out her tongue.

Mrs. Fletcher could hardly believe her eyes. "Well! How's Mrs. Pike, your attractive new friend with the sharp eyes who spreads it around town that perfect strangers are pregnant?" she asked in a sweetened tone.

"Oh, Mizziz Pike." Leota combed Mrs. Fletcher's hair with heavy strokes.

"You act like you're tired," said Mrs. Fletcher.

"Tired? Feel like it's four o'clock in the afternoon already," said Leota. "I ain't told you the awful luck we had, me and Fred? It's the worst thing you ever heard of. Maybe *you* think Mrs. Pike's got sharp eyes. Shoot, there's a limit! Well, you know, we rented out our room to this Mr. and Mrs. Pike from New Orleans when Sal an' Joe Fentress got mad at us 'cause they drank up some home-brew we had in the closet—Sal an' Joe did. So, a week ago Sat'day Mr. and Mrs. Pike moved in. Well, I kinda fixed up the room, you know—put a sofa pillow on the couch and picked some ragged robbins and put in a vase, but they never did say they appreciated it. Anyway, then I put some old magazines on the table."

"I think that was lovely," said Mrs. Fletcher.

"Wait. So, come night 'fore last, Fred and this Mr. Pike, who Fred just took up with, was back from they said they was fishin', bein' as neither one of 'em has got a job to his name, and we was all settin' around in their room. So Mrs. Pike was settin' there, readin' a old *Startling G-Man Tales* that was mine, mind you, I'd bought it myself, and all of a sudden she jumps!—into the air—you'd 'a' thought she'd set on a spider—an' says, 'Canfield'—ain't that silly, that's Mr. Pike— 'Canfield, my God A'mighty,' she says, 'honey,' she says, 'we're rich, and you won't have to work.' Not that he turned one hand anyway. Well, me and Fred rushes over to her, and Mr. Pike, too, and there she sets, pointin' her finger at a photo in my copy of *Startling G-Man*. 'See that man?' yells Mrs. Pike. 'Remember him, Canfield?' 'Never forget a face,' says Mr. Pike. 'It's Mr. Petrie, that we stayed with him in the apartment next to ours in Toulouse Street in N.O. for six weeks. Mr. Petrie.' 'Well,' says Mrs. Pike, like she can't hold out one secont longer, 'Mr. Petrie is wanted for five hundred dollars cash, for rapin' four women in California, and I know where he is.' "

"Mercy!" said Mrs. Fletcher. "Where was he?"

At some time Leota had washed her hair and now she yanked her up by the back locks and sat her up.

"Know where he was?"

"I certainly don't," Mrs. Fletcher said. Her scalp hurt all over.

Leota flung a towel around the top of her customer's head. "No-where else but in that freak show! I saw him just as plain as Mrs. Pike. *He* was the petrified man!"

"Who would ever have thought that!" cried Mrs. Fletcher sympathetically.

"So Mr. Pike says, 'Well whatta you know about that,' an' he looks real hard at the photo and whistles. And she starts dancin' and singin' about their good luck. She meant our bad luck! I made a point of tellin' that fortune-teller the next time I saw her. I said, 'Listen, that magazine was layin' around the house for a month, and there was the freak show runnin' night an' day, not two steps away from my own beauty parlor, with Mr. Petrie just settin' there waitin'. An' it had to be Mr. and Mrs. Pike, almost perfect strangers.' "

"What gall," said Mrs. Fletcher. She was only sitting there, wrapped in a turban, but she did not mind.

"Fortune-tellers don't care. And Mrs. Pike, she goes around actin' like she thinks she was Mrs. God," said Leota. "So they're goin' to leave tomorrow, Mr. and Mrs. Pike. And in the meantime I got to keep that mean, bad little ole kid here, gettin' under my feet ever' minute of the day an' talkin' back too."

"Have they gotten the five hundred dollars' reward already?" asked Mrs. Fletcher.

"Well," said Leota, "at first Mr. Pike didn't want to do anything about it. Can you feature that? Said he kinda liked that ole bird and said he was real nice to 'em, lent 'em money or somethin'. But Mrs. Pike simply tole him he could just go to hell, and I can see her point. She says, 'You ain't worked a lick in six months, and here I make five hundred dollars in two seconts, and what thanks do I get for it? You go to hell, Canfield,' she says. So," Leota went on in a despondent voice, "they called up the cops and they caught the ole bird, all right, right there in the freak show where I saw him with my own eyes, thinkin' he was petrified. He's the one. Did it under his real name— Mr. Petrie. Four women in California, all in the month of August. So Mrs. Pike gits five hundred dollars. And my magazine, and right next door to my beauty parlor. I cried all night, but Fred said it wasn't a bit of use and to go to sleep, because the whole thing was just a sort of coincidence—you know: can't do nothin' about it. He says it put him clean out of the notion of goin' to Vicksburg for a few days till we rent out the room agin—no tellin' who we'll git this time."

"But can you imagine anybody knowing this old man, that's raped four women?" persisted Mrs. Fletcher, and she shuddered audibly. "Did Mrs. Pike *speak* to him when she met him in the freak show?"

Leota had begun to comb Mrs. Fletcher's hair. "I says to her, I says, 'I didn't notice you fallin' on his neck when he was the petrified man— don't tell me you didn't recognize your fine friend?' And she says, 'I didn't recognize him with that white powder all over his face. He just looked familiar,' Mrs. Pike says, 'and lots of people look familiar.' But she says that ole petrified man did put her in mind of somebody. She wondered who it was! Kep' her awake, which man she'd ever knew it reminded her of. So when she seen the photo, it all come to her. Like a flash. Mr. Petrie. The way he'd turn his head and look at her when she took him in his breakfast."

"Took him in his breakfast!" shrieked Mrs. Fletcher. "Listen—don't tell me. I'd 'a' felt something."

"Four women. I guess those women didn't have the faintest notion at the time they'd be worth a hunderd an' twenty-five bucks a piece some day to Mrs. Pike. We ast her how old the fella was then, an' she says he musta had one foot in the grave, at least. Can you beat it?"

"Not really petrified at all, of course," said Mrs. Fletcher meditatively. She drew herself up. "I'd 'a' felt something," she said proudly.

"Shoot! I did feel somethin'," said Leota. "I tole Fred when I got home I felt so funny. I said, 'Fred, that ole petrified man sure did leave me with a funny feelin'.' He says, 'Funny-haha or funny-peculiar?' and I says, 'Funny-peculiar.'" She pointed her comb into the air emphatically.

"I'll bet you did," said Mrs. Fletcher.

They both heard a crackling noise.

Leota screamed, "Billy Boy! What you doin' in my purse?"

"Aw, I'm just eatin' these ole stale peanuts up," said Billy Boy.

"You come here to me!" screamed Leota, recklessly flinging down the comb, which scattered a whole ashtray full of bobby pins and knocked down a row of Coca-Cola bottles. "This is the last straw!"

"I caught him! I caught him!" giggled Mrs. Fletcher. "I'll hold him on my lap. You bad, bad boy, you! I guess I better learn how to spank little old bad boys," she said.

Leota's eleven o'clock customer pushed open the swing-door upon Leota paddling him heartily with the brush, while he gave angry but belittling screams which penetrated beyond the booth and filled the whole curious beauty parlor. From everywhere ladies began to gather round to watch the paddling. Billy Boy kicked both Leota and Mrs. Fletcher as hard as he could, Mrs. Fletcher with her new fixed smile.

Billy Boy stomped through the group of wild-haired ladies and went out the door, but flung back the words, "If you're so smart, why ain't you rich?"

Mac Hyman

EXCERPTS FROM
NO TIME FOR SERGEANTS

["No Time for Sergeants" *recounts the army adventures of Draftee Will Stockdale, of Georgia. Stockdale is willing, genial, incredibly strong—but not very bright, and unused to discipline of any kind. He is the nemesis of Sergeant King, whose effort to fob him off on permanent latrine duty culminates in the first episode reprinted here. The second episode takes place after Stockdale and his buddy, Ben, are assigned to practice missions. Sergeant King thinks he is rid of them for good—but proves wrong indeed.*

No Time for Sergeants, *published in October* 1954, *and a selection of the Book-of-the-Month Club, is, in my opinion, one of the most hilarious books of the past ten years.—*EDITOR'S NOTE]

1.

THE next day for inspection I cleaned up everything real white, except the tops which warnt supposed to be white, and Sergeant King went pacing all round the place examining bunks and getting wrinkles out of them and things like that, and telling everybody how to act, and just what the officers would do and everything. He worried a good bit about inspection like that, and he explained it to everybody again, and it happened just like he said it would too. The door opened and some Lieutenants and the Captain and the Colonel come in, and Sergeant King called out "Attention!" and everybody stood real stiff like they warnt breathing, and the Lieutenants peeped and sniffed around here and there, and the Captain went around looking over the men in their fresh uniforms, but the Colonel, *he* didnt waste no time at all—he only glanced at things and headed right past, coming for the latrine where I was standing at attention by myself, just like Sergeant King said he would do.

And he really was the most interested in latrines of any man you ever seen in your life. He was a nice old fellow too, gray-headed with a little moustache and looked like an uncle of mine, but I knowed it warnt as my uncle hadnt been drafted that I had heered—anyhow, he headed right back for the latrine and went in and looked around, nodding his head and smiling, and seemed mighty pleased with it. And I was myself when I seen the look on his face and seen Sergeant King kind of cutting his eyes around at him. But I didnt want to take all the credit for myself, so when he come back by me on the way out, I said, "Colonel, I hope you like how we fixed up the latrine for you."

And when he turned to me and said, "What?" I said, "The reason it is so clean was mainly because of Sergeant King there. He's the one behind it all; I just done the cleaning. He said he had never seen a man in his life care more about latrines than you do, and that's the reason . . ."

"Attention!" the Captain yelled out. "You're at attention there!" and he come bounding over with his face all red like he was going to jump all over me.

But I didnt pay much attention to him because I warnt talking to him nohow, and besides the Colonel held up his hand at the Captain to shut him up, and then he looked at me for a while and asked me to go over what I had said again. So I did, and this time I really laid it on good too. I told him how Sergeant King had told me to clean it up so good because he had never seen a man in his life that would come back and stick his head right down in the bowls the way *he* done, and I think the Colonel kind of appreciated it too, because he looked around and said, "And which one is Sergeant King?"

So I pointed him out, though Sergeant King was right embarrassed and kind of white in the face, and the Colonel went over to speak with him for a minute. I couldnt make out what he said, though, because the Captain begun talking to me, and seemed like he had got kind of interested in the latrine himself. He asked me if I had been doing all the cleaning by myself, and I told him, "Yessir, I been cleaning it for about two weeks now. I'm the permanent latrine orderly."

"You mean you havent even started *classification* yet? You've been here two weeks and havent even *started* . . . Oh, Sergeant King, step over here a minute, will you, when the Colonel finished speaking with you."

So we all kind of gathered around, the Colonel and the Captain and the Lieutenants and Sergeant King and myself, and had a real nice chat about it. They wanted to know about what I had been doing and I told them about the latrine and how Sergeant King let me work there, and how at first I was on KP for a while, and how nice Sergeant King had been to me, not making me bother with classification but letting me help wash his car and all; and we kept talking about it, only Sergeant King didnt say much but kept his head ducked down and kept blushing and acting modest and everything—anyhow, we talked and talked—and finally they got ready to leave, and the Captain said, "King, you come over and wait in the office. I want to talk to you a little while," and Sergeant King come to attention and said, "Yessir," so it all seemed to come off all right. And they was about the nicest bunch of officers I had ever seen and must have knowed me from somewhere too because just as they were leaving, the Captain looked at me and said, "You must be Stockdale."

And I said, "Yessir, that's right, but I dont recall meeting you . . ." but he didnt stay around no longer; he only turned to the Lieutenant and said, "That one's Stockdale," and the Lieutenant looked at me and said, "Oh, yeah," and I said, "Yessir, that's right, but I don't recall meeting . . ." but they were already headed out about that time.

Anyhow, you could never tell how Sergeant King would feel about things, as changeable as he was, and when he come back from talking with the Captain, he was most *wild*-looking in a way. He stood in his room and kept blinking his eyes and shaking his head like he didnt even know I was there. "You didnt have to do it," he finally said. "You really didnt have to do that."

"I know it," I said. "But I didnt see no sense in me taking all the credit when it was your idea and all. You done a lot for me and I thought I could help out some and . . ."

But he kept shaking his head, and said, "Yes, but did you think that would be *helping* . . ." and then he stopped and rubbed his hands over his face and said, "Yes, I guess you would. I'm not surprised at all. But look here now, you dont have to help me out no more, see? I get along all right here. I got three stripes and my own barracks and I dont really need no help. You've done enough for me already. Look, you help somebody else out for a while. Look, I know a loud-mouthed, low-down, four-striper over in the orderly room, why dont you help *him* out a little bit? Why . . . ?" But then he waved his hand like he didnt want to talk about it no more, and I said I would if I got the chance, but he waved his hand again and turned back around and said, "Look, Will, just forget everything else now. The main thing now is to get you *classified*. That's something we've *got* to do."

And then he seemed to get all upset about that too. He got to pacing up and down talking about it, seeming right anxious about it, and looking all worried again. So I tried to calm him down a bit; I said it probably didnt amount to much and that there really warnt that much to worry about because I liked the latrine fine and had just as soon stay right there as long as I was on the field.

But that seemed to upset him too. He said, "No, Will, no! You wouldnt want to spend the rest of your hitch here, would you? You want to get out and do something. Nosir, what we want to do is get you classified and shipped out of here, because the Captain said that if you didnt, you would stay right here and . . . Look, Will, if it's the last thing we ever do, I think we ought to get you classified. It's the *only* thing."

"Well, I was only thinking about the latrine and helping you out and . . ."

But he was the most upset I ever seen him. He said, "Nosir! Nosir! Absolutely not! The Captain said . . ." and then he got all jumbled up with it all. He shouted "Nosir!" a few more times, and then, "They'll ship you a thousand miles away from here!" and a lot of other stuff like that, getting more and more upset. And finally he wore himself out and just laid down on the bunk and covered up his face with his arms, upset the way he was. So just as I was leaving, I said, "Well, if they *do* ship me a thousand miles away from here, I might manage to hitch a ride back every once in a while," but it didnt do no good. He only moaned, his face still covered up and didnt answer me at all.

2.

After we got assigned to gunnery, me and Ben both got to be airmans-third-class which means you wear a stripe on your arm, only we didnt get to wear it long because of this Captain that was in charge of our crew in transition. He was pilot of the plane and was always real particular, wanting you to wear neckties and such most of the time, which I didnt care nothing about. Anyhow, he stopped me and Ben up town one day and I didnt have my tie on, and we had a few words about that when I tried to explain to him how it was, which I found out later I warnt supposed to do—Ben said all I was supposed to do was stand there and say "No excuse, sir," which sounded like a kind of foolish way to talk to a man—so one thing led to another and we was recruits again; and besides that he changed us off his crew and put us in another crew. And Ben didnt like that too much because he said we was now on the *sorriest* crew on the base. He said everybody knowed it was the worst crew there, but I didnt much think so myself because I got along with them pretty good. They was real easygoing compared to the other one; it didnt make much difference with them whether you showed up for a mission or not. Lieutenant Bridges was the pilot and he was a Reserve and was the only one of the officers I knowed much at first because the planes was so monstrously big and because we flew in the back and they flew in the front so that we didnt see much of the others, and didnt know them usually when we did. But Lieutenant Bridges was a mighty easygoing fellow and didnt care much what you done; he went around most of the time with his eyes about half-opened and half-closed, just kind of dragging himself around like he was walking in his sleep, only he just seemed that way, I think; he warnt really asleep but probably only half drunk, even though it was kind of hard to tell the difference most of the time. And as far as I was concerned, I had ruther been on his crew than the first one because he was so easy to work for. If you took it in your head you didnt want to go on a mission, he never would notice you warnt there nohow. I mean like this one fellow we had; he didnt fly hardly any and one day when he come out to the plane, Lieutenant Bridges didnt remember him and wouldnt let him fly with us until he went back to Operations and got a card showing he was supposed to be on our crew.

Anyhow, Sergeant King had got back to being a sergeant again by that time and had got himself a job in the Orderly Room, and me and Ben hung around a good bit, not doing much but going on practice missions, and Ben finally quit worrying about losing his stripe, and we had a right nice time. Ben still didnt like the crew much—he was mighty disappointed in them most of the time and said it was a good thing most of the officers warnt like them and all like that, but he liked flying a lot, so we went on most of the missions, not skipping them the way about half the crew did. And I didnt mind it much myself—it warnt much trouble because there warnt nothing to do in the back of the plane but sleep or play cards or set there and watch the country go under you. Finally I got a checkerboard and took that along, and me and Ben and this other fellow took turns playing each other, only the other fellow didnt play much because he was working on a model airplane that he took along with him. We never did get to know him too good, though, because he finally just quit coming altogether, and I guess he must have dropped off the crew because we didn't see him around nowhere for a long time.

Anyhow, there warnt much to it; when we was scheduled for a mission, me and Ben went and crawled in the back of the plane, and when it landed, we crawled back out, and never had anything to say to anybody except sometimes when Lieutenant Bridges would call back to see if anybody else was around, and I was kind of enjoying it. And then one day I happened to meet the co-pilot up in Operations, which was a right peculiar thing because we was just standing there talking together and his voice sounded familiar and he said mine did too, and finally we found out we was on the same crew together. His name was Lieutenant Gardella and he seemed like a real nice fellow, and when I asked him what they done up in the front of the plane, he said, "Nothing much. What do yall do in the back?"

So I told him about the checkers and the cards that we played sometimes and he said that sounded mighty good to him and that he would come back and play with us sometimes, and I told him I would like to have him and that I wanted him to meet Ben besides. I asked him what his job was and he said, "Oh, I do different things. Mainly, I just let the wheels up and down and I stick to that pretty much as I dont care to take on anything more right now."

"How long you been letting them up and down?"

"A pretty good while," he said. "About six weeks now, ever since I got out of cadets. Next time we fly I'm going to let the flaps up and down too. Say, why dont you come up front and fly with us next time? Why dont you ask Bridges about it?"

"Well, that's mighty nice of you. I'd sho like to see you let them wheels up and down."

"Sure," he said. "I'll show you all about it."

He was a real obliging kind of fellow that way and you wouldnt think he was an officer at all just to look at him—he looked like he was only about thirteen years old and you would probably think he was a Boy Scout instead of an officer if you seen him, only he always had this big cigar in his mouth and usually didnt seem real sober neither, which of course aint like most Boy Scouts as they usually seem right sober most of the time.

So I went out and finally found Lieutenant Bridges in the BOQ and he was laying down on his bunk and I had to stand around a while before I could tell whether he was asleep or awake with his eyes half open the way they always was, but finally he set up and looked at me, and I told him what I wanted. And he said, "Look here, you cant just go around flying here and there. Why dont you ask your own pilot?"

And I told him *he* was my pilot, and so he looked at me for a while and finally said, "Oh, yeah, I thought I had seen you around somewhere before. What did you say your name was now?"

So we talked for a while and he said I could ride up front with them on the next trip, and then I asked about Ben, and he said, "Ben who?" and I explained to him that Ben was another one of his gunners, and he said it was all right by him, that it didnt make no difference to him one way or the other.

But when I went back and told Ben about it, Ben said, "No, I'll stay in the back where I'm supposed to stay. I never seen officers care as little about things as this bunch does. I wish we had never got off the other crew myself."

So I told him I would ride in the back too, but he said, "No, there aint any use in that. After all, the pilot is in charge of the plane and what he says goes, I guess, even if he dont seem to know what he is talking about half the time."

But they warnt all that bad, I didnt think, and I really enjoyed watching them work when I flew up front. We took off that day about dark and Lieutenant Bridges got the plane off the ground real good and Lieutenant Gardella let the wheels up and done a right good job of it too, right smack up in the sides like he had been borned doing it; we went skimming out over the end of the runway and then Lieutenant Gardella got out a cigar and stuck it in his mouth and rared back and begun reading a magazine, while Lieutenant Bridges flew back over the field and then set it on the automatic, and then propped his feet up and leaned his seat back to go to sleep. I watched it all and it seemed like they done right good, and then I went back to talk with Lieutenant Kendall, the engineer, only he said he was sleepy and was getting his parachute under his head and sticking his feet out in the aisle trying to get comfortable. So I finally went back and set in the radio operators seat, because he hadnt showed up, and watched Lieutenant Cover while he navigated; and he was the one I wished Ben could have seen because he was probably the hardest-working man I ever seen in my life. He was bounding all over the back of the plane navigating even before it was over the end of the runway, peeping down tubes and looking out the window and writing things down on maps that he had scattered all over the desk, then grabbing up one of them three watches that he had scattered around and checking the time, and writing that down, and then taking this camera-looking thing he had, and running back to the dome and pointing it out at the stars that was just coming out, and then running back to write that down too. He wrote so fast and so hard that twice the lead flew off the pencil and flipped across the plane and nearly hit me in the eye; and another time he snatched up a map that had this weight on it that sailed across the desk and caught me right beside the head; so I got up and moved down a ways after that as it did seem right dangerous being close to him working that hard but I still watched him a good while and got a kick out of it.

Anyhow, I wished Ben could have seen it the way he went at things; he was so busy most of the time he wouldnt even talk to me. Most people that work hard usually like to talk about it a good bit, but when I asked him where he was navigating to, he snapped real quick, "Biloxi, Mississippi. Dont bother me, I'm busy," and wouldnt even look at me. After a little bit, we was well on the way and it was dark and the plane was quiet the way it gets at night, with only the sounds of the engines and no lights to speak of except little blue dials and the lamp that come down over Lieutenant Cover's head; but watching him work was enough to wear you out, so I got a little bit sleepy, and must have dozed off for a good while because when I woke up there was a big disturbance going on with people walking around and talking, and I didnt know what was going on.

Anyhow, I woke up and felt the plane going in these big circles, and then I looked over to the desk and there was Lieutenant Bridges standing holding one of the maps in his hand and looking at it, and Lieutenant Cover arguing with him, rattling papers around and trying to show him how he had figured this and that. Lieutenant Kendall was setting over there watching them with his chin propped up on his hands, and Lieutenant Gardella was up front flying the plane in these big circles, looking around every once in a while to see what was going on with the big cigar stuck out of his mouth; they was talking loud and everybody seemed real interested in it, and it seemed like Lieutenant Bridges knowed a lot about navigation himself even though he was the pilot. He was waving the map around saying, "I dont care what your figures show. I guess I can look out the window and *see*, cant I?"

"Well, you just check the figures for yourself," Lieutenant Cover said. "I got a fix about thirty minutes ago and that showed us right here, and thirty minutes later, we're supposed to be right *here*. You can check every figure down there. I figured that position by Dead Reckoning and I figured it thirty minutes from that fix, and I know it's right!"

But Lieutenant Bridges kept on shaking his head and saying, "Well, by God, I can *see*, cant I? I can look right out the window and *see*, cant I?"

So they talked a good bit about navigation that way and both took a lot of interest in it, it seemed like. Lieutenant Kendall was setting back there listening to the whole thing and he was right interested too, even though he was the engineer, and so I stepped back there and asked him what the discussion was all about. And he said, "What do you think it's about? They're lost again naturally. I been in this plane seven times and five of them we been lost. All I know is how much gas we got and if they want to know that, I'll be glad to tell them, but I aint going to worry about it anymore. They can ditch the plane or jump out for all I care; the only thing I know is about how much gas we got."

Then Lieutenant Gardella called back and asked how much gas *did* we have, and Lieutenant Kendall said, "Tell him we can fly another forty minutes. I dont want to talk with him because every time we do, we get in an argument over where we are, and I'm tired of talking about it."

"I know what you mean," I said. "I dont like to argue about things neither, but it is good to see everybody taking such an interest in things; old Ben would be surprised to see it."

"Who is Ben?"

"He's one of the gunners," I said. "He rides in the back of the plane."

"Well," Lieutenant Kendall said. "I hope he knows how to use a parachute."

"Sho," I said. "I bet Ben knows about as much about parachutes as anybody you ever seen."

Anyhow we chatted a while and then I went back and listened to Lieutenant Bridges and Lieutenant Cover some more. Lieutenant Cover was still talking about his DR position where he said we ought to be; he turned to Lieutenant Bridges and said, "Well, who's been navigating, you or me? I got a fix no moren thirty minutes ago and that means our DR position is right here, about a hundred miles out over the Gulf of Mexico . . ."

And then Lieutenant Bridges come in with *his* side of the argument, saying, "Well, I might not have been navigating but I got eyes in my head, and I guess I can look out the window right now and see we're circling over a town half the size of New York; and according to this map or none I ever saw in my life, there aint a town at *all* in the middle of the Gulf of Mexico, much less one half the size of New York and . . ."

"Well, just look then," Lieutenant Cover said. "Dont argue with me, just look. You can check every figure I got here. My DR position puts . . ."

"Well, I dont care anything about that," Lieutenant Bridges said. "All I want to know is what town we're circling over, and if you can tell me that, we can land this thing because we cant fly here all night long while you try to tell me there is a town of that size in the middle of the Gulf of Mexico!"

So they took on that way for a while, and then Lieutenant Gardella and Lieutenant Kendall had a pretty good argument about one of the engines going out; so they discussed that a good while too until Lieutenant Kendall said, "Well, there's not any sense in arguing about it; I'm going to feather the thing." And after a little bit, they changed positions, and Lieutenant Bridges come up front and looked out and seen that one of the engines warnt working, and went back to see Lieutenant Kendall and they had a long talk over the engine being feathered too. Lieutenant Bridges said, "You are not supposed to go around feathering engines like that. I'm the one that's supposed to feather the engine. I'm the pilot, aint I?"

"Yeah, but you was too busy trying to navigate the plane when you're supposed to be up there flying it and . . ."

"All right," Lieutenant Bridges said, "But at least you could have *told* me we had lost an engine. I am the *pilot*, aint I?"

So they talked about that a good while too, and I set back and watched and listened, only I must have dozed off again because when I woke up, we was coming in for a landing. We hit and bounced once pretty hard so that I got throwed halfway across the plane, and then bounced again so that it throwed me back where I started from, but then I grabbed on and didnt get throwed no more on the rest of the bounces. We taxied up the runway with the wheels squeaking and finally stopped and started getting out, but nobody was talking much by then except Lieutenant Gardella—he kept telling Lieutenant Bridges that he thought the *third* bounce was the smoothest of all, but Lieutenant Bridges didnt seem to care about talking about it none, and I noticed in a minute that none of the others did either.

Anyhow, we got out and they had this truck waiting for us and we got on that, and nobody was discussing nothing by this time, and I was right sorry for that because I wanted Ben to hear them because they was right interesting to listen to. But everybody just set there and then Lieutenant Cover come out with all his maps and everything folded up, and he got in and didnt say a word to nobody either. The truck finally started up and we headed across the ramp with everybody real quiet until finally Lieutenant Bridges leaned over and tapped Lieutenant Cover on the shoulder and said, "Look, Cover, I dont mean to run this thing into the ground, but I would appreciate it if you would try to find out where this place is. I mean if it is in the middle of the Gulf of Mexico, we've damn well discovered something."

And then Lieutenant Cover said, "Well, the way you fly, it's a wonder we didnt end up there anyhow."

So we drove up and got off and everybody stood around for a while hemming and hawing, and Lieutenant Bridges went over and asked Lieutenant Cover again if he had figured out where we was, and Lieutenant Cover said, "I thought you was the one who knew so much about it. If you want to find out, why dont you ask the driver?"

But then Lieutenant Bridges said, "Ask the driver? You expect me to land a plane and then go over and ask a truck driver where I landed it?" and got right stubborn about it. But then he turned to me and said, "Hey, what was your name now?"

"Stockdale," I said.

"Look, Stockdale," he said. "How about scouting around here somewhere and see if you cant find out what place this is, will you? Be kind of casual about it, you know."

So I went down the way and asked a fellow and he told me Houston, Texas, and I come back and told Lieutenant Bridges and he seemed to feel much better about things then. "Well, Houston aint such a bad town after all," he said. "By gosh, Cover, you're getting better every day. You didn't miss the field but about four hundred and fifty miles this time."

Then Lieutenant Cover said, "Well, what I figgered was that you would bounce the rest of the way—it looked like it from the way we landed . . ."

And then Lieutenant Bridges had something to say to that, and after a while they begun squabbling a little bit, which I didnt like to hear. Me and Ben stood around waiting while they went at it and Ben said to me, "I never heered a bunch of officers argue so much in my life!"

"Yeah, Ben, they do now, but you ought to have been in the front of that plane and seen the way they worked. That was something else. If you could have seen that, you would have thought a lot more of them. Why, I'll bet they are about as good a crew as you can find, when they're sober like that."

"Which aint often," Ben said.

Anyhow, I hated for Ben to hear the squabbling and kept on talking to him until they had finished up with it because he got so digusted about things like that. But they was finally finished; all of them heading across the ramp except Lieutenant Cover who had lost the argument because they had all jumped on him together before it was over —he was getting all his charts and stuff up and mumbling to himself. And I felt right sorry for him the way he had lost out on the argument and everything; I went over to him and said, "Well, I wouldnt worry about it none. I dont see how it amounts to too much. I had just as soon land at this field as any other one, and we aint going to be here but one day nohow . . ."

But he was right down on things and turned around and looked at me like he was almost mad with me, and said, "Look, do you want to check my figures? Do you want to check them and see for yourself? I got them all right here!"

"Well, I dont know nothing about it," I said. "If you say they're right, I guess they is."

"I can show you my DR position," he said. "It shows us right out in the Gulf."

"Well, I wouldnt know about that," I said. "If you say your DR position is out in the Gulf, I reckon that's where it is all right. How long do you expect it to be out there?"

But he was pretty much down on things; he turned away and stomped off without even answering me—nothing you could say would make him feel any better.

V. THE MIDWEST

James Thurber

THE NIGHT THE BED FELL

I SUPPOSE that the high-water mark of my youth in Columbus, Ohio, was the night the bed fell on my father. It makes a better recitation (unless, as some friends of mine have said, one has heard it five or six times) than it does a piece of writing, for it is almost necessary to throw furniture around, shake doors, and bark like a dog, to lend the proper atmosphere and verisimilitude to what is admittedly a somewhat incredible tale. Still, it did take place.

It happened, then, that my father had decided to sleep in the attic one night, to be away where he could think. My mother opposed the notion strongly because, she said, the old wooden bed up there was unsafe: it was wobbly and the heavy headboard would crash down on father's head in case the bed fell, and kill him. There was no dissuading him, however, and at a quarter past ten he closed the attic door behind him and went up the narrow twisting stairs. We later heard ominous creakings as he crawled into bed. Grandfather, who usually slept in the attic bed when he was with us, had disappeared some days before. (On these occasions he was usually gone six or eight days and returned growling and out of temper, with the news that the federal Union was run by a passel of blockheads and that the Army of the Potomac didn't have any more chance than a fiddler's bitch.)

We had visiting us at this time a nervous first cousin of mine named Briggs Beall, who believed that he was likely to cease breathing when he was asleep. It was his feeling that if he were not awakened every hour during the night, he might die of suffocation. He had been accustomed to setting an alarm clock to ring at intervals until morning, but I persuaded him to abandon this. He slept in my room and I told him that I was such a light sleeper that if anybody quit breathing in the same room with me, I would wake instantly. He tested me the first night—which I had suspected he would—by holding his breath after my regular breathing had convinced him I was asleep. I was not asleep, however, and called to him. This seemed to allay his fears a little, but he took the precaution of putting a glass of spirits of camphor on a little table at the head of his bed. In case I didn't arouse him until he was almost gone, he said, he would sniff the camphor, a powerful reviver. Briggs was not the only member of his family who had his crotchets. Old Aunt Melissa Beall (who could whistle like a man, with two fingers in her mouth) suffered under the premonition that she was destined to die on South High Street, because she had been born on South High Street and married on South High Street. Then there was Aunt Sarah Shoaf, who never went to bed at night without the fear that a burglar was going to get in and blow chloroform under her door through a tube. To avert this calamity—for she was in greater dread of anesthetics than of losing her household goods—she always piled her money, silverware, and other valuables in a neat stack just outside her bedroom, with a note reading: "This is all I have. Please take it and do not use your chloroform, as this is all I have." Aunt Gracie Shoaf also had a burglar phobia, but she met it with more fortitude. She was confident that burglars had been getting into her house every night for forty years. The fact that she never missed anything was to her no proof to the contrary. She always claimed that she scared them off before they could take anything, by throwing shoes down the hallway. When she went to bed she piled, where she could get at them handily, all the shoes there were about her house. Five minutes after she had turned off the light, she would sit up in bed and say "Hark!" Her husband, who had learned to ignore the whole situation as long ago as 1903, would either be sound asleep or pretend to be sound asleep. In either case he would not respond to her tugging and pulling, so that presently she would arise, tiptoe to the door, open it slightly and heave a shoe down the hall in one direction and its mate down the hall in the other direction. Some nights she threw them all, some nights only a couple of pair.

But I am straying from the remarkable incidents that took place during the night that the bed fell on father. By midnight we were all in bed. The layout of the rooms and the disposition of their occupants is important to an understanding of what later occurred. In the front room upstairs (just under father's attic bedroom) were my mother and my brother Herman, who sometimes sang in his sleep, usually "Marching Through Georgia" or "Onward, Christian Soldiers." Briggs Beall and myself were in a room adjoining this one. My brother Roy was in a room across the hall from ours. Our bull terrier, Rex, slept in the hall.

My bed was an army cot, one of those affairs which are made wide enough to sleep on comfortably only by putting up, flat with the middle section, the two sides which ordinarily hang down like the sideboards of a drop-leaf table. When these sides are up, it is perilous to roll too far toward the edge, for then the cot is likely to tip completely over, bringing the whole bed down on top of one with a tremendous banging crash. This, in fact, is precisely what happened, about two o'clock in the morning. (It was my mother who, in recalling the scene later, first referred to it as "the night the bed fell on your father.")

Always a deep sleeper, slow to arouse (I had lied to Briggs), I was at first unconscious of what had happened when the iron cot rolled me onto the floor and toppled over on me. It left me still warmly bundled up and unhurt, for the bed rested above me like a canopy. Hence I did not wake up, only reached the edge of consciousness and went back. The racket, however, instantly awakened my mother, in the next room, who came to the immediate conclusion that her worst dread was realized: the big wooden bed upstairs had fallen on father. She therefore screamed, "Let's go to your poor father!" It was this shout, rather than the noise of my cot falling, that awakened my brother Herman, in the same room with her. He thought that mother had become, for no apparent reason, hysterical. "You're all right, mamma!" he shouted, trying to calm her. They exchanged shout for shout for perhaps ten seconds: "Let's go to your poor father!" and "You're all right!" That woke up Briggs. By this time I was conscious of what was going on, in a vague way, but did not yet realize that I was under my bed instead of on it. Briggs, awakening in the midst of loud shouts of fear and apprehension, came to the quick conclusion that he was suffocating and that we were all trying to "bring him out." With a low moan, he grasped the glass of camphor at the head of his bed and instead of sniffing it poured it over himself. The room reeked of camphor. "Ugf, ahfg!" choked Briggs, like a drowning man, for he had almost succeeded in stopping his breath under the deluge of pungent spirits. He leaped out of bed and groped toward the open window, but he came up against one that was closed. With his hand, he beat out the glass, and I could hear it crash and tinkle in the alleyway below. It was at this juncture that I, in trying to get up, had the uncanny sensation of feeling my bed above me! Foggy with sleep, I now suspected, in my turn, that the whole uproar was being made in a frantic endeavor to extricate me from what must be an unheard-of and perilous situation. "Get me out of this!" I bawled. "Get me out!" I think I had the nightmarish belief that I was entombed in a mine. "Gugh!" gasped Briggs, floundering in his camphor.

By this time my mother, still shouting, pursued by Herman, still shouting, was trying to open the door to the attic, in order to go up and get my father's body out of the wreckage. The door was stuck, however, and wouldn't yield. Her frantic pulls on it only added to the general banging and confusion. Roy and the dog were now up, the one shouting questions, the other barking.

Father, farthest away and soundest sleeper of all, had by this time been awakened by the battering on the attic door. He decided that the house was on fire. "I'm coming, I'm coming!" he wailed in a slow, sleepy voice—it took him many minutes to regain full consciousness. My mother, still believing he was caught under the bed, detected in his "I'm coming!" the mournful, resigned note of one who is preparing to meet his Maker. "He's dying!" she shouted.

"I'm all right!" Briggs yelled, to reassure her. "I'm all right!" He still believed that it was his own closeness to death that was worrying mother. I found at last the light switch in my room, unlocked the door, and Briggs and I joined the others at the attic door. The dog, who never did like Briggs, jumped for him—assuming that he was the culprit in whatever was going on—and Roy had to throw Rex and hold him. We could hear father crawling out of bed upstairs. Roy pulled the attic door open, with a mighty jerk, and father came down the stairs, sleepy and irritable but safe and sound. My mother began to weep when she saw him. Rex began to howl. "What in the name of God is going on here?" asked father.

The situation was finally put together like a gigantic jigsaw puzzle. Father caught a cold from prowling around in his bare feet but there were no other bad results. "I'm glad," said mother, who always looked on the bright side of things, "that your grandfather wasn't here."

James Thurber

THE NIGHT THE GHOST GOT IN

THE ghost that got into our house on the night of November 17, 1915, raised such a hullabaloo of misunderstandings that I am sorry I didn't just let it keep on walking, and go to bed. Its advent caused my mother to throw a shoe through a window of the house next door and ended up with my grandfather shooting a patrolman. I am sorry, therefore, as I have said, that I ever paid any attention to the footsteps.

They began about a quarter past one o'clock in the morning, a rhythmic, quick-cadenced walking around the dining-room table. My mother was asleep in one room upstairs, my brother Herman in another; grandfather was in the attic, in the old walnut bed which, as you will remember, once fell on my father. I had just stepped out of the bathtub and was busily rubbing myself with a towel when I heard the steps. They were the steps of a man walking rapidly around the dining-room table downstairs. The light from the bathroom shone down the back steps, which dropped directly into the dining-room; I could see the faint shine of plates on the plate-rail; I couldn't see the table. The steps kept going round and round the table; at regular intervals a board creaked, when it was trod upon. I supposed at first that it was my father or my brother Roy, who had gone to Indianapolis but were expected home at any time. I suspected next that it was a burglar. It did not enter my mind until later that it was a ghost.

After the walking had gone on for perhaps three minutes, I tiptoed to Herman's room. "Psst!" I hissed, in the dark, shaking him. "Awp," he said, in the low, hopeless tone of a despondent beagle—he always half suspected that something would "get him" in the night. I told him who I was. "There's something downstairs!" I said. He got up and followed me to the head of the back staircase. We listened together. There was no sound. The steps had ceased. Herman looked at me in some alarm: I had only the bathtowel around my waist. He wanted to go back to bed, but I gripped his arm. "There's something down there!" I said. Instantly the steps began again, circled the dining-room table like a man running, and started up the stairs toward us, heavily, two at a time. The light still shone palely down the stairs; we saw nothing coming; we only heard the steps. Herman rushed to his room and slammed the door. I slammed shut the door at the stairs top and held my knee against it. After a long minute, I slowly opened it again. There was nothing there. There was no sound. None of us ever heard the ghost again.

The slamming of the doors had aroused mother: she peered out of her room. "What on earth are you boys doing?" she demanded. Herman ventured out of his room. "Nothing," he said, gruffly, but he was, in color, a light green. "What was all that running around downstairs?" said mother. So she had heard the steps, too! We just looked at her. "Burglars!" she shouted, intuitively. I tried to quiet her by starting lightly downstairs.

"Come on, Herman," I said.

"I'll stay with mother," he said. "She's all excited."

I stepped back onto the landing.

"Don't either of you go a step," said mother. "We'll call the police." Since the phone was downstairs, I didn't see how we were going to call the police—nor did I want the police—but mother made one of her quick, incomparable decisions. She flung up a window of her bedroom which faced the bedroom windows of the house of a neighbor, picked up a shoe, and whammed it through a pane of glass across the narrow space that separated the two houses. Glass tinkled into the bedroom occupied by a retired engraver named Bodwell and his wife. Bodwell had been for some years in rather a bad way and was subject to mild "attacks." Most everybody we knew or lived near had *some* kind of attacks.

It was now about two o'clock of a moonless night; clouds hung black and low. Bodwell was at the window in a minute, shouting, frothing a little, shaking his fist. "We'll sell the house and go back to Peoria," we could hear Mrs. Bodwell saying. It was some time before Mother "got through" to Bodwell. "Burglars!" she shouted. "Burglars in the house!" Herman and I hadn't dared to tell her that it was not burglars but ghosts, for she was even more afraid of ghosts than of burglars. Bodwell at first thought that she meant there were burglars in his house, but finally he quieted down and called the police for us over an extension phone by his bed. After he had disappeared from the window, mother suddenly made as if to throw another shoe, not because there was further need of it but, as she later explained, because the thrill of heaving a shoe through a window glass had enormously taken her fancy. I prevented her.

The police were on hand in a commendably short time: a Ford sedan full of them, two on motorcycles, and a patrol wagon with about eight in it and a few reporters. They began banging at our front door. Flashlights shot streaks of gleam up and down the walls, across the yard, down the walk between our house and Bodwell's. "Open up!" cried a hoarse voice. "We're men from Headquarters!" I wanted to go down and let them in, since there they were, but mother wouldn't hear of it. "You haven't a stitch on," she pointed out. "You'd catch your death." I wound the towel around me again. Finally the cops put their shoulders to our big heavy front door with its thick beveled glass and broke it in: I could hear a rending of wood and a splash of glass on the floor of the hall. Their lights played all over the living-room and crisscrossed nervously in the dining-room, stabbed into hallways, shot up the front stairs and finally up the back. They caught me standing in my towel at the top. A heavy policeman bounded up the steps. "Who are you?" he demanded. "I live here," I said. "Well, whattsa matta, ya hot?" he asked. It was, as a matter of fact, cold; I went to my room and pulled on some trousers. On my way out, a cop stuck a gun into my ribs. "Whatta you doin' here?" he demanded. "I live here," I said.

The officer in charge reported to mother. "No sign of nobody, lady," he said. "Musta got away—whatt'd he look like?" "There were two or three of them," mother said, "whooping and carrying on and slamming doors." "Funny," said the cop. "All ya windows and doors was locked on the inside tight as a tick."

Downstairs, we could hear the tramping of the other police. Police were all over the place; doors were yanked open, drawers were yanked open, windows were shot up and pulled down, furniture fell with dull thumps. A half-dozen policemen emerged out of the darkness of the front hallway upstairs. They began to ransack the floor: pulled beds away from walls, tore clothes off hooks in the closets, pulled suitcases and boxes off shelves. One of them found an old zither that Roy had won in a pool tournament. "Looky here, Joe," he said, strumming it with a big paw. The cop named Joe took it and turned it over. "What is it?" he asked me. "It's an old zither our guinea pig used to sleep on," I said. It was true that a pet guinea pig we once had would never sleep anywhere except on the zither, but I should never have said so. Joe and the other cop looked at me a long time. They put the zither back on a shelf.

"No sign o' nuthin'," said the cop who had first spoken to mother. "This guy," he explained to the others, jerking a thumb at me, "was nekked. The lady seems historical." They all nodded, but said nothing; just looked at me. In the small silence we all heard a creaking in the attic. Grandfather was turning over in bed. "What's 'at?" snapped Joe. Five or six cops sprang for the attic door before I could intervene or explain. I realized that it would be bad if they burst in on grandfather unannounced, or even announced. He was going through a phase in which he believed that General Meade's men, under steady hammering by Stonewall Jackson, were beginning to retreat and even desert.

When I got to the attic, things were pretty confused. Grandfather had evidently jumped to the conclusion that the police were deserters from Meade's army, trying to hide away in his attic. He bounded out of bed wearing a long flannel nightgown over long woolen underwear, a nightcap, and a leather jacket around his chest. The cops must have realized at once that the indignant white-haired old man belonged in the house, but they had no chance to say so. "Back, ye cowardly dogs!" roared grandfather. "Back t' the lines, ye goddam lily-livered cattle!" With that, he fetched the officer who found the zither a flat-handed smack alongside his head that sent him sprawling. The others beat a retreat, but not fast enough; grandfather grabbed Zither's gun from its holster and let fly. The report seemed to crack the rafters; smoke filled the attic. A cop cursed and shot his hand to his shoulder. Somehow, we all finally got downstairs again and locked the door against the old gentleman. He fired once or twice more in the darkness and then went back to bed. "That was grandfather," I explained to Joe, out of breath. "He thinks you're deserters." "I'll say he does," said Joe.

The cops were reluctant to leave without getting their hands on somebody besides grandfather; the night had been distinctly a defeat for them. Furthermore, they obviously didn't like the "layout"; something looked—and I can see their viewpoint—phony. They began to poke into things again. A reporter, a thin-faced, wispy man, came up to me. I had put on one of mother's blouses, not being able to find anything else. The reporter looked at me with mingled suspicion and interest. "Just what the hell is the real lowdown here, Bud?" he asked. I decided to be frank with him. "We had ghosts," I said. He gazed at me a long time as if I were a slot machine into which he had, without results, dropped a nickel. Then he walked away. The cops followed him, the one grandfather shot holding his now-bandaged arm, cursing and blaspheming. "I'm gonna get my gun back from that old bird," said the zither-cop. "Yeh," said Joe. "You—and who else?" I told them I would bring it to the station house the next day.

"What was the matter with that one policeman?" mother asked, after they had gone. "Grandfather shot him," I said. "What for?" she demanded. I told her he was a deserter. "Of all things!" said mother. "He was such a nice-looking young man."

Grandfather was fresh as a daisy and full of jokes at breakfast next morning. We thought at first he had forgotten all about what had happened, but he hadn't. Over his third cup of coffee, he glared at Herman and me. "What was the idee of all them cops tarryhootin' round the house last night?" he demanded. He had us there.

Ellis Parker Butler

PIGS IS PIGS

MIKE FLANNERY, the Westcote agent of the Interurban Express Company, leaned over the counter of the express office and shook his fist. Mr. Morehouse, angry and red, stood on the other side of the counter, trembling with rage. The argument had been long and heated, and at last Mr. Morehouse had talked himself speechless. The cause of the trouble stood on the counter between the two men. It was a soap box across the top of which were nailed a number of strips, forming a rough but serviceable cage. In it two spotted guinea-pigs were greedily eating lettuce leaves.

"Do as you loike, then!" shouted Flannery, "pay for thim an' take thim, or don't pay for thim and leave thim be. Rules is rules, Misther Morehouse, an' Mike Flannery's not goin' to be called down fer breakin' of thim."

"But, you everlastingly stupid idiot!" shouted Mr. Morehouse, madly shaking a flimsy printed book beneath the agent's nose, "can't you read it here—in your own plain printed rates? 'Pets, domestic.

Franklin to Westcote, if properly boxed, twenty-five cents each.'" He threw the book on the counter in disgust. "What more do you want? Aren't they pets? Aren't they domestic? Aren't they properly boxed? What?"

He turned and walked back and forth rapidly, frowning ferociously.

Suddenly he turned to Flannery, and forcing his voice to an artificial calmness spoke slowly but with intense sarcasm.

"Pets," he said. "P-e-t-s! Twenty-five cents each. There are two of them. One! Two! Two times twenty-five are fifty! Can you understand that? I offer you fifty cents."

Flannery reached for the book. He ran his hand through the pages and stopped at page sixty-four.

"An' I don't take fifty cints," he whispered in mockery. "Here's the rule for ut. 'Whin the agint be in anny doubt regardin' which of two rates applies to a shipment, he shall charge the larger. The consign-ey may file a claim for the overcharge.' In this case, Misther Morehouse, I be in doubt. Pets thim animals may be, an' domestic they be, but pigs I'm blame sure they do be, an' me rules says plain as the nose on yer face, 'Pigs Franklin to Westcote, thirty cints each.' An', Misther Morehouse, by me arithmetical knowledge two times thirty comes to sixty cints."

Mr. Morehouse shook his head savagely. "Nonsense!" he shouted, "confounded nonsense, I tell you! Why, you poor ignorant foreigner, that rule means common pigs, domestic pigs, not guinea-pigs!"

Flannery was stubborn.

"Pigs is pigs," he declared firmly. "Guinea-pigs or dago pigs or Irish pigs is all the same to the Interurban Express Company an' to Mike Flannery. Th' nationality of the pig creates no differentiality in the rate, Misther Morehouse! 'Twould be the same was they Dutch pigs or Rooshun pigs. Mike Flannery," he added, "is here to tind to the ex-priss business and not to hould conversation wid dago pigs in sivinteen languages fer to discover be they Chinese or Tipperary by birth an' nativity."

Mr. Morehouse hesitated. He bit his lip and then flung out his arms wildly.

"Very well!" he shouted, "you shall hear of this! Your president shall hear of this! It is an outrage! I have offered you fifty cents. You refuse it! Keep the pigs until you are ready to take the fifty cents, but, by George, sir, if one hair of those pigs' heads is harmed I will have the law on you!"

He turned and stalked out, slamming the door. Flannery carefully lifted the soap box from the counter and placed it in a corner. He was not worried. He felt the peace that comes to a faithful servant who has done his duty and done it well.

Mr. Morehouse went home raging. His boy, who had been awaiting the guinea-pigs, knew better than to ask him for them. He was a normal boy and therefore always had a guilty conscience when his father was angry. So the boy slipped quietly around the house. There is nothing so soothing to a guilty conscience as to be out of the path of the avenger.

Mr. Morehouse stormed into the house. "Where's the ink?" he shouted at his wife as soon as his foot was across the doorsill.

Mrs. Morehouse jumped guiltily. She never used ink. She had not seen the ink, nor moved the ink, nor thought of the ink, but her husband's tone convicted her of the guilt of having borne and reared a boy, and she knew that whenever her husband wanted anything in a loud voice the boy had been at it.

"I'll find Sammy," she said meekly.

When the ink was found Mr. Morehouse wrote rapidly, and he read the completed letter and smiled a triumphant smile.

"That will settle that crazy Irishman!" he exclaimed. "When they get that letter he will hunt another job, all right!"

A week later Mr. Morehouse received a long official envelope with the card of the Interurban Express Company in the upper left corner. He tore it open eagerly and drew out a sheet of paper. At the top it bore the number A6754. The letter was short. "Subject—Rate on guinea-pigs," it said. "Dear Sir,—We are in receipt of your letter regarding rate on guinea-pigs between Franklin and Westcote, addressed to the president of this company. All claims for overcharge should be addressed to the Claims Department."

Mr. Morehouse wrote to the Claims Department. He wrote six pages of choice sarcasm, vituperation and argument, and sent them to the Claims Department.

A few weeks later he received a reply from the Claims Department. Attached to it was his last letter.

"Dear Sir," said the reply. "Your letter of the 16th inst., addressed to this Department, subject rate on guinea-pigs from Franklin to Westcote, rec'd. We have taken up the matter with our agent at Westcote, and his reply is attached herewith. He informs us that you refused to receive the consignment or to pay the charges. You have therefore no claim against this company, and your letter regarding the proper rate on the consignment should be addressed to our Tariff Department."

Mr. Morehouse wrote to the Tariff Department. He stated his case clearly, and gave his arguments in full, quoting a page or two from the encyclopedia to prove that guinea-pigs were not common pigs.

With the care that characterizes corporations when they are systematically conducted, Mr. Morehouse's letter was numbered, O.K.'d, and started through the regular channels. Duplicate copies of the bill of lading, manifest, Flannery's receipt for the package and several other pertinent papers were pinned to the letter, and they were passed to the head of the Tariff Department.

The head of the Tariff Department put his feet on his desk and yawned. He looked through the papers carelessly.

"Miss Kane," he said to his stenographer, "take this letter. 'Agent, Westcote, N. J. Please advise why consignment referred to in attached papers was refused domestic pet rates.'"

Miss Kane made a series of curves and angles on her notebook and waited with pencil poised. The head of the department looked at the papers again.

"Huh! guinea-pigs!" he said. "Probably starved to death by this time! Add this to that letter: 'Give condition of consignment at present.'"

He tossed the papers on to the stenographer's desk, took his feet from his own desk and went out to lunch.

When Mike Flannery received the letter he scratched his head.

"Give prisint condition," he repeated thoughtfully. "Now what do thim clerks be wantin' to know, I wonder! 'Prisint condition,' is ut? Thim pigs, praise St. Patrick, do be in good health, so far as I know, but I niver was no veternairy surgeon to dago pigs. Mebby thim clerks wants me to call in the pig docther an' have their pulses took. Wan thing I do know, howiver, which is, they've glorious appytites for pigs of their soize. Ate? They'd ate the brass padlocks off of a barn door! If the paddy pig, by the same token, ate as hearty as these dago pigs do, there'd be a famine in Ireland."

To assure himself that his report would be up to date, Flannery went to the rear of the office and looked into the cage. The pigs had been transferred to a larger box—a dry goods box.

"Wan,—two,—t'ree,—four,—foive,—six,—sivin,—eight!" he counted. "Sivin spotted an' wan all black. All well an' hearty an' all eatin' loike ragin' hippypottymusses." He went back to his desk and wrote.

"Mr. Morgan, Head of Tariff Department," he wrote, "why do I say dago pigs is pigs because they is pigs and will be til you say they ain't which is what the rule book says stop your jollying me you know it as well as I do. As to health they are all well and hoping you are the same. P. S. There are eight now the family increased all good eaters. P. S. I paid out so far two dollars for cabbage which they like shall I put in bill for same what?"

Morgan, head of the Tariff Department, when he received this letter, laughed. He read it again and became serious.

"By George!" he said, "Flannery is right, 'pigs is pigs.' I'll have to get authority on this thing. Meanwhile, Miss Kane, take this letter: 'Agent, Westcote, N. J. Regarding shipment guinea-pigs, File No. A6754. Rule 83, General Instructions to Agents, clearly states that agents shall collect from consignee all costs of provender, etc., etc., required for live stock while in transit or storage. You will proceed to collect same from consignee.' "

Flannery received this letter next morning, and when he read it he grinned.

"Proceed to collect," he said softly. "How thim clerks do loike to be talkin'! *Me* proceed to collect two dollars and twenty-foive cints off Misther Morehouse! I wonder do thim clerks *know* Misther Morehouse? I'll git it! Oh, yes! 'Misther Morehouse, two an' a quarter, plaze.' 'Cert'nly, me dear frind Flannery. Delighted!' *Not!*"

Flannery drove the express wagon to Mr. Morehouse's door. Mr. Morehouse answered the bell.

"Ah, ha!" he cried as soon as he saw it was Flannery. "So you've come to your senses at last, have you? I thought you would! Bring the box in."

"I hev no box," said Flannery coldly. "I hev a bill agin Misther John C. Morehouse for two dollars and twenty-foive cints for kebbages aten by his dago pigs. Wud you wish to pay ut?"

"Pay—Cabbages—!" gasped Mr. Morehouse. "Do you mean to say that two little guinea-pigs——"

"Eight!" said Flannery. "Papa an' mamma an' the six childer. Eight!"

For answer Mr. Morehouse slammed the door in Flannery's face. Flannery looked at the door reproachfully.

"I take ut the con-*sign*-y don't want to pay for thim kebbages," he said. "If I know signs of refusal, the con-*sign*-y refuses to pay for wan dang kebbage leaf an' be hanged to me!"

Mr. Morgan, the head of the Tariff Department, consulted the president of the Interurban Express Company regarding guinea-pigs, as to whether they were pigs or not pigs. The president was inclined to treat the matter lightly.

"What is the rate on pigs and on pets?" he asked.

"Pigs thirty cents, pets twenty-five," said Morgan.

"Then of course guinea-pigs are pigs," said the president.

"Yes," agreed Morgan, "I look at it that way, too. A thing that can come under two rates is naturally due to be classed as the higher. But are guinea-pigs, pigs? Aren't they rabbits?"

"Come to think of it," said the president, "I believe they are more like rabbits. Sort of half-way station between pig and rabbit. I think the question is this—are guinea-pigs of the domestic pig family? I'll ask Professor Gordon. He is authority on such things. Leave the papers with me."

The president put the papers on his desk and wrote a letter to Professor Gordon. Unfortunately the Professor was in South America collecting zoological specimens, and the letter was forwarded to him by his wife. As the Professor was in the highest Andes, where no white man had ever penetrated, the letter was many months in reaching him. The president forgot the guinea-pigs, Morgan forgot them, Mr. Morehouse forgot them. But Flannery did not. One half of his time he gave to the duties of his agency; the other half was devoted to the guinea-pigs. Long before Professor Gordon received the president's letter Morgan received one from Flannery.

"About them dago pigs," it said, "what shall I do they are great in family life, no race suicide for them, there are thirty-two now shall I sell them do you take this express office for a menagerie, answer quick."

Morgan reached for a telegraph blank and wrote:

"Agent, Westcote. Don't sell pigs."

He then wrote Flannery a letter calling his attention to the fact that the pigs were not the property of the company but were merely being held during a settlement of a dispute regarding rates. He advised Flannery to take the best possible care of them.

Flannery, letter in hand, looked at the pigs and sighed. The dry goods box cage had become too small. He boarded up twenty feet of the rear of the express office to make a large and airy home for them, and went about his business. He worked with feverish intensity when out on his rounds, for the pigs required attention and took most of his time. Some months later, in desperation, he seized a sheet of paper and wrote "160" across it and mailed it to Morgan. Morgan returned it asking for explanation. Flannery replied:

"There be now one hundred sixty of them dago pigs, for heaven's sake let me sell off some, do you want me to go crazy, what?"

"Sell no pigs," Morgan wired.

Not long after this the president of the express company received a letter from Professor Gordon. It was a long and scholarly letter, but the point was that the guinea-pig was the *Cavia aparoea*, while the common pig was the genus *Sus* of the family *Suidae*. He remarked that they were prolific and multiplied rapidly.

"They are not pigs," said the president, decidedly, to Morgan. "The twenty-five cent rate applies."

Morgan made the proper notation on the papers that had accumulated in File A6754, and turned them over to the Audit Department. The Audit Department took some time to look the matter up, and after the usual delay wrote Flannery that as he had on hand one hundred and sixty guinea-pigs, the property of consignee, he should deliver them and collect charges at the rate of twenty-five cents each.

Flannery spent a day herding his charges through a narrow opening in their cage so that he might count them.

"Audit Dept.," he wrote, when he had finished the count, "you are way off there may be was one hundred and sixty dago pigs once, but wake up don't be a back number. I've got even eight hundred, now shall I collect for eight hundred or what, how about sixty-four dollars I paid out for cabbages."

It required a great many letters back and forth before the Audit Department was able to understand why the error had been made of billing one hundred and sixty instead of eight hundred, and still more time for it to get the meaning of the "cabbages."

Flannery was crowded into a few feet at the extreme front of the office. The pigs had all the rest of the room and two boys were employed constantly attending to them. The day after Flannery had counted the guinea-pigs there were eight more added to his drove, and by the time the Audit Department gave him authority to collect for eight hundred Flannery had given up all attempts to attend to the receipt or the delivery of goods. He was hastily building galleries around the express office, tier above tier. He had four thousand and sixty-four guinea-pigs to care for. More were arriving daily.

Immediately following its authorization the Audit Department sent another letter, but Flannery was too busy to open it. They wrote another and then they telegraphed:

"Error in guinea-pig bill. Collect for two guinea-pigs, fifty cents. Deliver all to consignee."

Flannery read the telegram and cheered up. He wrote out a bill as rapidly as his pencil could travel over paper and ran all the way to the Morehouse home. At the gate he stopped suddenly. The house stared at him with vacant eyes. The windows were bare of curtains and he could see into the empty rooms. A sign on the porch said, "To Let." Mr. Morehouse had moved! Flannery ran all the way back to the express office. Sixty-nine guinea-pigs had been born during his absence. He ran out again and made feverish inquiries in the village. Mr. Morehouse had not only moved, but he had left Westcote. Flannery returned to the express office and found that two hundred and six guinea-pigs had entered the world since he left it. He wrote a telegram to the Audit Department.

"Can't collect fifty cents for two dago pigs consignee has left town address unknown what shall I do? Flannery."

The telegram was handed to one of the clerks in the Audit Department, and as he read it he laughed.

"Flannery must be crazy. He ought to know that the thing to do is to return the consignment here," said the clerk. He telegraphed Flannery to send the pigs to the main office of the company at Franklin.

When Flannery received the telegram he set to work. The six boys he had engaged to help him also set to work. They worked with the haste of desperate men, making cages out of soap boxes, cracker boxes, and all kinds of boxes, and as fast as the cages were completed they filled them with guinea-pigs and expressed them to Franklin. Day after day the cages of guinea-pigs flowed in a steady stream from Westcote to Franklin, and still Flannery and his six helpers ripped and nailed and packed—relentlessly and feverishly. At the end of the week they had shipped two hundred and eighty cases of guinea-pigs, and there were in the express office seven hundred and four more pigs than when they began packing them.

"Stop sending pigs. Warehouse full," came a telegram to Flannery. He stopped packing only long enough to wire back, "Can't stop," and kept on sending them. On the next train up from Franklin came one of the company's inspectors. He had instructions to stop the stream of guinea-pigs at all hazards. As his train drew up at Westcote station he saw a cattle-car standing on the express company's siding. When he reached the express office he saw the express wagon backed up to the door. Six boys were carrying bushel baskets full of guinea-pigs from the office and dumping them into the wagon. Inside the room Flannery, with his coat and vest off, was shoveling guinea-pigs into bushel baskets with a coal scoop. He was winding up the guinea-pig episode.

He looked up at the inspector with a snort of anger.

"Wan wagonload more an' I'll be quit of thim, an' niver will ye catch Flannery wid no more foreign pigs on his hands. No, sur! They near was the death o' me. Nixt toime I'll know that pigs of whativer nationality is domestic pets—an' go at the lowest rate."

He began shoveling again rapidly, speaking quickly between breaths.

"Rules may be rules, but you can't fool Mike Flannery twice wid the same thrick—whin ut comes to live stock, dang the rules. So long as Flannery runs this expriss office—pigs is pets—an' cows is pets—an' horses is pets—an' lions an' tigers an' Rocky Mountain goats is pets—an' the rate on thim is twinty-foive cints."

He paused long enough to let one of the boys put an empty basket in the place of the one he had just filled. There were only a few guinea-pigs left. As he noted their limited number his natural habit of looking on the bright side returned.

"Well, annyhow," he said cheerfully, "'tis not so bad as ut might be. What if thim dago pigs had been elephants!"

Ring Lardner

MR. FRISBIE

I AM Mr. Allen Frisbie's chauffeur. Allen Frisbie is a name I made up because they tell me that if I used the real name of the man I am employed by that he might take offense and start trouble though I am sure he will never see what I am writing as he does not read anything except the American Golfer but of course some of his friends might call his attention to it. If you knew who the real name of the man is it would make more interesting reading as he is one of the 10 most wealthiest men in the United States and a man who everybody is interested in because he is so famous and the newspapers are always writing articles about him and sending high salary reporters to interview him but he is a very hard man to reproach or get an interview with and when they do he never tells them anything.

From *Round Up*, copyright, 1929, by Charles Scribner's Sons.

That is how I come to be writing this article because about two weeks ago a Mr. Kirk had an appointment to interview Mr. Frisbie for one of the newspapers and I drove him to the station after the interview was over and he said to me your boss is certainly a tough egg to interview and getting a word out of him is like pulling turnips.

"The public do not know anything about the man," said Mr. Kirk. "They know he is very rich and has got a wife and a son and a daughter and what their names are but as to his private life and his likes and dislikes he might just as well be a monk in a convent."

"The public knows he likes golf," I said.

"They do not know what kind of a game he plays."

"He plays pretty good," I said.

"How good?" said Mr. Kirk.

"About 88 or 90," I said.

"So is your grandmother," said Mr. Kirk.

He only meant the remark as a comparison but had either of my grandmothers lived they would both have been over 90. Mr. Kirk did not believe I was telling the truth about Mr. Frisbie's game and he was right though was I using real names I would not admit it as Mr. Frisbie is very sensitive in regards to his golf.

Mr. Kirk kept pumping at me but I am used to being pumped at and Mr. Kirk finally gave up pumping at me as he found me as closed mouth as Mr. Frisbie himself but he made the remark that he wished he was in my place for a few days and as close to the old man as I am and he would then be able to write the first real article which had ever been written about the old man. He called Mr. Frisbie the old man.

He said it was too bad I am not a writer so I could write up a few instances about Mr. Frisbie from the human side on account of being his caddy at golf and some paper or magazine would pay me big. He said if you would tell me a few instances I would write them up and split with you but I said no I could not think of anything which would make an article but after Mr. Kirk had gone I got to thinking it over and thought to myself maybe I could be a writer if I tried and at least there is no harm in trying so for the week after Mr. Kirk's visit I spent all my spare time writing down about Mr. Frisbie only at first I used his real name but when I showed the article they said for me not to use real names but the public would guess who it was anyway and that was just as good as using real names.

So I have gone over the writing again and changed the name to

Allen Frisbie and other changes and here is the article using Allen Frisbie.

When I say I am Mr. Frisbie's chauffeur I mean I am his personal chauffeur. There are two other chauffeurs who drive for the rest of the family and run errands. Had I nothing else to do only drive I might well be turned a man of leisure as Mr. Frisbie seldom never goes in to the city more than twice a week and even less oftener than that does he pay social visits.

His golf links is right on the place an easy walk from the house to the first tee and here is where he spends a good part of each and every day playing alone with myself in the roll of caddy. So one would not be far from amiss to refer to me as Mr. Frisbie's caddy rather than his chauffeur but it was as a chauffeur that I was engaged and can flatter myself that there are very few men of my calling who would not gladly exchange their salary and position for mine.

Mr. Frisbie is a man just this side of 60 years of age. Almost 10 years ago he retired from active business with money enough to put him in a class with the richest men in the United States and since then his investments have increased their value to such an extent so that now he is in a class with the richest men in the United States.

It was soon after his retirement that he bought the Peter Vischer estate near Westbury, Long Island. On this estate there was a 9 hole golf course in good condition and considered one of the best private 9 hole golf courses in the United States but Mr. Frisbie would have had it plowed up and the land used for some other usage only for a stroke of chance which was when Mrs. Frisbie's brother came over from England for a visit.

It was during while this brother-in-law was visiting Mr. Frisbie that I entered the last named employee and was an onlooker when Mr. Frisbie's brother-in-law persuaded his brother-in-law to try the game of golf. As luck would have it, Mr. Frisbie's first drive was so good that his brother-in-law would not believe he was a new beginner till he had seen Mr. Frisbie shoot again but that first perfect drive made Mr. Frisbie a slave of the game and without which there would be no such instance as I am about to relate.

I would better explain at this junction that I am not a golfer but I have learned quite a lot of knowledge about the game by cadding for Mr. Frisbie and also once or twice in company with my employer have picked up some knowledge of the game by witnessing players like Bobby Jones and Hagen and Sarazen and Smith in some of their matches. I have only tried it myself on a very few occasions when I was sure Mr. Frisbie could not observe me and will confide that in my own mind I am convinced that with a little practise that I would have little trouble defeating Mr. Frisbie but will never seek to prove same for reasons which I will leave it to the reader to guess the reasons.

One day shortly after Mr. Frisbie's brother-in-law had ended his visit I was cadding for Mr. Frisbie and as had become my custom keeping score for him when a question arose as to whether he had taken 7 or 8 strokes on the last hole. A 7 would have given him a total of 63 for the 9 holes while a 8 would have made it 64. Mr. Frisbie tried to recall the different strokes but was not certain and asked me to help him.

As I remembered it he had sliced his 4th. wooden shot in to a trap but had recovered well and got on to the green and then had taken 3 putts which would make him a 8 but by some slip of the tongue when I started to say 8 I said 7 and before I could correct myself Mr. Frisbie said yes you are right it was a 7.

"That is even 7s," said Mr. Frisbie.

"Yes," I said.

On the way back to the house he asked me what was my salary which I told him and he said well I think you are worth more than that and from now on you will get $25.00 more per week.

On another occasion when 9 more holes had been added to the course and Mr. Frisbie was playing the 18 holes regular every day he came to the last hole needing a 5 to break 112 which was his best score.

The 18th. hole is only 120 yards with a big green but a brook in front and traps in back of it. Mr. Frisbie got across the brook with his second but the ball went over in to the trap and it looked like bad business because Mr. Frisbie is even worse with a niblick than almost any club except maybe the No. 3 and 4 irons and the wood.

Well I happened to get to the ball ahead of him and it laid there burred in the deep sand about a foot from a straight up and down bank 8 foot high where it would have been impossible for any man alive to oust it in one stroke but as luck would have it I stumbled and gave the ball a little kick and by chance it struck the side of the bank and stuck in the grass and Mr. Frisbie got it up on the green in one stroke and was down in 2 putts for his 5.

"Well that is my record 111 or 3 over 6s," he said.

Now my brother had a couple of tickets for the polo at Meadowbrook the next afternoon and I am a great lover of horses flesh so I said Mr. Frisbie can I go to the polo tomorrow afternoon and he said certainly any time you want a afternoon off do not hesitate to ask me but a little while later there was a friend of mine going to get married at Atlantic City and Mr. Frisbie had just shot a 128 and broke his spoon besides and when I mentioned about going to Atlantic City for my friend's wedding he snapped at me like a wolf and said what did I think it was the xmas holidays.

Personally I am a man of simple tastes and few wants and it is very seldom when I am not satisfied to take my life and work as they come and not seek fear or favor but of course there are times in every man's life when they desire something a little out of the ordinary in the way of a little vacation or perhaps a financial accommodation of some kind and in such cases I have found Mr. Frisbie a king amongst men provide it one uses discretion in choosing the moment of their reproach but a variable tyrant if one uses bad judgment in choosing the moment of their reproach.

You can count on him granting any reasonable request just after he has made a good score or even a good shot where as a person seeking a favor when he is off his game might just swell ask President Coolidge to do the split.

I wish to state that having learned my lesson along these lines I did not use my knowledge to benefit myself alone but have on the other hand utilized same mostly to the advantage of others especially the members of Mr. Frisbie's own family. Mr. Frisbie's wife and son and daughter all realized early in my employment that I could handle Mr. Frisbie better than anyone else and without me ever exactly divulging the secret of my methods they just naturally began to take it for granted that I could succeed with him where they failed and it became their habit when they sought something from their respective spouse and father to summons me as their adviser and advocate.

As an example of the above I will first sight an example in connection with Mrs. Frisbie. This occurred many years ago and was the instance which convinced her beyond all doubt that I was a expert on the subject of managing her husband.

Mrs. Frisbie is a great lover of music but unable to perform on any instrument herself. It was her hope that one of the children would be a pianiste and a great deal of money was spent on piano lessons for both Robert the son and Florence the daughter but all in vain as neither of the two showed any talent and their teachers one after another gave them up in despair.

Mrs. Frisbie at last became desirous of purchasing a player piano and of course would consider none but the best but when she brooched the subject to Mr. Frisbie he turned a deaf ear as he said pianos were made to be played by hand and people who could not learn same did not deserve music in the home.

I do not know how often Mr. and Mrs. Frisbie disgust the matter pro and con.

Personally they disgust it in my presence any number of times and finally being a great admirer of music myself and seeing no reason why a man of Mr. Frisbie's great wealth should deny his wife a harmless pleasure such as a player piano I suggested to the madam that possibly if she would leave matters to me the entire proposition might be put over. I can no more than fail I told her and I do not think I will fail so she instructed me to go ahead as I could not do worse than fail which she had already done herself.

I will relate the success of my plan as briefly as possible. Between the house and the golf course there was a summer house in which Mrs. Frisbie sat reading while Mr. Frisbie played golf. In this summer house she could sit so as to not be visible from the golf course. She was to sit there till she heard me whistle the strains of "Over There" where at she was to appear on the scene like she had come direct from the house and the fruits of our scheme would then be known.

For two days Mrs. Frisbie had to console herself with her book as Mr. Frisbie's golf was terrible and there was no moment when I felt like it would not be courting disaster to summons her on the scene but during the 3rd. afternoon his game suddenly improved and he had shot the 1st. 9 holes in 53 and started out on the 10th. with a pretty drive when I realized the time had come.

Mrs. Frisbie appeared promptly in answer to my whistling and walked rapidly up to Mr. Frisbie like she had hurried from the house and said there is a man at the house from that player piano company and he says he will take $50.00 off the regular price if I order today and please let me order one as I want one so much.

"Why certainly dear go ahead and get it dear," said Mr. Frisbie and that is the way Mrs. Frisbie got her way in regards to a player piano. Had I not whistled when I did but waited a little longer it would have spelt ruination to our schemes as Mr. Frisbie took a 12 on the 11th. hole and would have bashed his wife over the head with a No. 1 iron had she even asked him for a toy drum.

I have been of assistance to young Mr. Robert Frisbie the son with reference to several items of which I will only take time to touch on one item with reference to Mr. Robert wanting to drive a car. Before Mr. Robert was 16 years of age he was always after Mr. Frisbie to allow him to drive one of the cars and Mr. Frisbie always said him nay on the grounds that it is against the law for a person under 16 years of age to drive a car.

When Mr. Robert reached the age of 16 years old however this excuse no longer held good and yet Mr. Frisbie continued to say Mr. Robert nay in regards to driving a car. There is plenty of chauffeurs at your beckon call said Mr. Frisbie to drive you where ever and when ever you wish to go but of course Mr. Robert like all youngsters wanted to drive himself and personally I could see no harm in it as I personally could not drive for him and the other 2 chauffeurs in Mr. Frisbie's employee at the time were just as lightly to wreck a car as Mr. Robert so I promised Mr. Robert that I would do my best towards helping him towards obtaining permission to drive one of the cars.

"Leave it to me" was my bequest to Mr. Robert and sure enough my little strategy turned the trick though Mr. Robert did not have the patience like his mother to wait in the summer house till a favorable moment arrived so it was necessary for me to carry through the entire proposition by myself.

The 16th. hole on our course is perhaps the most difficult hole on our course at least it has always been a variable tartar for Mr. Frisbie.

It is about 350 yards long in lenth and it is what is called a blind hole as you can not see the green from the tee as you drive from the tee up over a hill with a direction flag as the only guide and down at the bottom of the hill there is a brook a little over 225 yards from the tee which is the same brook which you come to again on the last hole and in all the times Mr. Frisbie has played around the course he has seldom never made this 16th. hole in less than 7 strokes or more as his tee shot just barely skins the top of the hill giving him a down hill lie which upsets him so that he will miss the 2d. shot entirely or top it and go in to the brook.

Well I generally always stand up on top of the hill to watch where his tee shot goes and on the occasion referred to he got a pretty good tee shot which struck on top of the hill and rolled half way down and I hurried to the ball before he could see me and I picked it up and threw it across the brook and when he climbed to the top of the hill I pointed to where the ball laid the other side of the brook and shouted good shot Mr. Frisbie. He was overjoyed and beamed with joy and did not suspect anything out of the way though in realty he could not hit a ball more than 160 yards if it was teed on the summit of Pike's Peak.

Fate was on my side at this junction and Mr. Frisbie hit a perfect mashie shot on to the green and sunk his 2d. put for the only 4 of his career on this hole. He was almost delirious with joy and you may be sure I took advantage of the situation and before we were fairly off the green I said to him Mr. Frisbie if you do not need me tomorrow morning do you not think it would be a good time for me to learn Mr. Robert to drive a car.

"Why certainly he is old enough now to drive a car and it is time he learned."

I now come to the main instance of my article which is in regards to Miss Florence Frisbie who is now Mrs. Henry Craig and of course Craig is not the real name but you will soon see that what I was able to do for her was no such childs play like gaining consent for Mr. Robert to run a automobile or Mrs. Frisbie to purchase a player piano but this was a matter of the up most importance and I am sure the reader will not consider me a vain bragger when I claim that I handled it with some skill.

Miss Florence is a very pretty and handsome girl who has always had a host of suiters who paid court to her on account of being pretty as much as her great wealth and I believe there has been times when no less than half a dozen or more young men were paying court to her at one time. Well about 2 years ago she lost her heart to young Henry Craig and at the same time Mr. Frisbie told her in no uncertain turns that she must throw young Craig over board and marry his own choice young Junior Holt or he would cut her off without a dime.

Holt and Craig are not the real names of the two young men referred to though I am using their real first names namely Junior and Henry. Young Holt is a son of Mr. Frisbie's former partner in business and a young man who does not drink or smoke and has got plenty of money in his own rights and a young man who any father would feel safe in trusting their daughter in the bands of matrimony. Young Craig at that time had no money and no position and his parents had both died leaving nothing but debts.

"Craig is just a tramp and will never amount to anything," said Mr. Frisbie. "I have had inquirys made and I understand he drinks when anyone will furnish him the drinks. He has never worked and never will. Junior Holt is a model young man from all accounts and comes of good stock and is the only young man I know whose conduct and habits are such that I would consider him fit to marry my daughter."

Miss Florence said that Craig was not a tramp and she loved him and would not marry anyone else and as for Holt he was terrible but even if he was not terrible she would never consider undergoing the bands of matrimony with a man named Junior.

"I will elope with Henry if you do not give in," she said.

Mr. Frisbie was not alarmed by this threat as Miss Florence has a little common sense and would not be lightly to elope with a young man who could hardly finance a honeymoon trip on the subway. But neither was she showing any signs of yielding in regards to his wishes in regards to young Holt and things began to take on the appearance of a dead lock between father and daughter with neither side showing any signs of yielding.

Miss Florence grew pale and thin and spent most of her time in her room instead of seeking enjoyment amongst her friends as was her custom. As for Mr. Frisbie he was always a man of iron will and things began to take on the appearance of a dead lock with neither side showing any signs of yielding.

It was when it looked like Miss Florence was on the verge of a serious illness when Mrs. Frisbie came to me and said we all realize that you have more influence with Mr. Frisbie than anyone else and is there any way you can think of to get him to change his status towards Florence and these 2 young men because if something is not done right away I am afraid of what will happen. Miss Florence likes you and has a great deal of confidence in you said Mrs. Frisbie so will you see her and talk matters over with her and see if you can not think up some plan between you which will put a end to this situation before my poor little girl dies.

So I went to see Miss Florence in her bedroom and she was a sad sight with her eyes red from weeping and so pale and thin and yet her face lit up with a smile when I entered the room and she shook hands with me like I was a long lost friend.

"I asked my mother to send you," said Miss Florence. "This case looks hopeless but I know you are a great fixer as far as Father is concerned and you can fix it if anyone can. Now I have got a idea which I will tell you and if you like it it will be up to you to carry it out."

"What is your idea?"

"Well," said Miss Florence, "I think that if Mr. Craig the man I love could do Father a favor why Father would not be so set against him."

"What kind of a favor?"

"Well Mr. Craig plays a very good game of golf and he might give Father some pointers which would improve Father's game."

"Your father will not play golf with anyone and certainly not with a good player and besides that your father is not the kind of a man that wants anyone giving him pointers. Personally I would just as leaf go up and tickle him as tell him that his stance is wrong."

"Then I guess my idea is not so good."

"No," I said and then all of a sudden I had a idea of my own. "Listen Miss Florence does the other one play golf?"

"Who?"

"Young Junior Holt."

"Even better than Mr. Craig."

"Does your father know that?"

"Father does not know anything about him or he would not like him so well."

Well I said I have got a scheme which may work or may not work but no harm to try and the first thing to be done is for you to spruce up and pretend like you do not feel so unkindly towards young Holt after all. The next thing is to tell your father that Mr. Holt never played golf and never even saw it played but would like to watch your father play so he can get the hang of the game.

And then after that you must get Mr. Holt to ask your father to let him follow him around the course and very secretly you must tip Mr. Holt off that your father wants his advice. When ever your father does anything wrong Mr. Holt is to correct him. Tell him your father is crazy to improve his golf but is shy in regards to asking for help.

There is a lot of things that may happen to this scheme but if it should go through why I will guarantee that at least half your troubles will be over.

Well as I said there was a lot of things that might have happened to spoil my scheme but nothing did happen and the very next afternoon Mr. Frisbie confided in me that Miss Florence seemed to feel much better and seemed to have changed her mind in regards to Mr. Holt and also said that the last named had expressed a desire to follow Mr. Frisbie around the golf course and learn something about the game.

Mr. Holt was a kind of a fat pudgy young man with a kind of a sneering smile and the first minute I saw him I wished him the worst.

For a second before Mr. Frisbie started to play I was certain we were lost as Mr. Frisbie remarked where have you been keeping yourself Junior that you never watched golf before. But luckily young Holt took the remark as a joke and made no reply. Right afterwards the storm clouds began to gather in the sky. Mr. Frisbie sliced his tee shot.

"Mr. Frisbie," said young Holt, "there was several things the matter with you then but the main trouble was that you stood too close to the ball and cut across it with your club head and besides that you swang back faster than Alex Smith and you were off your balance and you gripped too hard and you jerked instead of hitting with a smooth follow through."

Well, Mr. Frisbie gave him a queer look and then made up his mind that Junior was trying to be humorous and he frowned at him so as he would not try it again but when we located the ball in the rough and Mr. Frisbie asked me for his spoon young Holt said Oh take your mashie Mr. Frisbie never use a wooden club in a place like that and Mr. Frisbie scowled and mumbled under his breath and missed the ball with his spoon and missed it again and then took a midiron and just dribbled it on to the fairway and finally got on the green in 7 and took 3 putts.

I suppose you might say that this was one of the quickest golf matches on record as it ended on the 2d. tee. Mr. Frisbie tried to drive and sliced again. Then young Holt took a ball from my pocket and a club from the bag and said here let me show you the swing and drove the ball 250 yards straight down the middle of the course.

I looked at Mr. Frisbie's face and it was puffed out and a kind of a purple black color. Then he burst and I will only repeat a few of the more friendlier of his remarks.

"Get to hell and gone of my place. Do not never darken my doors again. Just show up around here one more time and I will blow out what you have got instead of brains. You lied to my girl and you tried to make a fool out of me. Get out before I sick my dogs on you and tear you to pieces."

Junior most lightly wanted to offer some word of explanation or to demand one on his own account but saw at a glance how useless same would be. I heard later that he saw Miss Florence and that she just laughed at him.

"I made a mistake about Junior Holt," said Mr. Frisbie that evening. "He is no good and must never come to this house again."

"Oh Father and just when I was beginning to like him," said Miss Florence.

Well like him or not like him she and the other young man Henry

Craig were married soon afterwards which I suppose Mr. Frisbie permitted the bands in the hopes that same would rile Junior Holt.

Mr. Frisbie admitted he had made a mistake in regards to the last named but he certainly was not mistaken when he said that young Craig was a tramp and would never amount to anything.

Well I guess I have rambled on long enough about Mr. Frisbie.

Emily Kimbrough

CINCINNATI AND I

NOT long ago, I returned from a six-weeks lecture tour, and, looking back on it, I feel that two facts emerge emphatically: first, that I am what my Grandmother Kimbrough used to call "not right sharp" about schedules, and second, that Cincinnati and I are not happy together.

On this tour, I had my second lecture date in Cincinnati. My first was in 1946, when I arrived there on February 26th at 8:30 a.m. from an engagement in Pittsburgh the night before. That time, I stayed at the Netherland Plaza. This season, I was at the Hotel Gibson. I can understand, in view of my demolition of a portion of the Netherland Plaza, why the lecture bureau should have put me in another hotel on my second trip. But until the morning of October 31, 1947, I thought that the grotesque 1946 Cincinnati incidents were only a kind of three-day northeaster that had blown itself out there. In the light of what happened this year, I am inclined to believe that Cincinnati is a storm center for me and that hereafter I will do better to skirt around it.

The 1946 grotesqueries actually began on February 25th, on the day train from Philadelphia to Pittsburgh. I was well along in a six-weeks tour. It had been strenuous but, on the whole, pleasant and uneventful. I had had a week-end interim at home in Philadelphia, and was starting out on the middle lap of the tour, rested, and comfortably settled in my parlor-car seat. I was, I remember, knitting when I first smelled smoke.

Craning my neck around toward the back of my chair, I sniffed. I could not smell any smoke there, and none of the passengers were sniffing, so I went back to my knitting. Then I smelled it again, and this time I was sure that it came from burning leather. I summoned the porter and said to him that I didn't wish to alarm either him or the other passengers, but did he smell smoke? He chuckled reassuringly, but stopped abruptly to point to a thin line of smoke that was drifting up from the mouth of my black suede handbag, which I had wedged between my chair and the window. It was a bag I kept out of sight as much as possible—a difficult thing to do, considering its size.

The bag had been made in Hollywood at a famous suede shop, and it wasn't finished until the day I left for the East and the lecture tour. I had ordered a pouch-style bag, with suede drawstrings long enough for me to wear over my shoulder. It was to be eight inches wide and ten inches deep, but when I went to the shop to get it—one of the fifteen last-minute errands that day—I found the saleslady holding it in her hand and looking at it in awe. At the sight of me, she said, "Miss Kimbrough, I don't know if you'll want this. We've got a new cutter, and I think she's exaggerated." We measured the bag, and it was twenty-two inches wide and twenty-seven inches deep. I took it, because there was no time to have it changed, but I kept it out of sight whenever I could.

The porter grabbed the bag and turned it upside down in the aisle. Besides the ordinary things any woman has in her bag—purse, compact, lipstick, cigarettes, Kleenex, handkerchief, theater-ticket stubs, shopping lists, and swatches of material—there was a large tin of Postum and a folding spoon. I do not like to admit that I cannot drink coffee, and the suede pouch had seemed a good place to hide the Postum I always carry with me. This time it didn't work. The tin rolled all the way down the aisle to the men's room.

The last thing to come out of the bag was a book of blazing matches that had burned through a corner of the lining and into the suede. It took a great deal longer to gather up the items shaken out in the aisle than it did to stamp out the fire, although the other passengers pitched in and helped. After I had thanked them all and explained about the Postum and the size of the bag, I was glad we were coming into Pittsburgh.

The clerk at the desk of my hotel sniffed a little while I was asking about my reservation, so I felt that I had to explain the episode to him. The bellboy, too, wanted to know about the smell, so I held the bag up for both of them to see. Once in my room, I bathed, dressed (formal evening dress requested, it said on my contract; women's clubs are always explicit), had my dinner sent up, and was called for at half past seven by the chairman of the evening and her husband. He was, he told me, in charge of the backstage arrangements, and he proved to be very genial. I constantly marvel at the patience and cooperation of the husbands of women's club ladies. This Pittsburgh husband delivered me and his wife at the door of the auditorium and joined us backstage after he had parked the car. He asked me how I wanted the lights, and since I know nothing whatever about lighting, I said that I thought overhead and footlights would be just right, and he said that those were exactly what he had turned on, which I had noticed. His wife interrupted us with the announcement "If we wait for late-comers, the early ones get restless," and strode onto the stage. I followed her.

We got off to a fine start. Her introduction was hearty, and she remembered it. "It gives me great pleasure—" she ended, and we bowed each other into reverse positions, she to the chair I had quitted and I behind the lectern.

About three-quarters of the way through my lecture, I had occasion to illustrate a point I was making by holding up my hands on either side of my face, like blinders, and in doing this I leaned my elbows on the lectern. There was a ripping, crunching sound, and the lectern disintegrated under me. The rim, breaking up into pieces that looked like the kind of kindling wood that is full of nails, flew down into the front row, where the unhappy people dodged in surprise. For a moment, it looked as if I would join them there. As the lectern sank to the floor, its component parts spreading out at my feet, I lost my balance and gave every appearance of an inexperienced diver about to plunge reluctantly over the footlights. But by rotating my arms vigorously —though I was hampered by the tightness across the upper arms of my off-the-shoulder dress—I brought myself back to an upright position. I had, however, lost the thread of my lecture, and so had the audience. I made a few efforts to find it but it seemed better just to wish them good evening and leave the stage. Their sportsmanship brought me back to take a bow. The janitor accompanied me, and after my bow we both squatted down while he helped me paw out from the rubble my handkerchief, gloves and bag—not my knapsack but a small evening bag that was harder to find. He helped me to my feet and glared at the audience.

"I told you ladies to tell your speakers not to touch that lectern," he shouted. "It's got worms in it."

The chairman and her husband were garrulously distressed all the way back to the hotel. He said she ought to have warned me, but she said that because she'd noticed I didn't carry notes, she'd thought I probably wouldn't lay a hand on the thing, and hadn't wanted to make me nervous.

I boarded a late train that night, slept fitfully, and rose early to get out at Cincinnati at seven-thirty. Following the redcap who had my bag, I stepped briskly along the corridor that leads from the train sheds into the main waiting room. The floor of this corridor is smooth white marble—or something like marble—and felt slippery. It dips down decidedly the last few yards before you get to the waiting room, and when I reached this incline, I veered to the left impulsively to walk on a black band about two feet wide that extends the whole length of the corridor. I thought it was a rubber carpeting put down as a safeguard against slipping, but it was of the same kind of stone— apparently just a decorative note. I had hardly set a tentative foot on it when something caught me behind the knees, upended me, and carried me on it smoothly down the slope and into the waiting room, my feet in the air and my hat over my face. I heard running footsteps behind me and a man's voice calling indistinguishable words.

As I was slowing down to a stop a hand grabbed my arm and pulled me to my feet. I pushed up my hat and looked into the anxious face of a Marine. He was out of breath, but he apologized and explained in a rush of words that his bag here—he pointed to the piece of luggage on which I had just been recumbent—was so heavy that when he saw the incline ahead he had set it down, hauled off, and given it a big boot. Then I had crossed over without warning in front of it. . . . And if there was anything he could do. . . . He hoped I knew how bad he felt to have done such a thing. . . .

I think he was going to offer to see me to my hotel, but as I was assuring him that I was not hurt, a lady's troubled voice interrupted us. "This *is* Miss Kimbrough, isn't it?" She injected a nervous giggle. "I was just *sure* it was." After she had introduced me to two friends on the hospitality committee who had come with her to meet me, I turned back to the Marine, but he had gone.

We four ladies rode together to the Netherland Plaza in a car belonging to one of them, who drove. I was put into the back seat with the lady who had claimed me, but the driver and her friend in the front seat were so interested to know how I had "*ever* happened to come down into the station on top of that big black bag" that they kept turning around, in order not to miss any of the story. I am always nervous in a car I'm not driving myself, even behind the most skillful of drivers, which this one was not, so I was tired when we reached the hotel. The ladies said that they would come back for me about half past twelve to take me out to their club for the luncheon before my speech. The driver interrupted with a suggestion that if they came a little early, she could point out the sights as we drove along, and perhaps take in one or two places not directly on the route. In the face of their enthusiasm, I could hardly say that if I were given my choice, I would prefer to start out right then on foot, however far the club might be. I promised to be ready when they came, and they drove off, waving.

The luncheon was no more shrill than any women's gathering. The hostesses were charming and hospitable. My speech passed off uneventfully, and we had tea afterward. My ladies would have taken me out to dinner, rounding up some of the other "girls" to go along, but I told them about my Great-Aunt Wilmina, who lives near Cincinnati and was coming in to have dinner with me at the hotel, so they drove me back to the Netherland Plaza. When I left them, I said emphatically that I wouldn't dream of allowing them to go to the inconvenience of driving me to the train; I was leaving early in the morning for Louisville, and it would be much simpler for everyone if I got a taxi. They were prettily reluctant, but I was firm, and we parted with a rondo of good-bys and thank-yous.

Aunt Wilmina came to dinner, and I saw her off in a taxi at nine-thirty. When I got back to my room, I was tired, and very thirsty after a day of talking. I felt that I could drink an entire quart of ginger ale, and perhaps two, so I telephoned for two quarts, and a waiter brought them. I asked if he had an opener, and he told me there was one in the bathroom.

After he left, I found the opener in the bathroom—a metal lip an inch and a half long, fastened with two screws to the frame of the medicine cabinet. One of the screws was loose and the opener sagged, but, nevertheless, I slipped the cap of the ginger-ale bottle underneath it and pulled down. Nothing happened, so I took a firmer grip on the bottle, inserted it again, and gave a quick jerk with all my strength. The opener came away from the medicine cabinet and fell into the washbasin. So did the quart of ginger ale, and with such force that it split the washbasin into two parts. One part toppled over into the toilet and splintered. The other dropped against the side of the bathtub and broke into four large chunks. The ginger ale bottle was not even nicked, but the cap was loosened enough to send the liquid in a thin, powerful stream toward the ceiling and all over my head. It shot up with such violence that I couldn't pound the cap on again. I covered the top of the bottle with my hand, but the liquid squirted out over my dress, legs and feet. Ginger ale is sweet and sticky, and there is more of it in a quart than I had ever dreamed. When the last of it was out of the bottle, I mopped up as much of myself and the floor as I could with the one towel the ginger ale hadn't reached. Then I went into the bedroom, called the desk, and asked the clerk if he could spare the time to come up for a moment, because something had happened that I found difficult to explain over the telephone. When he arrived, another man was with him, but the clerk did not say who he was. I took them to the door of the bathroom and pointed to the empty ginger-ale bottle, which I had set down on the shelf above the toilet, thinking that if I started with the bottle, I could perhaps describe the accident step by step, and thus make it sound credible. The strange man picked up the bottle and held it all the time I talked. He kept looking at it, and then at the walls, where the ginger ale was dripping, and at the floor, where the remains of the washbasin lay. When I had finished my story, the clerk said that nothing like this had ever happened in the Netherland Plaza before. This did not surprise me. He also said there wasn't another room available in the hotel and that they couldn't get the washstand replaced that night, which also did not surprise me. He would send up a chambermaid to sweep up, he said, and to give me fresh towels. The other man was still holding the ginger ale bottle when they left. He hadn't spoken at all.

The chambermaid wanted to know what in the name of conniption had happened, and when I explained it to her, she said that it didn't seem to her it could have happened that way. But she telephoned the linen room to send me a box in which to pack the clothes I was wearing, because, she said, I certainly couldn't wear them again before they had been cleaned and couldn't pack them with my other clothes; the best thing would be to mail them home. She got the bathroom pretty well mopped and swept, and she brought me fresh towels. But she cautioned me not to step on the floor in bare feet, because there might still be a lot of chips around.

As soon as she had left, I got out of my clothes and into the tub and washed my hair. It took three separate washings and rinsings to get all the ginger ale out. My hair is long, and it was three in the morning when I had finished drying it. I put in a call to be waked at seven o'clock, because I was afraid I might oversleep and miss my train for Louisville. I caught the Louisville train by running up the incline at the station and all the rest of the length of the marble corridor.

When I reached home, a couple of weeks later, I found a letter from the Netherland Plaza Hotel. It read:

Dear Miss Kimbrough:
   On February 26, while you were a guest at the Netherland Plaza in Room 2522, it appears that you broke a lavatory in the bathroom. The cost of replacing this lavatory is $55.17. We trust that we will receive an early reply.

                                        Yours very truly.

I replied, protesting the charge, because, I explained, the accident had been caused by a defective opener that was the property of the hotel. "I do not therefore feel responsible," I wrote, "though I regret exceedingly that it happened."

A week later, I received a courteous answer cancelling the charges for the broken lavatory. One more letter from me, thanking them for their understanding and generosity, presumably closed the incident. This year, though, as I said, I was booked at the Gibson Hotel, and I do not know whether it was by request of the Netherland Plaza or because of a delicate sense of consideration on the part of the man in the lecture bureau who makes my reservations.

I think I shall remember for a long time that I arrived in Cincinnati for my lecture there this season on Thursday, October 30th, at 6:20 p.m. I spent that evening at the theater, where I met some old friends who were in Cincinnati for a brief visit. They were at the Netherland Plaza and were sorry I wasn't staying there. I said only that I was comfortable at the Gibson and had stayed at the Netherland Plaza on a previous trip. They insisted on taking me back to their rooms after the play, and I looked wistfully around the familiar lobby as I went in.

I did not leave them until long after midnight, and found, when I got outside, that it had started to rain. My taxi-driver said he would just as soon it rained hard for the next twenty-four hours, on account of its being Hallowe'en the next night. He explained that the whole downtown district of Cincinnati was always turned over to Hallowe'en celebrations. Everybody came out, either in costume or just to see the sights, and the crowds were so heavy that taxis weren't even allowed on some of the streets. He said it seemed like anywhere you wanted to go, it took you ten blocks out of your way to get there, and, what with the crowds, you couldn't get through anyhow. But that was the way Hallowe'en was in Cincinnati.

I was very sleepy the next morning. I had breakfast in my room, got into a gray wool dress that, with gold necklace and earrings, was as near as I could approximate what was stipulated in the contract as "short, formal, daytime dress." I glanced at my lecture-bureau schedule hastily to make sure of the hour and address. It read, "Friday, November 1, Cincinnati, Ohio, Southwest Ohio Teachers' Association, 9:30 a.m., Scottish Rite Auditorium." By rushing, I managed to get to the Scottish Rite building at nine-twenty. It is a very large place, and I had some difficulty in finding the way to my auditorium, which was a lesser one. I had particular difficulty because there seemed to be no one else going there. I came upon it eventually, through a door that took me onto the stage, and found myself alone, except for a janitor who was sweeping one of the aisles. I asked him what was going on, and he said nothing, as far as he knew. He was irritated, because his back had been turned to me when I called him, and he said I had made him jump. I had no trouble finding my way out of the building, but it was hard to get a taxi. It was still raining and there were puddles on the sidewalk. I was wearing thin, black suede, open-toed slippers, and the water splashed in the toes and up over my insteps. As soon as I got back to my hotel room, I telephoned Mr. R. W. Cadwallader, whose name, as Executive Secretary of the Southwestern Ohio Teachers' Association, was on my contract. Mrs. Cadwallader answered the telephone. She didn't know where Mr. Cadwallader was, she said. Had I tried the auditorium? I told her I had. Well, then, she said, she didn't know where to find him, he was so busy with these meetings. Up to this moment, I had been calm, I think, but now I became a little high-pitched. Could she tell me, then, I demanded, where I was supposed to be? My lecture engagement was at nine-thirty and it was now quarter to ten.

"Wait a minute," she said, and left the telephone. In a moment, she was back. "I'm looking at my bulletin," she told me, "and you are speaking at the Scottish Rite Auditorium tomorrow morning at nine-thirty—Saturday, November 1st. I'm reading it right here."

"I'm sure my schedule says Friday, November 1st," I said, and I think my voice was trembling.

Mrs. Cadwallader was patient. "But Friday isn't November 1st. To-day is Hallowe'en—you know, the thirty-first of October. Tomorrow is November 1st."

I was sitting on the edge of my bed, and after I had put down the telephone, I kept on sitting there for some time. I felt suddenly over-dressed in formal daytime dress at 9:50 a.m. in a hotel bedroom, and I had twenty-four hours to go. Of course this was the thirty-first of October! The taxi-driver's talk about Hallowe'en the night before should have warned me. But it was Friday. I looked at my schedule again. It read, "Friday, November 1." I took out my pencil and cor-rected the schedule to read, "Saturday, November 1." It was too late to do any good. I should have checked and corrected my dates long before, especially since, on a previous tour for the same lecture bureau, I had got to Shreveport, Louisiana, three days ahead of time. But that mixup was my own fault. This at least was one-half the fault of the lecture bureau. I studied the schedule again and tried to figure out why I had been rushed from Mansfield, Ohio, the day before if I was to have a twenty-four-hour wait in Cincinnati. I had had to leave Mansfield in the middle of lunch after a morning lecture and drive fifteen miles to catch a New York Central train at two-ten, in order to reach Cincinnati at six-twenty on Thursday, October 30th. They knew I had a great-aunt near Cincinnati. I had written about her. They thought I would like to see her. As simple as that! It suddenly occurred to me to wonder whether my Pullman ticket for the train that was to take me to my next engagement might not be wrong, too. I got it out of the leather folder in which I always keep my tickets, with the schedule and my lecture contracts. It was for New York Central train No. 405, leaving Cincinnati for Chicago at 3:20, p.m., Saturday, No-vember 1st. They knew, then, all along, at the lecture bureau, that I was speaking on November 1st, and that it came on a Saturday. Friday was just a slip of the typewriter—or a Hallowe'en prank.

I know now that it is not enough to read my schedule carefully; it is necessary to check it with the railroad accommodations. I evidently learn one thing at a time. It has taken two visits to Cincinnati to show me that that city and I do not blend.

Max Shulman

EXCERPTS FROM
BAREFOOT BOY WITH CHEEK

THE morning of the big day dawned bright and clear. As the rosy fingers of the sun crept through my window and illuminated the C&H on my homemade bed sheet, I could scarcely contain myself. "Huzzah!" I shouted. "Huzzah!"

I bounded joyously from my bed. I bounded right back again. My drop-seat pajamas had become entangled in a bedspring during the night. Disengaging myself, I ran to wake Mother. "Mother," I called. "Mother, give me to eat."

But lovable old Mother had anticipated me. She had been up for hours. While I had lain in drowsyland, she had slaughtered the brood sow and bustled about preparing the morning meal. When I came into the kitchen, my favorite breakfast was already on the table.

"Mother!" I cried. "Johnson grass and brala suet. Just for me."

"Set down and eat, slugabed," she chided gently. "You don't want to be late the first day."

I could not help taking her in my arms and kissing her careworn cheek. A person can choose his friends and select a wife, but he has only one mother, I always say. The trouble with many of us is that we don't appreciate our mothers. I think that a certain day should be set aside each year and dedicated to mothers. It could be called "Mother's Day."

"Son," she said, "you ain't my baby no more."

"The hell you say, Mother," I said. "The hell you say."

"You're agoin' off to thet air university and get your haid all full of l'arnin', and you're gonna fergit your pore old igerant mother."

"Aw, you're not so dumb," I protested.

"Yes, I be," she declared. "I don't know no more than your old houn' dog Edmund layin' over there by the stove."

I jumped up from the table. "Now just you be careful what you're saying about Edmund. I don't mean to have that dog run down when I'm here. He's a mighty smart dog." I whistled to him. "Play dead, Edmund," I said. "See," I told Mother. "Look at how he obeys. All four feet sticking up in the air."

"He ain't playin', son," Mother said softly. "I didn't want to tell you. He's been dead since Friday."

Edmund dead! I couldn't believe it. Why, only last Friday I had seen him happily flushing grouse. In his excitement he had flushed too many, and we had had to call a plumber. But it was all fixed now, and Edmund was forgiven. Naturally, I had punished him, but—— No. No! I couldn't have——

"Mother!" I cried.

"Yes, son," she said. "He died right after. That last time you ran over him with the car did it."

I stumbled over to the window and pressed my hot forehead against the pane. A cloud passed over the sun, and it began to rain. The room was oppressively quiet. A loon cried over the lake.

Father came into the kitchen. "Good morning, son," he said. "I came to say good-by before you went off to the University."

"Thank you," I said simply.

"Button your fly," Mother said.

"Oh, button your lip," Father exclaimed testily, and hit her in the mouth with a skillet. Mother went to weld her dentures.

Father came over and put his arm around me. "Son, today you are entering a new phase of your life."

"Oh, can't you leave me alone?" I snapped. "Can't anybody leave me alone?"

Father drew back. "Why, son, what's the matter? This should be the happiest day in your life."

I laughed ironically. "The happiest day of your life, he says."

"No, no," Father interrupted. "I said the happiest day *in* your life. Not *of—in!*"

"Oh. Excuse me. The happiest day in your life, he says." I lifted my clenched fists. "Oh, ironical gods! What a mockery you have made of this day."

"Why, son, what——"

I pointed mutely to Edmund.

"I understand," said Father simply.

The door opened and two men from the animal rescue league came in. They took Edmund. "Neighbors been complaining," one of them explained.

Father put an arm around my shaking shoulders. "You know, son," he said, "I had a dog once. A little Pekingese bitch named Anna May."

"Is it true what they say about the Pekingese, Father?" I asked.

He winked obscenely and continued: "She wasn't much of a dog, I guess. She couldn't hunt. She was no good as a watchdog. All she did all day long was lie on a chaise longue reading slim yellow French novels and eating bonbons. But when I came home at night from a hard day at the egg candlery, Anna May was always waiting, wagging her little tail and being sick on the rug. I—I guess I loved her, that's all," Father said.

"I understand," I said simply.

"But I didn't have Anna May long. One day my cousin May Fuster came to visit me. You remember May, don't you, son?"

"Of course," I said. "Whatever became of her?"

"It's a long story. She ran off with a full-blooded Chippewa named Alf Mountainclimbing. He took her to La Paz, Bolivia, where he found employment as a clerk in an Adam hat store. At first May loved it down there. She used to watch the colorful *pesos* riding around in their old-fashioned *tortillas*. Every afternoon she used to lie down and take a *hacienda*. During the carnival season she would put on her *vincent lopez* and dance in the street with the rest of the happy natives. In her own words she was, as the expression goes, very *muy Usted*.

"But a cloud passed over the sunshine of her life. Alf's Chippewa heritage manifested itself. He started to drink heavily. One could always find him sprawled drunkenly over a table in one of the lower-class *cojones* of La Paz. He lost his position at the hat store. Poor May, in order to keep body and soul together, was forced into inter-American relations with the natives.

"Alf grew progressively worse. His alcoholic brain cells finally failed him. One day he dropped to all fours and declared that he was a pinball machine. From that day on he remained in that position, complaining occasionally that he was being tilted.

"May's sultry Northern beauty brought her a large and varied clientele. One of her patrons was Ed Frenesi, the local bullfight impressario. Frenesi remarked the supple grace of her limbs and suggested to her that she should become a female bullfighter.

"Of course she scoffed at the idea. But after he offered her 5,000 *muchachas* (about thirty-four hundred dollars) while she was learning and 5,000 more for every bull she killed, May accepted."

"I understand," I said simply.

"Then began a rigorous training period. First she trained with less dangerous bulls from which the horns had been removed. May was up early every morning making passes at the dehorns. All day long she practiced in the hot sun with a draped cape and a gored sword. She retired every evening at eight, and after reading Hemingway for an hour fell into the deep sleep of fatigue.

"Frenesi watched her progress with considerable satisfaction. He saw how easily she mastered the intricate art of dominating the bull, and he knew that if everything went right he would have a great attraction. He taught May by easy stages until she learned the ultimate accomplishment in the bullfighter's craft—the Veronica, or killing a bull while your hair hangs over one eye. Then Frenesi knew that she was ready for her debut. He Latinized her name to Yanqui Imperialismo, and splashed posters all over La Paz.

"Frenesi's shrewd showmanship had its desired effect. For weeks before the bullfight nobody in La Paz talked about anything but *el toreador broad*—the lady bullfighter. From all the surrounding territories people poured into La Paz. Hotel rooms were filled almost immediately, and thousands of visitors had to sleep on makeshift *frijoles* in the lobbies. The wineshops and cafés were unable to handle all their trade. Alf, May's husband, took in a considerable sum posing as a pinball machine in a downtown tavern. La Paz's choked streets resounded with good-natured cries of 'I spit in the milk of your motor,' and 'I this and that on your this.' The land office did a land-office business."

Father took a guitar from the mantel and struck chords as he continued his narrative. "The day of the big fight dawned bright and clear. In the morning Frenesi went down to the bull pen and selected a crowd pleaser named Harry Holstein as May's opponent. May went to her dressing room at the arena where her cross-eyed seamstress named Pilar helped her with the involved business of dressing. May was nervous and frightened, but Pilar reassured her. 'Do not be afraid, my little,' she said. 'We all got to go sometime.'

"At last May heard the fanfare, and she knew that the *Presidente* had entered his box. The fight was about to begin. Suddenly May was in the center of the hot white sand of the arena. A roar rose from a hundred thousand throats. A gate swung open, and Harry Holstein, pawing and snorting, charged into the ring.

"Now the fear left May. Coolly she prepared to nimbly sidestep the initial charge of the beast. But, alas, her cross-eyed seamstress had tied the laces of her two shoes together. She could not move.

"May was impaled on the horns of the bull. What a dilemma! The attendants rushed from the sidelines to rescue her. The angry, cheated people in the stands cut off their ears and threw them into the arena with enraged cries of '*Olé! Olé!*'

"May eventually recovered. As soon as she could, she left La Paz. Her name was anathema in the town. She tried to see Frenesi once, but he instructed his housekeeper to pour hot water on her.

"So she wandered from one South American city to another, eking out a bare living tuning guitars and dealing double Canfield. Today, a broken woman, she earns a meager subsistence as a harbor buoy in Havana."

"But what about your Pekingese, Father?" I asked.

"Gad, son, look at the time!" Father exclaimed. "You'll be late for school."

*　　*　　*

St. Paul and Minneapolis extend from the Mississippi River like the legs on a pair of trousers. Where they join is the University of Minnesota.

I stood that day and gazed at the campus, my childish face looking up, holding wonder like a cup; my little feet beating time, time, time, in a sort of runic rhyme. A fraternity man's convertible ran me down, disturbing my reverie. "Just a flesh wound," I mumbled to disinterested passersby.

With eager steps I proceeded to explore the campus. All around me was the hum of happy men at work. Here were masons aging a building so they could hang ivy on it. There were chiselers completing the statue of Cyrus Thresher, first regent of the University. It was Thresher, as you know, who said, "It takes a heap o' learnin' to make a school a school." Yonder were landscapers cleverly trimming a twelve-foot hedge to spell "Minnesota, Minnesota, rah, rah, ree. Little brown jug, how we love thee."

The architecture at Minnesota is very distinctive, and thereby hangs a tale. It goes back a good many years, back to the time when the mighty, sprawling University was just an infant. At that time Art Chaff, the son of a wealthy Minneapolis flour miller named Elihu Chaff, was expelled from Harvard for playing buck euchre on the Sabbath. Old Elihu was deeply incensed by the indignity. He was determined that Art should go to college, and, moreover, to a bigger college than Harvard.

So Elihu went to work on the University of Minnesota campus. He erected twenty buildings. They all looked like grain elevators, for that is what Elihu intended to use them for after Art had been graduated. But Elihu never fulfilled his plan.

One week end Elihu went fishing, accompanied only by an Indian guide named Ralph Duckhonking. They went into a deep forest, and after two days Duckhonking came out alone. He was wearing Elihu's suit and carrying all of his valuables. He said he knew nothing about Elihu's disappearance. Duckhonking was indicted for murder, but he was never tried because it was impossible to obtain twelve English-speaking veniremen in that judicial district. Duckhonking walked about free until he died more than twenty years later of nepotism. This case later became famous as the *Crédit Mobilier* scandal.

Elihu's elevators, therefore, remained part of the University. In fact, out of respect to Elihu, all the buildings which were subsequently erected on the campus were built to resemble grain elevators.

But this was no time to be gawking about the campus. I had things to do. First I had to see Mr. Ingelbretsvold, my freshman adviser, about making out a program of studies for the year. Obtaining directions from a friendly upperclassman who sold me a freshman button, freshman cap, subscription to *Ski-U-Mah*, the campus humor magazine, a map of the campus, and a souvenir score card of last year's home-coming game, I proceeded to the office of Mr. Ingelbretsvold.

A line of freshmen stood in front of his door. I knew how they must feel, about to embark on this great adventure, and I could not help cheerily hollering "Halloa" to them. They stoned me in an amiable fashion.

At last a voice came from behind the door bidding me come in. How my heart beat as I opened the door and trod across the luxuriant burlap rug to Mr. Ingelbretsvold's desk.

"My name is Asa Hearthrug and I've come for advice," I said.

He stood up and smiled at me kindly. "Sit down, young man," he said.

"Thank you," I said, making a low curtsey.

"Well, it's certainly a nice day."

"Yes," I agreed. "Almost twelve inches of rain since sunup."

"That's what I meant," he said. "It's a nice rain. It will help the potato crop."

"Yes," I agreed, "it should wash out every potato in Minnesota."

"That's what I meant," he said. "It will get rid of those damn potatoes. People are eating altogether too many potatoes. But enough of this meteorological chitchat. Let's get down to business. First of all, I want you to know that I'm your friend."

I licked his hand gratefully.

"You are about to enter a new phase of your life. I wonder whether you realize just how important this is."

"Oh, I do, sir, I do," I exclaimed.

"Shut up when I'm talking," he said. "Now, I have a little story that I like to tell to freshmen to impress them with the importance of college. I have had a great many students who were graduated from Minnesota and went out to take their places in the world come back after many years and say to me, 'Mr. Ingelbretsvold, I can never thank you enough for that little story you told me when I first came to the University.' Yes, young man, this story has helped a great many people, and I hope it will help you."

"So tell it already," I said.

"Well, sir, when I was a boy I had a good friend named Kyrie Eleison. We went through grade school and high school together, and on the night we were graduated from high school I said to him, 'Well, Kyrie, what are you going to do now?'

"'Oh,' he said, 'I've got a chance to get a job in a nepotism business in North Dakota.'

"'Kyrie,' I told him, 'don't take it. Come to college with me, or else you'll always regret it.'

"But he didn't choose to take my advice. I went to college, and he took the job. Yes, he did well at his work. By the time he was thirty he had seventy-five million dollars, and he has been getting richer ever since. He built a fine big house in which he holds the most lavish social affairs in the whole Northwest.

"Well, sir, one night I was invited to a party at Kyrie's house. I rented a suit and went. The house was filled with prominent people. A hundred-and-twenty-piece orchestra was playing. When we went in for dinner the table groaned with all sorts of expensive delicacies. And at the head of the table sat Kyrie, the monarch of all he surveyed.

"But during the course of the dinner a well-dressed young woman leaned over and said to Kyrie, 'Who was the eighth avatar of Vishnu?' and Kyrie, for all his wealth and power, did not know the answer."

"How ghastly!" I cried, throwing up my hands.

"Yes," said Mr. Ingelbretsvold. "You will find that sort of thing all through life. People come up to you on the street and say, 'Does a paramecium beat its flagella?' or 'How many wheels has a fiacre?' or

'When does an oryx mate?' and if you have not been to college, you simply cannot answer them."

"But that cannot happen to me. I am going to the University," I said.

"Ah, but it can," Mr. Ingelbretsvold answered. "It happens to many who go to college."

"But how?"

"You see, my boy, a great many people go to college to learn how to *do* something. They study medicine or law or engineering, and when they are through they know how to trepan a skull or where to get a writ of estoppel or how to find the torque of a radial engine. But just come up to them and ask how many caliphs succeeded Mohammed or who wrote *Baby Duncan's Whistling Lung* and they stare at you blankly."

I shuddered. "Oh, please, Mr. Ingelbretsvold," I begged, "what must I do?"

"You must do like I tell you. You must let college make you a well-rounded-out personality. That is the chief function and purpose of this University: to make you a well-rounded-out personality. Now you get out a pencil and paper and write down the names of the courses I am going to give you. If you follow this program you will find yourself a well-rounded-out personality."

I took out a pencil and poised it over my dickey bosom.

"Ready. Here they are: Races and Cultures of Arabia, Egypt, and North Africa; Ethnology of India; History of Architecture; Greek; Latin; Sixteenth-Century Literature; Seventeenth-Century Literature; Eighteenth-Century Literature; Nineteenth-Century Literature; Twentieth-Century Literature; Geography; Ancient History; Medieval History; Modern History; Ancient Philosophy; Modern Philosophy; Contemporary Philosophy; History of Religion; American Government; British Government; Chinese Government; Japanese Government; Lett Government; First Aid; Public Health; General Psychology; Psychology of Learning; Psychology of Advertising; Psychology of Literature; Psychology of Art; Psychology of Behavior; Animal Psychology; Abnormal Psychology; Norwegian; Swedish; Danish; French; German; Russian; Italian; Lett; Urban Sociology; Rural Sociology; Juvenile Sociology; Statistical Sociology; Criminology; Penology; Elocution; Speech Pathology; and Canoe Paddling.

"That will do for a start. As you go into these courses you will find others that will interest you too."

"And these will make me a well-rounded-out personality?" I asked.

He laughed gently. "Oh no, my boy. That is only a small but essential part of rounding out your personality. There is the social life too." He nudged me and winked. "A fellow can have a good time here."

"Sir," I said, and blushed.

"But you'll soon find out all about that. Now, one more thing. In addition to the work you do for these courses I have named you should do a lot of reading that has not been assigned in your classes. Do you read anything now?"

"A mystery story now and then," I confessed.

"Oh, have you read Rex Snout's latest, *The Case of the Gelded Gnu?*"

"No, but I read the one before that, *The Case of the Missing Lynx.*"

"I missed that one. What was it about?"

"Well, a horribly mutilated corpse is found on the railroad tracks near Buffalo. This corpse is in such a state that it is impossible to identify it or even to tell whether it is a man or a woman. The story is concerned almost entirely with trying to establish the identity of the corpse. In the end it is discovered that it is not a corpse at all, but a pan of waffle batter that fell out of the window of a New York Central dining car."

"How interesting. Well, I guess that's all the time I can give you. Others are waiting," he said, taking cognizance of the stones they were throwing through the window.

"Just one more thing, Mr. Ingelbretsvold," I said. "I don't know quite how to say this, but I think I would like to be a writer when I grow up. Will the program you made out for me help me to be a writer?"

"Why, bless you, child," Mr. Ingelbretsvold said, "you follow that program and there's nothing else you can be."

*   *   *

The University of Minnesota builds not only minds; it also builds bodies. Before you can enter the University you must undergo a thorough and rigorous examination at the Student Health Service. Minnesota has one of the finest health services in the country. Here prominent doctors, serving without compensation, give unstintingly of their time and wisdom that youth of Minnesota might be strong.

I shall always remember, with a mixture of gratitude and admiration, the day I went through the Health Service for my examination. I was extensively examined by not one, but many doctors, each an expert in his particular branch of medicine.

First I was sent to the bone surgeon. He was sitting at his desk reading a copy of *Film Fun*. "How many arms and legs you got?" he asked, without putting down the *Film Fun*.

"Two," I answered.

"Two altogether?"

"No sir, two of each."

"O.K. You're all right. Go ahead," he said, still looking at the *Film Fun*.

I proceeded to the office of the heart doctors. Because heart examination is a delicate, involved process, two doctors are assigned to that duty. When I came into the office, they were standing by the window dropping paper bags filled with water on pedestrians.

"I had an interesting case the other day," said one to the other. "I was listening to a kid's heart and it was the damnedest thing I ever heard. It didn't thump. It chimed in three notes."

"What do you know?" said the second. "What caused that?"

"I couldn't find out for a long time," answered the first. "It wasn't until I went way back into the kid's history that I found the solution. His mother was frightened by an NBC station break."

"Well, what do you know?" said the second. "Say, I heard of another interesting case yesterday. Dr. Curette in plastic surgery told me about it. A man came in to see him. The fellow didn't have a nose."

"No nose?" said the first. "How did he smell?"

"Terrible," said the second.

"Oh, Harold," said the first, "you're more fun than a barrel of monkeys."

I cleared my throat. They turned and noticed me for the first time.

"I've come for a heart examination," I said.

"You look all right. Go ahead," they said.

They went over to the sink to fill some more bags with water.

My next stop was the weighing room. I stepped on the scale, my weight was recorded, and a doctor said, "You make friends easily. You are a good worker although you are a little inclined to put things off. You are going to make a long trip on water."

I gave him a penny and proceeded to the abdominal clinic. The doctor was sitting at a table building a boat in a bottle. "Ever have to get up in the middle of the night?" he asked.

"Yes sir," I answered.

"Hmm," he said. "I'm going to have a little trouble with the mizzen-mast. Know anything about boats?"

"Some," I confessed modestly.

"I love boats," he said. "I love the sea. Right now I'd love to be on a trim little schooner hauling a cargo of oscars from the levant. I love the good feel of a stout ship on a rough sea. Perhaps a nor'wester would blow up, and all the hearty mates would be on the deck pulling together while the grizzled old skipper stood on the bridge and yelled his orders: 'Keelhaul the bosun! Jettison the supercargo!' "

"My, you certainly know a lot about boats," I said admiringly.

He lowered his eyes. "I should. I was cuckold on the Yale crew in 1912. But enough of this. So you have to get up in the middle of the night?"

"Yes sir. You see, my sister Morningstar keeps company with an engineer on the Natchez, Mobile, and Duluth railroad. About a year ago he got put on a night run, and Morningstar never used to get to see him. She complained so much that he finally had a sidetrack built into our back yard.

"Now when he comes by at night he runs the train into our back yard for a while. I have to get up in the middle of the night and go out and keep his steam up while he comes in the house and trifles with Morningstar."

But he wasn't listening. He was fiddling with his boat in the bottle. "Wonder which side is starboard," he mumbled.

I left quietly for the chiropodist's office.

The doctor was sitting behind his desk playing "Your Feets Too Big" on a jew's-harp when I came in.

"How did you get here?" he asked.

"Why, I walked."

"Well, then," he said, "your feet are all right. You're lucky. There was a girl in here the other day whose feet were in terrible shape. She had been wearing such high heels that she constantly leaned forward at a forty-five-degree angle. Gave the impression of being on a ski slide."

"What did you do for her?" I asked.

"Cut off her legs, naturally. She's much happier now. She's made a lot of new friends who affectionately call her 'Shorty.' "

I made as if to go.

"Wait a minute. Know how I got interested in chiropody?"

"No sir," I said, for I did not.

He giggled. "I got webbed feet, that's why." He leaped up from his chair and ran around the room quacking wildly. Water was rolling off his back.

Now I went to the last office, the psychiatrist's. He was driving golf balls through the window. An angry crowd was collecting outside. "Any insanity in your family?" he asked.

"Oh, not really insanity," I said. "Maybe some of them act a little funny sometimes, but I wouldn't call it insanity. Uncle Bert, for instance, he's in Washington now circulating a petition to free Sacco and Vanzetti.

"And Cousin Roger. He's got a little farm near Des Moines. Every day he hauls his produce to Des Moines in a square-wheeled cart.

"And Uncle Donald. He started a million-dollar suit against the Reynolds Tobacco Company last year. He says he got a hump on his back from smoking Camels.

"And Aunt Yetta. Every time she needs a little money, she pulls out a tooth and puts it under her pillow.

"And then there's Cousin Booker, who thinks he's got a diamond in his navel, and Aunt Melanie who burns churches, and Uncle Alex who hangs on the wall and says he's a telephone, and Uncle Milton who has been standing in a posthole since 1924.

"But I wouldn't call that insanity exactly, would you, Doctor?"

"Oh, certainly not," he said. "They're probably just a little tired. Well, my boy, the examination is all over. Let me congratulate you. You are now a student at the University of Minnesota."

Tears filled my eyes and my throat was all choked up.

"Don't try to talk," said the doctor. "Just hold me tight. I want to remember you always, just like this."

In a little while I was all right, and I left, hoping with all my heart that I would prove worthy of the consideration that my new alma mater had lavished upon me.

VI. THE SOUTHWEST

Will Rogers

FROLICS AND FOLLIES

IN 1915 I went up on Mr. Ziegfeld's roof in the Midnight Frolic
show. I got two-fifty a week, and got my first car, an Overland,
and drove it out on Long Island every night about two thirty. It got
to knocking so much that one night the cop arrested me. "Hey, you
can go down the road at night, Rogers, but you got to leave that
thing. You're like an alarm clock at three A.M."

Ever know how the Midnight Shows started? Well I can tell you
for I was in the first one.

The Midnight Frolic was the start of all this Midnight and late style
of entertainment. That has since degenerated into a drunken orgy
of off-colored songs, and close-formation dancing. It was the first midnight show. It started right on the stroke of twelve, it could have 50
or 75 people in the cast, bigger than all the modern day shows given
at regular hours. It had the most beautiful girls of any show Ziegfeld
ever put on, for the beautiful ones wouldent work at a matinee for
they never got up that early.

We used to have a time getting em up for the midnight show. I
dont mean I did, I dident have to go round waking any of em up
but somebody did.

The same bunch of folks, that is about 50 per cent of the main ones,
were up there every night.

It was for folks with lots of money. And plenty of insomnia. He
would have great big musical numbers, all written especially for the
show, maby 40 girls in em, led by some well known local Broadway
star at that time.

From *Autobiography of Will Rogers*, edited by Donald Day, copyright, 1949, by
The Rogers Company. Reprinted by permission of Houghton Mifflin Company,
authorized publishers.

We would put on a new show about every four months. Costumes and all. There has never been anything to equal it since then.

My act at that time consisted generally of the same jokes each night, all pertaining to the place or to the other acts in the show. Then Mr. Ford started his memorable peace trip. Well, I doped out a lot of gags on it, and the first one I used turned out to be about the best one I ever had.

"If Mr. Ford had taken this bunch of girls, in this show, and let 'em wear the same costumes they wear here, and marched them down between the trenches, believe me, the boys would have been out before Christmas!"

After that line of stuff died out, I wished somebody else would start something, but I thought at that time there would never be anything as funny as that. One day my wife said:

"Why don't you talk about what you read? Goodness knows! you're always reading the papers!"

So I started to reading about Congress; and, believe me, I found they are funnier three hundred and sixty-five days a year than anything I ever heard of.

Now here's the point: if I had been in a regular show where they have a different audience every night, I wouldn't have had to change my stuff; but on the roof we got a lot of repeaters each night, and a man won't laugh at the same joke more than once. So that was what made me dig. I would read the papers for hours, trying to dope out a funny angle to the day's news, and I found that they would laugh easiest at the stuff that had just happened that day. A joke don't have to be near as funny if it's up to date.

So that's how I learned that my own stuff, serving only strictly fresh-laid jokes, as you might say, goes better than anything else.

I use only one set method in my little gags, and that is to try and keep to the truth. Of course you can exaggerate it, but what you say must be based on truth. And I have never found it necessary to use the words "hell" or "damn" to get a laugh, either.

Personally, I don't like the jokes that get the biggest laughs, as they are generally as broad as a house and require no thought at all. I like one where, if you are with a friend, and hear it, it makes you think, and you nudge your friend and say; "He's right about that." I would rather have you do that than to have you laugh—and then forget the next minute what it was you laughed at.

I like all kinds of audiences excepting the convention kind, the lodge brand, the sort of crowd that wants itself praised. That kind gives me a pain. There's always some fellow sends you a note framing your gag for you, asking you to mention this and that and not to forget a certain name. It's sure to be the name of the fellow that writes the note—some modest business guy that wants to get his name incorporated in the libretto of the Follies. It is usually a great pleasure to pan him—if only you can remember his unknown name, which mostly you can't.

We played for President Wilson and I used one joke which he repeated in his Boston speech on his return from France. He said:

"As one of our American humorists says [up to that time I had only been an ordinary rope thrower], Germany couldn't understand how we could get men over there and get them trained so quick. They didn't know that in our manual there's nothing about retreating! And when you only have to teach an army to go one way, you can do it in half the time."

Of course you know how much truth there was in that. See Pershing's reports.

President Wilson was my best audience. I have played to him five times, and always used lots of things about him. I want to speak and tell of him as I knew him for he was my friend. We of the stage knew that our audiences are our best friends, and he was the greatest Audience of any Public Man we ever had. I want to tell of him as I knew him across the footlights. A great many Actors and Professional people have appeared before him, on various occasions in wonderful high-class endeavors. But I don't think that any person met him across the footlights in exactly the personal way that I did.

Every other Performer or Actor did before him exactly what they had done before other audiences on the night previous, but I gave a great deal of time and thought to an Act for him, most of which would never be used again and had never been used before.

It just seemed by an odd chance for me every time I played before President Wilson that on that particular day there had been something of great importance that he had just been dealing with. For you must remember that each day was a day of great stress with him. He had no easy days. So when I could go into a Theatre and get laughs out of our President by poking fun at some turn in our National affairs, I don't mind telling you it was the happiest moments of my entire career on the stage.

The first time I shall never forget, for it was the most impressive and for me the most nervous one of them all. The Friars Club of New York one of the biggest Theatrical Social Clubs in New York had decided to make a whirlwind Tour of the Principal Cities of the East all in one week. We played a different City every night. We made a one-night stand out of Chicago and New York. We were billed for Baltimore but not for Washington. President Wilson came over from Washington to see the performance. It was the first time in Theatrical History that the President of the United States came over to Baltimore just to see a Comedy.

It was just at the time we were having our little Set Too, with Mexico, and when we were at the height of our Note Exchanging career with Germany and Austria. The house was packed with the Elite of Baltimore.

The Show was going great. It was a collection of clever Skits, written mostly by our stage's greatest Man, George M. Cohan, and even down to the minor bits was played by Stars with big Reputations. I was the least-known member of the entire aggregation, doing my little specialty with a Rope and telling Jokes on National Affairs, just a very ordinary little Vaudeville act by chance sandwiched in among this great array.

I was on late, and as the show went along I would walk out of the Stage door and out on the Street and try to kill the time and nervousness until it was time to dress and go on. I had never told Jokes even to a President, much less about one, especially to his face. Well, I am not kidding you when I tell you that I was scared to death. I am always nervous. I never saw an Audience that I ever faced with any confidence. For no man can ever tell how a given Audience will ever take anything.

But here I was, nothing but a very ordinary Oklahoma Cowpuncher who had learned to spin a Rope a little and who had learned to read the Daily Papers a little, going out before the Aristocracy of Baltimore, and the President of the United States, and kid about some of the Policies with which he was shaping the Destinies of Nations.

How was I to know what the audience would rise up in mass and resent it? I had never heard, and I don't think any one else had ever heard of a President being joked personally in a Public Theatre about the Policies of his administration.

The nearer the time came the worse scared I got. George Cohan, and Willie Collier, and others, knowing how I felt, would pat me on the back and tell me, "Why he is just a Human Being; go on out and do your stuff." Well if somebody had come through the dressing room and hollered "Train for Claremore Oklahoma leaving at once," I would have been on it. This may sound strange but any who have had the experience know, that a Presidential appearance in a Theatre, especially outside Washington, D.C., is a very Rare and unique feeling even to the Audience. They are keyed up almost as much as the Actors.

At the time of his entrance into the House, everybody stood up, and there were Plain Clothes men all over the place, back stage and behind his Box. How was I to know but what one of them might not take a shot at me if I said anything about him personally?

Finally a Warden knocked at my dressing-room door and said: "You die in 5 more minutes for kidding your Country." They just literally shoved me out on the Stage.

Now, by a stroke of what I call good fortune (for I will keep them always), I have a copy of the entire Acts that I did for President Wilson on the Five times I worked for him. My first remark in Baltimore was, "I am kinder nervous here tonight." Now that is not an especially bright remark, and I don't hope to go down in History on the strength of it, but it was so apparent to the audience that I was speaking the truth that they laughed heartily at it. After all, we all love honesty.

Then I said, "I shouldn't be nervous, for this is really my second Presidential appearance. The first time was when Bryan spoke in our town once, and I was to follow his speech and do my little Roping Act." Well, I heard them laughing, so I took a sly glance at the President's Box and sure enough he was laughing just as big as any one. So I went on, "As I say, I was to follow him, but he spoke so long that it was so dark when he finished, they couldn't see my Roping." That went over great, so I said, "I wonder what ever became of him." That was all right, it got over, but still I had made no direct reference to the President.

Now Pershing was in Mexico at the time, and there was a lot in the Papers for and against the invasion. I said "I see where they have captured Villa. Yes, they got him in the morning Editions and the Afternoon ones let him get away." Now everybody in the house before they would laugh looked at the President, to see how he was going to take it. Well, he started laughing and they all followed suit.

"Villa raided Columbus New Mexico. We had a man on guard that night at the Post. But to show you how crooked this Villa is, he sneaked up on the opposite side." "We chased him over the line 5 miles, but run into a lot of Government Red Tape and had to come back." "There is some talk of getting a Machine Gun if we can borrow one. The one we have now they are using to train our Army with in Plattsburg. If we go to war we will just about have to go to the trouble of getting another Gun."

Now, mind you, he was being criticized on all sides for lack of preparedness, yet he sat there and led that entire audience in laughing at the ones on himself.

At that time there was talk of forming an Army of 2 hundred thousand men, so I said, "we are going to have an Army of 2 hundred thousand men. Mr. Ford makes 3 hundred thousand Cars every year. I think, Mr. President, we ought to at least have a Man to every Car." "See where they got Villa hemmed in between the Atlantic and Pacific. Now all we got to do is to stop up both ends." "Pershing located him at a town called Los Quas Ka Jasbo. Now all we have to do is to locate Los Quas Ka Jasbo." "I see by a headline that Villa escapes Net and Flees. We will never catch him then. Any Mexican that can escape Fleas is beyond catching." "But we are doing better toward preparedness now, as one of my Senators from Oklahoma has sent home a double portion of Garden Seed."

After various other ones on Mexico I started in on European affairs which at that time was long before we entered the war. "We are facing another Crisis tonight, but our President here has had so many of them lately that he can just lay right down and sleep beside one of those things."

Then I first pulled the one which I am proud to say he afterwards repeated to various friends as the best one told on him during the war. I said, "President Wilson is getting along fine now to what he was a few months ago. Do you realize, People, that at one time in our negotiations with Germany that he was 5 Notes behind?"

How he did laugh at that! Well, due to him being a good fellow and setting a real example, I had the proudest and most successful night I ever had on the stage, I had lots of Gags on other subjects but the ones on him were the heartiest laughs with him, and so it was on all the other occasions I played for him. He come back Stage at intermission and chatted and shook hands with all.

For a long time after the war we always had so many returned men at the shows that I used something about them like:

"I see where they are going to muster all you boys out as soon as they investigate the morale of your homes."

"The reason they leave some of our boys over there so long is so they can get the mail that was sent to them during the war."

"If they had divided up all the money they spent on parades for you boys, you wouldent have to be looking for a job."

"If they really wanted to honor the boys, why dident they let them sit on the stands and have the people march by?"

Lots of good subjects would be in the papers for days[1] and I couldnt think of a thing on them. Some of the best things came to me when I was out on the stage. I figured out the few subjects that I would touch on and always had a few gags on each one, but the thing I went out to say might fall flat, and some other gag I just happened to put in out there went great. For instance here is an example! "Mr. Edison is perfecting a submarine destroyer. Well they say he only sleeps three or four hours out of the twenty-four. That gives him plenty of time to invent . . ." That was only a little laugh, but I used it to show the audience that I had read about the invention which had only been announced that day. It happened that at this time New York cafés were closed at one o'clock so I casually added to the remark my sudden thought: "Suppose Mr. Edison lived in New York and Mayor Mitchell made him go to bed at one o'clock; where would our invention come from?" And that was the big laugh.

This illustrates my work. I had to have my idea—all extemporaneous speakers do—but my laugh came quickly and apparently out of nowhere.

Another thing I read, was that submarines could not operate in the Warm Gulf Stream—so I said: "If we can only heat the ocean we will have them licked." That didn't get much of a laugh and I was kinda stuck—but happened to add, "Of course, that is only a rough idea. I haven't worked it out yet." This last went big and covered up the other.

I was talking of the income tax and how hard it hit our girls in the show, and just happened to mention, "A lot of them have figured out it would be cheaper to lay off."

I would start on a subject and if it was no good then I would switch quick and lots of times when I come off the stage I would have done an entirely different act from what I intended when I went on. Sometimes an audience is not so good and my stuff that night might not have been very good, so it is then you would see the old ropes commence to do something. It got their mind off the bum stuff I was telling and as I often said to the folks in the show, "I reach away back in my hip pocket and dig up a sure-fire gag, as I always try to save some of my best gags—just like a prohibition State man will his last drink."

In the four years I was with Mr. Ziegfeld in his Follies and Midnight Frolic where we played to a great many repeaters, I never did

[1] Much of the following was taken from an interview reported by George Martin, "Wit of Will Rogers," *American Magazine*, November, 1919.

the same act any two nights. I always changed parts of it and in the Frolics a great many times I did an entirely new act.

Another thing, I think I did the shortest act of any monologue man and that recommended it. On the Amsterdam Roof I never did over six minutes and in the Follies nine or ten, generally eight.

I like the stage, and as long as I can hang and rattle with it, some farmer is losing about a twenty-eight-per-cent efficient farmhand. If I can keep on my friendly relations with the audience and not have them suffer, I will stick to my job on what is in the newspapers, and not try to put over any outside propaganda as von Bernstorff did; and when I do get my papers—in the nature of the audience not liking my little act—I will not pull one of those strategic victories, by saying the people don't know a good act when they see one. I will bundle up my wife and three little Cherokees and burn the breeze for the tall grass of Oklahoma, get me one of those long-distance shooting guns, that some of our boys will have captured and brought home from Berlin, and point it down the main road. If ever I see a man coming down the road with a newspaper I will cut the gun loose and just keep on living in ignorance.

Will Rogers

TAKING THE CURE,
BY THE SHORES OF CAT CREEK

NOW, in my more or less checkered career before the more or less checkered Public, I have been asked to publicly indorse everything from Chewing Gum, Face Beautifiers, Patent Cocktail Shakers, Ma Junk Sets, even Corsets, Cigarettes, and Chewing Tobacco, all of which I didn't use or know anything about. But I always refused.

You never heard me boosting for anything, for I never saw anything made that the fellow across the street didn't make something just as good.

But, at last, I have found something that I absolutely know no one else has something just as good as, for an all-seeing Nature put this where it is and it's the only one he had, and by a coincidence it is located in the Town near the ranch where I was born and raised.

So I hereby and hereon come out unequivocally (I think that's the way you spell it) in favor of a place that has the water that I *know* will cure you. You might ask, cure me of what? Why, cure you of anything—just name your disease and dive in.

Claremore, Oklahoma, is the birthplace of this Aladdin of health waters. Some misguided Soul named it RADIUM WATER, but Radium will never see the day that it is worth mentioning in the same breath as this Magic Water. Why, to the afflicted and to all suffering Humanity, a Jug of this Water is worth a wheelbarrow full of Radium. Still, even under the handicap of a cheap name, this liquid Godsend has really cured thousands.

Now you may say, "Oh you boost it because you live there," but I don't want you to think so little of me that you would think I would misguide a sick person, just for the monetary gain to my Home Town. We don't need you that bad. The city is on a self supporting basis without Patients, just by shipping the Water to Hot Springs, Ark., Hot Springs, Va., West Baden, Ind., and Saratoga, N. Y.

Now, as to a few of the Ignorant who might still be in the dark as to where the Home of this Fountain of Youth is located, I will tell you. I shouldn't waste my time on such Low Brows, but unfortunately they get sick and need assistance the same as the 95 Million others who already know where Claremore is located.

It is located, this Mecca of the ill, about 17 hundred miles west of New York, (either City or State, depends on which ever one you happen to be in). You bear a little south of west, after leaving New York, till you reach Sol McClellan's place, which is just on the outskirts of Claremore. Before you get into the City proper, if you remember about 500 miles back, you passed another Town. Well, that was St. Louis, most of which is in Illinois.

Now, if you are in the North, and happen to get something the matter with you, we are 847 and a half miles South by West from Gary, Indiana. We have cured hundreds of people from Chicago, Ill. from Gun shot wounds inflicted in attempted murders and robberies. There is only one way to avoid being robbed of anything in Chicago and that is not to have anything.

If you are from Minneapolis, our Radium Water guarantees to cure you of everything but your Swedish accent. If you are from St. Paul, we can cure you of everything but your ingrown hatred for Minneapolis.

I will admit that these waters have quite a peculiar odor as they have a proportion of Sulphur and other unknown ingredients, but visitors from Kansas City, who are used to a Stock Yard breeze, take this wonderful water home as a Perfume.

Approaching this City from the North, don't get it confused with Oolagah, Oklahoma, my original Birthplace, which is 12 miles to the north, as both towns have Post Offices.

From the west, if you are afflicted and you are sure to be or you wouldn't have gone out there, why Claremore is just 1900 miles due east of Mojave, California, one of the few Towns which Los Angeles has not voted into their Cafeteria. You come east till you reach an Oil Station at a road crossing. This oil station is run by a man named St. Clair. You will see a lot of men pitching Horseshoes. Well, that is the Post Office of Tulsa, Oklahoma, and the men are Millionaires pitching Horseshoes for Oil Wells or for each other's wives.

You should, by this description, have the place pretty well located in your minds. Now, if you are living in the South and are afflicted with a Cotton Crop under a Republican Administration, or with the Ku Klux, or with the Hook Worm, we guarantee to rid you of either or all of these in a course of 24 Baths.

Claremore is located just 905 miles north of Senator Pat Harrison's Mint Bed in Mississippi. In coming from the Gulf Country some have got off the road and had to pass through Dallas, Texas, but have found out their mistake and got back on the main road at Ft. Worth before losing all they had. You easily can tell Ft. Worth. A fellow will be standing down in front of the Drug Store making a speech.

Now, before reaching Claremore, you will pass, even though it's in the middle of the day, a place where you think it's night and you won't know what is the matter. Well, that's Muskogee, Oklahoma, and this darkness is caused by the Color scheme of the population, so put on your headlights and go on in. This Muskogee is really a parking space for cars entering Claremore. Of course, if you want to drive on into the Town of Claremore proper, it's only 60 miles through the suburbs from here.

The City is located on Cat Creek, and instead of having a lot of Streets like most Towns and Cities, we have combined on one street. In that way no Street is overlooked.

You might wonder how we discovered this Blarney Stone of Waters. In the early days, us old timers there, always considered these Wells more as an Odor than as a Cure. But one day a man come in there who had been raised in Kansas and he had heard in a roundabout way of people bathing, although he had never taken one. So, by mistake, he got into this Radium Water.

He was a one armed man—he had lost an Arm in a rush to get into a Chautauqua Tent in Kansas to hear Bryan speak on Man Vs. Monkey. Well he tried this Bath and it didn't kill him and he noticed that he was beginning to sprout a new arm where he had lost the old one, so he kept on with the Baths and it's to him that we owe the discovery of this wonderful curative Water. Also he was the Pioneer of Bathers of Kansas, as now they tell me it's no uncommon thing to have a Tub in most of their larger towns.

Now, it has been discovered that you can carry a thing too far and overdo it, so we don't want you there too long. A man come there once entirely Legless and stayed a week too long and went away a Centipede.

I want to offer here my personal Testimonial of what it did to me. You see, after this Kansas Guy started it, why, us old Timers moved our bathing from the River into a Tub. Now, at that time, I was practically Tongue tied and couldn't speak out in private much less in Public. Well, after 12 baths, I was able to go to New York and make after dinner speeches. I stopped in Washington on the way and saw how our Government was run and that gave me something funny to speak about.

So, in thanking the Water, I also want to thank the Government for making the whole thing possible. Now, had I taken 24 baths I would have been a Politician, so you see I stopped just in time.

The only thing I get out of this is I have the "Thrown Away Crutch Privilege." If you don't get well and throw away your Invalid Chair or crutches I get nothing out of it, so that is why we give you a square deal. If you are not cured, I don't get your Crutches. There is no other resort in the World that works on that small a margin.

W. J. Bryan drank one drink of this Water and turned against Liquor. Senator La Follette drank two drinks of it and turned against everything. So remember Claremore, The Carlsbad of America, where the 'Frisco Railroad crosses the Iron Mountain Railroad, not often, but every few days.

George Sessions Perry

EDGAR AND THE DANK MORASS

DRESSED in forty-three dollars' worth of fishing togs, and leading a donkey packed with articles relevant to the occasion, Edgar Selfridge stopped where the wooded road reached an opening. In the clearing before him he saw a three-room house sitting on stilts. Before it, across the scrubby yard, was a pile of new split cypress posts and a man in the act of splitting others from the giant cypress heart before him. To the left of the house lay the bayou, and across it, the swamp, gray and yellow and pale blue in the late-afternoon sun. Sitting on a log at the boat landing, a woman in a calico dress and a sunbonnet caught a pumpkin-seed perch.

"Hello," Edgar called.

The upraised ax did not fall. It was lowered slowly halfway, and then held. The woman stopped rebaiting her hook and turned to look. A girl, lovely, ripe, sixteen perhaps, barefooted, and with a half-emptied pea pod in her hand, came out on the top step. She stood there, her mouth slightly open, watching the stranger.

The man took a few steps toward Edgar. He was tall and thin and slightly wavy in physique. His chin was hardly worth mentioning. His eyes goggled like those of the perch in the woman's hand.

"Whut was it?" he asked.

The woman and the girl watched.

"I'd like to spend the night," Edgar said.

"Whut fer?"

"I like it here."

"Aw," the man said incredulously.

"I'm on a walking tour," Edgar explained.

"I don't b'lieve I know whut that is."

"Ever hear of Washington Irving?"

"Well, it seems like I is an' it seems like I ain't."

"There's nothing to it," Edgar said. "I'm just walking through the bayou country. Besides, I like to fish."

"You's talkin' my kind o' talk now," the man said, apparently glad the conversation was coming down out of the clouds. "We got them critters here."

"Well, will you let me stay? I'll pay what you think is right."

"God knows, if you can stand it, we orter could. Reckon would a dollar a week be too high?"

"It wouldn't be enough."

"It is, fer whut you're a-gonna get. A right dainty hog couldn't stand up to it."

"We'll make it nice, if he'll stay," the girl on the steps said, looking down.

"Don't pay no 'tention to her," the man said. "That's jest Virginia, our girl. I guess she gets kind of lonesome."

Edgar smiled at Virginia. Somehow, the paradoxical idea came to him that she could not have been so naturally, disarmingly lovely had she not been the least bit grimy.

If ever there was a swamp angel—he thought.

He said, "Thank you, Virginia. I think it's fine."

Out on the bayou, gars slithered through the surface of the water. A mud hen created a commotion in some near-by reeds. Jimbo, the cat, went down to ogle the perch the woman had caught.

"Well, onhitch yer jackass," the man said, pushing the blade of the ax into the grass, "and make yourself at home."

It was still two hours until dark. Half an hour later, after Edgar had unpacked his gear and learned that his hosts were the Frank Copelands, Frank said: "Since you come a-fishin', we better go get some bait an' get at it. This is the time o' day they bite."

"Oh, I won't need bait," Edgar said, showing his array of artificial lures.

For a moment, Frank studied the variegated articles. Once he brought himself almost to the point of touching one of them, but withdrew his hand before actually doing so.

"Well, I've heard tell o' folks fishin' with them chips," he said, "but I ain't never actually seed it. I'm kinda feared these ole countrified fish o' ourn won't know whut to do."

Edgar laughed. "We'll have to find out," he said.

If Edgar Selfridge's mentality was not so great as that of an Einstein, he could still probably beat an Einstein catching fish. For if there was one thing Edgar understood, it was the soul and longings of a bass.

"Lemme go with y'all, Pap?" Virginia asked.

Pap was exasperated. He turned to Edgar.

"How long you plan to stay?" he asked.

"A week."

"An' you ain't going to run off, are you?"

"No."

"Now, you hear that, Virginia?"

"Yeah."

"Well, jest calm down then. You can visit with him when the fish ain't bitin'. He'll keep."

"Well, take care of him, Pap."

"You go shell them peas," Pap said.

Seventy-five yards from the place where they got in the skiff there was an immense cypress stump out in the bayou. It was a veritable catacomb of crevices where a bass might hide from the gars and yet partake of passing minnows. It was at this stump that Edgar won the respect of Frank Copeland.

"Looks good," Edgar said.

"They's a ole rusty one belongs to be there."

"Hold the boat."

Edgar cast a large floating plug fifty feet through the air, dropping it neatly in the largest crevice. The bait rolled the water. Then, as if it were a crippled minnow, struggling to escape from what it had just seen below, it fluttered and struggled eighteen or nineteen inches from the stump before the explosion took place. Into the air from behind the bait came the bass, and down on top of it. For a fraction of a second, Edgar waited. Then he set the hooks, and the battle was on.

The fish was strong, as bayou bass are strong. He wanted loose and he meant to get that way if he had to destroy all of Edgar's expensive but delicate tackle. Four minutes later, however, he was doing his wanting in the boat.

Edgar was happy.

"What'll he go?" he asked Frank.

"Four pounds and odd ounces."

"That's my guess. . . . What are you looking at me like that for?"

"Well," Frank said, "even if you do wear a mighty queer kind of clothes and traipse around over the country leading a jackass, I'll say one thing for you."

"What, Frank?"

"You's a mighty bright somebody when hit comes to catchin' ole Mr. Bass on a dappled cawncob."

As night was beginning to thicken over the swamp, where it ultimately achieves its greatest density and becomes almost adhesive, and as the first gray wisps began to rise from the surface of the bayou, Virginia saw the skiff moving toward the landing.

"They're comin', Ma!" she shouted. "Put in the hoe cake!"

Jimbo, the cat, who always met the skiff, hopefully meowed.

"You still got him with you, Pap?" Virginia called.

"Yep," Frank answered, paddling the boat up to the landing, where Virginia pulled it up and tied it. "An' many a time I wished it was Friday 'stead o' Saturday. We throwed 'em all back 'cep' one big one."

"Why Friday?" Edgar asked.

"That's jest our feudin' day an' we could use more fish. . . . Virginia, get a stick and whip the snakes off of our live box and put that bass in it. I'm a-going on to the house."

"Maybe Mr. Edgar will help me."

"Now don't be a-doggin' him ever' second, Virginia."

"I want to help her, Frank."

"Well, be careful y'all don't get snake bit," Frank said, walking on to the house.

When, despite the dark, the live box had been pulled out of the water and the bass put inside, Edgar fastened the door and put the box back in the bayou. Then as he stood up, Virginia, with no verbal warning, put her arms around his neck and began kissing him. Had Ma not called "Vittles!" only daylight and the necessity to gather the eggs would have stopped her. She had kissed Edgar eighteen times when the call came.

"Gee!" Virginia said, as they started to the house. "That was wonderful!"

Said the groggy and slightly limp Edgar, "It was that."

At the lamp-lit table, all Frank said was, "I had hoped our company wouldn't have to be bothered with it, but hit looks like he's a-gonna have to start packin' a club."

Later, while the women washed the dishes, Edgar said: "What about that feud you mentioned?"

" 'Tain't much of a feud. Fact is, I'm kinda ashamed of it."

"I see. You feel it's out of date."

"Naw, Edgar. Jest sorry. Jest run-down. We done feuded aroun' twell there ain't nobody left on our side but me and Ma and Virginia, an' Virginia ain't no account to us 'cause the rules say unmarried girls got to keep out of it. They liable to get all scarred up, and then they can't get 'em no husband."

"I see."

"And the Whittakers—that's the other side—they're down to jest old Bart and his wife Fanny an' a occasional visitin' relative. They're right bad about that. It ain't fair, but they figger it's one way er entertainin' their company, so they ring 'em in an' wallop up the earth with us. 'Cause, you see, since we done got down to what you might call jest the old nest eggs, we had to change it from a gun feud to a fist feud, er they very soon wouldn't a' been no feud a-tall."

"Stands to reason," Edgar Selfridge said.

"So, such as it is, we meet at the Whittakers' one Friday an' here the next. An' after we finish fightin', we eat supper together. God knows I'se 'shamed of it. I don't reckon you could find a sissier feud anywhere, but it's jest another case of 'the sins of the fathers.' "

"You mean they should have loved their neighbors as——"

"Naw, dern it; effen the old folks had sorter rationed theirselves out, ain't no tellin' how long it could 'a' gone on bein' a first-rate gun feud. But they'd get drunk an' mow down a half a dozen at a time, and so this is what they left us with—a nasty stinkin' little ole fist feud."

Edgar tried to comfort his host, but with little success. A fist feud was still a fist feud. But soon the focus of the conversation turned on Edgar and his doings.

He told them about Uncle Grover, his guardian, in as sympathetic a way as he could, stressing such things as Uncle Grover's position at the bank and his wealth, neglecting to mention his parsimony and his inability to understand the viewpoint of youth. Edgar even touched on life at the university and in New York, and gave them a brief account of his experiences with the Russian grand duchess, Tanya Alanovna Vollivollivov.

Virginia's eyes stood out on stems to such an extent that, as her father remarked, "you could rope 'em with a grapevine."

It comforted Edgar to feel that within this humble bayou haven he was weaving a spell of glamour, of romance and of mystery. A little later, however, the idea struck him that he could be seen in two lights—not only as the gay Prince Charming passing a night in a poor man's cottage, but, just as easily, as the glib, leering city slicker come to undo their honest Nell, or Virginia, as the case might be. He shuddered and ended his story.

So, peacefully, did the mellow days flow by in the unprogressive tempo of the swamps. True, Edgar did spend the long hot midday hours trying to teach Virginia to spell the simpler words in a mail-order catalogue. It was one of his few annoying habits to try to mend affairs for his friends that they did not care to have mended. But since Virginia's mind was occupied entirely with matters that had no connection with spelling, little real harm came of it.

It was on Thursday after dinner, when the family was assembled on the porch around the smudge pot which was intended to asphyxiate the pterodactyl-like mosquitoes instead of, as the case was, the human beings around it, that Ma said: "It's mighty businesslike of you to of thought of it, Pap, but I don't know as it seems altogether right to me."

"Well, if we don't, we'll have Virginia to bury, an' then who'll do the chores?"

"It ain't only Virginia you're thinking of."

"God knows it ain't. It's that wealth. With that two hundred dollars I could retire."

"From what?" Virginia asked.

"You want me to take a chunk to you, you sassy thing?" Pap asked absently, mechanically, unoffended.

"Maybe you've got some family matter to discuss," Edgar said. "I can go for a stroll, if you like."

"Set," Pap said. "It concerns you, in a way."

"Any way I can help?"

"Well, to tell the truth, an' I hope you ain't goin' to be disappointed in me, Edgar, 'cause I dern sho like you, and so does all my outfit, but what I mean to say is, we're kind of studyin' about holdin' you fer ransom. Whut do you think about it?"

Edgar was stunned. "I hadn't thought," he said.

"Don't you reckon that ole hard-shelled uncle o' yourn would pay two hunderd dollars to deransomize you, Edgar?"

"He might."

"Well, you see, if he would, we could go up on the river or out in the swamps som'ers and live mighty comfortable fer a long time."

"How're you going to keep me here?"

"I got a gun, ain't I?"

"Frank, you wouldn't shoot me!"

"I'd hate it like pizen, Edgar. An' I ain't sayin' I would nur I wouldn't. But I'd point it at you an' it might go off."

"True," Edgar said.

"As Gospel," Frank said.

"Then you'll stay?" Virginia said hopefully.

"Now listen," Frank said, "he's my prisoner, and don't be a-askin' him if he'll stay. Ask me."

"What would you do with two hundred dollars, Frank?" Edgar asked.

"Well, first I'd get me somep'n I ain't ever had in my whole life."

"What's that?"

"A two-bit bottle o' snuff, that's what. Not no nickel can, but a big brown two-bit bottle."

"What if my Uncle Grover puts the law on you?"

"He don't know where you're at, in the first place. And in the second, it's one thing to put the law after me an' a dern diffunt one to put 'em on me. They ain't gonna catch me, Edgar."

"The G-men will."

"Whut's that?"

"Federal men."

"He means revenooers," Frank said, glancing at the rifle in the corner. Then he added, "Ha-ha."

"Wait a minute, Frank," Ma said, picking up the gun and examining the stock. Then she said, "Like I thought. You made a mistake. It ain't ha-ha. It's ha-ha-ha, an' a winged one that got away."

"Them things is allus hard for me to keep straight," Frank said.

"No," she said proudly. "You're jest bein' modest about it, Pap, and I love you fer it."

"They'll call it kidnaping," Edgar said, still interested in his ransoming, "and hang you, Frank."

"Well, dern 'em, they'd be lyin' if they did. This ain't no kidnapin'. This is a ransomin', pure an' simple. An' furthermore, yore room rent stops today. We certainly ain't goin' to charge no prisoner of ourn any rent."

"When are you going to notify Uncle Grover?"

"Later. The time ain't come yet. . . . Now, Ma, le's us git to bed an' try to rest up for our feudin' tomorrow. . . . You young'uns can set out here an' spoon a spell if you want to."

"Gee. Thanks, Pap," Virginia said.

"You're welcome. An', Edgar, don't you feel like I'm abandonin' you. When she gets too rough on you, jest holler, an' I'll come with the gun."

"Thanks, Frank," Edgar said.

The next morning, when Frank and his prisoner returned from fishing with ample fish for the feudin' supper, Frank said: "We better run over to the still now, Edgar, on account of we'll need somethin' in the gourd 'sides water after the feud meets."

They set out in the skiff. After going a few hundred yards up the bayou, Frank turned the boat into one of those narrow shallow ditches made in the swamp floor for the navigation of row boats and individual cypress logs, and known as a "pull-boat road." He turned the boat at a dozen intersections, and once or twice it seemed to Edgar they were passing places they had passed before.

"Don't be 'spectin' nothin' fancy," Frank said. "Hit's only a family still. I don't sell nothin', but jest try to keep a little, so we don't dry plum up."

At the still, which lay in a small clearing, Frank found the mash at a propitious stage, and with Edgar's help soon had it in the still. It was while Frank was building the fire that Edgar eased the rifle up off of the log beside Frank and withdrew to the other side of the clearing.

When the fire was going, Frank turned and saw the gun leveled at him. For a moment, he was speechless. At last he managed to say: "Why, confound yore sneaky hide, Edgar. An' me just fixin' to offer you a drink."

"Looks like I'm the boss now, doesn't it, Frank?"

"It jest looks like dern pore manners, if you ask me."

"I'm not going to tell on you when I get back, Frank."

"Thanks, Edgar. Back where?"

"Home."

"I see. But I'm kinda curious to know how you're gonna get out o' this swamp."

"I hadn't thought of that. I'll make you show me the way."

"Whut if I won't make?"

"What if I shoot you?"

"You'd get powerful lonesome out here with just my corpse and the alligators and the moccasins. Specially at night, I imagine."

Edgar walked over and handed Frank the gun.

"How about that drink you mentioned, Frank?"

Frank smiled. "Dog my cats, Edgar," he said, "I ain't never liked nobody better than you."

After lunch, Edgar began to notice that Frank was behaving peculiarly.

"What's the matter, Frank?" Edgar inquired.

"Oh, I don't know," Frank said, dropping his eyes and marking a figure on the floor with his toe. "I reckon I'm kind of ashamed of myself, Edgar."

"Because of the ransom?"

"Naw, on account of this afternoon. I hate to tell you, Edgar, but I got to tie you up durin' the feud."

"That's nothing. Prisoners expect that."

Frank's face brightened. "Then yore feelin's won't be hurt about it?"

"Not at all."

"Gee, Pap," Virginia said earnestly, "ain't he wonderful?"

"He certainly is," Frank said. "And he has certainly took a load off of my mind."

Later then, when the Whittakers drove up in their hack, Edgar was lying bound to his bed, but the window was open and he heard Frank say: "Who that in that hack with y'all?"

"Our nephew, Willie, from over in Jasper County. He's come for the feudin'."

"Well, jest let 'im watch," Frank said. "Last time he was here I got two ribs broke."

"He come to enter in, not jest to watch, an' we ain't gonna have Willie disappointed."

"I can't stand the thought o' that lummox a-whalin' me in the back while ole Whittaker is a-workin' on my front," Frank was saying.

"You got to stand it, or quit the feud."

"Well, I ain't quittin' no feud, but I'm liable to turn this'n into a gun feud if that Willie o' yourn gets out of that hack."

"You can't. We ain't got no gun."

"Well," Frank screamed, "we ain't got no Willie!"

"The rules is the rules."

"Long as they read in the Whittakers' favor."

"Get out of the hack, Willie."

"No, you don't. I tell you I jest can't stand the thought of no such beatin' up. I ain't forgot the time I was clenched with Bart Whittaker, an' that blame Willie tried to gnaw my ear off."

"Well, Willie's fightin' with us today and there ain't no ifs and ands about it."

"Shore, I am!" a voice which must have been Willie's roared. "I got my dander up, an' won't nothin' do me short of a good fight!"

Frank groaned. "I'd give a thousand dollars for me a nephew right this minute," he said.

"Would you give two hundred?" Edgar called out the window.

"I never said that much," said the startled Frank.

Silence.

Then, in a considerably different tone, Frank's voice said: "What's the matter with y'all? Does the thought of a good fair fight make you oneasy?"

"No, by dern," old Whittaker said. "It's jest that we'd expected some pretty easy pickin's today."

"I thought so," Frank said. "An' look at yore big brave rib-bustin' Willie. His face looks like he fell in the flour barrel."

"It does not," Willie said.

"Dog it," Frank said, "it's extravagant as package coffee, but I'm comin' after you, Edgar."

When Edgar's fetters were removed and he stood on the porch, he said, "I want to thank you, Frank. All through history good men have allowed their slaves and prisoners to fight for their freedom. If today I besmirch this house's honorable name, laughter will never pass my lips again."

Frank screamed like a Comanche.

Then solemnly he said, "Ain't he a man fer you?"

"I wish that I could say I was a boxing champion at school," Edgar said. "But I wasn't. I'll sort of have to pick it up as I go along. Now, one thing more."

"What, Edgar?"

"Who is that creature shaking in the hack?"

"Willie," Frank said.

"The one who busted your ribs from behind, Frank?"

"The selfsame Willie."

"The one who gnawed your ear while you were clenched with another opponent?"

"It was him."

There was a pause.

Frank was beaming as Napoleon would have beamed at Waterloo had his re-enforcements arrived more punctually than they did.

Then Edgar said: "Alight, Willie."

"Aw, that's all right," Willie said. "I'll jest look on from the hack. I don't guess I've got any business in this feud. It ain't none of mine."

"No new business," Edgar said, "just some old unfinished. As for me, my freedom is at stake. Again I invite you to alight."

"No."

In answer to no accusation whatever, Ma Whittaker said, "Willie ain't afraid."

"Pull 'im out o' there, Bart," Frank said. "He's yore nephew. My side's ready."

Frank made a line on the ground.

Bart Whittaker removed the reluctant Willie from the buggy. Soon the forces of both sides stood in battle formation, Ma Whittaker opposite Ma Copeland, Frank opposite the leader of the invaders, and before Edgar stood, or, more precisely, quaked Willie.

On the porch, Virginia held the dishpan in one hand and an iron cooking spoon in the other.

"Ready, visitors?" she called.

"Ready!" Bart Whittaker called.

"How about us, Pap?"

"Ready!" Frank shouted.

Virginia brought the spoon down on the dishpan, and the battle was on.

Grunts and groans filled the air. For a while it was anybody's battle. Ma Copeland was the first to go down, having been induced to do so by a left to the solar plexus and an elbow to the jaw. Proudly, Ma Whittaker, who passionately believed that the best defense was a withering offense, watched her adversary sink earthward.

Willie was the second to go. As he relaxed upon the Copelands' yard, his mouth opened and two bicuspids and an incisor fluttered to the ground.

"Change partners!" Frank shouted, leaving Pa Whittaker to Edgar and heroically facing Ma Whittaker himself.

A minute and a half later Frank was stretched out beside Willie, to be joined a second later by Pa Whittaker. Slumber possessed the three of them, as it also possessed Ma Copeland. This left Edgar to face that Amazon, Ma Whittaker.

But at the same time he was faced by something else: his code of gentlemanly behavior, which frowned upon fisticuffs with members of the fairer sex.

"I can't hit a woman," he said, striking an attitude only a second before Ma Whittaker's fist struck him and he, in turn, struck the ground.

"Get up an' fight," she said. "We bayou gals don't ask no favors nur give no quarter."

"Well," Edgar reasoned, "when in Rome—"

He arose and, with a vigor even the doughty Ma Whittaker could not long withstand, went for her.

Three minutes later she had joined the others who were reclining on the turf.

The supper that night was one the bayou would never see surpassed either in respect to the abundance of fish and liquor or in the spirit of friendliness and jocularity that pervaded it.

"If there was more fights like that one today," Ma Whittaker said, depressed, "our feud would amount to something."

"Whut I saw of it," Frank agreed, "was downright beautiful."

"I wish that we could have Edgar every Friday," Ma Copeland said wistfully, realizing it was too good to be true.

"Well, it's rough on the carcass," Ma Whittaker said, like the old sport she was, "but by jucks it's a honor to get a lickin' from a man like that."

Edgar blushed. "Stop it," he said. "You are giving me the swell head."

"H'ist up yore gourds," Willie said, not to be outdone, "an' drink off a slug o' licker to the fist-fightin'est, fish-catchin'est man on this whole bayou."

The bones on his plate and the color and swelling around his eyes endorsed the truth of his statement.

The toast was drunk, and a cheer rang out through the moss-draped limbs of the cypresses that put the swamp denizens on the alert as much as a mile away.

That night when the Whittakers were gone, Edgar submitted to a final session of spooning on the front porch with Virginia. Certainly he was in no condition to receive such treatment, but heroism in Edgar knew no bounds.

The next day he left them, after kissing Ma and Virginia—as if one kiss more or less would make any difference to her—and promising Frank he would come back the next summer.

At the first store he passed, Edgar bought Ma and Virginia each a dress and sent his fishing tackle to Frank.

He was on the verge of leaving the store when the extent of his own thoughtlessness occurred to him. He returned to the counter and said: "Who's going to deliver this?"

"The errand boy."

"Well, here's a dollar extra for him. Ask him please to kiss Miss Virginia for me."

"All right, sir. But what's that extra quarter for?"

A tear came into Edgar's eye. "A bottle of snuff," he said. "Not jest no nickel can, but a big brown two-bit bottle."

Outside the store, he took up the donkey's lead rein, and they walked on down the road.

Frank Sullivan

AN INNOCENT IN TEXAS

I HAD heard so much about Texas that I was consumed with curiosity about our great sister republic to the south. Was it true for instance that all Texans are seven feet tall except the football players at Texas Christian and Southern Methodist, who are eight? Was it true that Rhode Island would fit 220 times into Texas, as Texas friends had so often assured me? Was it true that in the early years of the war there were so many Texans in the Royal Canadian Air Force that Canadians were often tempted to call it the Royal Texan Air Force? Did Oveta Culp Hobby . . .

I wanted to learn the answers. I wanted to see Texas in action. There was only one way to do so. Throwing a few things into my bag I took off for Houston. I travelled light—a spare ten-gallon hat, two pairs of chaps, one for business and one for formal evening wear, a lariat, a few other necessaries, and Rhode Island, which I brought along because, in the interests of accuracy, I was eager to check on that 220 story.

On a typical sparkling Texas morning I debarked at Houston. Two glorious suns were shining, the regular one and the special Texas sun. Above the hum of the city's traffic rose the pleasant susurrus of Texas voices exchanging matutinal howdies in their melodious Confederate drawl.

From the distance came the agreeable gurgle of gushers gushing in the gusheries scattered about the city, with occasionally the triumphant yodel of an oil millionaire who had just discovered a new gusher. Anon, the crack of rifle fire and the sight of a fleeing cattle rustler with a posse at his heels told me plainer than words that Texas could still dispense frontier justice.

"Yippee!" I cried, for I speak Texan fluently, and, drawing two or three six-shooters from my belt, I fired a volley of twenty-one guns in salute to Pecos Bill, John Nance Garner, General Santa Anna, Stephen F. Austin, Maury Maverick and the Alamo.

I made Houston my first port of call because it is the metropolis and chief city of the Texan republic, although I add instantly that Dallas, San Antonio, Galveston, Waco, Wichita Falls, Fort Worth, Austin, Abilene and El Paso are also the chief cities of Texas. Other chief cities may have sprung up since I left. If so, I beg their pardon for not mentioning them.

Houston has a population of 600,000 and, Houstonians informed me, is growing at the rate of 10,000 inhabitants a day, 5000 of them oil millionaires. Texas grows the largest and most luscious grapefruit in the world and the richest millionaires. Jesse Jones of Houston is the richest Jones in recorded history. At its present rate of growth Houston will outstrip London and New York in a decade. Perhaps sooner, since Texans are twice as big as Londoners or New Yorkers.

My day in Houston was packed with excitement. No sooner was I settled in my suite at one of the city's finer hotels than they struck oil in the cellar and immediately started tearing down the twenty-eight-story hotel to make way for the more profitable gusher. The hospitable Chamber of Commerce quickly found me agreeable quarters in a twenty-nine-story hotel and after washing up I still had time before lunch to measure Rhode Island into Houston. It goes seven times.

I shall not soon forget that lunch. We had steak. Steak is the state flower of Texas. Texas has the finest steaks and the best department stores in the country. I had heard of the Gargantuan meals to which the lusty Texans are accustomed, but after all I come from New York, the home of the late Diamond Jim Brady, who thought nothing of consuming, at one sitting, twelve dozen oysters, eight quarts of orange juice, four adult lobsters, two planked steaks and Lillian Russell, so I set to work with a will and in no time at all was pridefully chasing the last shred of tenderloin around my plate with a piece of bun.

"Yippee!" I remarked. "Here's one dam-yank that can tie on the old feedbag with any varmint in Houston."

Just then a waiter put a steak in front of me twice as big as the steak I had just eaten. The waiter was twice as big as a New York waiter.

"What's that thar, pardner?" says I.

"That thar's yore steak, pardner," says he.

"What was that thar I just et?" says I.

"That thar was jest yore hors d'oeuvre," says he.

"Yippee!" says I, but in a more chastened tone, you may be sure, and that was the last time I bragged of my appetite in Texas.

I tried to tell my hosts how overjoyed I was to be having my first glimpse of their great republic.

"Perhaps no other planet in the universe has contributed as many notable figures to history as Texas," I enthused. "Look at the roster—Martin Dies, Ma Ferguson, Sam Houston, Chester A. Nimitz, Ensign Gay, Abraham Lincoln, George Washington, Queen Victoria, Amon G. Carter, Napoleon Bonaparte, O. Henry, Charlemagne, John the Baptist, the Twelve Apostles . . ."

"Excuse me, pardner," interrupted a Texan, "only nine of the Twelve Apostles was from Texas."

After lunch my hosts asked me if there was anything in particular I wished to see, and I was able to answer them precisely.

"Before I leave Houston I want to see a new gusher come into being," I said.

"Easiest thing in the world. Step this way."

We went to a vacant lot down back of the post office, and the chairman of the Houston Gusher Commission took a folding divining rod from his pocket.

"What kind of oil would you all care to see, pardner?" he asked.

"Some of that black gold I've heard so much about, if you please," said I.

Thereupon the chairman mumbled a few charms, dangled the rod over a cactus plant nearby, and within seconds there was a grumble. There followed a restless groaning and heaving as of oil struggling to reach the surface, the cactus plant hurried off in a kind of panic, and a second later on that very spot a fine geyser of high-octane black gold shot ninety-two feet into the air before us.

"Golly!" I exclaimed, in awesome admiration. "Congratulations. I'll wager this gusher will bring you fellows a pretty penny in royalties."

"Why, she's yours," cried the chairman, jovially.

"Oh, no. Really, I couldn't think . . ."

"Nonsense. It's your luncheon favor. Compliments of the Chamber of Commerce of Houston. We always give gushers to visitors. Why don't you christen her?"

"I christen thee the Pappy O'Daniel," I said to the oil well, and instantly it gulped, gasped and retreated into the bowels of the earth.

"Better try another name," the chairman suggested.

"I christen thee the Davy Crockett," I amended, and this time the gusher gushed joyfully again. I can only add that that gusher has to date brought me $4,390,000 in royalties. As far as I am concerned the accounts of the legendary hospitality of Houston are definitely not exaggerated.

Nor are the accounts of the legendary hospitality of Dallas exaggerated. Dallas, named for Stella Dallas, is 187 light years distant from Houston and is the finest city in Texas. By a stroke of good fortune I visited Dallas just at a time when the traditional rivalry between itself and Fort Worth, the finest city in Texas, had reached one of its periodical boiling points. It seems that the night before I got there a band of marauders from Fort Worth had made a surprise attack on the famous Nieman-Marcus department store in Dallas and with shouts of "Yippee!" and "Southern Methodist is no good, chop 'em up for kindling wood!" had carried off the entire contents of the notion counter, along with several hundred pounds of pecan pralines. Feeling was running high in Dallas and there was talk of reprisals on the Fort Worth Cowboy Lament Works, the great sprawling industrial plant where 20,000 musicians work in three shifts composing the dirges which have made the name of Texas so—what shall I say?—throughout the world.

The rivalry between the various cities of Texas is an interesting phenomenon and, I was told, is the main reason why the founders of the republic felt it wise to place each city at least 800 miles from its nearest neighbor. In telling a Dallasian his community is not as matchless a civic gem as Fort Worth you run an even greater risk than if you told an Irishman from Connemara that County Mayo is the flawless emerald in Erin's diadem.

The Easterner, or tenderfoot, will not comprehend this keen, internecine rivalry. A resident of, let us say, Rochester has no fear of not being made welcome when he visits New York City (one of the larger cities in the state). True, his wallet may be extracted from his pants before he has got three blocks from the Grand Central Terminal, but it is done quietly and with a minimum of discomfort to him. He will be overcharged at hotels and restaurants and will pay one of the better kings' ransoms for theatre tickets and on his way home he may be mugged by an acquisitive thug, but it is all in a spirit of detachment, like a surgeon removing a gall bladder. There is absolutely no bias against him simply because he comes from Rochester. In fact, the driver of the taxi which clips him as he crosses Fifth Avenue may himself be a Rochester boy. Truly it is a small world in New York.

Not soon shall I forget my first sight of Fort Worth. I neared the city on foot from the east, meaning east of Fort Worth, at about sunset. My two slaves, Caesar and Pompey, whom I had picked up for a song in one of the large Houston department stores, followed me at a respectful distance, carrying Rhode Island. On the western horizon, enclosing the city in a shimmering, iridescent halo, was a sight of such beauty as to take away my breath—and I had little of it to spare after the day's hike. Reds, golds, crimsons, purples, pinks, mauves, oranges, bananas, a thousand delicate hues intermingled in what cannot but be described as a veritable riot of color. Never, not even over the Hackensack meadows, had I seen so gorgeous a sunset, and for that reason if for none other my disappointment was the keener when I learned that it was not a sunset at all but the great Fort Worth Cowboy Shirt Plant, where they make all those beautiful, vivid shirts that cowboys wear to frighten steers into submission. What I mistook for a sunset was the day's output of the shirt mills, hung out to air. I shall never again see a sunset that will not seem tame.

One of the most agreeable episodes of my trip to Texas was the day I spent on the Regal Ranch, the largest cattle, or any kind of, ranch in the world. Rhode Island fitted into it sixty-seven times. It is so large that although there are 949 billion trillions of blades of grass on it, each blade is three feet from its nearest neighbor. (I am indebted to Professor Harlow Shapley of the Harvard Department of Astronomy for the use of these figures.) The cattle have to be flown in jet planes from one pasturage to another. If they tried to walk they would either die of fatigue or become so tough and muscle-bound that they would be useless for anything except one of those $8 table d'hôte dinners at a swank New York hotel. No matter how large you think the Regal Ranch is, it is twice as large as that. In fact the cowboys from the northern part of the ranch can scarcely understand the dialect spoken by their colleagues from its southern shires.

Last year the Regal exported 5,476,397 head of cattle to Kansas City and 2,397,739 head of cowboy to the Hollywood mart. Of the latter, 726,387 were pure Roy Rogers, 327,835 were Gene Autrys and 14,397 were genuine, antique Gary Coopers. The foreman of one of the counties in the ranch told me they are experimenting on an improved breed of cowboy, who will combine the best features of all cowboys since William S. Hart and will, as one improved feature, have fingernails four times as durable as the present ones, and therefore be better equipped for successful plunking of guitars. Many an otherwise magnificent specimen of cowboy, the foreman told me, has had to be shot because of brittle fingernail, an occupational defect which renders a cowhand useless as a guitar strummer and hence useless. The fingernail snaps off in the middle of "Home on the Range," and lasting shame is the lot of the unfortunate cowboy, through no fault of his own.

With his plunking fingernail thus bolstered, the last defect will be removed from the Texas cowboy, and he will be the most perfect specimen of fine upstanding manhood the world has known. He is eight feet tall, of course. No cowhand under that height can hope to win his lariat. He is not only a paragon of manly beauty but he has a pure mind and worships the ground that women walk on. Womankind, whom he traditionally and respectfully addresses as "Ma'am," takes second place in his affections only to the little dogies whose virtues he has lyricised to the envy of all the rest of the animal kingdom, no species of which has found so eloquent a minstrel to sing its praises. The Texas cowhand is generous to a fault and, unless you are wary, he will give you the shirt off his back. Quick to resent an affront he nevertheless has a heart of gold, and no widow or orphan ever appealed to him for succor in vain.

I shall not name, for I would not dignify him by doing so, a certain viper whom I encountered at a luncheon given for me by the Chamber of Commerce of one of the larger cattle ranches. Chatting casually with this person, who had been introduced to me as a Texan, I said, "You've got a mighty fine state down here, pardner."

"Oh, it's all right," he said, in a tone of diffidence which I did not quite like.

"It's the biggest state in the Union," I said, bridling slightly.

"Size isn't everything," he remarked.

I was now pretty nettled, for in my stay I had come to look upon Texas with great affection.

"Texas has won every war for the United States," I challenged.

"Pooh!" This from a Texan!

"You pooh Texas!" I cried, astounded.

"Yes, and I re-pooh it," said he.

"You deny Texas won the World wars in addition to the Spanish-American, Civil and Revolutionary wars?"

"I do. Where do you come from?"

"Round Lake, New York."

"I thought so. You foreigners who become enamored of Texas brag worse than our own Chamber of Commerce. Texas is just another state."

I know I acted hastily. I should have turned him over to the Chamber of Commerce. But I couldn't help it. I shot him. No jury convicted me.

A week had passed and my visit to the Lonesome Star State was coming to a close. I do not pretend to have seen all of Texas in my week there. It would take at least another week to do that. But I had completed my research with Rhode Island. It really does go 220 times into Texas. In fact, I had Deaf Smith County left over.

Bennett Cerf

A TEXAS SAMPLER

TEXANS are, on the average, so tall, handsome, and full of vitality there's something unbelievable about them—and that goes double for the myriad of stories by and about them.

There's no need to ask a man in those parts what state he's from. If he's from Texas, he'll tell you himself; if he's not, why embarrass him? The state is so big that El Paso natives refer to citizens of Texarkana as "effete Easterners" and Brownsville folk regard Dallasites as "Northern white trash." Roads leading South bear signs marked "This way to Texas." Those who can read keep on going; the others settle in Arkansas.

Even Texas sandstorms are something special. A farmer went to town to borrow money on his farm. The banker said, "I'll have to ride out and look over your place." "That won't be necessary," said the farmer. "Here comes the place now." On his way out, the farmer's hat blew off. He just reached up into the air and pulled down another one.

A Texas rancher shot a man dead and telegraphed a slick lawyer in Fort Worth, three hundred miles away, offering a $5000 fee. The attorney wired back, "Leaving for your town on next train, bringing three eye-witnesses."

Sam Houston is the hero of a thousand Texas anecdotes. At a big outdoor dinner in his honor, somebody handed him a plate of sizzling hot rice pudding. In the midst of an oration, Houston lifted a huge spoonful to his mouth, let out a roar, and then spat the rice to the ground. "You see, folks," he explained, "many a durn fool woulda swallowed that!"

The court house at Stephenville has a large clock that is the pride of the town. It is illuminated at night. One citizen staggered up to a mail box, dropped a penny in the slot, glanced at the clock, and exclaimed, "Jehoshaphat, I'm nine pounds overweight."

They say the air is so bracing in Texas that the State Chamber of Commerce had to hire an Easterner to shoot himself so they could start a cemetery. At the last minute he rued his bargain and ran for his life. Pistol Pete lassoed him, and declared when he brought him in, "This dude was runnin' so fast his vest pocket was dippin' up sand."

In a remote corner of the state, the first motorcycle Sam'l ever had seen chugged by. Sam'l seized his rifle and fired. "Git the varmint?" asked his wife. "Nope," said Sam'l. "I still hear the critter but I shore made it turn that man loose."

A Fort Worth newspaper printed a personal ad that read, "If John Blank, who deserted his wife and baby twenty-one years ago, will return, said baby will knock hell out of him." A cub reporter on the same sheet referred in his first story to a "local schoolteacher." The editor advised, "Son, always use the name of the city; never use the word 'local.'" The next day the youngster covered the operation on a tycoon and reported, "The surgeon used a Fort Worth anaesthetic."

In the early days in Texas when frontier justice was the rule, there was one two-fisted judge who ruled his court with an iron hand plus a pair of six-shooters. The only book in the whole town was an authentic first edition of a Sears Roebuck catalogue. The judge kept it on his desk and whenever it came time to give a sentence, he would consult its pages. One morning he opened the book at random, glanced at the open page, and shook a gnarled finger at a prisoner. "I fine you," he said, "$3.49."
The prisoner started to protest. "Shut up," whispered his lawyer.

"You're the luckiest coot in town. Supposin' he had turned to 'pianos' instead of 'babies' dresses'?"

Wall Street financier Arthur Goodman asked a Texas oil tycoon, "How's business holding up in your sector?" "Son," drawled the Texan, "in Houston we do more business by accident than you do in Wall Street on purpose."

A Texas dowager presented herself at the Pearly Gates, and when Saint Peter asked for her credentials, proudly presented a membership card to the Symphony, receipted bills from Neiman-Marcus and the Shamrock Hotel, and a picture of herself shaking hands with Ted Dealey of the Dallas News. Saint Peter, duly impressed, remarked, "Come in, Madam, by all means—but I don't think you'll like it."

Vice-President Barkley was engaged in hot debate with one of those fabulous Texas oil millionaires over the merits of a neighboring Houstonian. "I'll bet he's as rich as you are," needled Barkley. "Don't let that fourflusher fool you," retorted the Texan angrily. "He's never had over thirty million dollars in his pocket at one time in his whole life."

A New Yorker was driving through a barren wilderness in West Texas when a fancy bird skittled past the car. "What kind of fowl do you call that?" he asked. The driver answered proudly, "That's a bird of paradise." "Hm-m-m," mused the New Yorker. "Kind of far from home, isn't he?"

The citizens of the gay and booming metropolis of Dallas buy more books and accord more hospitality to visiting literati than any other place on earth. This is due partly to the fact that, in Elizabeth Ann McMurray, John McGinnis, Jimmie Albright, and Lon Tinkle, it harbors four of the outstanding personalities in the American book world. It is also due to the Dallasites' insatiable craving for culture. Good books, good paintings, good music not only stimulate their souls, but engender an intoxicating feeling of superiority over their hated neighbors in Fort Worth, thirty miles to the west. Dallas was vaguely pleased when a local wit dubbed it "The Athens of the Alfalfa Fields."

In 1936, Texas staged a mammoth centennial celebration. Dallas wanted it very much; so did Fort Worth. Dallas won, and laid out a series of exhibits that plumbed deep in the arts of Texas. Fort Worth countered with a garden of beautiful girls, planted by an inspired horticulturist named Billy Rose, and broadcast its defy, "Dallas for education; Fort Worth for entertainment." That left everybody happy, particularly Billy Rose, who got a thousand dollars a day for his efforts, and was worth it. The only time they had to call out the Texas Rangers was when one incredulous patron hit the jackpot on a slot machine.

One of the most colorful figures in Dallas is Everette Lee De Golyer, pre-eminent geophysicist, and authority on oil. His six-year-old granddaughter is a chip off the old block. Mrs. De Golyer told her one day about her great-grandmother, something of a family legend. The little girl asked to see her. "You can't," said Mrs. De Golyer, "she's dead." The granddaughter asked, "Who shot her?"

The Dallas institution that every woman visits first is the fabulous Neiman-Marcus store. It is really a collection of superb specialty shops under one roof, featuring merchandise that could be obtained only, if at all, by visits to a score of different establishments on Fifth Avenue, Michigan Boulevard, or Wilshire. Mr. De Golyer once asked Neiman-Marcus to send some costume jewelry over to his office. He wanted to make a modest anniversary gift to his wife. A suave salesman arrived with several pieces, priced from forty to sixty dollars each. He saved until last an emerald ring. Mr. De Golyer has always had a weakness for emeralds. "I think I like this best," he said. "How much is it?" The salesman coughed discreetly and murmured, "$55,000." De Golyer challenged Stanley Marcus another time to find him one item in the store that sold for a dollar. Stanley searched for some time, and finally came up with a pocket handkerchief.

An oil tycoon's wife visited Neiman-Marcus one day in search of a new fur coat and Stanley Marcus waited on her in person.

She inclined to a modest number that bore a price tag of exactly $32,000. Marcus told her, "We must warn everybody who picks out a coat of this particular fur that while it is very, very rare and uncommonly beautiful, it doesn't wear as well as, say, mink or sable, and may no longer look its best after two or three seasons. That being the case, I suppose you'll reconsider the purchase."

"On the contrary," said the customer promptly, "that being the case, I'd better have two of them!"

The last Southern Methodist-Notre Dame football game was a sell-out. Hordes of excited fans yelled their lungs out as the tide of fortune swayed now one way, now the other. And nobody yelled louder for SMU than a young priest who had a seat on the 35-yard line. During a time-out the man next to him admitted, "I can't figure, Father, why you are rooting for SMU. Surely you realize Notre Dame is a Catholic institution! How come?" The priest explained proudly, "First, suh, Ah am a Texan!"

VII. THE FAR WEST

Bret Harte

AN INGENUE OF THE SIERRAS

I

WE ALL held our breath as the coach rushed through the semi-darkness of Galloper's Ridge. The vehicle itself was only a huge lumbering shadow; its side-lights were carefully extinguished, and Yuba Bill had just politely removed from the lips of an outside passenger even the cigar with which he had been ostentatiously exhibiting his coolness. For it had been rumored that the Ramon Martinez gang of "road agents" were "laying" for us on the second grade, and would time the passage of our lights across Galloper's in order to intercept us in the "brush" beyond. If we could cross the ridge without being seen, and so get through the brush before they reached it, we were safe. If they followed, it would only be a stern chase with the odds in our favor.

The huge vehicle swayed from side to side, rolled, dipped, and plunged, but Bill kept the track, as if, in the whispered words of the Expressman, he could "feel and smell" the road he could no longer see. We knew that at times we hung perilously over the edge of slopes that eventually dropped a thousand feet sheer to the tops of the sugar-pines below, but we knew that Bill knew it also. The half visible heads of the horses, drawn wedge-wise together by the tightened reins, appeared to cleave the darkness like a ploughshare, held between his rigid hands. Even the hoof-beats of the six horses had fallen into a vague, monotonous, distant roll. Then the ridge was crossed, and we plunged into the still blacker obscurity of the brush. Rather we no longer seemed to move—it was only the phantom night that rushed

Reprinted by permission of Houghton Mifflin Company, authorized publishers.

by us. The horses might have been submerged in some swift Lethean stream; nothing but the top of the coach and the rigid bulk of Yuba Bill arose above them. Yet even in that awful moment our speed was unslackened; it was as if Bill cared no longer to *guide* but only to drive, or as if the direction of his huge machine was determined by other hands than his. An incautious whisperer hazarded the paralyzing suggestion of our "meeting another team." To our great astonishment Bill overheard it; to our greater astonishment he replied. "It 'ud be only a neck and neck race which would get to h—ll first," he said quietly. But we were relieved—for he had *spoken!* Almost simultaneously the wider turnpike began to glimmer faintly as a visible track before us; the wayside trees fell out of line, opened up, and dropped off one after another; we were on the broader tableland, out of danger, and apparently unperceived and unpursued.

Nevertheless in the conversation that broke out again with the relighting of the lamps, and the comments, congratulations, and reminiscences that were freely exchanged, Yuba Bill preserved a dissatisfied and even resentful silence. The most generous praise of his skill and courage awoke no response. "I reckon the old man waz just spilin' for a fight, and is feelin' disappointed," said a passenger. But those who knew that Bill had the true fighter's scorn for any purely purposeless conflict were more or less concerned and watchful of him. He would drive steadily for four or five minutes with thoughtfully knitted brows, but eyes still keenly observant under his slouched hat, and then, relaxing his strained attitude, would give way to a movement of impatience. "You ain't uneasy about anything, Bill, are you?" asked the Expressman confidentially. Bill lifted his eyes with a slightly contemptuous surprise. "Not about anything ter *come*. It's what *hez* happened that I don't exactly *sabe*. I don't see no signs of Ramon's gang ever havin' been out at all, and ef they were out I don't see why they didn't go for us."

"The simple fact is that our ruse was successful," said an outside passenger. "They waited to see our lights on the ridge, and, not seeing them, missed us until we had passed. That's my opinion."

"You ain't puttin' any price on that opinion, air ye?" inquired Bill politely.

"No."

"'Cos thar's a comic paper in 'Frisco pays for them things, and I've seen worse things in it."

"Come off, Bill," retorted the passenger, slightly nettled by the tittering of his companions. "Then what did you put out the lights for?"

"Well," returned Bill grimly, "it mout have been because I didn't keer to hev you chaps blazin' away at the first bush you *thought* you saw move in your skeer, and bringin' down their fire on us."

The explanation, though unsatisfactory, was by no means an improbable one, and we thought it better to accept it with a laugh. Bill, however, resumed his abstracted manner.

"Who got in at the Summit?" he at last asked abruptly of the Expressman.

"Derrick and Simpson of Cold Spring, and one of the 'Excelsior' boys," responded the Expressman.

"And that Pike County girl from Dow's Flat, with her bundles. Don't forget her," added the outside passenger ironically.

"Does anybody here know her?" continued Bill, ignoring the irony.

"You'd better ask Judge Thompson; he was mighty attentive to her; gettin' her a seat by the off window, and lookin' after her bundles and things."

"Gettin' her a seat by the *window?*" repeated Bill.

"Yes, she wanted to see everything, and wasn't afraid of the shooting."

"Yes," broke in a third passenger, "and he was so d—d civil that when she dropped her ring in the straw, he struck a match agin all your rules, you know, and held it for her to find it. And it was just as we were crossin' through the brush, too. I saw the hull thing through the window, for I was hanging over the wheels with my gun ready for action. And it wasn't no fault of Judge Thompson's if his d—d foolishness hadn't shown us up, and got us a shot from the gang."

Bill gave a short grunt, but drove steadily on without further comment or even turning his eyes to the speaker.

We were now not more than a mile from the station at the crossroads where we were to change horses. The lights already glimmered in the distance, and there was a faint suggestion of the coming dawn on the summits of the ridge to the west. We had plunged into a belt of timber, when suddenly a horseman emerged at a sharp canter from a trail that seemed to be parallel with our own. We were all slightly startled; Yuba Bill alone preserving his moody calm.

"Hullo!" he said.

The stranger wheeled to our side as Bill slackened his speed. He seemed to be a "packer" or freight muleteer.

"Ye didn't get 'held up' on the Divide?" continued Bill cheerfully.

"No," returned the packer, with a laugh. "I don't carry treasure. But I see you're all right, too. I saw you crossin' over Galloper's."

"*Saw* us?" said Bill sharply. "We had our lights out."

"Yes, but there was suthin' white—a handkerchief or woman's veil, I reckon—hangin' from the window. It was only a movin' spot agin the hillside, but ez I was lookin' out for ye I knew it was you by that. Good-night!"

He cantered away. We tried to look at each other's faces, and at Bill's expression in the darkness, but he neither spoke nor stirred until he threw down the reins when we stopped before the station. The passengers quickly descended from the roof; the Expressman was about to follow, but Bill plucked his sleeve.

"I'm goin' to take a look over this yer stage and these yer passengers with ye, afore we start."

"Why, what's up?"

"Well," said Bill, slowly disengaging himself from one of his enormous gloves, "when we waltzed down into the brush up there I saw a man, ez plain ez I see you, rise up from it. I thought our time had come and the band was goin' to play, when he sorter drew back, made a sign, and we just scooted past him."

"Well?"

"Well," said Bill, "it means that this yer coach was *passed through free* to-night."

"You don't object to *that*—surely? I think we were deucedly lucky."

Bill slowly drew off his other glove. "I've been riskin' my everlastin' life on this d—d line three times a week," he said with mock humility, "and I'm allus thankful for small mercies. *But*," he added grimly, "when it comes down to being passed free by some pal of a hoss thief, and thet called a speshal Providence, *I ain't in it!* No, sir, I ain't in it!"

II

It was with mixed emotions that the passengers heard that a delay of fifteen minutes to tighten certain screw-bolts had been ordered by the autocratic Bill. Some were anxious to get their breakfast at Sugar Pine, but others were not averse to linger for the daylight that promised greater safety on the road. The Expressman, knowing the real cause of Bill's delay, was nevertheless at a loss to understand the object of it. The passengers were all well known; any idea of complicity with the road agents was wild and impossible, and, even if there was a confederate of the gang among them, he would have been more likely to precipitate a robbery than to check it. Again, the discovery of such a confederate—to whom they clearly owned their safety—and his arrest would have been quite against the Californian sense of justice, if not actually illegal. It seemed evident that Bill's quixotic sense of honor was leading him astray.

The station consisted of a stable, a wagon shed, and a building containing three rooms. The first was fitted up with "bunks" or sleeping berths for the employees; the second was the kitchen; and the third and larger apartment was dining-room or sitting-room, and was used as general waiting-room for the passengers. It was not a refreshment station, and there was no "bar." But a mysterious command from the omnipotent Bill produced a demijohn of whiskey, with which he hospitably treated the company. The seductive influence of the liquor loosened the tongue of the gallant Judge Thompson. He admitted to having struck a match to enable the fair Pike Countian to find her ring, which, however, proved to have fallen in her lap. She was "a fine, healthy young woman—a type of the Far West, sir; in fact, quite a prairie blossom! yet simple and guileless as a child." She was on her way to Marysville, he believed, "although she expected to meet friends—a friend, in fact—later on." It was her first visit to a large town—in fact, any civilized centre—since she crossed the plains three years ago. Her girlish curiosity was quite touching, and her innocence irresistible. In fact, in a country whose tendency was to produce "frivolity and forwardness in young girls, he found her a most interesting young person." She was even then out in the stable-yard watching the horses being harnessed, "preferring to indulge a pardonable healthy young curiosity than to listen to the empty compliments of the younger passengers."

The figure which Bill saw thus engaged, without being otherwise distinguished, certainly seemed to justify the Judge's opinion. She appeared to be a well-matured country girl, whose frank gray eyes and large laughing mouth expressed a wholesome and abiding gratification in her life and surroundings. She was watching the replacing of luggage in the boot. A little feminine start, as one of her own parcels was thrown somewhat roughly on the roof, gave Bill his opportunity. "Now there," he growled to the helper, "ye ain't carting stone! Look out, will yer! Some of your things, miss?" he added, with gruff courtesy, turning to her. "These yer trunks, for instance?"

She smiled a pleasant assent, and Bill, pushing aside the helper, seized a large square trunk in his arms. But from excess of zeal, or some other mischance, his foot slipped, and he came down heavily, striking the corner of the trunk on the ground and loosening its hinges and fastenings. It was a cheap, common-looking affair, but the accident discovered in its yawning lid a quantity of white, lace-edged feminine apparel of an apparently superior quality. The young lady uttered another cry and came quickly forward, but Bill was profuse in his apologies, himself girded the broken box with a strap, and declared his intention of having the company "make it good" to her with a new one. Then he casually accompanied her to the door of the waiting-room, entered, made a place for her before the fire by simply lifting the nearest and most youthful passenger by the coat collar from the stool that he was occupying, and, having installed the lady in it, displaced another man who was standing before the chimney, and, drawing himself up to his full six feet of height in front of her, glanced down upon his fair passenger as he took his waybill from his pocket.

"Your name is down here as Miss Mullins?" he said.

She looked up, became suddenly aware that she and her questioner were the centre of interest to the whole circle of passengers, and, with a slight rise of color, returned, "Yes."

"Well, Miss Mullins, I've got a question or two to ask ye. I ask it straight out afore this crowd. It's in my rights to take ye aside and ask it—but that ain't my style; I'm no detective. I needn't ask it at all, but act as ef I knowed the answer, or I might leave it to be asked by others. Ye needn't answer it ef ye don't like; ye've got a friend over there—Judge Thompson—who is a friend to ye, right or wrong, jest as any other man here is—as though ye'd packed your own jury. Well, the simple question I've got to ask ye is *this*: Did you signal to anybody from the coach when we passed Galloper's an hour ago?"

We all thought that Bill's courage and audacity had reached its climax here. To openly and publicly accuse a "lady" before a group of chivalrous Californians, and that lady possessing the further attractions of youth, good looks, and innocence, was little short of desperation. There was an evident movement of adhesion towards the fair stranger, a slight muttering broke out on the right, but the very boldness of the act held them in stupefied surprise. Judge Thompson, with a bland propitiatory smile began: "Really, Bill, I must protest on behalf of this young lady"—when the fair accused, raising her eyes to her accuser, to the consternation of everybody answered with the slight but convincing hesitation of conscientious truthfulness:—

"I *did*."

"Ahem!" interposed the Judge hastily, "er—that is—er—you allowed your handkerchief to flutter from the window,—I noticed it myself,—casually—one might say even playfully—but without any particular significance."

The girl, regarding her apologist with a singular mingling of pride and impatience, returned briefly:—

"I signaled."

"Who did you signal to?" asked Bill gravely.

"The young gentleman I'm going to marry."

A start, followed by a slight titter from the younger passengers, was instantly suppressed by a savage glance from Bill.

"What did you signal to him for?" he continued.

"To tell him I was here, and that it was all right," returned the young girl, with a steadily rising pride and color.

"Wot was all right?" demanded Bill.

"That I wasn't followed, and that he could meet me on the road beyond Cass's Ridge Station." She hesitated a moment, and then, with a still greater pride, in which a youthful defiance was still mingled, said: "I've run away from home to marry him. And I mean to! No one can stop me. Dad didn't like him just because he was poor, and dad's got money. Dad wanted me to marry a man I hate, and got a lot of dresses and things to bribe me."

"And you're taking them in your trunk to the other feller?" said Bill grimly.

"Yes, he's poor," returned the girl defiantly.

"Then your father's name is Mullins?" asked Bill.

"It's not Mullins. I—I—took that name," she hesitated, with her first exhibition of self-consciousness.

"Wot *is* his name?"

"Eli Hemmings."

A smile of relief and significance went round the circle. The fame of Eli or "Skinner" Hemmings, as a notorious miser and usurer, had passed even beyond Galloper's Ridge.

"The step that you're taking, Miss Mullins, I need not tell you, is one of great gravity," said Judge Thompson, with a certain paternal seriousness of manner, in which, however, we were glad to detect a glaring affectation; "and I trust that you and your affianced have fully weighed it. Far be it from me to interfere with or question the natural affections of two young people, but may I ask you what you know of the—er—young gentleman for whom you are sacrificing so much, and, perhaps, imperiling your whole future? For instance, have you known him long?"

The slightly troubled air of trying to understand,—not unlike the vague wonderment of childhood,—with which Miss Mullins had received the beginning of this exordium, changed to a relieved smile of comprehension as she said quickly, "Oh yes, nearly a whole year."

"And," said the Judge, smiling, "has he a vocation—is he in business?"

"Oh yes," she returned; "he's a collector."

"A collector?"

"Yes; he collects bills, you know,—money," she went on, with childish eagerness, "not for himself,—*he* never has any money, poor Charley,—but for his firm. It's dreadful hard work, too; keeps him out for days and nights, over bad roads and baddest weather. Sometimes, when he's stole over to the ranch just to see me, he's been so bad he could scarcely keep his seat in the saddle, much less stand. And he's got to take mighty big risks, too. Times the folks are cross with him and won't pay; once they shot him in the arm, and he came to me, and I helped do it up for him. But he don't mind. He's real brave,—jest as brave as he's good." There was such a wholesome ring of truth in this pretty praise that we were touched in sympathy with the speaker.

"What firm does he collect for?" asked the Judge gently.

"I don't know exactly—he won't tell me; but I think it's a Spanish firm. You see"—she took us all into her confidence with a sweeping smile of innocent yet half-mischievous artfulness—"I only know because I peeped over a letter he once got from his firm, telling him he must hustle up and be ready for the road the next day; but I think the name was Martinez—yes, Ramon Martinez."

In the dead silence that ensued—a silence so profound that we could hear the horses in the distant stable-yard rattling their harness—one of the younger "Excelsior" boys burst into a hysteric laugh, but the fierce eye of Yuba Bill was down upon him, and seemed to instantly stiffen him into a silent, grinning mask. The young girl, however, took no note of it. Following out, with lover-like diffusiveness, the reminiscences thus awakened, she went on:—

"Yes, it's mighty hard work, but he says it's all for me, and as soon as we're married he'll quit it. He might have quit it before, but he won't take no money of me, nor what I told him I could get out of dad! That ain't his style. He's mighty proud—if he is poor—is Charley. Why, thar's all ma's money which she left me in the Savin's Bank that I wanted to draw out—for I had the right—and give it to him, but he wouldn't hear of it! Why, he wouldn't take one of the things I've got with me, if he knew it. And so he goes on ridin' and ridin', here and there and everywhere, and gettin' more and more played out and sad, and thin and pale as a spirit, and always so uneasy about his business, and startin' up at times when we're meetin' out in the South Woods or in the far clearin', and sayin': 'I must be goin' now, Polly,' and yet always tryin' to be chiffle and chipper afore me. Why, he must have rid miles and miles to have watched for me thar in the brush at the foot of Galloper's to-night, jest to see if all was safe; and Lordy! I'd have given him the signal and showed a light if I'd died for it the next minit. There! That's what I know of Charley—that's what I'm running away from home for—that's what I'm running to him for, and I don't care who knows it! And I only wish I'd done it afore—and I would—if—if—if—he'd only *asked me!* There now!" She stopped, panted, and choked. Then one of the sudden transitions of youthful emotion overtook the eager, laughing face; it clouded up with the swift change of childhood, a lightning quiver of expression broke over it, and—then came the rain!

I think this simple act completed our utter demoralization! We smiled feebly at each other with that assumption of masculine superiority which is miserably conscious of its own helplessness at such moments. We looked out of the window, blew our noses, said: "Eh—what?" and "I say," vaguely to each other, and were greatly relieved, and yet apparently astonished, when Yuba Bill, who had turned his back upon the fair speaker, and was kicking the logs in the fireplace, suddenly swept down upon us and bundled us all into the road, leaving Miss Mullins alone. Then he walked aside with Judge Thompson for a few moments; returned to us, autocratically demanded of the party a complete reticence towards Miss Mullins on the subject-matter under discussion, reëntered the station, reappeared with the young lady, suppressed a faint idiotic cheer which broke from us at the spectacle of her innocent face once more cleared and rosy, climbed the box, and in another moment we were under way.

"Then she don't know what her lover is yet?" asked the Express-man eagerly.

"No."

"Are *you* certain it's one of the gang?"

"Can't say *for sure.* It mout be a young chap from Yolo who bucked agin the tiger[1] at Sacramento, got regularly cleaned out and busted, and joined the gang for a flier. They say thar was a new hand in that job over at Keeley's,—and a mighty game one, too; and ez there was some buckshot onloaded that trip, he might hev got his share, and

[1] Gambled at faro.

that would tally with what the girl said about his arm. See! Ef that's the man, I've heered he was the son of some big preacher in the States, and a college sharp to boot, who ran wild in 'Frisco, and played himself for all he was worth. They're the wust kind to kick when they once get a foot over the traces. For stiddy, comf'ble kempany," added Bill reflectively, "give *me* the son of a man that was *hanged!*"

"But what are you going to do about this?"

"That depends upon the feller who comes to meet her."

"But you ain't going to try to take him? That would be playing it pretty low down on them both."

"Keep your hair on, Jimmy! The Judge and me are only going to rastle with the sperrit of that gay young galoot, when he drops down for his girl—and exhort him pow'ful! Ef he allows he's convicted of sin and will find the Lord, we'll marry him and the gal offhand at the next station, and the Judge will officiate himself for nothin'. We're goin' to have this yer elopement done on the square—and our waybill clean—you bet!"

"But you don't suppose he'll trust himself in your hands?"

"Polly will signal to him that it's all square."

"Ah!" said the Expressman. Nevertheless in those few moments the men seemed to have exchanged dispositions. The Expressman looked doubtfully, critically, and even cynically before him. Bill's face had relaxed, and something like a bland smile beamed across it, as he drove confidently and unhesitatingly forward.

Day, meantime, although full blown and radiant on the mountain summits around us, was yet nebulous and uncertain in the valleys into which we were plunging. Lights still glimmered in the cabins and few ranch buildings which began to indicate the thicker settlements. And the shadows were heaviest in a little copse, where a note from Judge Thompson in the coach was handed up to Yuba Bill, who at once slowly began to draw up his horses. The coach stopped finally near the junction of a small crossroad. At the same moment Miss Mullins slipped down from the vehicle, and, with a parting wave of her hand to the Judge, who had assisted her from the steps, tripped down the crossroad, and disappeared in its semi-obscurity. To our surprise the stage waited, Bill holding the reins listlessly in his hands. Five minutes passed—an eternity of expectation, and, as there was that in Yuba Bill's face which forbade idle questioning, an aching void of silence also! This was at last broken by a strange voice from the road:—

"Go on—we'll follow."

The coach started forward. Presently we heard the sound of other wheels behind us. We all craned our necks backward to get a view of the unknown, but by the growing light we could only see that we were followed at a distance by a buggy with two figures in it. Evidently Polly Mullins and her lover! We hoped that they would pass us. But the vehicle, although drawn by a fast horse, preserved its distance always, and it was plain that its driver had no desire to satisfy our curiosity. The Expressman had recourse to Bill.

"Is it the man you thought of?" he asked eagerly.

"I reckon," said Bill briefly.

"But," continued the Expressman, returning to his former skepticism, "what's to keep them both from levanting together now?"

Bill jerked his hand towards the boot with a grim smile.

"Their baggage."

"Oh!" said the Expressman.

"Yes," continued Bill. "We'll hang on to that gal's little frills and fixin's until this yer job's settled, and the ceremony's over, jest as ef we waz her own father. And, what's more, young man," he added, suddenly turning to the Expressman, *"you'll* express them trunks of hers *through to Sacramento* with your kempany's lables, and hand her the receipts and checks for them, so she *can get 'em there.* That'll keep *him* outer temptation and the reach o' the gang, until they get away among white men and civilization again. When your hoary-headed ole grandfather, or, to speak plainer, that partikler old whiskey-soaker known as Yuba Bill, wot sits on this box," he continued, with a diabolical wink at the Expressman, "waltzes in to pervide for a young couple jest startin' in life, thar's nothin' mean about his style, you bet. He fills the bill every time! Speshul Providences take a back seat when he's around."

When the station hotel and straggling settlement of Sugar Pine, now distinct and clear in the growing light, at last rose within rifleshot on the plateau, the buggy suddenly darted swiftly by us, so swiftly that the faces of the two occupants were barely distinguishable as they passed, and keeping the lead by a dozen lengths, reached the door of the hotel. The young girl and her companion leaped down and vanished within as we drew up. They had evidently determined to elude our curiosity, and were successful.

But the material appetites of the passengers, sharpened by the keen mountain air, were more potent than their curiosity, and, as the breakfast-bell rang out at the moment the stage stopped, a majority of them rushed into the dining-room and scrambled for places without giving much heed to the vanished couple or to the Judge and Yuba Bill, who had disappeared also. The through coach to Marysville and Sacramento was likewise waiting, for Sugar Pine was the limit of Bill's ministration, and the coach which we had just left went no farther. In the course of twenty minutes, however, there was a slight and somewhat ceremonious bustling in the hall and on the veranda, and Yuba Bill and the Judge reappeared. The latter was leading, with some elaboration of manner and detail, the shapely figure of Miss Mullins, and Yuba Bill was accompanying her companion to the buggy. We all rushed to the windows to get a good view of the mysterious stranger and probable ex-brigand whose life was now linked with our fair fellow-passenger. I am afraid, however, that we all participated in a certain impression of disappointment and doubt. Handsome and even cultivated-looking, he assuredly was—young and vigorous in appearance. But there was a certain half-shamed, half-defiant suggestion in his expression, yet coupled with a watchful lurking uneasiness which was not pleasant and hardly becoming in a bridegroom—and the possessor of such a bride. But the frank, joyous, innocent face of Polly Mullins, resplendent with a simple, happy confidence, melted our hearts again, and condoned the fellow's shortcomings. We waved our hands; I think we would have given three rousing cheers as they drove away if the omnipotent eye of Yuba Bill had not been upon us. It was well, for the next moment we were summoned to the presence of that soft-hearted autocrat.

We found him alone with the Judge in a private sitting-room, standing before a table on which there were a decanter and glasses. As we filed expectantly into the room and the door closed behind us, he cast a glance of hesitating tolerance over the group.

"Gentlemen," he said slowly, "you was all present at the beginnin' of a little game this mornin', and the Judge thar thinks that you oughter be let in at the finish. I don't see that it's any of *your* d—d business—so to speak; but ez the Judge here allows you're all in the secret, I've called you in to take a partin' drink to the health of Mr. and Mrs. Charley Byng—ez is now comf'ably off on their bridal tower. What *you* know or what *you* suspects of the young galoot that's married the gal ain't worth shucks to anybody, and I wouldn't give it to a yaller pup to play with, but the Judge thinks you ought all to promise right here that you'll keep it dark. That's his opinion. Ez far as my opinion goes, gen'l'men," continued Bill, with greater blandness and apparent cordiality, "I wanter simply remark, in a keerless, offhand gin'ral way, that ef I ketch any God-forsaken, lop-eared, chuckleheaded blatherin' idjet airin' *his* opinion"—

"One moment, Bill," interposed Judge Thompson with a grave smile; "let me explain. You understand, gentlemen," he said, turning to us, "the singular, and I may say affecting, situation which our good-hearted friend here has done so much to bring to what we hope will be. a happy termination. I want to give here, as my professional opinion, that there is nothing in his request which, in your capacity as good citizens and law-abiding men, you may not grant. I want to tell you, also, that you are condoning no offense against the statutes; that there is not a particle of legal evidence before us of the criminal antecedants of Mr. Charles Byng, except that which has been told you by the innocent lips of his betrothed, which the law of the land has now sealed forever in the mouth of his wife, and that our own actual experience of his acts has been in the main exculpatory of any previous irregularity—if not incompatible with it. Briefly, no judge would charge, no jury convict, on such evidence. When I add that the young girl is of legal age, that there is no evidence of any previous undue influence, but rather of the reverse, on the part of the bridegroom, and that I was content, as a magistrate, to perform the ceremony, I think you will be satisfied to give your promise, for the sake of the bride, and drink a happy life to them both."

I need not say that we did this cheerfully, and even extorted from Bill a grunt of satisfaction. The majority of the company, however, who were going with the through coach to Sacramento, then took their leave, and, as we accompanied them to the veranda, we could see that Miss Polly Mullins's trunks were already transferred to the other vehicle under the protecting seals and labels of the all-potent Express Company. Then the whip cracked, the coach rolled away, and the last traces of the adventurous young couple disappeared in the hanging red dust of its wheels.

But Yuba Bill's grim satisfaction at the happy issue of the episode seemed to suffer no abatement. He even exceeded his usual deliberately regulated potations, and, standing comfortably with his back to the centre of the now deserted bar-room, was more than usually loquacious with the Expressman. "You see," he said, in bland reminiscence, "when your old Uncle Bill takes hold of a job like this, he puts it straight through without changin' hosses. Yet thar was a moment, young feller, when I thought I was stompt! It was when we'd made up our mind to make that chap tell the gal fust all what he was! Ef she'd rared or kicked in the traces, or hung back only ez much ez that, we'd hev given him jest five minits' law to get up and get and leave her, and we'd hev toted that gal and her fixin's back to her dad again! But she jest gave a little scream and start, and then went off inter hysterics, right on his buzzum, laughin' and cryin' and sayin' that nothin' should part 'em. Gosh! if I didn't think *he* woz more cut up than she about it; a minit it looked as ef *he* didn't allow to marry her arter all, but that passed, and they was married hard and fast—you bet! I reckon he's had enough of stayin' out o' nights to last him, and ef the valley settlements hevn't got hold of a very shinin' member, at least the foothills hev got shut of one more of the Ramon Martinez gang."

"What's that about the Ramon Martinez gang?" said a quiet potential voice.

Bill turned quickly. It was the voice of the Divisional Superintendent of the Express Company,—a man of eccentric determination of character, and one of the few whom the autocratic Bill recognized as an equal,—who had just entered the bar-room. His dusty pongee cloak and soft hat indicated that he had that morning arrived on a round of inspection.

"Don't care if I do, Bill," he continued, in response to Bill's invitatory gesture, walking to the bar. "It's a little raw out on the road. Well, what were you saying about Ramon Martinez gang? You haven't come across one of 'em, have you?"

"No," said Bill, with a slight blinking of his eye, as he ostentatiously lifted his glass to the light.

"And you *won't*," added the Superintendent, leisurely sipping his liquor. "For the fact is, the gang is about played out. Not from want of a job now and then, but from the difficulty of disposing of the results of their work. Since the new instructions to the agents to identify and trace all dust and bullion offered to them went into force, you see, they can't get rid of their swag. All the gang are spotted at the offices, and it costs too much for them to pay a fence or a middleman of any standing. Why, all that flaky river gold they took from the Excelsior Company can be identified as easy as if it was stamped with the company's mark. They can't melt it down themselves; they can't get others to do it for them; they can't ship it to the Mint or Assay Offices in Marysville and 'Frisco, for they won't take it without our certificate and seals; and *we* don't take any undeclared freight *within* the lines that we've drawn around their beat, except from people and agents known. Why, *you* know that well enough, Jim," he said, suddenly appealing to the Expressman, "don't you?"

Possibly the suddenness of the appeal caused the Expressman to swallow his liquor the wrong way, for he was overtaken with a fit of coughing, and stammered hastily as he laid down his glass, "Yes—of course—certainly."

"No, sir," resumed the Superintendent cheerfully, "they're pretty well played out. And the best proof of it is that they've lately been robbing ordinary passengers' trunks. There was a freight wagon 'held up' near Dow's Flat the other day, and a lot of baggage gone through. I had to go down there to look into it. Darned if they hadn't lifted a lot o' woman's wedding things from that rich couple who got married the other day out at Marysville. Looks as if they were playing it rather low down, don't it? Coming down to hardpan and the bed rock—eh?"

The Expressman's face was turned anxiously towards Bill, who, after a hurried gulp of his remaining liquor, still stood staring at the window. Then he slowly drew on one of his large gloves. "Ye didn't," he said, with a slow, drawling, but perfectly distinct, articulation, "happen to know old 'Skinner' Hemmings when you were over there?"

"Yes."

"And his daughter?"

"He hasn't got any."

"A sort o' mild, innocent, guileless child of nature?" persisted Bill, with a yellow face, a deadly calm, and Satanic deliberation.

"No. I tell you he *hasn't* any daughter. Old man Hemmings is a confirmed old bachelor. He's too mean to support more than one."

"And you didn't happen to know any o' that gang, did ye?" continued Bill, with infinite protraction.

"Yes. Knew 'em all. There was French Pete, Cherokee Bob, Kanaka Joe, One-eyed Stillson, Softy Brown, Spanish Jack, and two or three Greasers."

"And ye didn't know a man by the name of Charley Byng?"

"No," returned the Superintendent, with a slight suggestion of weariness and a distraught glance towards the door.

"A dark, stylish chap, with shifty black eyes and a curled-up merstache?" continued Bill, with dry, colorless persistence.

"No. Look here, Bill, I'm in a little bit of a hurry—but I suppose you must have your little joke before we part. Now, what *is* your little game?"

"Wot you mean?" demanded Bill, with sudden brusqueness.

"Mean? Well, old man, you know as well as I do. You're giving me the very description of Ramon Martinez himself, ha! ha! No—Bill! you didn't play me this time. You're mighty spry and clever, but you didn't catch on just then."

He nodded and moved away with a light laugh. Bill turned a stony face to the Expressman. Suddenly a gleam of mirth came into his gloomy eyes. He bent over the young man, and said in a hoarse, chuckling whisper:—

"But I got even after all!"

"How?"

"He's tied up to that lying little she-devil, hard and fast!"

S. J. Perelman

STRICTLY FROM HUNGER

YES I was excited, and small wonder. What boy wouldn't be, boarding a huge, mysterious, puffing steam train for golden California? As Mamma adjusted my reefer and strapped on my leggings, I almost burst with impatience. Grinning redcaps lifted my luggage into the compartment and spat on it. Mamma began to weep into a small pillow-case she had brought along for the purpose.

"Oh, son, I wish you hadn't become a scenario writer!" she sniffled.

"Aw, now, Moms," I comforted her, "it's no worse than playing the piano in a call-house." She essayed a brave little smile, and, reaching into her reticule, produced a flat package which she pressed into my hands. For a moment I was puzzled, then I cried out with glee.

"Jelly sandwiches! Oh, Moms!"

"Eat them all, boy o' mine," she told me, "they're good for boys with hollow little legs." Tenderly she pinned to my lapel the green tag reading "To Plushnick Productions, Hollywood, California." The whistle shrilled and in a moment I was chugging out of Grand Central's dreaming spires followed only by the anguished cries of relatives who would now have to go to work. I had chugged only a few feet when I realized that I had left without the train, so I had to run back and wait for it to start.

As we sped along the glorious fever spots of the Hudson I decided to make a tour of inspection. To my surprise I found that I was in the only passenger car of the train; the other cars were simply dummies snipped out of cardboard and painted to simulate coaches. Even "passengers" had been cunningly drawn in colored crayons in the "window," as well as ragged tramps clinging to the blinds below and drinking Jamaica ginger. With a rueful smile I returned to my seat and gorged myself on jelly sandwiches.

At Buffalo the two other passengers and I discovered to our horror that the conductor had been left behind. We finally decided to divide up his duties; I punched the tickets, the old lady opposite me wore a conductor's hat and locked the washroom as we came into stations, and the young man who looked as if his feet were not mates consulted a Hamilton watch frequently. But we missed the conductor's earthy conversation and it was not until we had exchanged several questionable stories that we began to forget our loss.

A flicker of interest served to shorten the trip. At Fort Snodgrass, Ohio, two young and extremely polite road-agents boarded the train and rifled us of our belongings. They explained that they were modern Robin Hoods and were stealing from the poor to give to the rich. They had intended to rape all the women and depart for Sherwood Forest, but when I told them that Sherwood Forest as well as the women were in England, their chagrin was comical in the extreme. They declined my invitation to stay and take a chance on the train's pool, declaring that the engineer had fixed the run and would fleece us, and got off at South Bend with every good wish.

The weather is always capricious in the Middle West and although it was midsummer, the worst blizzard in Chicago's history greeted us on our arrival. The streets were crowded with thousands of newsreel cameramen trying to photograph one another bucking the storm on the Lake Front. It was a novel idea for the newsreels and I wished them well. With only two hours in Chicago I would be unable to see the city, and the thought drew me into a state of composure. I noted with pleasure that a fresh coat of grime had been given to the Dearborn Street station, though I was hardly vain enough to believe that it had anything to do with my visit. There was the usual ten-minute wait while the porters withdrew with my portable typewriter to a side room and flailed it with hammers, and at last I was aboard the "Sachem," crack train of the B.B.D. & O. lines.

It was as if I had suddenly been transported into another world. "General Crook," in whom I was to make my home for the next three days, and his two neighbors, "Lake Tahoe" and "Chief Malomai," were everything that the word "Pullman" implies; they were Pullmans. Uncle Eben, in charge of "General Crook," informed me that the experiment of air-cooling the cars had been so successful that the road intended trying to heat them next winter.

"Ah suttinly looks fo'd to dem roastin' ears Ah's gwine have next winter, he, he, he!" he chuckled, rubbing soot into my hat.

The conductor told me he had been riding on trains for so long that he had begun to smell like one, and sure enough, two brakemen waved their lanterns at him that night and tried to tempt him down a siding in Kansas City. We became good friends and it came as something of a blow when I heard the next morning that he had fallen off the train during the night. The fireman said that we had circled about for an hour trying to find him but that it had been impossible to lower a boat because we did not carry a boat.

The run was marked by only one incident out of the ordinary. I had ordered breaded veal cutlet the first evening, and my waiter, poking his head into the kitchen, had repeated the order. The cook, unfortunately, understood him to say "*dreaded* veal cutlet," and resenting the slur, sprang at the waiter with drawn razor. In a few seconds I was the only living remnant of the shambles, and at Topeka I was compelled to wait until a new shambles was hooked on and I proceeded with dinner.

It seemed only a scant week or ten days before we were pulling into Los Angeles. I had grown so attached to my porter that I made him give me a lock of his hair. I wonder if he still has the ten-cent piece I gave him? There was a gleam in his eye which could only have been insanity as he leaned over me. Ah, Uncle Eben, faithful old retainer, where are you now? Gone to what obscure ossuary? If this should chance to meet your kindly gaze, drop me a line care of *Variety*, won't you? They know what to do with it.

II

The violet hush of twilight was descending over Los Angeles as my hostess, Violet Hush, and I left its suburbs headed toward Hollywood. In the distance a glow of huge piles of burning motion-picture scripts lit up the sky. The crisp tang of frying writers and directors whetted my appetite. How good it was to be alive, I thought, inhaling deep lungfuls of carbon monoxide. Suddenly our powerful Gatti-Cazazza slid to a stop in the traffic.

"What is it, Jenkin?" Violet called anxiously through the speaking-tube to the chauffeur (played by Lyle Talbot).

A *suttee* was in progress by the roadside, he said—did we wish to see it? Quickly Violet and I elbowed our way through the crowd. An enormous funeral pyre composed of thousands of feet of film and scripts, drenched with Chanel Number Five, awaited the torch of Jack Holt, who was to act as master of ceremonies. In a few terse words Violet explained this unusual custom borrowed from the Hindus and never paid for. The worst disgrace that can befall a producer is an unkind notice from a New York reviewer. When this happens, the producer becomes a pariah in Hollywood. He is shunned by his friends, thrown into bankruptcy, and like a Japanese electing hara-kiri, he commits *suttee*. A great bonfire is made of the film, and the luckless producer, followed by directors, actors, technicians, and the producer's wives, immolate themselves. Only the scenario writers are exempt. These are tied between the tails of two spirited Caucasian ponies, which are then driven off in opposite directions. This custom is called "a conference."

Violet and I watched the scene breathlessly. Near us Harry Cohn, head of Columbia Studios, was being rubbed with huck towels preparatory to throwing himself into the flames. He was nonchalantly smoking a Rocky Ford five-center, and the man's courage drew a tear to the eye of even the most callous. Weeping relatives besought him to eschew his design, but he stood adamant. Adamant Eve, his plucky secretary, was being rubbed with crash towels preparatory to flinging herself into Cohn's embers. Assistant directors busily prepared spears, war-bonnets and bags of pemmican which the Great Chief would need on his trip to the "Happy Hunting Grounds." Wampas and beads to placate the Great Spirit (played by Will Hays) were piled high about the stoical tribesman.

Suddenly Jack Holt (played by Edmund Lowe) raised his hand for silence. The moment had come. With bowed head Holt made a simple invocation couched in one-syllable words so that even the executives might understand. Throwing his five-center to a group of autograph-hunters, the great man poised himself for the fatal leap. But from off-scene came the strident clatter of cocoanut shells, and James Agee, Filmdom's fearless critic, wearing the uniform of a Confederate guerrilla and the whiskers of General Beauregard, galloped in on a foam-flecked pinto. It was he whose mocking review had sent

Cohn into Coventry. It was a dramatic moment as the two stood pitted against each other—Cohn against Agee, the Blue against the Gray. But with true Southern gallantry Agee was the first to extend the hand of friendship.

"Ah reckon it was an unworthy slur, suh," he said in manly tones. "Ah-all thought you-all's pictuah was lousy but it opened at the Rialto to sensational grosses, an' Ah-all 'pologizes. Heah, have a yam." And he drew a yam from his tunic. Not to be outdone in hospitality, Cohn drew a yam from his tunic, and soon they were exchanging yams and laughing over the old days.

When Violet and I finally stole away to our waiting motor, we felt that we were somehow nearer to each other. I snuggled luxuriously into the buffalo lap-robe Violet had provided against the treacherous night air and gazed out at the gleaming neon lights. Soon we would be in Beverly Hills, and already the quaint native women were swarming alongside in their punts urging us to buy their cunning beadwork and mangoes. Occasionally I threw a handful of coppers to the Negro boys, who dove for them joyfully. The innocent squeals of the policemen as the small blackamoors pinched them were irresistible. Unable to resist them, Violet and I were soon pinching each other till our skins glowed. Violet was good to the touch, with a firm fleshy texture like a winesap or pippin. It seemed but a moment before we were sliding under the porte-cochère of her home, a magnificent rambling structure of beaverboard patterned after an Italian ropewalk of the sixteenth century. It had recently been remodeled by a family of wrens who had introduced chewing-gum into the left wing, and only three or four obscure Saxon words could do it justice.

I was barely warming my hands in front of the fire and watching Jimmy Fidler turn on a spit when my presence on the Pacific Slope made itself felt. The news of my arrival had thrown international financial centers into an uproar, and sheaves of wires, cables, phone messages, and even corn began piling up. An ugly rumor that I might reorganize the motion-picture industry was being bruited about in the world's commodity markets. My brokers, Whitelipped & Trembling, were beside themselves. The New York Stock Exchange was begging them for assurances of stability and Threadneedle Street awaited my next move with drumming pulses. Film shares ricocheted sharply, although wools and meats were sluggish, if not downright sullen. To the reporters who flocked around me I laughingly disclaimed that this was a business trip. I was simply a scenario writer to whom the idea of work was abhorrent. A few words murmured into the transatlantic telephone, the lift of an eyebrow here, the shrug of a shoulder there, and equilibrium was soon restored. I washed sparsely, curled my mustache with a heated hairpin, flicked a drop of Sheik Lure on my lapel, and rejoined my hostess.

After a copious dinner, melting-eyed beauties in lacy black under-things fought with each other to serve me kümmel. A hurried apology, and I was curled up in bed with the Autumn, 1927, issue of *The Yale Review*. Halfway through an exciting symposium on Sir Thomas Aquinas' indebtedness to Professors Whitehead and Spengler, I suddenly detected a stowaway blonde under the bed. Turning a deaf ear to her heartrending entreaties and burning glances, I sent her packing. Then I treated my face to a feast of skin food, buried my head in the pillow and went bye-bye.

III

Hollywood Boulevard! I rolled the rich syllables over on my tongue and thirstily drank in the beauty of the scene before me. On all sides nattily attired boulevardiers clad in rich stuffs strolled nonchalantly, inhaling cubebs and exchanging epigrams stolen from Martial and Wilde. Thousands of scantily draped but none the less appetizing extra girls milled past me, their mouths a scarlet wound and their eyes clearly defined in their faces. Their voluptuous curves set my blood on fire, and as I made my way down Mammary Lane, a strange thought began to invade my brain: I realized that I had not eaten breakfast yet. In a Chinese eatery cunningly built in the shape of an old shoe I managed to assuage the inner man with a chopped glove salad topped off with frosted cocoa. Charming platinum-haired hostesses in red pajamas and peaked caps added a note of color to the surroundings, whilst a gypsy orchestra played selections from Victor Herbert's operettas on musical saws. It was a bit of old Vienna come to life, and the sun was a red ball in the heavens before I realized with a start that I had promised to report at the Plushnick Studios.

Commandeering a taxicab, I arrived at the studio just in time to witness the impressive ceremony of changing the guard. In the central parade ground, on a snowy white charger, sat Max Plushnick, resplendent in a producer's uniform, his chest glittering with first mortgage liens, amortizations, and estoppels. His personal guard, composed of picked vice-presidents of the Chase National Bank, was drawn up stiffly about him in a hollow square.

But the occasion was not a happy one. A writer had been caught trying to create an adult picture. The drums rolled dismally, and the writer, his head sunk on his chest, was led out amid a ghastly silence. With the aid of a small stepladder Plushnick slid lightly from his steed. Sternly he ripped the epaulets and buttons from the traitor's tunic, broke his sword across his knee, and in a few harsh words demoted him to the mail department.

"And now," began Plushnick, "I further condemn you to eat . . ."

"No, no!" screamed the poor wretch, falling to his knees and embracing Plushnick's jackboots, "not that, not that!"

"Stand up, man," ordered Plushnick, his lip curling, "I condemn you to eat in the studio restaurant for ten days and may God have mercy on your soul." The awful words rang out on the still evening air and even Plushnick's hardened old mercenaries shuddered. The heartrending cries of the unfortunate were drowned in the boom of the sunset gun.

In the wardrobe department I was photographed, fingerprinted, and measured for the smock and Windsor tie which was to be my uniform. A nameless fear clutched at my heart as two impassive turnkeys herded me down a corridor to my supervisor's office. For what seemed hours we waited in an anteroom. Then my serial number was called, the leg-irons were struck off, and I was shoved through a door into the presence of Diana ffrench-Mamoulian.

How to describe what followed? Diana ffrench-Mamoulian was accustomed to having her way with writers, and my long lashes and peachblow mouth seemed to whip her to insensate desire. In vain, time and again, I tried to bring her attention back to the story we were discussing, only to find her gem-incrusted fingers straying through my hair. When our interview was over, her cynical attempt to "date me up" made every fiber of my being cry out in revolt.

"P-please," I stammered, my face burning, "I-I wish you wouldn't. . . . I'm engaged to a Tri Kappa at Goucher——"

"Just one kiss," she pleaded, her breath hot against my neck. In desperation I granted her boon, knowing full well that my weak defences were crumbling before the onslaught of this love tigree. Finally she allowed me to leave, but only after I had promised to dine at her penthouse apartment and have an intimate chat about the script. The basket of slave bracelets and marzipan I found awaiting me on my return home made me realize to what lengths Diana would go.

I was radiant that night in blue velvet tails and a boutonniere of diamonds from Cartier's, my eyes starry and the merest hint of cologne at my ear-lobes. An inscrutable Oriental served the Lucullan repast and my vis-à-vis was as effervescent as the wine.

"Have a bit of the wine, darling?" queried Diana solicitously, indicating the roast Long Island airplane with applesauce. I tried to turn our conversation from the personal note, but Diana would have none of it. Soon we were exchanging gay bantam over the mellow Vouvray, laughing as we dipped fastidious fingers into the Crisco parfait for which Diana was famous. Our meal finished, we sauntered into the rumpus room and Diana turned on the radio. With a savage snarl the radio turned on her and we slid over the waxed floor in the intricate maze of the jackdaw strut. Without quite knowing why, I found myself hesitating before the plate of liqueur candies Diana was pressing on me.

"I don't think I should—really, I'm a trifle faint——"

"Oh, come on," she urged masterfully. "After all, you're old enough to be your father—I mean I'm old enough to be my mother . . ." She stuffed a brandy bonbon between my clenched teeth. Before long I was eating them thirstily, reeling about the room and shouting snatches of coarse drunken doggerel. My brain was on fire, I tell you. Through the haze I saw Diana ffrench-Mamoulian, her nostrils dilated, groping for me. My scream of terror only egged her on, overturning chairs and tables in her bestial pursuit. With superhuman talons she tore off my collar and suspenders. I sank to my knees, choked with sobs, hanging on to my last shirt-stud like a drowning man. Her Svengali eyes were slowly hypnotizing me; I fought like a wounded bird—and then blissful unconsciousness.

When I came to, the Oriental servant and Diana were battling in the center of the floor. As I watched, Yen Shee Gow drove a well-aimed blow to her mid-section, following it with a right cross to the jaw. Diana staggered and rolled under a table. Before my astonished eyes John Chinaman stripped the mask from his face and revealed the features of Blanche Almonds a little seamstress I had long wooed unsuccessfully in New York. Gently she bathed my temples with Florida water and explained how she had followed me, suspecting Diana ffrench-Mamoulian's intentions. I let her rain kisses over my face and lay back in her arms as beaming Ivan tucked us in and cracked his whip over the prancing bays. In a few seconds our sleigh was skimming over the hard crust toward Port Arthur and freedom, leaving Plushnick's discomfited officers gnashing one another's teeth. The wintry Siberian moon glowed over the tundras, drenching my hair with moonbeams for Blanche to kiss away. And so, across the silvery steppes amid the howling of wolves, we rode into a new destiny, purified in the crucible that men call Hollywood.

John O'Hara

LIFE AMONG THESE
UNFORGETTABLE CHARACTERS

The constant rediscovery by Americans of lovable, unforgettable American characters is a challenge to any American writer. Up to now this writer has done little or nothing about it, but this condition could not long endure. The following, therefore, is submitted as the author's attempt to participate in the movement, or trend. It is sloppily written chiefly because the author was unable to decide whether to do the piece as a magazine article, a revue sketch, or a script for a motion-picture short. Any resemblance to real persons, living or dead, is fortuitous. The Author.

IT WAS with sighs of relief that Mr. and Mrs. Mort pulled up to the filling station. They had been told upon leaving the town of X—— that the tank of their Lincoln Continental convertible would hold enough gas to get them to the town of Y—— but that it would be a good idea to make a stop at Arthur James Witherspoon's filling station, the only filling station between X—— and Y——. It was pointed out (unnecessarily, since Mr. and Mrs. Mort were experienced motorists) that when driving in the desert it is a wise thing now and then to halt, let some of the air out of your tires, stretch your legs, wash up, see to the gas and oil and water, and inquire as to the condition of the highway. Driving fatigue is thus lessened, and the motorcar itself is in better shape for continuing the journey. Unfortunately, upon leaving the town of X——, the Morts observed a sign that read, "90 MI TO ARTHUR JAMES WITHERSPOON'S," and then ten miles farther another sign that said the same thing. Mr. Mort was doing the driving and he hoped his medium young and attractive wife had not noticed the sign but she had, all right. The third sign they saw reminded them that the next filling station was that of Arthur James Witherspoon, but gave no estimate of the distance. One thing the Morts knew: when they came upon a filling station it would be the only one, and it would be the one conducted by Arthur James Witherspoon.

The Morts kept an eye on the gas gauge and the speedometer and had a fairly unpleasant time trying to recall what mileage they got on a gallon at what speed, and Mr. Mort, with his somewhat vague technical information, had the added worry about the effect of altitude on gasoline consumption. Unhappily, he could not recall whether you used more, or less, gasoline at high altitudes, and moreover he was not sure whether this particular desert was one of the high-altitude deserts or low ones.

The result was that he had chewed the inside of his cheek to the point where he was developing another salivary gland when, in the distance about fifteen miles, he saw what could only be the filling station of Arthur James Witherspoon. He knew about mirages and suspected one, but when he turned to his wife she smiled; she, too, had seen the filling station, or what could only be the filling station. Praise God, they were right in their assumption.

When, some twelve or thirteen minutes later, they pulled up to the establishment of Arthur James Witherspoon, they at first saw no human being. But a moment after they stopped they saw an elderly man who had been half hidden by a rain barrel. He was sitting on a bench. Across his lap was an old .22 rifle, a Winchester octagonal-barrel pump gun. He wore a pair of levis and a blue shirt, both well bleached, a pair of white-and-brown saddle straps, and one of those cream-colored hats with half-inch bands that are affected by Westerners. The shoes were without laces. The man had what might be called a reluctant sunburn. His face and hands and arms were indeed sunburned, but not with the smoothness of the tan that indicates oils and lotions. He was sunburned because, in the desert, you just can't help it.

With the instinctive, well-mannered democracy that had got him into the Vine at Princeton, Mr. Mort called out to the elderly gentleman. "Howdy," he said.

"Hi ya," said the old gentleman.

"Fill 'er up," said Mr. Mort.

"Fill 'er up yourself," said the old gentleman.

Mr. Mort, as was his right, lightly punched his wife's thigh. "A character," he said, without moving his lips. Then, "Howdy," he repeated, starting to get out of the car. "Fill 'er up."

This time the old gentleman scratched himself and said, "I heard *you* the first time. Fill 'er up yourself."

"Oh," said Mr. Mort. He got out of the car and took the cap off the pipe leading to the tank of his car and unhooked the hose of the pump. He inserted the nozzle in the tank and then turned to Mr. Witherspoon. "Now what?" he asked.

"Just squeeze 'er, like a trigger. You seen it done a thousand times," said Mr. Witherspoon.

Mr. Mort smiled with almost boyish pleasure; he had seen it done a thousand times, but he never had done it himself. It came easy to him, and the fuel began pouring in the tank. The fun of it partly took away from his chagrin at Mr. Witherspoon's reception.

Mr. Witherspoon now seemed unaware of the presence of his clients, and when Mrs. Mort got out of the car and said, "Where can I wash my hands, please?" Mr. Witherspoon said, "Don't do much washin' here. We're in the desert. You wanta gota the toilet . . ." and he half turned his head in the direction of the back of the filling station.

Mrs. Mort started in that direction, but before she had gone very far Mr. Witherspoon said, "Look out for rattlers."

Mrs. Mort froze. "What?"

"You better look out for snakes. I try to keep them off the place, but I can't be everywhere." With that he raised his rifle and aimed at a spot just inside the clearing. He fired, pumped, and fired again. Mr. and Mrs. Mort looked toward the spot at which he had aimed. A five-foot rattlesnake lay quivering and forever ineffectual. "Most likely be anothern along soon, unless she's in the toilet." To Mr. Mort he said, "Your wife wants to gota the toilet. Take that stick."

Mr. Mort, who had paused in the fuelling of his car, said, "She doesn't need any stick to—"

"She don't, but maybe the she-rattler's in there. I don't know. Suit yourself."

"Oh," said Mr. Mort. He replaced the pump hose and took the stick and preceded his wife to the rest room. While he was gone he heard another shot, and when he came back he said to Mr. Witherspoon, "Get the other one?"

"Nup," said Mr. Witherspoon.

"Missed her, eh?"

"Nup. Wasn't shootin' at anything."

"You weren't *shooting* at anything? I thought I heard you fire the gun."

"Rifle," said Mr. Witherspoon.

"I mean rifle. I was sure I heard you fire it, the rifle."

"You did, but that don't say I was shootin' at anything."

"Oh," said Mr. Mort, pretending to understand. "Guess I'll let some air out of the tires. Can I borrow a gauge?"

"In there in the creel, on my cot."

"Creel? Any fishing around here?" said Mr. Mort. He was speaking with the enthusiasm of a fisherman, but tolerantly incredulous as well.

"You look in that creel, you'll find a pair of dice, too, but I don't shoot crap with myself. You wanta borrow a gauge, it's in the creel."

Mr. Mort found the gauge and went about the business of letting some air out of the tires.

While her husband was thus engaged, Mrs. Mort reappeared and sauntered up to Mr. Witherspoon. "My, it must get awfully lonely here. Do you get to town often?"

"Evvy Christmas," said Mr. Witherspoon.

"What?"

"Never miss a Christmas in town. Nineteen year now. Wouldn't think of missing a Christmas in town."

"Oh, really? I imagine the radio must be a great consolation here. I see you have one."

"Wouldn't be without it," said Mr. Witherspoon. "Forty-eight, we'll send that Truman back to Missouri, where he belongs, him and the rest of 'em. Yes, sir, I listen to all them campaigns."

"Well, I hope you're right. My husband and I are Republicans, too."

"Y'are? Hmm. Well, I don't ask a person their politics or religion or where they come from. Uh-uh. There she comes." He raised his rifle, fired, and lowered it. "There she goes." A second rattlesnake bit the dust.

"Oh! Good shot!" said Mrs. Mort.

"The othern wasn't. Took two. Skins ain't worth as much when you got two bullet holes in 'em," said Mr. Witherspoon. He pulled out an old hunting-case watch, studied it, looked toward the sun, and nodded. "Watch is right," he said, and frowned. "Say, Ma'am, your husband's probly gonna want to clean the windshield. Why don't you do it for him while he's fooling around with them tires? Rag over there. Water in that bottle. Don't waste the water."

"Oh, let him do it. I'd just like to sit and talk for a few minutes."

"Too late now," said Mr. Witherspoon. "Thu'll be a truck along here now pretty soon and I don't like to have the place all cluttered up with cars and people, where I can't give the proper attention to evvabody. You just take that rag and wipe them bugs off the windshield and you'll be outa here that much sooner."

Mrs. Mort did as she was told, greatly to the surprise and delight of her husband, who regretted that he was unable to see the expression on her face as she removed the corpses of insects from the windshield. He asked Mr. Witherspoon how much he owed him.

Mr. Witherspoon squinted and stared at the pump. "Looks like two forty-eight from here."

"That's about it," said Mr. Mort.

"Two forty-eight. That's four ninety-six. Make it five dollars."

"Five dollars?" said Mr. Mort.

"Well, four ninety-six, then, if you object to paying the extra four cents."

"It's not the four cents I object to. It's the extra two forty-eight. What's that for?"

"Double. I charge everything double here. In the desert it's worth it. Put your two forty-eight in the tank, bub, and your car won't run very far on it. I got the gazzoline, so—well, what's the use explaining matters?"

"I see," said Mr. Mort. He took a ten-dollar bill from his wallet.

Mr. Witherspoon looked at it. "In the desk inside, top drawer, you'll find some fives and singles. Get your change there and put the ten in the second drawer with the twenties and fifties. Hate to hurry you, but I got another customer almost due about now."

"I wish you'd make the change yourself. I don't like to handle somebody else's money."

"Why, I trust you, bub. Anyhow, you can't get very far on the desert. Only one road, bub, next town fifty-five mile from here."

"I see," said Mr. Mort. He did as instructed and then joined his wife in the car. Mr. Mort was now disagreeable. He started the motor, and as he was pulling away he heard the voice of Mr. Witherspoon.

"Hurry back," said Mr. Witherspoon, and looked again at his watch.

Will Rogers

IT'S TIME SOMEBODY SAID
A WORD FOR CALIFORNIA

I ATTENDED a dinner the other morning given for the Old Settlers of California. No one was allowed to attend unless he had been in the State 2 and one-half years.

I was the last speaker on the Menu. They put me last, figuring everybody would either be asleep or gone by the time I began.

Well sir, do you know, by the time it got to me there was nothing left to talk on! But I just happened to notice that in all the other speeches no one had mentioned California, so as that was all I had left I just had to go ahead and do the best I could with California.

Now, it ain't much of a speech but it is at least a novelty, because in all my time out here I had never heard the subject used before at any Dinners or Luncheons.

Mr. Toastmaster, Ladies and Gentlemen, and Members of the Old California Settlers Association: Your previous speakers have taken up so much time boosting and praising other States and their People that it is now most daylight, and I am at a loss to pick a subject, but at the last minute I just happened to remember that no one had said a word for California. So I will take up this very remote subject and see if I can't do something to drag it out of the obscurity in which it has been placed here tonight.

Being one of your old Timers (I have been a resident of this State now for nearly 4 years; there is only one other older member in the organization) I want to say right here that you often hear it said, "What is the matter with California?" Well, I will tell you what is the matter—it's MODESTY, that's what it is, too much MODESTY.

If we got out and blew our own Horns and Advertised and boosted our State like Delaware, and Rhode Island have, we wouldn't be so little heard of. So, whether you like it or not fellow Statesmen, I for one am going to throw Modesty to the winds and just tell the World off-hand a few of the things that we have got out here.

Now, just picking subjects at random, what do you suppose we could do if we wanted to say something about CLIMATE? Why, that item alone would draw people here. But what do we do? We just set here and say nothing. We go out of the State and we are so darn generous that all we do is brag on the place where we are. We never think of handing our own State a little free advertising.

But you take, as I say, a fellow from Delaware, and he is preaching Delaware and all its advantages from the time you meet him till you leave him, and by golly, it pays to do that. Look at Delaware today! So never mind this old good fellow spirit of giving the other fellow the best of it. I believe in throwing in a little boost for the old Native Heath.

Now I know you other members don't agree with me and think that we should think of our proud traditions and not stoop so low as to have to advertise but I tell you that this day and time is a commercial Age, and we have got to throw our Pride away and let the World know just what we have here.

There is no reason why other People from neighboring States shouldn't know of our Climate. Why keep it hid? It's here. We got it. They can't take it away with them.

Of course, I will admit that we have done a little good in a small way with Picture Post Cards. Five years ago Iowa was a prosperous and satisfied State. They had no idea of leaving. They had shoveled snow for 5 months every year and figured they would always shovel snow 5 months every year. But finally one day a Twenty Dollar Bill come into the State and a Farmer wanted to get change for it, so he started out trying to get it changed and wound up in Long Beach, California.

A fellow selling Roses in January changed it for him, and when the Farmer pulled off his Mittens to count the change he found that it was warm and he didn't have to put the mittens back on again. That made quite a hit with him and he decided to stay awhile. So he sent a Picture Post Card back with the Picture of a Man Picking Oranges off the trees in January, and told them how fine it was and everybody that read the Post Card, including the Postmaster come on out.

So when they came they sent back Picture Post Cards to all their Friends who liked Oranges, and in time they came too, and so on, each newcomer bringing out just as many more as he could afford

Post Cards. Now in the short space of 5 years look what has happened. The whole of the State of Iowa is here. The only ones left back there are the ones who can't read the Post Cards, or People who don't care for Oranges, and now I see where they have put in Schools to teach those others to read so that means we will eventually have them all, with the exception of the ones who don't like Oranges.

Now, as I say, if all of that can be done with just Picture Post Cards, what do you suppose could have been done if the Newspapers of our State had thought to have said something in praise of our Climate? So, Fellow Old Timers, if we can get the grand State of Iowa out here on a Picture Post Card of an Orange Tree, what could we do with some of these other States if we really devoted a little of our time to it!

Why, Oranges are a small time commodity with us. We raise more Beans on one farm here without Irrigating than we do Oranges in the whole State. If we had Picture Post Cards of Bean Fields instead of Orange Fields we could get the whole of Boston here the same as we did with Iowa. You will do even better with Boston than you did with Iowa because everybody there likes Beans. So let's get busy and let them know what we are doing in the Bean line.

Take the case of Oil. You all know we struck Oil here in Southern California. But did you let anybody else know it? No, you didn't say a word about it, and as a consequence, a man can't even find a place to buy an Oil Stock. Now there are lots of People would buy shares and Units, but no, you are so darn MODEST you won't let the World know what we have.

I would like to have seen what Delaware would have done if they had found this much Oil. They would have sold so much Stock that if the Pacific Ocean had been Oil it wouldn't have paid back the Buyers.

Look at Real Estate. Here we have the greatest Land and Lots that ever laid out of doors, but do we do anything with them? No! We just set here. We never advertise them; we never boost them. I wish you could see what the State of Delaware would do if they had the same class of lots that we have here. Why they would have Sub-Divisions all over the place. They would have Barbecues, and Drawings, and Scream Stars personally appearing, and men under umbrellas selling each lot. But no, we are too conservative; we like to sit here and let the stuff speak for itself. But I tell you, Fellow Old Timers, you can't do that nowadays. It's all right for a State to build up a Reputation for Modesty and be known as always having a good word to say for the other place, but I tell you we have carried it too far for our own good.

Of course I can appreciate you other old Timers' feelings in the matter. You have been here and helped build it to what it even is today, and you resent these Johnny Newcomers coming in and spoiling all of our old customs and Traditions. I know it is hard to change with the Times. We old Timers who have seen this place grow from what it was 2 and a half years ago to what it is today, must realize these stacks of young fellows coming in here the last two weeks must have the right idea, and we must begin to realize that after all it is the general welfare of the entire community we are after.

So, Fellow Members, if my little speech has been the means of changing just one of you from your Iron Clad rule of Modesty in regard to your Home state, why I will feel that my little efforts will not have been in vain.

So from now on I am for letting the World know of California, even if the rest of the State does disapprove of it, and I sit down amid HISSES from the MODEST Oldtimers.

Robert Lewis Taylor

AN EXCERPT FROM
W. C. FIELDS:
HIS FOLLIES AND FORTUNES

EARLY in his *Follies* career, W. C. Fields met Billy Grady, an agent, who was to represent him and travel with him off and on for fourteen years. Grady retains many vivid impressions of Fields, most of them quite sour. "Bill cheated me continuously throughout our association," he says. "He was the closest man with a dollar I ever met." Despite their endless wrangles over money, Grady stayed on, he thinks, because he was fascinated by the bizarre character of his client. "For sheer, unadulterated gall, Bill stood alone," Grady says. "He wasn't happy if he wasn't involved in a scrap of some kind. He thought everybody was trying to skin him, so he tried to skin them first. But he had class—I'll say that. Bill had class. His most larcenous acts were marked by a sort of brilliant dash."

During one period, when he was between contracts, Fields began to get uneasy. He had a mortal fear of unemployment; the threat of it almost drove him crazy. At the time, he and Grady were living in a sizable suite at the Hotel Astor. As he pondered his situation, Fields quickly saw that his salvation lay in accident insurance. He dropped into an insurance office and took out a big policy, with a remunerative clause about unemployment. Then he returned to the Astor, called the company doctor, and went to bed.

"What in the hell are you doing, you old goat?" asked Grady when he came in. (The relationship between the comedian and his agent was distinguished by an uninterrupted and rather abrasive exchange of billingsgate.)

"I've sprained my back," said Fields, regarding Grady steadily with his little frosty blue eyes. "The doctor's coming. Take a seat over in the corner."

The doctor arrived a few minutes later and conducted a search for symptoms.

"Where does it hurt?" he said.

"All over," Fields told him.

"How'd it happen?"

"I was juggling some chairs," Fields said.

The doctor took his temperature again and went over his back with a small rubber hammer. Then he said, "I'll have to come back at five o'clock. I need more equipment."

"When do the payments start?"

"See you around five," the doctor said, and left.

Fields and Grady had been playing handball in their living room for several days, for a dollar a game, and Fields was twelve dollars ahead. As soon as the doctor left, he arose and suggested that they continue. They played steadily until five o'clock, when Fields quit and got back in bed. He just made it. The doctor turned up and took his temperature again. By now, because of the exertion—Grady had been winning—Fields was overheated and sweaty.

"A singular case," the doctor said, reading the thermometer. "Your temperature seems to have gone up."

"Complete disability," Fields agreed, with a noisy rattle in his voice.

Greatly mystified, the doctor went over the patient's back with several additional instruments. He said he was having trouble locating the sprain, an ailment which, like beauty, sometimes exists largely in the eye of the sprainee, so to speak. "It may be going into something else, such as pneumonia or lockjaw," said the doctor.

He added that he would make a report right away, with the usual recommendations, and he left, with a worried look.

Fields got up again, threw off his robe, and said to Grady, "Now, damn you, let's get back at that handball." He served, and the game resumed.

At this point the doctor threw the door open and yelled, "Aha! I thought so, you faker!" He ducked back as Fields threw a lamp at him, then fled down the stairs.

"Bill was hopping mad for days," Grady says. "He took the attitude that he'd been defrauded. About a week later he said, 'I knew that insurance company was no good the minute I stuck my head in their door.'"

Fields' reaction to things was sometimes hard to figure out, according to Grady. Once when he was making out his income tax—an operation that put him in a blistering humor—Grady came in and looked over the papers. "Why, you can't deduct those things, you crook!" Grady said. "They'll put you in jail. How the hell can I make a living representing an inmate of a federal penitentiary?"

Fields ordered him out of the room and continued to sift the air for deductions. "He was too stingy to hire a lawyer," Grady says. "Besides, he was pretty sure the lawyers were secretly working for the government. I went in my room and sat down, but I was concerned. He was including things like depreciation on vaudeville houses where he'd played, salaries for ball rackers, and donations to churches in the Solomon Islands."

Fields completed his return, filed it with a look of satisfied pride, and continued with his engagements. "A few months later," says Grady, "he got a check from the government for $1100. They said he'd overcharged himself. I thought he'd blow up and crow about it, but he almost went out of his mind. He kept yelling, 'Think! *Think* of all the things I could have taken off in years past!'"

In this period of his *Follies* celebrity Fields took a fondness for big motor cars. "With anything of that sort he was far from stingy," Grady says. "He bought the most expensive cars, clothes, food, and so on he could find. It was mainly in his dealings with people that he began to act like a miser. But he wasn't consistent even with that. There were times when he'd sit in a restaurant all night rather than pick up the check. Other times, he wouldn't let anybody buy as much as a cigar. Bill was full of paradoxes." Fields' first car was a seven-passenger, custom-built Cadillac. He had the salesman from whom he bought it investigated by a detective agency. The man's record seemed to be all right, barring a few domestic spats, and Fields paid him in cash, but he insisted on getting a receipt signed in the presence of several witnesses, including a bootblack he brought in from the street. When the garage owner asked if he could drive, he said, with the kind of injured pomp that was making him famous, "I've been driving professionally since I was ten," or several years before automobiles were available. He added that his father had owned one of the first cars in Philadelphia, a purposeless lie. The garage people were relieved that he could drive. They shook hands with him and thanked him for the sale; then he got in the car and went about two hundred yards down the street, where he hit a parked laundry truck. He bawled out the driver, returned to the garage, and had a crushed fender repaired, while he delivered a mendacious account of how the laundryman had backed out of a driveway, at forty miles an hour, and hit him on the opposite side of the street. Although Fields had forked over $5000 cash for the car, he refused to pay a cent for repairs. He took the stand that the garage was liable until he got the automobile home. Before he left the second time, the garage people insisted on teaching him how to drive.

"Bill developed into a wonderful driver," Grady says. "He had, of course, natural co-ordination, and he was strong and athletic besides. He drove fast, took chances, and got into frequent arguments. During my fourteen years as his agent, I never knew him to be wrong. If he went around a curve, jumped up on a parkway and ran into a man's front porch, he'd find some reason why the house shouldn't have been there."

It was not hard for Fields to take on persecution complexes, and he managed a neat one about road hogs. Within six months after he bought the Cadillac he was convinced that 90 per cent of the people driving other cars were after his particular scalp. He rolled down the highway with a malevolent eye fixed on the opposite lane, ready to lock horns at the slightest hostile move. This bias, like most of his personal feelings, seeped into his work. In the movie If I Had a Million he worked out a sketch which represented one of his dreams of long standing. The plot directed that a number of persons, including Charles Laughton, Fields, Charles Ruggles, and George Raft, be capriciously given a million dollars by an elderly, cynical millionaire, who then studied the use each recipient made of the money. Most of the actors were content to abide by the ideas of the script writers; Fields conceived his own distribution of the windfall. Laughton, an obscure clerk for a corporation, walked humbly through several anterooms, to deliver a long pent-up Bronx cheer to his boss; Raft found himself in a position, as a hunted man, in which he couldn't cash his check without being caught; and Ruggles, in an immensely satisfying scene, smashed all the fragile wares in a high-class china shop where he'd worked for twenty-odd years. Fields, with Allison Skipworth, went to a secondhand car lot and bought a collection of wrecks, then asked the proprietor, "Can you furnish me some strong, brave drivers?" When his armored column was complete, he wheeled out onto the highways looking for trouble. "As Bill sat hunched down in that old Ford with his straw hat on, he looked just the way he always looked driving a car—mean as the devil," one of his friends says. It was a sketch that put the comedian in a roseate humor for weeks. In the movie he would sight a stranger getting across the line and hold up one hand, like a cavalry commander. One of his strong, brave drivers would wheel out of column, knock hell out of the offender, and the column would proceed to the next enemy of society. Fields himself hit two or three cars, for various breaches of conduct. His expression, as he rammed them, was demoniac in its glee, and he voiced a high, exultant, rallying cry as the fenders dropped.

During the *Follies*, too, Fields sharpened his taste for liquor. He had become discriminating; he wanted only the choicest brands. Consequently, he bought a third wardrobe trunk, had it fitted out with pigeonholes like a wine cellar, and stocked it with high-test beverages. He took it along wherever he went. Later on he decided he was carrying too many clothes, and he devoted another trunk to liquor. This balance working out about right—two trunks full of booze and one of equipment—he made it his standard traveling impedimenta for years. Even when he and Grady moved between engagements by car, he took one of the dispensaries in the back seat.

Once, when they were driving to Boston in the winter, Fields swerved to miss some children who were coasting, and struck a Ford. The Ford's driver, a farmer, was badly dazed. Fields offered to take care of him while Grady walked to a police station. "Bill had his trunk in the back and had been drinking a little," Grady says, "but I hadn't had a drink all evening. I found a sergeant named O'Malley at the station and we fell into a pleasant discussion about the Church. I figured we were going to get off scot-free. The sergeant was sympathetic when he heard about the crash. He said those things were sometimes unavoidable. I was about ready to leave when Fields and the farmer burst in through the door. They were both lit up to the sky. Bill had spent half an hour getting him drunk. When he saw me, he yelled, 'What are you doing, you Irish bum?' The sergeant thought he meant him and threw all three of us in jail. It cost us fifty dollars apiece. Bill made me pay the farmer's fine out of my own pocket. He said I'd handled it undiplomatically."

Grady was driving the car through the South one night while Fields sat in the back seat on the trunk. The comedian was drinking what he described as "martinis"; he had a bottle of gin in one hand and a bottle of vermouth in the other, and he took alternate pulls, favoring the gin. At an intersection in a country town they saw a man with a satchel making signals under a street lamp. Grady said, "Fellow wants a ride."

"Pick him up," cried Fields. "Where's your sense of charity?"

Grady slowed down, called out, "Hop in the back," and waited till the man got aboard. As they drove off, Fields extended the gin bottle to him, but the man refused, with a look of offended piety. About five miles down the road the stranger took some tracts out of his coat pocket and said, "Brothers, I'm a minister of the gospel."

Fields blew a mouthful of gin on the floor and the man went on, "You're sinning in this automobile and though I don't ordinarily do no free preaching, I'm going to preach a free sermon right here." He examined the tracts and added, "To tell you the truth, I'm a-going to give you Number Four."

"What's Number Four?" said Fields.

"Called the 'Evils of Alcohol,' " said the minister.

Fields leaned forward and said to Grady, "Pull up beside the first ditch you see."

The minister's narrative had reached a point where a roustabout had pawned his small daughter's shoes to raise money for a drink when Grady slammed on the brakes. "*Aus! Aus!*" Fields began to cry, harking back to his German period, and he kicked the minister into the ditch. Then he opened his trunk, removed an unopened bottle of gin, and tossed it down beside him. "There's my Number Three," he yelled. "Called 'How to Keep Warm in a Ditch.' "

Grady drove on. Fields told him afterward that he'd suspected the minister might be a Methodist. He'd had a lot of trouble with Methodists, he said, but he refused to describe it in detail.

Fields loved to motor through the South. He admired the Southern customs and traditions. He had a story, which shifted from month to month, about a terrible fight he got into with a crossing watchman. "I was on my way to Homosassa, Florida," he would say, dwelling lovingly on the name. ("That was probably a lie right there," Grady says. "He just liked the name Homosassa. He managed to ring it in every time he mentioned Florida.") Fields said he was en route to Homosassa on a fishing expedition and, on a back road, came on a blocked railroad crossing—a spur line grown up with weeds. There was a shack about twenty yards down the track. He stopped, and a watchman strolled up leisurely.

"You expecting a train?" Fields asked.

"Why, no," said the watchman, knocking the tops off some weeds with a stick. "I can't rightly say that I am."

"Not expecting one, hey?" said Fields.

"No. We only get a train along here on Tuesdays and Thursdays."

"Unless I'm mistaken," said Fields, "this is Wednesday. Why the hell have you got the gate down?"

"Well, they've been known to turn up early," said the watchman.

"Open that damned gate," roared Fields.

"My suggestion would be to try it on the main road. Used to be, they didn't put the gate down only on Tuesdays and Thurdays, but I hain't been up that way in three or four year."

Fields said he gave the man an average cursing and got out to do battle. The fellow was tougher than he looked. With his face fixed in a mournful, resigned expression, he hit Fields alongside the head with his stick every time Fields swung. "It's my bounden duty to pertect railroad prop'ty," he'd say, and, using his stick skillfully, duck a haymaker.

"I finally had to trip him up and brain him with a rock." Fields said later. "Then I tore down the crossing gate and went on to Homosassa. It was a nerve-racking experience for me." In other accounts, he said that he'd also destroyed the watchman's shack before he left and that he'd "put to rout" a large section gang that had come to the man's aid.

Fields prided himself on his knowledge of Southern history. He always tied it up with his own experiences. He could explain the entire South by means of a few personal observations. One time at his Hollywood home he got into a brisk argument with a college professor, a "doctor" of history, who was outlining the technical reasons why Sherman had got through to the sea, with statistics on such things as logistics, ordnance, lines of communication, and so on. Fields rejected the explanation, substituting a theory of his own. It hinged on deliberation. "They move in slow motion down there," he said. "I studied Sherman's march—read a lot of books about it—and the reason he made it was because Southern troops didn't get up till around noon, and most of them had breakfast in bed." Later on it developed that Fields was still smarting from a near-escape he'd once had from a Southern railroad accident. Driving through Georgia with Grady and a girl, he skidded on a railroad track and came to rest crossways on the rails. The car refused to start. They worked at it apprehensively for five minutes or so and a cracker came along in a wagon.

"A train ever pass along here?" Fields asked.

The man pulled out an Ingersoll watch, studied it, shook it, looked at the sun, wound his watch, and said, "The six-fifteen's due right now."

"Well, get a rope!" Fields yelled. "Pull me out of here."

The man climbed down from his wagon and tied his horse to a sapling, after which he got an old curtain out of the wagon and put it over the horse's back to keep off the flies. Then he found a piece of rope. He ambled over to the car, sat down on the front bumper, and, while he untied a knot in the end of the rope, asked pleasantly, "Yawl from the Nawth?"

Fields, who was in back of the car, futilely shoving, screamed at him to quit talking and hurry, and the man tied the rope on. Then he untied his horse, put the curtain back in the bed, led the horse over, and fixed the other end of the rope to the wagon.

The horse leaned half-heartedly into the traces, but the car still stuck fast. They heard a train whistle far down the tracks.

"She's coming!" Fields screamed. "We'll have to lighten the load." He and Grady started tossing out objects like press booklets, hampers, rugs, the girl, borrowed watermelons, and even liquor.

By now the cracker was down with an ear to a rail. "Yes, sir," he said, straightening up, "she sure is coming."

The train, an antediluvian shambles, came clanking around a curve at about fifteen miles an hour and stopped. The engineer and fireman got out deliberately. They introduced themselves, chatted a few minutes, and shoved the car back onto the road.

As the engine labored off down the tracks, the cracker permitted himself an observation. "I figured they wasn't any use gittin' worked up," he said. "We might as well wait till we got some he'p."

Nearly everywhere he went in the South, Fields ran into alligators. He had a fixation on the subject. Often, he said, he came dangerously close to being eaten. To hear him tell it, the entire South was overrun by alligators, most of which had a strong personal grudge against him. Grady believes that Fields actually did encounter one alligator in the South, at a time when he was driving through with Grady and a lady passenger. The day was warm and the lady wanted a drink. Fields pulled up beside a rotting farmhouse and made inquiries.

"You'll have to go down to the spring," said the farmer, rousing himself from a nap on the front porch and pointing to the path through the woods.

Fields took a thermos bottle and stepped down to the spring, "about a two-day trip by pack train," he said later. "I figured they'd have to get me out with bloodhounds."

He eventually found the spring, a rivulet of fresh water that trickled into a rusty, sunken kettle and then into a slough. But as he leaned over to dip in the thermos, an alligator coughed and slid off a log on the bank near by.

"We heard a dreadful cry and Bill came running out of the woods, white as a sheet," Grady says. "The thermos was missing and he was yelling, 'Start up the motor! Start up the motor!' It took a long time to get him quieted down."

It was not uncommon for Fields to be bullied by animals other than dogs. His trouble with a swan, later on in Hollywood, was notorious. He had rented a large establishment on Toluca Lake, a body of water inhabited by a peevish, noisy, outsized white swan, which took an instant dislike to Fields. Mary Brian, Bing Crosby, and Richard Arlen, who had houses on the lake, recall many interesting sights of the comedian fitted out for combat. For several days after he moved in, the swan would catch him near the shore and chase him back to his house. Then Fields got a cane with a curved handle and took to hiding in the reeds near the water. He would produce noises that he fancied were recognizable as authentic swan talk, and, when the bird came in to investigate, he would rush out and try to get the cane around its neck.

"Mr. Fields was sure enough scared of that swan," one of his former servants says. "Almost every time they met, he wound up runnin'."

After three or four futile brushes with the cane, he decided on heavier ordnance, and he switched to a golf club, selecting a number-four iron. The bird showed considerable respect for the iron, and Fields went on the offensive. He bought a canoe and chased the swan all over the lake every day. But no matter how hard he paddled, the bird managed to stay out in front. It was hot work, and Fields, on one occasion, lay back to rest and get his strength up. He dozed off, and the swan circled around, like Nelson at Trafalgar, and fell on him from the rear.

The comedian returned home in a homicidal humor. He stormed around the house trying to enlist sympathy for his cause. "The god-damned bird broke all the rules of civilized warfare," he kept saying. He got a revolver and loaded it up, but one of his household talked him into sticking to the golf club.

Grady cannot be too profuse in his praise of Fields' driving. One time during prohibition the comedian heard that a friend on Long Island had just received two cases of contraband Irish whisky. He and Grady drove out immediately. They and the friend spent the night making sure the government would be unable to recover part of the whisky, at least, and Fields and Grady left for home around dawn. Owing to their host's generosity, they took five or six quarts along with them, externally. Both Fields and Grady later recalled that it was snow-ing when they left, and they settled down for an exhausting drive. En route they took frequent pulls at the whisky and remarked at the surprising length of Long Island. Their heads were pretty fuzzy during the trip. They put in at filling stations now and then, gassed up, and sought information about the route. However, in response to a ques-tion like "How far's the Queensboro Bridge?" the attendants would only laugh, or stare stupidly. Also, as time wore on, the travelers got the cloudy impression that many people they talked to were essaying dia-lects, for some reason. "I don't recollect no place name of Man-hasset," a man would tell them, and they would applaud, then careen on down the road, drinking his health. Their heads finally cleared, and Grady found himself looking out of a window at a palm tree. They seemed to be in a hotel room. He dressed quickly and, while Fields slept on, exhausted by the Long Island roads, went down in search of a newspaper. The first intelligence he gleaned, when he got one, was that Ocala, Florida, was expecting no more than a moderate rain-fall for that time of year, and that things looked good for a big citrus crop.

He went back to the hotel room and shook up Fields.

"Paper here says we're in Ocala, Florida," he reported.

"I always said those Long Island roads were poorly marked," Fields replied.

They lingered on for a week and went on several picnics. They left after Fields had been fined two hundred and seven dollars for remov-ing two hundred and seven dogwood blossoms from the municipal park.

Herb Caen

THERE'LL ALWAYS BE A CABLE CAR

I KNOW, you've heard it all before.

Those colorful, picturesque, utterly adorable little cable cars.

Running up and down the impossible hills, filled with ding-dings and cluck-clucks and brave passengers clinging precariously to the outside steps, to each other, to anything, and sometimes nothing. Sentimental curios, riveted to the heart of every San Franciscan with strands of steel. Noisy, illogical, quaint, outmoded, hard to operate, harder yet to maintain, getting in everybody's way while getting somewhere in the slowest possible fashion.

The green Powell Street line and the red California Street line—photographed so often by delighted tourists that they seem almost to yawn as they waddle past the lenses. Breaking down crankily and stupidly in the middle of the heaviest traffic crushes, sitting in the middle of the street and listing slightly to one side in a smug attitude that plainly says: "Don't try to make us hurry. You know and we know that you can't get along without us." Jolting, shoving, jerking along the narrow streets, carrying the past heavily on their shoulders and the present as uncomfortably as possible.

But don't get me wrong. I love the cable cars. What other mode of public transportation brings smiles to the faces of the people who have to ride them? (Even though the smiles are sometimes a little pained and strained.) What other type of municipal conveyance is babied along like a rich old aunt, and tolerated overlong in a job that calls for brisk efficiency instead of gingerbread sentimentality? Only the cable cars of San Francisco—for a variety of reasons, some of them practical, some of them neurotic.

As a tourist attraction, the cables are the greatest thing that has happened to San Francisco since the Chinese decided they liked the local climate. They help make the city look "different," an adjective

From *Baghdad by the Bay*, copyright, 1949, by Herb Caen. Reprinted by permission of Doubleday & Company, Inc.

that would prove a lot less simple to apply without them. And as a way of getting people to and fro (forward motion not always guaranteed) they still do a pretty fair job.

But mainly it is a city's abject sentimentality that gets all fouled up in the cable lines. The citizens want the "dinkies" around as a constant working reminder of a supposedly glorious past that keeps fading away, elusive as fog. As R. L. Duffus once put it, today's San Franciscans know there was some special magic about yesterday's city, but they're no longer sure what it was, or where it was. However, they think the cable cars had something to do with it, and so they insist on seeing them toddling around the streets as long as possible—even to the point of impossibility.

There has always been humor connected with the slightly comical cable cars. Back in the 1880s the whole town giggled about the Chinese cook named Ching Pon, who, upon seeing a Washington Street cable stalled at Polk, hurried over to the gripman and inquired: "Whatsa malla—sling bloke?" For a couple of decades after delighted San Franciscans hurled that pidgin sentence whenever they spotted a cable car stalled in its tracks.

The children of that pre-automobile age had fun with the clacking cables too. A favorite sport of the roller-skating set was to drop a bent wire through the slot, hook onto the strand, and get themselves a free pull up a hill. Other inventive moppets conceived the fanciful idea of hitching empty boxes on a string and snagging them to the cable. It was no uncommon sight to see as many as thirty cartons galloping bravely over a hilltop, while the young gagsters stood cheering and yelling at the bottom.

And the gripmen, apparently, have always been as unique as their vehicles. Obligingly, they'd stop in the middle of a block to let a steady customer dismount directly in front of his home—a courtesy that was usually amply repaid. At Christmastime in the must-have-been-Gay Nineties, every gripman from the California Cable Company would line up at Braunschweiger's Whiskey House to get a gift bottle of rock and rye, as thanks for stopping daily in front of the Braunschweiger mansion at 2216 California Street.

Today's gripmen do their best to continue the colorful traditions. Once out of the traffic crush, they'll occasionally let an old-time passenger off in front of his door. But they have most of their fun with street names. For instance, there's a Negro gripman on the Powell Street line who gets an occasional gift carton of Lucky Strikes for singing out "Ellis—MFT!" as he approaches that intersection. And a California cable conductor steadfastly shouts "Paul Jones" (at Jones) and "Old Taylor" (at the next street), even though he has yet to be rewarded for his commercials.

I saw my favorite cable-car sight one day in 1946, at the corner of Powell and Jackson streets. As the car approached the rugged, right-angle turn there, the conductor leaned out and hollered the traditional "Hang on! 'Kout for the curve!" Then *he* fell off.

Incidentally, I believe I am the only San Franciscan who has ever been bitten by a cable car—and at that very same intersection. The story is short and painful. I was sitting in one of the slatted outside seats on a particularly loose-in-the-joints Powell car, and as it creaked around the curve—well, all I can say is that I was bitten, and I still have a small scar to prove it. I plan to leave this private blemish to the Smithsonian Institution, where, I hope, it will be displayed over a sign reading "San Francisco Cable Scar."

Of course practically every San Franciscan has his own gag about the cables. For instance, if you're a tourist, don't walk up to a San Franscynic and ask him how the cars operate. A favorite, bored retort is: "Well, you see that gimmick there in the middle? It's got a gizmo on the end that hooks onto the dingbat in the slot—that's all there is to it."

Another phenomenon of the cable car is that you generally see two or three pedestrians running after one, and for a very good reason. The cars seem never to stop in the same place twice. Sometimes they halt at the traditional corner, but if there are automobiles in the way, or they have an intersecting cable line to cross, they'll come to rest on the next corner, without signal, without explanation. John Wright, a seasoned observer of the local scene, recently defined a San Franciscan as "a person who can predict where a cable car is going to stop."

However, sometimes even the operators aren't sure. On California Street last year my friend Leah Siewert saw a cable car arrive at Franklin Street three times in one trip. The jam-packed car started up the hill from Van Ness Avenue, and just as the conductor yelled "Franklin!" it went into a slip and slid back to the bottom. Taking a deep breath, the cable started up again. The conductor called out "Franklin again!" And once more it lost its grip at the crest of the hill. This time the passengers on the steps dismounted and walked alongside as the crate slowly got to the top, whereupon the conductor groaned loudly: "For the third and last time—Franklin!"

Nevertheless, those who know the cable cars best love 'em the most. A Powell Street conductor one day explained to me why he's so crazy about the rickety ground grippers. "Look," he said. "I'm standing on the back platform, and my cap falls off. So do I get excited? Do I signal for a halt? Nyah. I jump off, pick up my cap, run back, and jump on again. What other kind of transportation moves so slow and easy-like these days?"

Another conductor I know is in the habit of jumping off his cable as it trundles past the Dunkit Donut Shop on Columbus Avenue near Chestnut. He runs inside, yells "Gimme six!" grabs the bag of doughnuts and catches up with his still-moving car without even a sprint. A third conductor holds up three fingers as he passes Bruno's Lunchroom at Columbus and Taylor, which is the signal for Bruno to get three hamburgers ready. Then, on the cable's return trip from the Bay-Taylor turntable, the conductor dashes in, picks up his 'burgers, and gallops back to his car.

But any discussion of the cable cars must return inevitably to the tourist aspect. They still fascinate the outsider. Even so seasoned a traveler as Phil Baker, the radio comedian, was incensed at the recent hullabaloo over abandoning the lines in favor of busses. "Why," he said indignantly, "San Francisco without its cable cars would be like a kid without his yo-yo."

The best description I've encountered of the typical tourist reaction was contained in a memo written recently by an employee of a large San Francisco firm to his boss, to explain why he was late to work one day. It went like this:

DEAR BOSS: I was late to work this morning. Why?

Boarded Washington-Jackson cable at Fillmore. Man, wife, eight-year-old boy, and a young couple—all tourists—aboard. At Webster, gripman stopped car so the father could walk ahead and take movies of his wife and kid as the car passed. Stopped again, of course, so Father could board car again. When gripman stopped to let Mother off to take pictures of Dad and kid, I offered to take the movies, figuring if I got the whole group in at once, we'd get along on time. I got the pictures.

But when we reached the top of the hill (by Lafayette Park) the gripman pointed out Alcatraz. That did it. We stopped at each of the next two intersections for movies of the Bay view and the Rock.

Meanwhile, the gripman was playing with the boy, who was much *more interested in the cable car than the view. Kid would shout "ding da-ding ding," and the gripman would add the last two bongs on the car's bell.*

We stopped again at the carbarn on Mason, where a pair of overalled workmen appeared with a grip to replace the one on our car. The tourists, as expected, stayed aboard to watch the transfer. I and a few other San Franciscans boarded a passing Bay-Taylor cable after our conductor shouted to the other that it was okay, we all had paid our fares.

Anyway, boss, that's why I was late to work this morning. But one thing I'm sure of. That pixie cable-car crew made friends for San Francisco—and gave those tourists the high spot of their vacation.

In fairness to the anti-cable car contingent, though, I suppose I should note that an occasional visitor experiences that letdown feeling. For instance, Mrs. Stewart Brown recently entertained as her house guest an Eastern woman who had never before visited San Francisco; so the first thing she wanted to do, of course, was see the cables. Mrs. Brown walked her over to California Street, where the visitor watched for a few minutes, then shrugged and sighed in a deeply disappointed tone:

"Let's go home. I thought they were *suspended* from cables!"

Betty MacDonald

AN EXCERPT FROM *THE EGG AND I*

I Learn to Hate Even Baby Chickens

PRIOR to life with Bob my sole contact with baby chickens had been at the age of eleven. Lying on my stomach in our hammock which was swung between two Gravenstein apple trees in the orchard by the house in Laurelhurst, I pulled out grass stems, ate the tender white part and watched Layette, Gammy's favorite Barred Rock hen, herd her fourteen home-hatched fluffy yellow chicks through the drifting apple blossoms and under the low flowering quince trees. This sentimental fragment of my childhood was a far cry from the hundreds and hundreds of yellowish white, yeeping, smelly little nuisances which made my life a nightmare in the spring.

I confess I could hardly wait for our chicks to come and spent many happy anticipatory hours checking the thermometer and reveling in the warmth and cleanliness of the new brooder house. But I learned to my sorrow that baby chickens are stupid; they smell; they have to be fed, watered and looked at, at least every three hours. Their sole idea in life is to jam themselves under the brooder and get killed; stuff their little boneheads so far into their drinking fountains they drown; drink cold water and die; get B. W. D., coccidiosis or some other disease which means sudden death. The horrid little things pick out each other's eyes and peck each other's feet until they are bloody stumps.

My chick manual, speaking from the fence said, "Some chicks have a strong tendency to pick and some don't." (I was reminded of the mushroom book's, "Some are poisonous and some are not.") The chick manual went on to say, "The causes of picking are overcrowding, lack of ventilation or cannibalism." Our chicks, according to the standards set by the manual, had plenty of air and space so I added plain meanness to their list of loathsome traits. From the time of their contemplation, our baby chickens were given the utmost in care and consideration and their idea of appreciation was to see how many of them could turn out to be cockerels and how high they could get the percentage of deaths. I knew that Layette's babies never acted like that, which was a flaw-proof argument for environment over heredity and against any form of regimentation.

I really did my badly organized best to follow my chicken manual to the letter, even though it required that I spend one out of every three hours in the brooder house—measuring feed, washing water fountains, removing the bloody and the dying to the first-aid corner —and all of my leisure time nailing a dead chicken to a shingle, splitting the carcass from stem to stern and by peering alternately inside the chicken and at a very complicated chart, trying to figure out what in the world it died of. I always drew a blank. In my little Death and Food Record book, I, in my prankish way, wrote opposite the date and number of deaths, "Chickenpox-Eggzema and Suicide." When he checked the records, Bob noted this fun-in-our-work, and unsmilingly erased it and neatly wrote, "Not determined." Men are quite humorless about their own businesses.

My chick manual was detailed to the extent that it gave the number of minutes it should take so many chicks to clean up so much food —what to feed every single day until the chickens were six weeks old; even what to do about the floors, hovers, founts, hoppers, etc., four weeks before brooding. From my experience I would supplement this prior-to-brooding advice to read, "Four weeks before brooding, leave on an extended trip to the Baranof Islands."

I well remember how the Lucrezia Borgia in me boiled to the surface as I read in my chick manual, "A single drink of cold water may be fatal to a baby chick." "You don't say," I thought, licking my fevered lips and glancing longingly at the little lake filled with icy water. But my poultricidal tendencies were replaced with pure hysteria as I read on, "Water may be warm when you put it in the founts, but will it stay warm?"

"My God, isn't it enough that my hands will soon be dragging on the ground from carrying buckets and buckets and buckets of water, and that Stove has acquired a permanent list on his reservoir side, without being further tortured with trick questions? Why don't you get underneath the brooder and see if the water stays warm, you big bore? Me, I'll fill the fountains with warm water and curses every three hours and take a chance." That was my reaction to my chick manual.

The next cozy paragraph was headed "Dopey Chicks." "If many chicks are 'dopey' and you are sure they are not overheated or gassed, those chicks and the chicks that continually chirp should be sent to the nearest pathological laboratory (to see who's dopey?). If the report says B.W.D., it is better to disinfect the premises and start new chicks." I could find no explanation of B.W.D., but to me it was code for the best news in the world. It might have been better to start new chicks, but it might have been best to take the next train for Mexico.

I wondered how other chicken ranchers' wives reacted to baby chickens. Was there something in my background which kept me from becoming properly adjusted to the chicken, or was there just that too wide a gulf separating a woman and a chicken? I was delighted therefore, one spring morning, to have Mrs. Hicks halloo from the road and invite me to ride down to Mrs. Kettle's with her while she returned some bread pans. Both Mrs. Kettle and Mrs. Hicks were raising baby chickens and I thought this would be a splendid opportunity to make comparisons and to slip out of harness for a little while.

I had bathed and fed small Anne and put her to sleep in her carriage in the orchard, so I took a quick look at all of my other babies to be sure they were well fed and asleep, threw Bob a few hazy instructions, hung my apron on the gatepost, and we were off. Mrs. Hicks, full to the lip with some new and wonderful bile primer, was cheerful to the point of gaiety. Not so Mrs. Kettle, who clumped morosely out to greet us, kicking at her beloved mongrels as she went by.

At first I thought it the heavy curtain of gloom which made the spacious kitchen seem so crowded—then I became conscious of a rising crescendo of twitterings from the vicinity of the stove. Mrs. Kettle was rearing her baby chickens in the kitchen. That area back of the large woodstove which ordinarily housed the woodbox, the house slippers and barn boots of Mr. Kettle and the boys, a couple of bicycles, bits of harness, the newspapers, the dogs and cats and the car parts, had been turned into a brooder house. Fenced off by rusty window screens leaning against chairs and heated by a varied assortment of jars, cans and bottles filled with hot water, two hundred baby chicks existed in apparent health and contentment. No B.W.D. there. No disinfectant, no thermometer—and no sickness either. "That manual writer should see this," I thought bitterly.

Mrs. Kettle was also harboring in her kitchen a little runt pig, the sole survivor of a litter eaten by its mother. "The old bitch ate 'em all but this little bastard," chronicled Mrs. Kettle, whose nomenclature was always colorful but at times confused.

The chicks she dismissed lightly with "Paw ordered 'em last fall but didn't git around to buildin' the brooder house before they come so I guess we'll just have to raise 'em in here." The chirping chickens and the little pig clicking around under foot on his little sharp hoofs, all completely innocent of any form of housebreaking, didn't bother Mrs. Kettle a whit. What did trouble her was the fact that her elder sister, who twenty-odd years before had had the good fortune to marry a man both wealthy and prominent, had had the effrontery to send Mrs. Kettle by the morning mail, in lieu of a rich gift, an enormous tinted portrait of herself in evening dress. This Mrs. Kettle had set up on the table, easeled by the cracked white sugar bowl and a jar of jam.

Scratching herself vigorously and gesticulating with her soup ladle, she sneered, "Look at that, would you—pretty fine ain't we with our dinners all bare like a whore's?" (The dress was cut in a very modest V.) "And covered with jools which your old man got from bribing the Government. Well, you can stuff your jools and your crooked husband and—" Mrs. Kettle's face brightened. "You know where I'm going to hang your goddamned pitchur? In the outhouse!"

Mrs. Hicks and I took our leave at this point, but as we drove over the hill we heard the sound of violent pounding as Mrs. Kettle hung sister's gilt-framed picture.

Mrs. Hicks invited me to go home with her for a cup of coffee and to see her baby chickens. I accepted instantly, of course, so we jounced right past our ranch and down the mountain on the other side.

The coffee, strong and delicious, with thick yellow cream, was accompanied by that heavenly and completely indigestible delicacy, fried bread. Apparently all Mrs. Hicks did was to drop twisted pieces of bread dough into hot fat and in a minute or two take out big golden brown puffs which she dipped in powdered sugar and covered with strawberry jam. They weren't small and had what I'd call body, but I ate three and Mrs. Hicks five before we made a move toward the chicken houses. Then I tried a sprightly leap off the back porch, only to find that I had suddenly been outfitted with ballbearings. The fried bread rolled from side to side giving me the feeling of sea legs. I glanced at Mrs. Hicks but she sailed ahead of me like a piece of thistledown. Thistledown or no, I already had a different conception of her liver and vowed that in the future I would be a little more careful of what was left of mine.

Mrs. Hicks' brooder house smelled so strongly of disinfectant it made my eyes water and the chickens, looking as if they had sprouted under boards, drooped listlessly around the edges of their immaculate modern house. Gammy used to say, "Too much scrubbing takes the life right out of things," but a perennial droop seemed to be Mrs. Hicks' yardstick of cleanliness.

On the ride home I clutched my fried bread on the rough places and shifted it left and right on the curves, while Mrs. Hicks, seemingly in perfect comfort, chatted gaily. I asked her about the percentage of deaths in her chicks and was amazed to learn that out of five hundred chicks she had lost only five. She said, "Those five died the day after we got the chicks and I don't think they was right, but just in case it was anything catching I put a little disinfectant in the drinking water and the rest pulled through fine." What I think really happened was that Mrs. Hicks called a meeting of her chicks right after they arrived and told them, "I'm the boss here and I'm not going to put up with any sickening or dying. The first chick I catch dying is going to get what for and I mean it." And the chicks, disinfected inside and out, stayed alive—or else.

Mrs. Hicks was really a remarkable woman. She was slender and frail-looking, but she did so much work that just to hear her tell about it made me tired. She took all of the care of the chickens, the calves, pigs, turkeys, ducks and eggs, in addition to keeping her house like an operating room, baking, cooking, cleaning, sewing, washing and ironing. In winter Mr. Hicks, as did most of the farmers, supplemented his income by longshoring at Docktown or working in the lumber camps. During these times Mrs. Hicks did all of her usual work and milked ten cows night and morning, separated the milk, fed and watered the horses and still had time to take the eggs to town and pick up her spy reports.

Often after a particularly gruelling day, as I banged my shins against the oven door and cursed the inadequacy of coal-oil lamps, I would think enviously of Mrs. Hicks, who at that moment was probably standing in her immaculate kitchen, in an immaculate apron and housedress, wondering, now that the dishes were done, if she shouldn't just bake an angel food cake or set some rolls for the basket social. Just thinking of her in her tireless efficiency sometimes made me think I had better give up smoking and take up bile priming in its stead.

Once Mr. Hicks got hurt in the woods and was sent to a hospital in town, Mrs. Hicks went in to stay with him and Bob and I took care of their ranch for them for a few days. I couldn't begin to take over all of Mrs. Hicks' duties, but between us we managed very well, except that I fixed the milk and cream which we bought from the Hicks and I evidently used the wrong faucet on the separator because the cream, instead of being the top-milk variety which we had been getting all spring and summer, oozed into the bottle, dark yellow and thick. I didn't say anything to Bob, for he leaned terribly toward fair play and would probably have left no stone unturned until he had located the error, but I noticed that for those few days he used cream on everything but his meat. Every day I unlocked Mrs. Hicks' back door and tiptoed into the house and dusted the golden oak furniture and resisted a strong impulse to rummage in her bureau drawers and pantry—a holdover from the days when I was a child-sitter and supplemented my 25¢-for-the-afternoon pay by eating everything not nailed down in the houses of my customers.

Working within the sacred bounds of Mrs. Hicks' cleanliness proved such a strong impetus for a while that I found myself going after corners in my own house with pins and washing the face of the kitchen clock. I waited for her return with the smug feeling of someone who has done something well and knows he is going to be praised. Mrs. Hicks was very grateful to Bob and me and she and Mr. Hicks told us over and over what kind neighbors we were, but the next day Bob and I stopped on our way to town to see if we could get them anything, and Mrs. Hicks had her washtub filled with boiling water and disinfectant and soapsuds and was scrubbing the walls and floors of the chicken houses, calf houses, pig houses, turkey houses, duck houses and brooder house which Bob and I thought we had kept so clean. I gave up.

Bob turned out to be the best chicken farmer in our community. He was scientific, he was thorough, and he wasn't hampered by a lot of traditions or old wives' tales. Bob didn't believe in mixing breeding and egg raising—he said that they were separate industries and should be treated as such. His theory was that an egg-raising flock should be kept to a 90-96 per cent lay as much of the year as possible, but that if you were also using the flock for breeding and hatching eggs, such a strenuous laying program weakened the stock and made for poor chicks. He evidently knew what he was doing for his chickens laid eggs and didn't get sick and we always made money. Bob said that he could make money if eggs dropped to 15¢ a dozen. They never did —I think that 19¢ was the lowest we ever got and that was in the spring when eggs were plentiful—but Bob was not one to make promises he couldn't keep. Bob said that the secret of success in the chicken business for one man was to keep the operation to a size that could be handled by one man. He estimated that one man could handle 1500 chickens (provided his wife was part Percheron) by himself and make a comfortable living—but most people's trouble was that they were so comfortable on 1500 chickens that they figured they might as well be luxurious and have 2500. Then the trouble started: they had to hire help; they had to have much more extensive buildings and equipment; and to warrant the extra expense they would have to have five or ten thousand chickens instead of 2500. It sounded reasonable, and if Bob said it, it probably was.

An average white Leghorn hen laid from 150 to 220 eggs a year. She cost from $2.25 to $2.50 to raise—this included cost of equipment and bird. Eggs averaged over the year 31¢ a dozen. Using this as a basis we figured that a hen the first year might, if she tried, lay 204 eggs or

17 dozen, which at 31¢ would be $5.27. Less her original cost of $2.35, less feed costs of around $2.40, this would leave a profit of about 50¢ per hen the first year. The second year the eggs were all profit except the feed, unless you wanted to split the cost of the new pullets and bring down the original cost per hen. There was a prize flock of 455 pullets in that vicinity which laid 243.5 eggs per hen per year, 111,-027 eggs per year per flock—and made a profit of $3.46 per fowl above feed costs. Our records showed that we were not too far behind this prize flock the second year and we had 1000 chickens.

I kept all of the egg records. I wrote on a large calendar in the kitchen the number of eggs we gathered at each gathering. At the end of the day these figures were entered in a daybook and later entered in a weekly column, along with the feed, which was delivered once a week. It was a very simple system, but when it came time to draw weekly and monthly percentages I was apt to find the hens in the throes of a 150 per cent lay and then I would have to go laboriously back and try to find out how far back and in which branch of my arithmetic, adding, multiplication or subtraction, the trouble lay.

The percentage of cockerels was a vital factor in determining the cost of each pullet, and I watched the baby chicks with beating heart for the first signs of the little combs which would tell me how we stood. As soon as we could tell them apart, we separated the cockerels and put them in fattening pens where they ate and fought and crowed until it was time to dress them for market. Anything else that I had cared for from birth would have become so embedded in my feelings I would have had to gouge it out, but I got so I actually enjoyed watching Bob stick his killing knife deep into the palates of fifty cockerels and hang them up to bleed. My only feeling was pride to see how firm and fat they were as we dressed them for market.

I got so I could dress chickens like an expert, but have wondered since how this ability to defeather a chicken in about two minutes without once tearing the skin, my only accomplishment, could ever be mentioned socially along with swimming and diving, or gracefully demonstrated as with violin and piano playing. Wouldn't you know that I would excel in chicken picking?

About the time the cockerels were ready for market, the pullets were ready to be taught to roost in their own little houses instead of in the trees, where they were easy prey for owls and wildcats. This meant that at dusk each night Bob and I had to go through the orchard plucking squawking, flapping birds out of the tops of the trees, holding them by the ankles with heads down. When we had as large a bouquet as we could hold, we took them to the pullet houses and planted them firmly on the roosts. At first I felt like a falconer and found the work rather exhilarating, but after about two weeks, when there was still a large group of boneheads who preferred to sleep out of doors and get killed, I found myself inclining toward the you've-made-your-bed-now-lie-in-it attitude.

Chickens are so dumb. Any other living thing which you fed 365 days in the year would get to know and perhaps to love you. Not the chicken. Every time I opened the chicken house door, SQUAWK, SQUAWK-SQUAAAAAAAAWK! And the dumbbells would fly up in the air and run around and bang into each other. Bob was a little more successful—but only a little more so and only because chickens didn't bother him or he didn't yell and jump when they did.

That second spring Bob built a large new yard for the big chickens— the old one was to be plowed and planted to clover, which disinfected the ground and provided greens for the hens. We eventually had four such yards so that by rotation our hens were always in a clean green playground. Other chicken ranchers shook their heads over this foolish waste of time and ground. They also scoffed at feeding the chickens buttermilk and greens the year round. They had been brought up to believe that women had tumors, babies had fits and chickens had croup; green food and fresh air were things to be avoided and a small dirty yard was all a chicken deserved.

Bob paid no attention to the other farmers, and when the new yard was finished we lifted the small runway doors and watched the hens come crowding out, scolding, quarreling, singing, squawking, choosing their favorite places and hurrying like mad to enjoy their playtime. They were gleaming white with health and spring, and didn't seem nearly so repulsive as usual.

When the pullets began laying, Bob and I culled the old hens. We did this at night. We'd lift an old hen off the roost, look at her head, the color of her comb, her shape, her legs, and if we were in doubt we'd measure the distance between her pelvic bones—two fingers was a good layer. Chickens could be culled in the yard except for the trouble encountered in catching them. The good layers looked motherly, their combs were full and bright red, their eyes large, beaks broad and short, and their bodies were well rounded, broad-hipped and built close to the ground. They were also the diligent scratchers and eaters and their voices seemed a little lower with overtones of lullaby. The non-producers, the childless parasites, were just as typical. Their combs were small and pale, eyes small, beaks sharp and pointed, legs long, hips narrow, and they spent all of their time gossiping, starting fights, and going into screaming hysterics over nothing. The non-producers also seemed subject to many forms of female trouble —enlarged liver, wire worms, and blowouts (prolapse of the oviduct). What a bitter thing for them that, unlike their human counterparts, their only operation was one performed with an axe on the neck.

I really tried to like chickens. But I couldn't get close to the hen either physically or spiritually, and by the end of the second spring I hated everything about the chicken but the egg. I especially hated cleaning the chicken house, which Bob always chose to do on ideal washing days or in perfect gardening weather. In fact, on a chicken ranch there never dawns a beautiful day that isn't immediately spoiled by some great big backbreaking task.

Our chicken house was very large and was complicated with rafters and ells and wings. Cleaning it meant first scrubbing off the dropping boards (which were scraped and limed daily) with boiling water and lye; then raking out all the straw and scraping at least a good half inch from the hard dirt floors; then with a small brush—a very small brush—I brushed whitewash into all the cracks on the walls, while Bob sprayed the ceiling. Then Bob sprayed the walls and criticized my work on the crevices (the only thing he failed to make me do was to catch the lice individually); then we put clean straw all over the floor; filled the mash hoppers; washed and filled the water jugs and at last turned in the hens, who came surging in filled with lice, droppings and, we hoped, eggs.

VIII. THIS SIDE OF PARODIES

Donald Ogden Stewart

THE WHISKY REBELLION

(In the Bedtime Story Manner of Thornton W. Burgess)

JUST the *day* for a Whisky Rebellion," said Aunt Polly and off she ran, lipperty-lipperty-lip, to get a few shooting rifles.

"Oh goody goody," cried little Emily. "Now we can all shoot at those horrid Revenue Officers," for the collectors of internal revenue were far from popular with these kindly Pennsylvania folk and Aunt Polly Pinkwood had often promised the children that if they were good some day they would be allowed to take a shot at a Revenue Officer.

Soon she returned, bearing in her arms a number of bright shiny new guns. The children crowded around in glee and soon all were supplied with weapons except little Frank who of course was too young to use a gun and was given a two-gallon jug of nice, old whisky to carry. Jed hitched up old Taylor, the faithful farm horse, and as quick as you could say Jack Robinson the little ones had piled into the old carryall. Round Mr. Sun was just peeping over the Purple Hills when the merry little party started on its way, singing and laughing at the prospect of the day's sport.

"I bet I kill five Revenue Officers," said little Edgar.

"Ha Ha Ha—you boaster, you," laughed Aunt Polly. "You will be lucky if you kill two, for I fear they will be hard to find today."

"Oh do you think so, Aunt Polly?" said little Elinor and she began to cry, for Elinor dearly loved to shoot.

"Hush dear," said Miss Pinkwood with a kindly pat, for she loved her little charges and it hurt her to see them unhappy. "I was only joking. And now children I will tell you a story."

"Oh goody goody," cried they all. "Tell us a true story."

"All right," said Aunt Polly. "I shall tell you a true story," and she began.

"Once there was a brave handsome man—"

"Mr. Welsbach," cried the children with one voice, for it was well known in the neighborhood that Aunt Polly had long been sweet on Julius Welsbach, the popular superintendent of the Sabbath School and the best whisky maker for miles around.

"Hush children," said Aunt Polly blushing in vexation. "Of course not. And if you interrupt me I shall not tell my story at all." But she was not really angry.

"And one day this brave handsome man was out making whisky and he had just sampled some when he looked up and what do you suppose he saw?"

"Snakes," cried little Elmer whose father had often had delirium tremens, greatly to the delight of his children.

"No, Elmer," said Miss Pinkwood, "not snakes."

"Pink lizards," cried little Esther, Elmer's sister.

"No," said Aunt Polly, with a hearty laugh, "he saw a—stranger. And what do you suppose the stranger had?"

"A snoot full," chorused the Schultz twins. "He was pie-eyed."

"No," replied Miss Pinkwood laughing merrily. "It was before noon. Guess again children. What did the stranger have?"

"Blind staggers," suggested little Faith whose mother had recently been adjudged insane.

"Come children," replied Aunt Polly. "You are not very wide awake this morning. The stranger had a gun. And when the brave handsome man offered the stranger a drink what do you suppose the stranger said?"

"I know," cried little Prudence eagerly. "He said, 'Why yes I don't care if I do.' That's what they all say."

"No, Prudence," replied Miss Pinkwood. "The stranger refused a drink."

"Oh come now, Aunt Polly," chorused the boys and girls. "You said you were going to tell us a true story." And their little faces fell.

"Children," said Miss Polly, "the stranger refused the drink because he was a Revenue Officer. And he pointed his gun at the brave handsome man and said he would have to go to jail because he had not paid the tax on his whisky. And the brave handsome man would have had to have gone to jail, too; but fortunately his brother came up just at the right time and—"

"Shot the Revenuer dead," cried the children in glee.

"Yes children," said Miss Polly. "He shot the Revenue Officer dead."

"Oh goody goody," cried all. "Now tell us another story. Tell us about the time your father killed a Revenue Officer with an ax."

"Oh you don't want to hear that again, do you children?" said Aunt Polly.

"Oh yes—yes—please," they cried, and Aunt Polly was just going to begin when Jed the driver stopped his horses and said:

"This hilltop is as good a place to shoot from as I know of, Miss Pinkwood. You can see both roads and nobody can see you."

"Thank you, Jed," said Aunt Polly giving him a kindly smile, and without more ado the children clambered out of the carryall and filled their guns with powder and bullets.

"I get first shot," proudly announced Robert, the oldest boy, and somewhat of a bully.

"Robert!" said Aunt Polly severely, and she looked almost ready to cry, for Aunt Polly had tried hard to teach the boys to be true knights of chivalry and it hurt her to have Robert wish to shoot a Revenue Officer before the girls had had a chance. Robert had not meant to hurt Aunt Polly's feelings but had only been thoughtless, and soon all was sunshine again as little Ellen the youngest made ready to fire the first shot.

The children waited patiently and soon they were rewarded by the sight of a Revenue Officer riding on horseback in the distant valley, as pretty a target as one could wish.

"Now do be careful, dear," whispered Miss Pinkwood, "for if you miss, he may take alarm and be off." But little Ellen did not miss. "Bang" went her gun and the little Merry Breezes echoed back and forth, "She got him. She got him," and old Mother West Wind smiled down at the happy sport. Sure enough, when old Mr. Smoke had cleared away there was a nice dead Revenue Officer lying in the road. "Well done, Ellen," said Miss Pinkwood patting her little charge affectionately which caused the happy girl to coo with childish delight.

Mary had next shot and soon all were popping away in great glee. All the merry wood folk gathered near to watch the children at their sport. There was Johnny Chuck and Reddy Fox and Jimmy Skunk and Bobby Coon and oh everybody.

Soon round Mr. Sun was high in the Blue Sky and the children began to tire somewhat of their sport. "I'm as hungry as a bear," said little Dick. "I'm as hungry as two bears," said Emily. "Ha Ha Ha," laughed Miss Pinkwood, "I know what will fix that," and soon she had spread out a delicious repast.

"Now children," said Miss Pinkwood when all had washed their faces and hands, "while you were busy washing I prepared a surprise for you," and from a large jug, before their delighted gaze, she poured out—what do you think? "Bronxes," cried little Harriet. "Oh goody goody." And sure enough Aunt Polly had prepared a jug of delicious Bronx cocktails which all pronounced excellent.

And after that there were sandwiches and olives and pie and good three year old whisky, too.

"That's awfully smooth rye, Aunt Polly," said little Prudence smacking her two red lips. "I think I'll have another shot."

"No dear," said Miss Pinkwood, pleased by the compliment, but firm withal. "Not now. Perhaps on the way home, if there is any left," for Aunt Polly knew that too much alcohol in the middle of the day is bad for growing children, and she had seen many a promising child spoiled by over-indulgent parents.

After lunch those children who could stand helped Aunt Polly to clear away the dishes and then all went sound asleep, as is the custom in Pennsylvania.

When they awoke round Mr. Sun was just sinking behind the Purple Hills and so, after taking a few more scattered shots at Revenue Officers, they piled once more into the carryall and drove back to town. And as they passed Mrs. Oliphant's house (Aunt Polly's sister) Aunt Flo Oliphant came out on the porch and waved her handkerchief at the merry party.

"Let's give her a cheer," said Fred.

"Agreed," cried they all, and so twelve little throats united in three lusty "huzzahs" which made Auntie Flo very happy you may be sure.

And as they drove up before the Pinkwoods' modest home twelve tired but happy children with one accord voted the Whisky Rebellion capital fun and Aunt Polly a brick.

S. J. Perelman

WAITING FOR SANTY

A CHRISTMAS PLAYLET

(With a Bow to Mr. Clifford Odets)

SCENE: *The sweatshop of S. Claus, a manufacturer of children's toys, on North Pole Street. Time: The night before Christmas.*

At rise, seven gnomes, Rankin, Panken, Rivkin, Riskin, Ruskin, Briskin, and Praskin, are discovered working furiously to fill orders piling up at stage right. The whir of lathes, the hum of motors, and the hiss of drying lacquer are so deafening that at times the dialogue cannot be heard, which is very vexing if you vex easily. (Note: the parts of Rankin, Panken, Rivkin, Riskin, Ruskin, Briskin, and Praskin are interchangeable, and may be secured directly from your dealer or the factory.)

RISKIN (*filing a Meccano girder, bitterly*)—A parasite, a leech, a bloodsucker—altogether a five-star nogoodnick! Starvation wages we get so he can ride around in a red team with reindeers!

RUSKIN (*jeering*)—Hey, Karl Marx, whyn'tcha hire a hall?

RISKIN (*sneering*)—Scab! Stool pigeon! Company spy! (*They tangle and rain blows on each other. While waiting for these to dry, each returns to his respective task.*)

BRISKIN (*sadly, to Panken*)—All day long I'm painting "Snow Queen" on these Flexible Flyers and my little Irving lays in a cold tenement with the gout.

PANKEN—You said before it was the mumps.

BRISKIN (*with a fatalistic shrug*)—The mumps—the gout—go argue with City Hall.

PANKEN (*kindly, passing him a bowl*)—Here, take a piece fruit.

BRISKIN (*chewing*)—It ain't bad, for wax fruit.

PANKEN (*with pride*)—I painted it myself.

BRISKIN (*rejecting the fruit*)—Ptoo! Slave psychology!

RIVKIN (*suddenly, half to himself, half to the Party*)—I got a belly full of stars, baby. You make me feel like I swallowed a Roman candle.

PRASKIN (*curiously*)—What's wrong with the kid?

RISKIN—What's wrong with all of us? The system! Two years he and Claus's daughter's been making googoo eyes behind the old man's back.

PRASKIN—So what?

RISKIN (*scornfully*)—So what? Economic determinism! What do you think the kid's name is—J. Pierpont Rivkin? He ain't even got for a bottle Dr. Brown's Celery Tonic. I tell you, it's like gall in my mouth two young people shouldn't have a room where they could make great music.

RANKIN (*warningly*)—Shhh! Here she comes now! (*Stella Claus enters, carrying a portable phonograph. She and Rivkin embrace, place a record on the turntable, and begin a very slow waltz, unmindful that the phonograph is playing "Cohen on the Telephone."*)

STELLA (*dreamily*)—Love me, sugar?

RIVKIN—I can't sleep, I can't eat, that's how I love you. You're a double malted with two scoops of whipped cream; you're the moon rising over Mosholu Parkway; you're a two weeks' vacation at Camp Nitgedaiget! I'd pull down the Chrysler Building to make a bobbie pin for your hair!

STELLA—I've got a stomach full of anguish. Oh, Rivvy, what'll we do?

PANKEN (*sympathetically*)—Here, try a piece fruit.

RIVKIN (*fiercely*)—Wax fruit—that's been my whole life! Imitations! Substitutes! Well, I'm through! Stella, tonight I'm telling your old man. He can't play mumblety-peg with two human beings! (*The tinkle of sleigh bells is heard offstage, followed by a voice shouting, "Whoa, Dasher! Whoa, Dancer!" A moment later S. Claus enters in a gust of mock snow. He is a pompous bourgeois of sixty-five who affects a white beard and a false air of benevolence. But tonight the ruddy color is missing from his cheeks, his step falters, and he moves heavily. The gnomes hastily replace the marzipan they have been filching.*)

STELLA (*anxiously*)—Papa! What did the specialist say to you?

CLAUS (*brokenly*)—The biggest professor in the country . . . the best cardiac man that money could buy . . . I tell you I was like a wild man.

STELLA—Pull yourself together, Sam!

CLAUS—It's no use. Adhesions, diabetes, sleeping sickness, decalcomania—oh, my God! I got to cut out climbing in chimneys, he says—me, Sanford Claus, the biggest toy concern in the world!

STELLA (*soothingly*)—After all, it's only one man's opinion.

CLAUS—No, no, he cooked my goose. I'm like a broken uke after a Yosian picnic. Rivkin!

RIVKIN—Yes, Sam.

CLAUS—My boy, I had my eye on you for a long time. You and Stella thought you were too foxy for an old man, didn't you? Well, let bygones be bygones. Stella, do you love this gnome?

STELLA (*simply*)—He's the whole stage show at the Music Hall, Papa; he's Toscanini conducting Beethoven's Fifth; he's—

CLAUS (*curtly*)—Enough already. Take him. From now on he's a partner in the firm. (*As all exclaim, Claus holds up his hand for silence.*) And tonight he can take my route and make the deliveries. It's the least I could do for my own flesh and blood. (*As the happy couple kiss, Claus wipes away a suspicious moisture and turns to the other gnomes.*) Boys, do you know what day tomorrow is?

GNOMES (*crowding around expectantly*)—Christmas!

CLAUS—Correct. When you look in your envelopes tonight, you'll find a little present from me—a forty-percent pay cut. And the first one who opens his trap—gets this. (*As he holds up a tear-gas bomb and beams at them, the gnomes utter cries of joy, join hands, and dance around him shouting exultantly. All except Riskin and Briskin, that is, who exchange a quick glance and go underground.*)

CURTAIN

Ira Wallach

THE KEEPER OF THE GELDED UNICORN

*An historical romance which breathes life into a little-known
episode in English history.*

*For readers who are interested in comparing money values,
one shekel is roughly equivalent to $2.98.*

"A HOGSHEAD of fine wine!"

The barmaid, her eyes wide with admiration, looked at the man
who had shouted his order with such an air of confident gaiety. He
was tall, lean, with broad shoulders, slender hips, eyes that blazed like
live coals, dark unruly hair, and a twinkle in the corner of a mouth
which could, at times, be stern enough to strike terror into the hearts
of the greatest swordsmen on the Continent and in very England itself.

"Come, maid, God wot, 'sblood, marry!" he called. "Did you not
hear me, maid? A hogshead of fine wine!" He pinched her lightly and
took her to bed, after which she brought the wine, her eyes tender and
moist with devotion.

Two public letter writers whispered in a corner. Outside, the cry of
the fishwives could be heard over the shouts of the children laughing
and clapping as the dancing bear performed in the streets thick with
cutpurses.

The barmaid slipped into the kitchen where her father awaited.
"Who is that young gentleman of noble mien, father?" she asked.

Old Robin, keeper of the inn, took one look and gasped. "The
Keeper of the Gelded Unicorn!" he whispered. "The finest sword in
England! 'Tis said he was born a foundling and raised in the court of
the Duc D'Ambert who lacked a son. The streets of London are paved
with the hearts he has broken, cemented by the blood he has spilled.

From *Hopalong Freud and Other Modern Literary Characters*, copyright, 1951,
by Ira Wallach. Reprinted by permission of Abelard-Schuman, Inc., New York.

But he is ever a friend to the poor, and a sworn enemy to Guise, the Earl of Essence!"

The barmaid's eyes filled with limpid tears. "Then he is not for me, father!"

Old Robin shook his head sadly. "God wot, no, daughter," he said. "Good Brogo, the blacksmith's half-witted son, will make you a fine husband."

At that moment Guise, the Earl of Essence, successor to many proud titles, strode into the inn, followed by his retinue. Guise might have been called handsome had not cruelty, avarice, and dissipation left their telltale marks on his countenance.

The barmaid hastened to serve him. Guise narrowed his eyes. "A fine ankle," he murmured. His courtiers smirked as Guise fondled the barmaid's left rump. In a moment a shining blade lay across the table.

"Aha! Meeting in rump session with your retinue! Wouldst cross blades now, my lord Guise?"

Guise looked up into a pair of burning eyes. Slowly, he removed his hand from the barmaid's rump. "Your time will come, Warren of Hastings," he spat, addressing the Keeper of the Gelded Unicorn by his true name, known only to those few who suspected from his demeanor that in his blood ran the cold skill of the English, the wild ferocity of the Scotch border chiefs, the lilting, carefree spirit of the Irish, and the soft and murmurous tenderness of the Latin.

Abruptly, Guise rose and left with his retinue. The barmaid approached the table and put her hand timidly upon that of Warren of Hastings. "You should not have done it, my lord," she murmured.

He snapped his fingers. "What if I do start the Thirty Years' War!" he exclaimed in his carefree manner.

England, in the Year of Our Lord 1746, was torn by dissension. The Queen's faction, headed by Warren of Hastings with the loyal aid of France's Count D'Même-Chose, was plotting an anti-Spanish alliance with the Holy Roman Empire and the Palatinate. The King's faction, led by Guise, Earl of Essence, sought instead an alliance with the Saracen, and the Earl was ready to go so far as to sign a secret treaty with the Czar. Richelieu, disturbed by the development of events, vacillated between the two, and only the Huguenots, tied as they were by bonds of kinship and blood to Austro-Hungary, and influenced by the sinister figure of Oliver Cromwell, followed an unswerving path. No one knew in which direction the Winter King would turn, and over all loomed the shadow of Napoleon. Into this maelstrom grimly strode Philip IV of Spain. Lenin remained noncommittal. Little wonder that heads rolled in the Tower, and that on the streets of London Warren of Hastings, at the head of his faithful band, often clashed with the hired cutthroats and Pomeranian mercenaries brought to England by Guise, the Earl of Essence.

Through a dark street, disguised only by a cloak over his face, Warren of Hastings sped toward the palace. Two public letter writers whispered in a corner. The cry of the fishwives could be heard over the shouts of the children laughing and clapping as the dancing bear performed in the streets thick with cutpurses. In a few moments, Warren of Hastings was in the Queen's bedchamber where he took the cloak from his face and murmured, "My lady!"

She walked toward him slowly, her dark hair gleaming under a caul of tinsel, her arms outstretched. "Warren of Hastings," she whispered, "swordsman, warrior, balladeer, courtier, pamphleteer, lover, poet, and patriot!"

He seized her roughly, importunately, and drew her to the window where he laid his cheek athwart her heaving bosom. She yielded momentarily, then turned her face to the darkening sky. "Not now," she whispered, "not now." Then, "Marry," she said, "notice yon white clouds."

"Not so white as thy teeth," he replied, "not half so regular."

Again she freed herself from his embrace. "God wot, Warren, even now my Earl of Guise is approaching Duncanfayne with a horde of Pomeranians. 'Tis said they will lay siege to Duncanfayne this night!"

Warren of Hastings leaped back, his hand instinctively clutching his sword's hilt. "Duncanfayne, where my lady has hidden her treasures!"

She nodded quietly and only a tear betrayed her thoughts.

"And my liege, the King?" asked Warren of Hastings.

"Carousing with Gisette of Lyons." She said it without bitterness although a trace of irony hardened her voice. "Little does he know that Gisette of Lyons is in the pay of Richelieu!"

"More fool he!" murmured Warren of Hastings.

"Sir!" cried the Queen, stirred to sudden wrath, "you are speaking of our lord, the King!"

Warren of Hastings dropped to his knees and pressed her hand against his lips. "Forgive me, dear lady," he pleaded. "I forgot myself."

"I forgive you," she said, forcing his head against the pillow.

"Even now Warren of Hastings, the Keeper of the Gelded Unicorn, is closeted in the Queen's chamber while we march on Duncanfayne," spat Guise as he rode his charger through the murky night, followed by a horde of Pomeranians.

Across the channel rose a faint glow from the fire whereon Joan of Arc was burning. Hammel de Vyl, the Earl's companion and master spy, smiled a dry smile. "More fool he," muttered Hammel.

The Earl snarled lightly. "Is all prepared?" he asked.

Again Hammel laughed, but with no trace of humor. "The guards are bribed, the moat is down, the bridge is up, and our agent has spavined all the spears in Duncanfayne. Warren of Hastings wots not of this."

"Well done, Hammel de Vyl," remarked the Earl, tossing him a bag of doubloons.

The four-master leaned to the wind, the night foam spraying her bow.

"Wet the sails, ye slobberers!" shouted the captain, his teeth trembling in the gale. "Jettison the cargo!"

The sailors sprang to, and overboard went casks, barrels of sprawns, cauls of lichen, two farthingales, and a huge tusk of billingsgate. Leaning against the mainmast, his feet on the mizzen, his face turned to the flying spray, was Warren of Hastings. Near him stood the faithful Edward Masterfield, a youth whose courage and sword most closely matched those of Warren himself.

"God wot, Edward," cried Warren, "little does Guise reck that we shall cut him off at Duncanfayne by sea this night!"

"More fool he," said Edward, his mouth making a grim line as his forefinger tested the edge of his sword.

From the crow's nest far aloft came a sudden call, "Land ahoy!" All eyes turned to the starboard where, across the bow, faintly glimmered the lights from the storm-tossed battlements of Duncanfayne.

Within an hour's time the good ship *Aphrodite* had tied up alongside and a group of silent men, their faces in their cloaks, slipped ashore.

In bloodstained Duncanfayne, Guise, the Earl of Essence, and Hammel de Vyl saw victory within their grasp. Then the Queen would sing a different tune indeed! Richelieu and the Winter King would have to retreat, and the counsel of the Earl of Essence would carry new weight in Venice before the whole province went to the Doges! Even the crown—it was not impossible, nay, it was probable—might revert to the Earl himself, once the King had become sufficiently involved in his wild dream of an *entente* with Bruit van Hotten of Holland!

The Earl himself led his men to the gates of the treasury. But suddenly the door swung open, a strong hand reached out and pulled the Earl within. The door immediately slammed shut against his Pomeranian followers.

Bewildered, the Earl looked about. The floors were strewn with the Queen's jewelry. Upon the table four candles gave the vault its only light. Lined against the walls were the followers of the Queen's faction, and there in the center, his merry eyes still twinkling, stood Warren of Hastings, Keeper of the Gelded Unicorn.

" 'Sblood!" cried Guise.

"How now, Guise," answered Warren, brushing back an unruly lock of curly hair.

"God wot!" retorted the Earl.

"Marry!" laughed Warren in rejoinder, "shall we try the temper of our swords?"

Guise blanched. "Your men," he said, indicating the band that stood against the walls.

"My retinue will not interfere, will you, retinue?"

"Nay, God wot!" they cried as one man.

"Then, have to!" shouted Warren, unsheathing his blade.

The Earl leaped back and bared his sword to the candlelight. For a moment they fenced cautiously. Then the swords locked at the hilt and the two faces met and almost touched. "I shall carve thee for a roast," hissed Guise.

"Let us see who does the roasting and who does the eating," rejoined Warren between clenched teeth.

They separated. The blades flashed. The Earl advanced, taking the offensive. Skillfully, Warren parried the quick thrusts as he retreated around the table. At that moment he caught the eye of Edward Masterfield and turned to smile. It was a mistake of overconfidence, for in that very moment of turning, Guise's swift blade thrust in, cut through doublet, lumpkin, ruffle, and wattles, drawing a thin line of blood upon Warren's shoulder.

" 'Sblood!" cried Warren of Hastings. Quickly he turned to the offensive and brought the duel to the Earl, his lightning blade catching the fine glints of the candlelight. Another bold thrust forward, and bright steel cut flesh on Guise's thigh. Guise withdrew, but Warren was relentless. A few sudden parries, a feint, an *entrechat*, and to the hoarse cry of "Long live the Queen!" a slender blade shot forward and pierced the Earl's throat.

Warren sighed. "Now open the doors," he ordered his men. The doors swung wide. The Pomeranians advanced, but catching sight of the Earl, now dead, they fell back with a cry of horror, and crossed the Channel.

"A good night's work," murmured Edward Masterfield weakly, as he drew a Pomeranian arrow, shot by a fleeing malcontent, from his abdomen.

It was a gay and lighthearted Warren of Hastings who brought the jewels to the Queen's chamber. Although she had lost neither whit nor tittle of her regal bearing, her eyes spoke for her as she said, "You may kiss me, Warren of Hastings."

Wilder and wilder grew Warren's passion. He heard her murmurous, "No, no," but he was his heart's puppet, and he could not deny his Irish, English, Scotch, or Latin blood. In the bed he drew her still closer as they lay in murmurous and ecstatic silence.

Outside the palace two public letter writers whispered in a corner. The cry of the fishwives could be heard over the shouts of the children laughing and clapping as the dancing bear performed in the streets thick with cutpurses.

"And now, beloved lady," cried Warren of Hastings, "on to the War of the Roses!"

Her eyes filled with tears. "Honor will always take thee further afoot than love," she sighed.

"God wot," he replied, bowing his head. Through the window the sun rose on the battlements and on the triumphant standards of the Queen.

Warren of Hastings silently arose from bed and removed his hat. England was safe.

Wolcott Gibbs

SHAD AMPERSAND

(A Novel of Time and the Writer, Tentatively Based On
Cass Timberlane, A Novel of Husbands and Wives)

CHAPTER I

THE city of Grand Revenant, in High Hope County and the
sovereign state of Nostalgia, has a population of 34,567, according
to the official census taker, a vast and bumbling liar, receiver of puny
bribes and secret high acolyte of the poems of Algernon Charles Swin-
burne.

Grand Revenant is 49.6 miles from Zenith and 99.2 from Gopher
Prairie.

It was founded in 1903, a year that also saw the birth, at Kitty Hawk,
N. C., of a strange, boxlike contrivance that held the bright seeds of
death for Coventry and Nagasaki and other proud cities, half the world
away.

Its pioneer settler was old Cornelius Ampersand, a prodigious
seducer of Indians along the thundering marge of Lake Prolix and on
the cold, improbable trails that lead from Baedeker and Larousse to
Mount Thesaurus. Corn was a He-Man, a Wowser, a High Anointed
Member of the Sacred and Splendiferous Tribe of Good Scouts, and
if his thin, despairing wife often wept alone in the night, nobody knew
—except perhaps her two or three hundred closest friends.

In the years since old Corn raped his last squaw (and how those
golden girls would giggle in the dusk!), Grand Revenant had grown
like an angry weed in the fertile soil of the prairie.

Factories came—Wilson & Fadiman, who ravaged the little, firm-
breasted hills for copper for moot points; Trilling & Cowley, who
made the smoothest, shiniest, most astoundingly complicated little
instruments for determining tension and slack (it was hard to say what
everybody did before it was possible to determine slack to one-ten-

thousandth part of an inch); Mencken & Nathan, who manufactured Hortex and were said to have the seventh largest mangle in the state of Nostalgia.

Stores were born—the Mad Mode Mart, Avis Cormorant, prop. (Miss Cormorant was a nymphomaniac and, very discreetly, a German spy, but her chic was the despair of her rival, Elsie Drear, who was a virgin and an Episcopalian); Blitberg's Department Store which sold everything from needles to yachts, and if one or two salesgirls died each week from a strange and terrible disease called Dreiser's Botch, there was surely no kinder or merrier man in all Revenant than old Sam Blitberg; Dirge & Mouseman (Mrs. Mouseman, née Birdie Jump, was that object of almost inconceivable grandeur, a former inmate of the *Social Register*), where you could buy, for very little more than it would cost to build supernal beauty or to stamp out Yaws, rare stones of devious and bloody history.

Other noble monuments—the Revenant Museum of Art, which boasted a Modigliani and a Dali and a whole roomful of Grant Woods, but which was chiefly notable for its swimming pool which was as deep and blue as a lake; Revenant Junior High School, which regularly and gratifyingly beat the upstart team from East Hemingway in the annual marathon, and if very few of her graduates could tell you who wrote *Thanatopsis* or even *Mantrap*, they usually proved astonishingly nimble at selling not too aqueous real estate and beautifully shiny automobiles, which often ran quite well; and, always and most particularly, Mme. Moriarity's bowling parlors, where the nickering males of Revenant betook themselves for curious delights, which sometimes they even actually enjoyed.

Churches sprang up, to the glory of a Fat God, whose other names were Baal and Moloch and Ahriman and Progress and Rugged Individualism.

Hotels and restaurants—the Revenant Inn, which travellers had been known to compare favorably with the glittering Bellevue-Stratford in Philadelphia, but at which there was no room for the Indians whose doomed campfires had once glowed where now its flying towers mocked the sky; Doug's Hotburger, where the cop on the beat, a cold and melancholy man, dropped in nightly to sigh: "Geez, you take my wife. A good woman, I guess, but no get-up-and-go to her like some of these peppy society dames. And *talk!* Golly! One of these days maybe I'll have to shut the ole girl up." At six o'clock one bitter January morning, he did, very neatly and irrevocably, using the old .44 service revolver with which he had sworn to uphold the law; the Heyday Grille, where Doc Kennicott and George Babbitt and Sam Dods-worth and all the glorious he-male company of competent seducers (about once a year, Babbitt conducted a fumbling, inconclusive ex-periment with some derisive young woman in a canoe) and two-fisted drinkers (sometimes, uneasily, they had a cocktail before lunch) met every Friday to bumble cheerfully: "Well, I dunno what you other, uh, homo sapiensibuses think, but it strikes this not-so-humble observer that this lil ole burg is sure goin' straight to the twenty-three skiddoos." Solemnly, they agreed that Grand Revenant could not compare in splendor with Zenith and Gopher Prairie and Paris and New York; se-cretly, they knew that she was strange and beautiful beyond all the other cities of the earth.

CHAPTER II

Shad Ampersand, old Corn's grandson, lived in a neat $26,500 bun-galow called Christmas Past, on Revenant Heights, overlooking the brisk, aspiring town. He was a tall, ramshackle hayrick of a man of fifty-six, copper red (a testimony, it was whispered, to old Corn's prow-ess with the squaws) and sad of eye, like a water spaniel or an early Donatello. An admirer of loneliness and rye whiskey and thin, hawk-vivid girls, who listened with vast politeness while he explained such recondite matters as Arbitrary Microcosm, Limited Frame of Refer-ence, Elementary Symbolism, and Dated or Synthetic Idiom, about all of which they knew precisely nothing and most enthusiastically cared even less.

Sitting on his tiny porch on one of the brightest, briefest, and most poignant of all October afternoons, Shad was very weightily consider-ing the profound mystery of Sex.

"I'm not one of these highbrow geezers like W. Somerset Maugham or John Q. Galsworthy," he plondered heavily, "and it sure gives me a pain in the ole bazookus to hear some long-haired so-called intel-lectual claiming that love and marriage and kiddies and everything a dumb ole roughneck like me has come to hold most sacred is nothing more nor less than something called the Biological Urge."

"Hey, you don't have to talk to *me* like that," said Trenda Boneside sharply. "I'm not the Pulitzer Prize Committee."

She was a small, fierce kitten of a girl, who had lived for nineteen eager, sniffing years with her parents on a farm in Remnant, just across the state line.

"M? Nope. See what you mean," he said placatingly. She was a passionate white flame on a cigar-store lighter. He tried to imagine her cooking his breakfast. Tried and most conspicuously failed.

"No, you don't at all," she snapped at him, this brisk fox terrier of a girl. "You listen to me, Shad Ampersand. I'm not one of those old girls of yours—Carol or Leora or that awful Dodsworth woman, whatever *her* name was."

"Fran," he said humbly.

"Fran. Well, anyway, I'm not. Maybe that old hillbilly talk was all right for them, and even the *American Mercury*. But with me you can just talk like anybody else."

"M."

"That's another thing!" she cried furiously. "That 'M'! What the hell is that supposed to be? The name of a moving picture?"

"Gee, Tren," he sighed. "It's only an experiment in phonetics. You know, how to get something down the way it really sounds. As I was telling ole Doc Bongflap . . ."

Now she was really a tigress.

" 'Bongflap,' " she wailed. "I've known you for a long time, Shad Ampersand, and I've certainly heard some terrible names—Vergil Gunch and Roscoe Geake and Adelbert Shoop—but that's the worst ever. Nobody in the world was ever called Bongflap."

"Well, maybe not, but, drat it, when an author wants to suggest how a character . . ."

"I know all about that," she said, "and I know all about Charles Dickens, too, and you both make me sick. My God, even *Tarkington* wouldn't call anybody Bongflap. Or Timberlane, either, for that matter. Timber*lane*. Timber*line*. Hansen and Chamberlain ought to be able to get that one, all right, but I think it stinks. I keep thinking it's Tamberlane or Timberleg."

"Aren't we getting a little off the subject, Tren?" he said mildly.

"I don't know. What *was* the subject?"

"Well, uh, love."

"Oh, *that*," she yawned. "What about it?"

"Well, uh," he fumbled. She was a laughing brook of a girl, cool, diamond-bright, a wanderer in secret loveliness. He dreamed of her in a gingham apron, cooking his breakfast. Golly! "Uh, I thought we might get married," he whinnied. It was so perhaps that Paris whispered to Helen before they came to the City of the Topless Towers, so the Roman gave his soul to Egypt's queen on the dreaming bosom of the

Nile. She looked at him and suddenly her heart was in her eyes.

"Shad!" she trilled, and now she was a bell.

"Wife!" he clamored through their urgent kiss, and miraculously it was a word in nowise stained with use.

CHAPTER III

The little orange cat called Pox stretched languorously in Shad Ampersand's lap.

"I know you're lonely since your wife, Trenda, left you last November to join Blight Grimes, the polo player and nimble seducer, at his hotel in Chicago, Illinois," she mewed. She was a very fetching device of a cat, an explanatory butler at curtain rise in a Lonsdale comedy.

Shad scratched her ears and thought: I should have known all along about Tren and Blight. The time they went away together for a week back in March and Trenda said—oh, she was very innocent and airy about it!—that they'd just gone up to Alaska to look at polo ponies; the time I found them upstairs in bed and they said they were just lying down because their feet hurt. I must have been pretty credulous, he decided, and Pox blinked her copper eyes in sardonic agreement.

"You're damn right," she purred, "but now, of course, she has delirium tremens and this Grimes character isn't exactly the kind of man you can picture running up and down stairs with paraldehyde and strait jackets. There's a strange streak of cruelty in him."

He nodded, but he was thinking despairingly: I must have failed her somehow. Maybe I was wrong to want to keep her here in Christmas Past, pasting up scrapbooks for an old galoot like me—Blight, doggone his hide, was only forty-nine and lithe and puissant as a sword—when she ought to be running around with kids her own age, going to the movies and coming out with her head all full of stars and dreams (as a matter of fact, he knew she loathed the movies), having a soda with the Gang at Bleeck's and feeding nickels into the juke box for "Smiles" and "Margie," maybe even being kissed, in sweet and childish innocence, in the back seat of a Chevrolet.

"Pope Hartford," said Pox, who was also a mind-reader.

"M?"

"Pope Hartford," repeated the cat irritably. "You might as well stick to the period. And while I think of it, you can lay off that 'M' with *me*, too."

Anyway, he had failed her, his lost and golden girl, and she was in Chicago with Blight. He looked at his watch. 11:46. Probably they were back from the theatre now and up in their suite and Blight was slipping the little silver-fox cape from her shoulders.

"His heart contracted," murmured Pox.

"M, uh, I mean what?"

"Don't keep making me say everything twice, for God's sake. 'His heart contracted.' That goes in there somewhere. In parentheses. After the second 'and,' I should say. It's one of your mannerisms, though not a very fortunate one. Also, you seem to have forgotten that she's on the sauce, if you'll pardon the expression."

Trenda spifflicated, swizzled, tiddly. He knew it was the truth, but the thought was a sharp agony, an unthinkable desecration, as if he saw the slender, terrible beauty of the Samothrace deep in foul mud and marred with the droppings of obscene and dreadful birds.

"I think you're overreaching yourself there," said Pox. "Too many modifiers, and it's a pretty elaborate image. After all, you aren't Henry James."

"Golly, Pox—"

"Ah, the hell with it. Let it go. It's your stream of consciousness, thank God, not mine."

In his despair, his cold, unutterable loss, Shad Ampersand began to think of all the world, and Pox looked at him sharply for a moment and then hopped off his lap and left the room. Shad thought: Marriage. A man and a woman—him and Tren, Romeo and Juliet, Philemon and Baucis, Ruth and, and, drat it, who *was* that guy—anyway, they fell in love—oh, Tren, sweet, we *must* have been in love the night we read "Gideon Planish" until the stars went out!—and they promised to love, honor, and obey—golly, the most beautiful words in the English language, except, of course, maybe some parts of Shakespeare—till death you did part. But then something happened. One day they woke up and the magic was gone. (He and Tren were having breakfast, Homogenized Virtex and Spookies, and suddenly, appallingly, she cried, "Shad! I'm going away with Blight! Right this minute! He's going to take me to London, Paris, Berlin— Gee, I've always wanted to see the Taj Mahal and all those cute little Androgynes or whatever you call 'em—and we're going to take along a sleeping bag, you know, like in that Hemingway book I read some of, and camp right out on the biggest darn ole Alp we can find." He had burbled, "Gee, that sounds mighty interesting, Tren. Yes, sir. Like to take a little trip sometime myself," but the Spookies were ashes in his mouth.) Anyway, it always ended—either in the hideous, clinging slime of the divorce court, or else—and this was unutterably worse—in the terrible, icy vacuum of indifference, the final, shameful acceptance of infidelity. ("You ought to get yourself a girl, Shad," she had told him one night; as usual, she was sitting on Blight's lap, knitting a new-fangled sock. "Why don't you call up Avis Cormorant? *There's* a cheerful little giver for you. Or maybe one of those Piutes you say old Corn was always talking about." He had almost struck her then.) It was this, this modern cynicism, this flat denial of marriage, not the Communists or the Fascists or the Technocrats or even the hot-eyed disciples of Fourier and Adam Smith, that was destroying America. In the ultimate scheme of things, the continuing marriage of Tren and Shad Ampersand, or, if you chose, of plain Helen and Robert Lynd, was more important than—

"Hey," said Pox, putting his head around the door, "I wouldn't disturb you, except you didn't seem to be getting anywhere in particular with that editorial. Anyway, she's back."

"Who?" spurted Shad, though his heart obliteratingly knew.

"Who the hell did you think?" said Pox scornfully. "Little Round Heels. With a hangover I could swing on by my tail."

She came in then, with a glad, unsteady rush, a broken cry, into his waiting arms, and if she was damaged, if she was no longer the bright, imperious child his dreams had known, but something harder, wiser, and infinitely sad, he had no eyes to see.

"Tren, baby!" he whispered fiercely in her hair.

"Shad!" she breathed, and gave him the ruined glory of her smile. After all, she thought, stroking the remembered kindness of his cheek, you always have to figure that the old horror is practically indestructible, there ought to be plenty of books still batting around in him for all the endless years to come.

"Nice going, sister," murmured Pox, and most discreetly shut the door.

E. B. White

ACROSS THE STREET
AND INTO THE GRILL

(*With respects to Ernest Hemingway*)

THIS is my last and best and true and only meal, thought Mr.
Perley as he descended at noon and swung east on the beat-up
sidewalk of Forty-fifth Street. Just ahead of him was the girl from the
reception desk. I am a little fleshed up around the crook of the elbow,
thought Perley, but I commute good.

He quickened his step to overtake her and felt the pain again. What
a stinking trade it is, he thought. But after what I've done to other
assistant treasurers, I can't hate anybody. Sixteen deads, and I don't
know how many possibles.

The girl was near enough now so he could smell her fresh receptive-
ness, and the lint in her hair. Her skin was light blue, like the sides of
horses.

"I love you," he said, "and we are going to lunch together for the
first and only time, and I love you very much."

"Hello, Mr. Perley," she said, overtaken. "Let's not think of anything."

A pair of fantails flew over from the sad old Guaranty Trust Company, their wings set for a landing. A lovely double, thought Perley,
as he pulled. "Shall we go to the Hotel Biltmore, on Vanderbilt Avenue, which is merely a feeder land for the great streets, or shall we go to
Schrafft's, where my old friend Botticelli is captain of girls and where
they have the mayonnaise in fiascos?"

"Let's go to Schrafft's," said the girl, low. "But first I must phone
Mummy." She stepped into a public booth and dialled true and well,
using her finger. Then she telephoned.

As they walked on, she smelled good. She smells good, thought
Perley. But that's all right, I add good. And when we get to Schrafft's,
I'll order from the menu, which I like very much indeed.

They entered the restaurant. The wind was still west, ruffling the edges of the cookies. In the elevator, Perley took the controls. "I'll run it," he said to the operator. "I checked out long ago." He stopped true at the third floor, and they stepped off into the men's grill.

"Good morning, my Assistant Treasurer," said Botticelli, coming forward with a fiasco in each hand. He nodded at the girl, who he knew was from the West Seventies and whom he desired.

"Can you drink the water here?" asked Perley. He had the fur trapper's eye and took in the room at a glance, noting that there was one empty table and three pretty waitresses.

Botticelli led the way to the table in the corner, where Perley's flanks would be covered.

"Alexanders," said Perley. "Eighty-six to one. The way Chris mixes them. Is this table all right, Daughter?"

Botticelli disappeared and returned soon, carrying the old Indian blanket.

"That's the same blanket, isn't it?" asked Perley.

"Yes. To keep the wind off," said the Captain, smiling from the backs of his eyes. "It's still west. It should bring the ducks in tomorrow, the chef thinks."

Mr. Perley and the girl from the reception desk crawled down under the table and pulled the Indian blanket over them so it was solid and good and covered them right. The girl put her hand on his wallet. It was cracked and old and held his commutation book. "We are having fun, aren't we?" she asked.

"Yes, Sister," he said.

"I have here the soft-shelled crabs, my Assistant Treasurer," said Botticelli. "And another fiasco of the 1926. This one is cold."

"Dee the soft-shelled crabs," said Perley from under the blanket. He put his arm around the receptionist good.

"Do you think we should have a green pokeweed salad?" she asked. "Or shall we not think of anything for a while?"

"We shall not think of anything for a while, and Botticelli would bring the pokeweed if there was any," said Perley. "It isn't the season." Then he spoke to the Captain. "Botticelli, do you remember when we took all the mailing envelopes from the stockroom, spit on the flaps, and then drank rubber cement till the foot soldiers arrived?"

"I remember, my Assistant Treasurer," said the Captain. It was a little joke they had.

"He used to mineograph pretty good," said Perley to the girl. "But that was another war. Do I bore you, Mother?"

"Please keep telling me about your business experiences, but not the rough parts." She touched his hand where the knuckles were scarred and stained by so many old mimeographings. "Are both your flanks covered, my dearest?" she asked, plucking at the blanket. They felt the Alexanders in their eyeballs. Eighty-six to one.

"Schrafft's is a good place and we're having fun and I love you," Perley said. He took another swallow of the 1926, and it was a good and careful swallow. "The stockroom men were very brave," he said, "but it is a position where it is extremely difficult to stay alive. Just outside that room there is a little bare-assed highboy and it is in the way of the stuff that is being brought up. The hell with it. When you make a breakthrough, Daughter, first you clean out the baskets and the half-wits, and all the time they have the fire escapes taped. They also shell you with old production orders, many of them approved by the general manager in charge of sales. I am boring you and I will not at this time discuss the general manager in charge of sales as we are unquestionably being listened to by that waitress over there who is setting out the decoys."

"I am going to give you my piano," the girl said, "so that when you look at it you can think of me. It will be something between us."

"Call up and have them bring the piano to the restaurant," said Perley. "Another fiasco, Botticelli!"

They drank the sauce. When the piano came, it wouldn't play. The keys were stuck good. "Never mind, we'll leave it here, Cousin," said Perley.

They came out from under the blanket and Perley tipped their waitress exactly fifteen per cent minus withholding. They left the piano in the restaurant, and when they went down the elevator and out and turned in to the old, hard, beat-up pavement of Fifth Avenue and headed south toward Forty-fifth Street, where the pigeons were, the air was as clean as your grandfather's howitzer. The wind was still west.

I commute good, thought Perley, looking at his watch. And he felt the old pain of going back to Scarsdale again.

IX. THE NEXT VERSE
YOU HEAR

Franklin P. Adams

SIGNAL SERVICE

Time-table! Terrible and hard
　　To figure! At some station lonely
We see this sign upon the card:
*

We read thee wrong; the untrained eye
　　Does not see always with precision.
The train we thought to travel by
†

Again, undaunted, we look at
　　The hieroglyphs, and as a rule a
Small double dagger shows us that
‡

And when we take a certain line
　　On Tues., Wednes., Thurs., Fri., Sat., or Monday,
We're certain to detect the sign:
§

Heck Junction—Here she comes! Fft! Whiz!
   A scurry—and the train has flitted!
Again we look. We find it—viz.,
‖

Through hieroglyphic seas we wade—
   Print is so cold and so unfeeling.
The train we await at Neverglade
¶

Now hungrily the sheet we scan
   Grimy with travel, thirsty, weary,
And then—nothing is sadder than
☞

Yet, cursèd as is every sign,
   The cussedest that we can quote is
This treacherous and deadly line:
    *
 * *

---

    * Train 20: stops on signal only.
  † Runs only on North-west division.
   ‡ Train does not stop at Ashtabula.
    § $10 extra fare ex. Sunday.
‖ Train does not stop where time omitted.
  ¶ Connects with C. & A. at Wheeling.
    ☞ No diner on till after Erie.
 *
* * Subject to change without our notice.

BASEBALL PLAYER

In Spring, when it's cold out
Appears the baseball hold-out;
In spring, when it's warm out
He gets his uniform out.

FREQUENTLY

I shot a poem into the air
It was reprinted everywhere
From Bangor to the Rocky Range
And always credited to (Exchange).

ADVICE TO YOUNG MEN

Never smash thy promise, lad;
Never break thy word;
Never kiss a lady's lips,
Lest thou seem absurd.
Be a rock the girls can trust;
Never tell a lie;
Never come thou back again
When they say goodby.
Never let them wonder, lad,
If thou'lt be on time;
Pay thy debts with diamonds,
Never with a rhyme.

Never be a wastrel, lad;
Never fool a maid;
Make of honor a business,
Make of truth a trade.
Do thou as I tell thee, lad;
Be the best of men:
And girls won't write of thee in verse,
Nor think of thee again.

Richard Armour

MINIATURE

My day-old son is plenty scrawny,
His mouth is wide with screams, or yawny,
His ears seem larger than he's needing,
His nose is flat, his chin's receding,
His skin is very, very red
He has no hair upon his head,
And yet I'm proud as proud can be
To hear you say he looks like me.

'TWAS THE NIGHT (LATE)
BEFORE CHRISTMAS

'Twas the night before Christmas, and all through the house
Two creatures were stirring—just me and my spouse.
To attic and cellar we secretly sped
As soon as the children lay safely in bed,
And in many a closet, as busy as elves,
Pulled down all the parcels stacked high on the shelves.

We brought in the tree, which we found much too tall,
And we topped it and lopped it and stopped it from fall;
We tore up some boxes and badly behaved
While seeking the tinsel we *thought* we had saved.
And then, upon chairs and with foothold precarious,
We hung up our ornaments many and various.

The tree now resplendent, except for the fact
That the lights wouldn't light (a connection we lacked),
We filled up the stockings—a job not done quickly—
And vacuumed the rugs, which were tinselled so thickly,
And then, when we'd read and reread the directions,
Assembled the toys that had come in all sections.

The hour was now midnight and quite a bit past,
But our labors, thank Heaven, were finished at last . . .
As we gazed at our efforts through lead-lidded eyes
And thought of the morrow and shouts of surprise,
We prayed that the children, the morn of St. Nick's
Would please not awaken at least until six!

Morris Bishop

AMBITION

I got pocketed behind 7X–3824;
He was making 65, but I can do a little more.
I crowded him on the curves, but I couldn't get past,
And on the straightaways there was always some truck coming
     fast.
Then we got to the top of a mile-long incline
And I edged her out to the left, a little over the white line,
And ahead was a long grade with construction at the bottom,
And I said to the wife, "Now by golly I got'm!"
I bet I did 85 going down the long grade,
And I braked her down hard in front of the barricade
And I swung in ahead of him and landed fine
Behind 9W–7679.

MERRY OLD SOULS

Old Ben Franklin was a merry old soul,
He walked up Market Street munching on a roll,
And a girl laughed loud, and her laughter was so ranklin'
That Old Ben Franklin made her Mrs. Ben Franklin.

Old Julius Caesar was a merry old soul,
To be a Roman Emperor was all his goal.
But he put away the crown; he was such an old teaser
That the mob put the finger on Caius Julius Caesar.

Old Isaac Newton was a merry old soul,
He invented gravitation when out for a stroll;
And no one up to now has succeeded in refutin'
The good old hypothesis of Old Isaac Newton.

Rabelais also was a merry old soul;
Many of his writings are very very droll.
Censors in the custom-house treat him rather shabbily
By cutting out the better bits of Master Francis Rabelais.

T. A. Daly

MIA CARLOTTA

Giuseppe, da barber, ees greata for "mash,"
He gotta da bigga, da blacka moustache,
Good clo'es an' good styla an' playnta good cash.

W'enevra Giuseppe ees walk on da street,
Da peopla dey talka, "how nobby! how neat!
How softa da handa, how smalla da feet."

He leefta hees hat an' he shaka hees curls,
An' smila weeth teetha so shiny like pearls;
Oh, manny da heart of da seelly young girls
> He gotta.
>> Yes, playnta he gotta—
>>> But notta
>>> Carlotta!

Giuseppe, da barber, he maka da eye,
An' lika da steam engine puffa an' sigh,
For catcha Carlotta w'en she ees go by.

Carlotta she walka weeth nose in da air,
An' look through Giuseppe weeth far-away stare,
As eef she no see dere ees som'body dere.

Giuseppe, da barber, he gotta da cash,
He gotta da clo'es an' da bigga moustache,
He gotta da seelly young girls for da "mash,"
> But notta—
> You bat my life, notta—
>> Carlotta.
>> I gotta!

Irwin Edman

ON HEARING FRENCH CHILDREN
SPEAK FRENCH

Children—a well-known circumstance—
Speak French extremely well in France;
Their accent, to the wondering ear,
Is perfect, and their diction clear.

But when I watch them at their play,
They might be kids in Deal, N. J.
Like girls and boys one sees about
At home, they tumble, run, and shout;
Like others of their age and ilk,
They dote on sweets, they thrive on milk;
They are, their mothers sadly sigh,
Petits bébés, as here they're styled,
Cry very like my neighbor's child.

I, noting thus what's said and done,
Judge the world is, or should be, one;
It is the planet's blackest blot
That it should be—and that it's not.

NOTE ON GERIATRICS

Few people know how to be old—*La Rochefoucauld*

Very few, so we are told,
Are skilled at all in being old,
And of those few, few will admit
To age, whatso they make of it,
And when they do admit it, sadly,
They act their years but do it badly.
Midnight, when they should be abed,
They're mostly on the town instead;
Their passions, which should now be
Quiet,
Break out anew in ill-timed riot;
The elders they should drowse among
They snub, to gambol with the young.
An old man is not, as a rule,
Too old to be much less a fool.

But as one looks about, one fears
Few manage well their middle years,

Or are, in their pretended prime,
Clever with love or wealth or time.
How awkward, too, and how uncouth,
The young are in their use of youth,
And babes, as anyone can see,
Make shambles of their infancy.

The old mess up their day, but, oh,
They're not alone, La Rochefoucauld!

Margaret Fishback

HELL'S BELLS

The ambulance flies at a furious gait
That registers utter defiance of Fate
As clanging through traffic quite agile and supple,
It picks up one person and knocks down a couple.

From *One to a Customer*, copyright, 1932, by E. P. Dutton & Co., Inc.

ATTENTION: SUNBURN ENTHUSIASTS

Blister your shoulders,
Blister your knees,
Blister yourself
Anywhere you damn please,
Turn yourself into
An ash or an ember,
But when you've done so
I hope you'll remember
I shall not feel
That my presence is vital,

From *One to a Customer*, copyright, 1931, by Margaret Fishback; copyright, 1932, by E. P. Dutton & Co., Inc. Originally in *The New Yorker*.

No matter where
You may stage your recital.

INFANT PRODIGY

At six weeks Baby grinned a grin
That spread from mouth to eyes to chin,
And Doc, the smartie, had the brass
To tell me it was only gas!

Arthur Guiterman

ANTHOLOGISTICS

Since one anthologist put in his book
Sweet things by Morse, Bone, Potter, Bliss and Brook,
All subsequent anthologists, of course
Have quoted Bliss, Brook, Potter, Bone and Morse.
For, should some rash anthologist make free
To print selections, say, from you and me,
Omitting with a judgment all his own
The classic Brook, Morse, Potter, Bliss and Bone,
Contemptuous reviewers, passing by
Our verses, would unanimously cry,
"What manner of anthology is this
That leaves out Bone, Brook, Potter, Morse and Bliss!"

Samuel Hoffenstein

POEMS IN PRAISE
OF PRACTICALLY NOTHING

From "Love Songs, at Once Tender and Informative"

Satyrs used to fall for nymphs,
Just the same as other symphs;
Same as many a modern goof,
Cupid kept them on the hoof.

A woman, like the touted Sphinx,
Sits, and God knows what she thinks;
Hard-boiled men, who never fall,
Say she doesn't think at all.

Breathes there a man with hide so tough
Who says two sexes aren't enough?

Maid of Gotham, ere we part,
Have a hospitable heart—
Since our own delights must end,
Introduce me to your friend.

She gave me her heart—
Oh, the sweetness of it!
She gave me her hand—
The petiteness of it!

Little bride, come over here,
Tell me where you'll be next year;
Quite unfearful of my doom,
I should like to know with whom.

If you love me, as I love you,
We'll both be friendly and untrue.

Your little hands,
Your little feet,
Your little mouth—
Oh, God, how sweet!

Your little nose,
Your little ears,
Your eyes, that shed
Such little tears!

Your little voice,
So soft and kind;
Your little soul,
Your little mind!

My mate, my friend, my love, my life,
My bosom's—as the phrase is—wife;
My comrade in the hour of woe—
An hour whose limits I don't know—
My star in darkness, solace, balm,
My prophylaxis, refuge, calm,
Companion of the million blights
That plague my liver, purse and lights;
My pleasant garden in the gloam,
My all—if you were ever home!
When you're away, I'm restless, lonely,
Wretched, bored, dejected; only
Here's the rub, my darling dear,
I feel the same when you are here.

Newman Levy

THAIS

One time, in Alexandria, in wicked Alexandria,
Where nights were wild with revelry and life was but a game,
There lived, so the report is, an adventuress and courtesan,
The pride of Alexandria, and Thais was her name.

Nearby, in peace and piety, avoiding all society,
There dwelt a band of holy men who'd built a refuge there;
And in the desert's solitude they spurned all earthly folly to
Devote their days to holy works, to fasting and to prayer.

Now one monk whom I solely mention of this group of holy men
Was known as Athanael; he was famous near and far.
At fasting bouts or prayer with him no other could compare with him;
At ground and lofty praying he could do the course in par.

One night while sleeping heavily (from fighting with the devil he
Had gone to bed exhausted while the sun was shining still),
He had a vision Freudian, and though he was annoyed he an-
Alyzed it in the well-known style of Doctors Jung and Brill.

He dreamed of Alexandria, of wicked Alexandria;
A crowd of men were cheering in a manner rather rude
At Thais, who was dancing there, and Athanael, glancing there,
Observed her do the shimmy in what artists call The Nude.

Said he, "This dream fantastical disturbs my thoughts monastical;
Some unsuppressed desire, I fear, has found my monkish cell.
I blushed up to the hat o' me to view that girl's anatomy,
I'll go to Alexandria and save her soul from Hell."

From *Opera Guyed*, copyright, 1923, by Alfred A. Knopf, Inc.

So, pausing not to wonder where he'd put his summer underwear,
He quickly packed his evening clothes, his tooth brush and a vest.
To guard against exposure he threw in some woollen hosiery,
And bidding all the boys good-by, he started on his quest.

The monk, though warned and fortified, was deeply shocked and
     mortified
To find, on his arrival, wild debauchery in sway.
While some lay in a stupor sent by booze of more than two per cent.,
The others were behaving in a most immoral way.

Said he to Thais, "Pardon me. Although this job is hard on me,
I gotta put you wise to what I come down here to tell.
What's all this sousin' gettin' you? Cut out this pie-eyed retinue;
Let's hit the trail together, kid, and save yourself from Hell."

Although this bold admonishment caused Thais some astonishment,
She coyly answered, "Say, you said a heaping mouthful, bo.
This burg's a frost, I'm telling you. The brand of hooch they're
     selling you
Ain't like the stuff we used to get, so let's pack up and go."

So forth from Alexandria, from wicked Alexandria,
Across the desert sands they go beneath the blazing sun;
Till Thais, parched and sweltering, finds refuge in the sheltering
Seclusion of a convent, and the habit of a nun.

But now the monk is terrified to find his fears are verified;
His holy vows of chastity have cracked beneath the strain.
Like one who has a jag on he cries out in grief and agony,
"I'd sell my soul to see her do the shimmy once again."

Alas! his pleadings clamorous, though passionate and amorous,
Have come too late; the courtesan has danced her final dance.
The monk says, "That's a joke on me, for that there dame to croak
     on me.
I hadn't oughter passed her up the time I had the chance."

David McCord

HIGHBOY, LOWBOY, OBOY!

"Come, my love, and let us stoppë
In our ancient jade jaloppë
At ye oldë moldë shoppë:
Fine Antiques—to sell or swappë.
Out you hoppë, in we poppë."

"Lawsy, what a table toppë!"
"Lazy Susan? That's a coppë."
"Grant's old razor!"   "Where's the stroppë?"
"Snuffbox . . . pewter . . . London foppë . . ."
Flip glass?"   "Careful, now. Don't droppë!"

"See that curious, *curious* moppë!"
"Buggy whips!—the old clip-cloppë
Days!"   "A pruning knife . . . to loppë?"
"Burbank owned it."   "Will you ploppë
Down five bucks for these sweet sloppë
Jars?"   "That's much too much—*de troppë!*"

EPITAPH ON A WAITER

By and by
God caught his eye.

TO A CERTAIN CERTAINLY
CERTAIN CRITIC

He takes the long review of things;
He asks and gives no quarter
And you can sail with him on wings
Or read the book. It's shorter.

Phyllis McGinley

I HATE BACHELORS

Married men have paunches
   And feeble repartee.
Their conversation launches
   Upon a charted sea.
Married men with loathing
   Regard the hour grown late
And cling to formal clothing
   Some seasons out of date.
But whether plump or harried,
   With thinning hair or hoar,
I love a man that's married
   Above a bachelor.

For, marital saints or domestic sinners,
They come on time to your festive dinners,
Come, unattended by hound or terrier,
And don't leave early for some place merrier.
Talk of your progeny doesn't bore them.

They're nice to the partner you've picked out *for* them.
At passing canapés they've a knack,
And they frequently entertain you back.

Now, bachelors are witty
    And elegantly browned.
The night-enchanted city
    They know their way around.
Through fretless days and gay days
    Admired of debutantes,
They stroll, the dole of pay days
    Augmented by their aunts.
At vintages they're clever
    And their responses quick.
But I prefer forever
    The guileless benedick.

For married men pummel their friends and hearties,
But they don't bring strangers to week-end parties,
Or lend their presence upon your stairs
As if the courtesy all were theirs.
When breakfast's ready they answer roll call.
They ask permission to make a toll call.
They drink your Scotch with a word of gratitude,
And ennui isn't their natural attitude.

So when the chops are breaded
    And next the wine is poured,
That male, alone, who's wedded
    Shall revel at my board.
For bachelors are slim men
    And expert at the dance;
They're tailor-made and trim men,
    With pleatings in their pants;
They neither fetch nor carry;
    At other's cost they dine,
But till they up and marry
    They'll be no guests of mine.

*　　*　　*

THIS ONE'S ABOUT TWO IRISHMEN, OR, OLIVER AMES IS A RACONTEUR

When meekly to Judgment I come,
    When marital virtues are passed on,
For comfort I'll cling to a crumb,
    One noble attainment stand fast on.
Though manifold duties remiss in,
    Addicted to phoning my folks,
I think that They'll have to put *this* in:
    I giggled at Oliver's jokes.

The new ones, the old ones,
    The couldn't-be-sillier;
The pure and the bold ones;
    The grimly familiar;
The dialect stories
    In dubious brogue;
Entire repertories
    Some months out of vogue;
The puns; the inventions—
    Whatever their worth,
At merest of mentions
    Convulsed me with mirth.

My prowess with thimble and thread,
    Inadequate doubtless They'll judge it.
From kitchen encounters I fled.
    I wasn't much good with a budget.
That vain was my nature and idle,
    I'll likely be forced to admit.
But Oliver, stanch at my side'll
    Recall how I relished his wit.

How raptly I harked to
    Each lengthy relation
Of what he remarked to

The boys at the station.
Will tell how I nodded
Not once at a jest,
But bravely applauded
The worst with the best,
No one of the crop, sir,
So whiskered and hoar,
I ever cried, "Stop, sir,
I've heard that before."

Let wives who are clever with bills
    Or versed in the pot and the kettle,
Deride me. I scoff at their skills,
    Convinced of superior mettle.
Yes, let them go ruffle a curtain
    Or trim their ineffable toques.
This marriage is solid and certain.
    I chuckle at Oliver's jokes.

Don Marquis

excerpts from archy and mehitabel

THE COMING OF ARCHY

The circumstances of archy's first appearance are narrated in the
following extract from the Sun Dial column of the New York *Sun.*

DOBBS FERRY possesses a rat which slips out of his lair at night
and runs a typewriting machine in a garage. Unfortunately, he
has always been interrupted by the watchman before he could produce
a complete story.

It was first thought that the power which made the typewriter run
was a ghost, instead of a rat. It seems likely to us that it was both

a ghost and a rat. Mme. Blavatsky's ego went into a white horse after she passed over, and someone's personality has undoubtedly gone into this rat. It is an era of belief in communications from the spirit land.

And since this matter had been reported in the public prints and seriously received we are no longer afraid of being ridiculed, and we do not mind making a statement of something that happened to our own typewriter only a couple of weeks ago.

We came into our room earlier than usual in the morning, and discovered a gigantic cockroach jumping about upon the keys.

He did not see us, and we watched him. He would climb painfully upon the framework of the machine and cast himself with all his force upon a key, head downward, and his weight and the impact of the blow were just sufficient to operate the machine, one slow letter after another. He could not work the capital letters, and he had a great deal of difficulty operating the mechanism that shifts the paper so that a fresh line may be started. We never saw a cockroach work so hard or perspire so freely in all our lives before. After about an hour of this frightfully difficult literary labor he fell to the floor exhausted, and we saw him creep feebly into a nest of the poems which are always there in profusion.

Congratulating ourself that we had left a sheet of paper in the machine the night before so that all this work had not been in vain, we made an examination, and this is what we found:

> expression is the need of my soul
> i was once a vers libre bard
> but i died and my soul went into the body of a cockroach
> it has given me a new outlook upon life
> i see things from the under side now
> thank you for the apple peelings in the wastepaper basket
> but your paste is getting so stale i cant eat it
> there is a cat here called mehitabel i wish you would have
> removed she nearly ate me the other night why dont she
> catch rats that is what she is supposed to be for
> there is a rat here she should get without delay
>
> most of these rats here are just rats
> but this rat is like me he has a human soul in him
> he used to be a poet himself

night after night i have written poetry for you
on your typewriter
and this big brute of a rat who used to be a poet
comes out of his hole when it is done
and reads it and sniffs at it
he is jealous of my poetry
he used to make fun of it when we were both human
he was a punk poet himself
and after he has read it he sneers
and then he eats it

i wish you would have mehitabel kill that rat
or get a cat that is onto her job
and i will write you a series of poems showing how things look
to a cockroach
that rats name is freddy
the next time freddy dies i hope he wont be a rat
but something smaller i hope i will be a rat
in the next transmigration and freddy a cockroach
i will teach him to sneer at my poetry then

dont you ever eat any sandwiches in your office
i havent had a crumb of bread for i dont know how long
or a piece of ham or anything but apple parings
and paste leave a piece of paper in your machine
every night you can call me archy

The Song of Mehitabel

this is the song of mehitabel
of mehitabel the alley cat
as i wrote you before boss
mehitabel is a believer
in the pythagorean
theory of the transmigration
of the soul and she claims
that formerly her spirit
was incarnated in the body

of cleopatra
that was a long time ago
and one must not be
surprised if mehitabel
has forgotten some of her
more regal manners

i have had my ups and downs
but wotthehell wotthehell
yesterday sceptres and crowns
fried oysters and velvet gowns
and today i herd with bums
but wotthehell wotthehell
i wake the world from sleep
as i caper and sing and leap
when i sing my wild free tune
wotthehell wotthehell
under the blear eyed moon
i am pelted with cast off shoon
but wotthehell wotthehell

do you think that i would change
my present freedom to range
for a castle or moated grange
wotthehell wotthehell
cage me and i d go frantic
my life is so romantic
capricious and corybantic
and i m toujours gai toujours gai

i know that i am bound
for a journey down the sound
in the midst of a refuse mound
but wotthehell wotthehell
oh i should worry and fret
death and i will coquette
there s a dance in the old dame yet
toujours gai toujours gai

i once was an innocent kit
wotthehell wotthehell

with a ribbon my neck to fit
and bells tied onto it
o wotthehell wotthehell
but a maltese cat came by
with a come hither look in his eye
and a song that soared to the sky
and wotthehell wotthehell
and i followed adown the street
the pad of his rhythmical feet
o permit me again to repeat
wotthehell wotthehell

my youth i shall never forget
but there s nothing i really regret
wotthehell wotthehell
there s a dance in the old dame yet
toujours gai toujours gai

the things that i had not ought to
i do because i ve gotto
wotthehell wotthehell
and i end with my favorite motto
toujours gai toujours gai

boss sometimes i think
that our friend mehitabel
is a trifle too gay

Ogden Nash

WHAT'S THE MATTER, HAVEN'T YOU GOT ANY SENSE OF HUMOR?

There is at least one thing I would less rather have in the neighborhood than a gangster,

And that one thing is a practical prankster.

I feel that we should differ more sharply than Montagues and Capulets or York and Lancaster,

Me and a practical prancaster.

If there is a concentration camp in limbo, that is the spot for which I nominate them,

Not because I don't like them, but simply because I abominate them.

The born practical prankster starts out in early youth by offering people a chair,

And when they sit down it isn't there,

And he is delighted and proceeds to more complicated wheezes,

Such as ten cent X-rays to see through people's clothes with and powders to give them itches and sneezes,

And his boutonniere is something that people get squirted in the eye out of,

And their beds are what he makes apple pie out of.

Then as he matures he widens his scope,

And he is no longer content to present people with exploding cigars and chocolate creams with centers of soap,

So he dresses up as an Oriental potentate and reviews the British fleet,

Or collects a little group of kinsprits and a few pickaxes and a STREET CLOSED sign and digs up a busy street,

And if people are jumpy about their past or present private lives he hints that he is writing his memoirs and is devoting an entire chapter to their particular skeleton,

And finally he reaches the apex of his career when he slips into somebody's bathroom and fills up all the modern conveniences with water and then adds raspberry gelatin.

I have recently read with complete satisfaction of a practical prankster two of whose friends had just been married,

Which was of course in itself simply a challenge to be harried,

And it was a challenge he was eager to meet,

And he went to the roof of their hotel and tied a rope around his waist and a colleague lowered him to where he could clash a pair of cymbals outside the window of the nuptial suite,

And he weighed two hundred and eighty pounds and the rope broke,

And that to my mind is the perfect practical joke.

GENEALOGICAL REFLECTION

No McTavish
Was ever lavish.

SONG OF THE OPEN ROAD

I think that I shall never see
A billboard lovely as a tree.
Indeed, unless the billboards fall,
I'll never see a tree at all.

REFLECTIONS ON ICE-BREAKING

Candy
Is dandy
But liquor
Is quicker.

REFLECTION ON BABIES

A bit of talcum
Is always walcum.

THE RABBITS

Here's a verse about rabbits
That doesn't mention their habits.

THE PANTHER

The panther is like a leopard,
Except it hasn't been peppered.
Should you behold a panther crouch,
Prepare to say Ouch.
Better yet, if called by a panther,
Don't anther.

THE TERMITE

Some primal termite knocked on wood
And tasted it, and found it good,
And that is why your Cousin May
Fell through the parlor floor today.

WHAT'S THE USE?

Sure, deck your lower limbs in pants;
Yours are the limbs, my sweeting.
You look divine as you advance—
Have you seen yourself retreating?

MY DADDY

I have a funny daddy
Who goes in and out with me,
And everything that baby does
My daddy's sure to see,
And everything that baby says
My daddy's sure to tell.
You *must* have read my daddy's verse.
I hope he fries in hell.

From *Many Long Years Ago*, copyright, 1933, by Ogden Nash. Reprinted by permission of Little, Brown & Company.

Dorothy Parker

UNFORTUNATE COINCIDENCE

By the time you swear you're his,
    Shivering and sighing,
And he vows his passion is
    Infinite, undying—
Lady, make a note of this:
    One of you is lying.

From *The Portable Dorothy Parker*, copyright, 1926, 1927, 1944, by Dorothy Parker. Reprinted by permission of The Viking Press, Inc., New York.

SONG OF ONE OF THE GIRLS

Here in my heart I am Helen;
    I'm Aspasia and Hero, at least.
I'm Judith, and Jael, and Madame de Staël;
    I'm Salome, moon of the East.

From *The Portable Dorothy Parker*, copyright, 1926, 1927, 1944, by Dorothy Parker. Reprinted by permission of The Viking Press, Inc., New York.

Here in my soul I am Sappho;
    Lady Hamilton am I, as well.
In me Récamier vies with Kitty O'Shea,
    With Dido, and Eve, and poor Nell.

I'm of the glamorous ladies
    At whose beckoning history shook.
But you are a man, and see only my pan,
    So I stay at home with a book.

PARABLE FOR A CERTAIN VIRGIN

Oh, ponder, friend, the porcupine;
    Refresh your recollection
And sit a moment, to define
    His means of self-protection.

How truly fortified is he!
    Where is the beast his double
In forethought of emergency
    And readiness for trouble?

Recall his figure, and his shade—
    How deftly planned and clearly
For slithering through the dappled glade
    Unseen, or pretty nearly.

Yet should an alien eye discern
    His presence in the woodland,
How little has he left to learn
    Of self-defense! My good land!

For he can run, as swift as sound,
    To where his goose may hang high;
Or thrust his head against the ground
    And tunnel half to Shanghai;

Or he can climb the dizziest bough—
  Unhesitant, mechanic—
And, resting, dash from off his brow
  The bitter beads of panic;

Or should pursuers press him hot,
  One scarcely needs to mention
His quick and cruel barbs, that got
  Shakespearean attention;

Or driven to his final ditch,
  To his extremest thicket,
He'll fight with claws and molars (which
  Is not considered cricket).

How amply armored, he, to fend
  The fear of chase that haunts him!
How well prepared our little friend!—
  And who the devil wants him?

BOHEMIA

Authors and actors and artists and such
Never know nothing, and never know much.
Sculptors and singers and those of their kidney
Tell their affairs from Seattle to Sydney.
Playwrights and poets and such horses' necks
Start off from anywhere, end up at sex.
Diarists, critics, and similar roe
Never say nothing, and never say no.
People Who Do Things exceed my endurance;
God, for a man that solicits insurance!

X. A WHIFF OF GREASE PAINT

[As in the chapter devoted to light verse, these few pages can serve only as a reminder of the wonderful vein of humor abounding in really top-grade American plays, vaudeville, motion pictures, radio, and television. Whole volumes are available on the subject, but in none of them, I believe, will you find more rewarding material than in these particular favorites of my own.—EDITOR'S NOTE]

Ben Hecht and
Charles MacArthur

THREE MEMORABLE SCENES FROM BROADWAY COMEDY HITS

THE LAST SCENE FROM "THE FRONT PAGE"

(HILDY JOHNSON, star-reporter on the Chicago *Herald-Examiner*, has been threatening for years to make an honest woman of his fiancée, PEGGY GRANT. At the last moment, however, Fate, or Hildy's love for the newspaper business, or, more usually, the machinations of WALTER BURNS, Hildy's managing editor, have prevented the nuptials. Now, at last, Love seems to have conquered all.)

HILDY. Walter, I'm all washed up. I mean it this time, Walter.

PEGGY. Oh, Hildy, if I only thought you did.

HILDY. Listen, Peggy,—if I'm not telling you the absolute truth may God strike me dead right now. I'm going to New York with you to-night—if you give me this one last chance! I'll cut out drinking and swearing and everything connected with the Goddamn newspaper business. I won't even *read* a newspaper.

WALTER. Listen, Hildy, I got an idea . . .

HILDY (*to* WALTER). There's nothing you can say can make me change my mind. This time I'm through, and I *mean* it. I know I don't deserve you, Peggy. I've done everything in the world to prove that, I guess.

PEGGY. Hildy, please! Don't say things like that.

HILDY. I've gotta hell of a nerve to ask you to marry me. I'm a prize package, all right. But if you'll take me, here I am.

PEGGY. Darling, don't talk that way. I want you just the way you are. (*Anyway* PEGGY *will always remember that she said this and always forget that she didn't mean it.*)

WALTER. God, Hildy, I didn't know it was anything like this. Why didn't you *say* something? I'd be the last person in the world to want to come between you and your happiness.

HILDY (*staggered*). What?

WALTER. You ought to know that. . . . (*As* HILDY *continues to blink*) I love you, you crazy Swede! (*To* PEGGY) You're getting a great guy, Peggy.

HILDY. Never mind the Valentines. Goodbye, you lousy bohunk. (*They shake hands.*)

WALTER. You're a great newspaperman, Hildy. I'm sorry to see you go. Damn sorry.

HILDY. Well, if I ever come *back* to the business . . . (*To* PEGGY) Which I won't . . . (*To* WALTER, *his arm around* PEGGY) There's only one man I'd work for. You know that, don't you?

WALTER. I'd kill you if you ever worked for anybody else.

HILDY. Hear that, Peggy? That's my diploma. (*He hesitates*) Well, Walter . . . I don't know what to say . . . except I'm going to miss you like hell.

WALTER. Same here, son.

HILDY (*to* PEGGY). Twelve years we've been knocking around together . . . before you were born. . . . (*To* WALTER, *his face lighting up*) Remember the time we hid the missing heiress in the sauerkraut factory?

WALTER. Do I! (*To* PEGGY) Get him to tell you some time about how we stole Old Lady Haggerty's stomach . . . off the coroner's physician. We *proved* she was poisoned. . . .

HILDY (*laughing*). We had to hide for a week!

PEGGY. Darling . . .

HILDY (*back to life*). What?

PEGGY. You don't want to go to New York . . . down deep.

HILDY. Aw . . . what do you mean? I was just talking. (*With a nervous laugh*) I'd feel worse if I stayed, I guess . . .

PEGGY. Hildy, if I thought you were going to be unhappy—I mean, if you really wanted to—(*Firmly*) No. No. It's your chance to have a home and be a human being—and I'm going to make you take it.

WALTER (*to* PEGGY). Why, I wouldn't let him stay . . . Go on, Hildy, before I make you city editor.

HILDY (*starting*). Hurry up, Peggy. He means it.

WALTER (*as* PEGGY *follows*). Any objection to my kissing the bride?

HILDY (*stopping*). It's O.K. with me. (*He looks at* PEGGY. *She smiles*) Go ahead, Mrs. Johnson.

WALTER (*removing his hat and kissing her chastely*). Thank you . . . What time does your train go?

PEGGY. There's another one at twelve-forty. (*To* HILDY) We came awfully near going without you.

WALTER. New York Central, eh? (*To* HILDY) I wish there was time to get you a little wedding present . . . but it's awful short notice.

PEGGY (*straining to be gone*). Thank you, Mr. Burns, but Hildy's all the wedding present I want. . . . (*Laughing a little*) If I've really got him.

HILDY. Ah, forget it, Walter. (*He too is leaving.*)

WALTER. Hold on. I want you to have something to remember me by. You can't just leave like this. . . . (*Thoughtfully reaching for his watch*) And I know what it's going to be. . . . (*Produces the watch.*)

HILDY (*embarrassed*). Aw, Jesus, no, Walter! You make me feel like a fairy or something!

WALTER (*with affected brusqueness*). Shut up! You're going to take it, I tell you! It was a present from the Big Chief himself! And if you'll look inside . . . (*Opening the watch*) You'll find a little inscription: "To the Best Newspaperman I know." When you get to New York you can scratch out my name and put yours in its place, if you want to. . . .

HILDY. You know I wouldn't do that. . . .

WALTER. Here. . . . (*Giving him the watch.*)

HILDY. Aw, Walter! It's too good for me! I can't take it!

WALTER. You *got* to! (*To* PEGGY) *Make* him!

PEGGY. Go on, Hildy . . . if Mr. Burns wants you to. You don't want to hurt his feelings. . . . (HILDY *takes it.* WALTER *pats him on the shoulder, his face averted.*)

HILDY (*a lump in his throat*). Well, this is the first and last thing I ever got from a newspaper. . . .

PEGGY. Goodbye, Mr. Burns . . . I always had a queer opinion of you, Mr. Burns. I *still* think you're a little peculiar, but you're all right . . . underneath. I mean I think you're a peach.

WALTER (*winningly*). So are you! You look just like a little flower!

HILDY (*ushering* PEGGY *out*). Goodbye, you big baboon. . . .

PEGGY. Goodbye. . . . (*They exit.*)

WALTER (*calling after, leaning against the door*). Goodbye, Johnson! Be good to yourself . . . and the little girl. . . .

HILDY'S VOICE. The same to you and many of them!

(WALTER *waits till* HILDY *and* PEGGY *are out of sight and earshot, then closes the door. He walks slowly to the telephone. The receiver is still off the hook, the obedient* DUFFY *still on the other end.* WALTER *hesitates sentimentally, the receiver in his hand. Then he heaves a huge sigh and speaks.*)

WALTER. Duffy! . . . (*He sounds a bit tired*) Listen. I want you to send a wire to the Chief of Police of La Porte, Indiana. . . . That's right. . . . Tell him to meet the twelve-forty out of Chicago . . . New York Central . . . and arrest Hildy Johnson and bring him back here. . . . Wire him a full description. . . . The son of a bitch stole my watch!

CURTAIN

Moss Hart and
George S. Kaufman

The Opening Scene From

"The Man Who Came To Dinner"

The curtain rises on the attractive living room in the home of MR. and
MRS. ERNEST W. STANLEY, in a small town in Ohio. The STANLEYS
are obviously people of means. The room is large, comfortable, taste-
fully furnished. Double doors lead into a library; there is a glimpse of a
dining room at the rear, and we see the first half dozen steps of a
handsome curved staircase. At the other side, bay windows, the entrance hall, the outer door.

MRS. STANLEY is hovering nervously near the library doors, which are
tightly closed. She advances a step or two, retreats, advances again
and this time musters up enough courage to listen at the door. Suddenly the doors are opened and she has to leap back.

A NURSE in full uniform emerges—scurries, rather, out of the room.

An angry voice from within speeds her on her way: "Great dribbling
cow!"

MRS. STANLEY (*eagerly*). How is he? Is he coming out?

(*But the* NURSE *has already disappeared into the dining room. Simultaneously the doorbell rings—at the same time a young lad of twenty-
one,* RICHARD STANLEY, *is descending the stairs.*)

RICHARD. I'll go, Mother.

(JOHN, *a white-coated servant, comes hurrying in from the dining
room and starts up the stairs, two at a time.*)

MRS. STANLEY. What's the matter? What is it?

JOHN. They want pillows. (*And he is out of sight.*)

(*Meanwhile the* NURSE *is returning to the sickroom. The voice is heard again as she opens the doors. "Don't call yourself a doctor in my presence! You're a quack if I ever saw one!"* RICHARD *returns from the hall, carrying two huge packages and a sheaf of cablegrams.*)

RICHARD. Four more cablegrams and more packages. . . . Dad is going crazy upstairs, with that bell ringing all the time.

(*Meanwhile* JUNE, *the daughter of the house, has come down the stairs. An attractive girl of twenty. At the same time the telephone is ringing.*)

MRS. STANLEY. Oh, dear! . . . June, will you go? . . . What did you say, Richard?

RICHARD (*examining the packages*). One's from New York and one from San Francisco.

MRS. STANLEY. There was something from Alaska early this morning.

JUNE (*at the telephone*). Yes? . . . Yes, that's right.

MRS. STANLEY. Who is it?

(*Before* JUNE *can answer, the double doors are opened again and the* NURSE *appears. The voice calls after her: "Doesn't that bird-brain of yours ever function?"*)

THE NURSE. I—I'll get them right away. . . . He wants some Players Club cigarettes.

MRS. STANLEY. Players Club?

RICHARD. They have 'em at Kitchener's. I'll run down and get 'em. (*He is off.*)

JUNE (*still at the phone*). Hello. . . . Yes, I'm waiting.

MRS. STANLEY. Tell me, Miss Preen, is he—are they bringing him out soon?

MISS PREEN (*wearily*). We're getting him out of bed now. He'll be out very soon . . . Oh, thank you.

(*This last is to* JOHN, *who has descended the stairs with three or four pillows.*)

MRS. STANLEY. Oh, I'm so glad. He must be very happy.

(*And again we hear the invalid's voice as* MISS PREEN *passes into the room. "Trapped like a rat in this hell-hole! Take your fishhooks off me!"*)

JUNE (*at the phone*). Hello. . . . Yes, he's here, but he can't come to the phone right now . . . London? (*She covers the transmitter with her hand*) It's London calling Mr. Whiteside.

MRS. STANLEY. London? My, my!

JUNE. Two o'clock? Yes, I think he could talk then. All right. (*She hangs up*) Well, who do you think that was? Mr. H. G. Wells.

MRS. STANLEY (*wild-eyed*). H. G. Wells? On our telephone? (*The doorbell again.*)

JUNE. I'll go. This is certainly a busy house.

(*In the meantime* SARAH, *the cook, has come from the dining room with a pitcher of orange juice.*)

MRS. STANLEY (*as* SARAH *knocks on the double doors*). Oh, that's fine, Sarah. Is it fresh?

SARAH. Yes, ma'am.

(*The doors are opened;* SARAH *hands the orange juice to the* NURSE. *The voice roars once more: "You have the touch of a sex-starved cobra!"*)

SARAH (*beaming*). His voice is just the same as on the radio.

(*She disappears into the dining room as* JUNE *returns from the entrance hall, ushering in two friends of her mother's,* MRS. DEXTER *and* MRS. MC CUTCHEON. *One is carrying a flowering plant, partially wrapped; the other is holding, with some care, what turns out to be a jar of calf's-foot jelly.*)

THE LADIES. Good morning!

MRS. STANLEY. Girls, what do you think? He's getting up and coming out today!

MRS. MC CUTCHEON. You don't mean it!

MRS. DEXTER. Can we stay and see him?

MRS. STANLEY. Why, of course—he'd love it. Girls, do you know what just happened?

JUNE (*departing*). I'll be upstairs, Mother, if you want me.

MRS. STANLEY. What? . . . Oh, yes. June, tell your father he'd better come down, will you? Mr. Whiteside is coming out.

MRS. DEXTER. Is he really coming out today? I brought him a plant—Do you think it's all right if I give it to him?

MRS. STANLEY. Why, I think that would be lovely.

MRS. MC CUTCHEON. And some calf's-foot jelly.

MRS. STANLEY. Why, how nice! Who do you think was on the phone just now? H. G. Wells, from London. And look at those cablegrams. He's had calls and messages from all over this country and Europe. The New York *Times*, and Radio City Music Hall—I don't know why *they* called—and Felix Frankfurter, and Dr. Dafoe, the Mount Wilson Observatory—I just can't tell you what's been going on.

MRS. DEXTER. There's a big piece about it in this week's *Time*. Did you see it? (*Drawing it out of her bag.*)

MRS. STANLEY. No—really?

MRS. MC CUTCHEON. Your name's in it too, Daisy. It tells all about the whole thing. Listen: "Portly Sheridan Whiteside, critic, lecturer, wit, radio orator, intimate friend of the great and near great, last week found his celebrated wit no weapon with which to combat a fractured hip. The Falstaffian Mr. Whiteside, trekking across the country on one of his annual lecture tours, met his Waterloo in the shape of a small piece of ice on the doorstep of Mr. and Mrs. Ernest W. Stanley, of Mesalia, Ohio. Result: Cancelled lectures and disappointment to thousands of adoring clubwomen in Omaha, Denver, and points west. Further result: The idol of the air waves rests until further notice in home of surprised Mr. and Mrs. Stanley. Possibility: Christmas may be postponed this year." What's *that* mean?

MRS. STANLEY. Why, what do you think of that? (*She takes the magazine; reads*) "A small piece of ice on the doorstep of Mr. and Mrs. Ernest"—think of it!

MRS. MC CUTCHEON. Of course if it were *my* house, Daisy, I'd have a bronze plate put on the step, right where he fell.

MRS. STANLEY. Well, of course I felt terrible about it. He just never goes to dinner anywhere, and he finally agreed to come here, and then *this* had to happen. Poor Mr. Whiteside! But it's going to be so wonderful having him with us, even for a little while. Just think of it! We'll sit around in the evening and discuss books and plays, all the great people he's known. And he'll talk in that wonderful way of his. He may even read "Good-bye, Mr. Chips" to us.

(MR. STANLEY, *solid, substantial—the American business man—is descending the stairs.*)

STANLEY. Daisy, I can't wait any longer. If—ah, good morning, ladies.

MRS. STANLEY. Ernest, he's coming out any minute, and H. G. Wells telephoned from London, and we're in *Time*. Look!

STANLEY (*taking the magazine*). I don't like this kind of publicity at all, Daisy. When do you suppose he's going to leave?

MRS. STANLEY. Well, he's only getting up this morning—after all, he's had quite a shock, and he's been in bed for two full weeks. He'll certainly have to rest a few days, Ernest.

STANLEY. Well, I'm sure it's a great honor, his being in the house, but it *is* a little upsetting—phone going all the time, bells ringing, messenger boys running in and out—

(*Out of the sickroom comes a business-like-looking young woman about thirty. Her name is* MARGARET CUTLER—MAGGIE *to her friends.*)

MAGGIE. Pardon me, Mrs. Stanley—have the cigarettes come yet?

MRS. STANLEY. They're on the way, Miss Cutler. My son went for them.

MAGGIE. Thank you.

MRS. STANLEY. Ah—this is Miss Cutler, Mr. Whiteside's secretary. (*An exchange of "How do you do's?"*)

MAGGIE. May I move this chair?

MRS. STANLEY (*all eagerness*). You mean he's—coming out now?

MAGGIE (*quietly*). He is indeed.

MRS. STANLEY. Ernest, call June. June! June! Mr. Whiteside is coming out!

(JOHN, *visible in the dining room, summons* SARAH *to attend the excitement.* "*Sarah! Sarah!*" SARAH *and* JOHN *appear in the dining-room entrance,* JUNE *on the stairs.* MRS. STANLEY *and the two other ladies are keenly expectant; even* MR. STANLEY *is on the qui vive. The double doors are opened once more, and* DR. BRADLEY *appears, bag in hand. He has taken a good deal of punishment, and speaks with a rather false heartiness.*)

DR. BRADLEY. Well, here we are, merry and bright. Good morning, good morning. Bring our little patient out, Miss Preen.

(*A moment's pause, and then a wheelchair is rolled through the door. It is full of pillows, blankets, and* SHERIDAN WHITESIDE. SHERIDAN WHITESIDE *is indeed portly and Falstaffian. He is wearing an elaborate velvet smoking jacket and a very loud tie, and he looks like every caricature ever drawn of him. There is a hush as the wheelchair rolls into the room. Welcoming smiles break over every face. The chair comes to a halt:* MR. WHITESIDE *looks slowly around, into each and every beaming face. His fingers drum for a moment on the arm of the chair. He looks slowly around once more. And then he speaks.*)

WHITESIDE (*quietly, to* MAGGIE). I may vomit.

MRS. STANLEY (*with a nervous little laugh*). Good morning, Mr. Whiteside. I'm Mrs. Ernest Stanley—remember? And this is Mr. Stanley.

STANLEY. How do you do, Mr. Whiteside? I hope that you are better.

WHITESIDE. Thank you. I am suing you for a hundred and fifty thousand dollars.

STANLEY. How's that? What?

WHITESIDE. I said I am suing you for a hundred and fifty thousand dollars.

MRS. STANLEY. You mean—because you fell on our steps, Mr. Whiteside?

WHITESIDE. Samuel J. Liebowitz will explain it to you in court. . . . Who are those two harpies standing there like the kiss of death? (MRS. MC CUTCHEON, *with a little gasp, drops the calf's-foot jelly. It smashes on the floor.*)

MRS. MC CUTCHEON. Oh, dear! My calf's-foot jelly.

WHITESIDE. Made from your own foot, I have no doubt. And now, Mrs. Stanley, I have a few small matters to take up with you. Since this corner druggist at my elbow tells me that I shall be confined in this mouldy mortuary for at least another ten days, due entirely to your stupidity and negligence, I shall have to carry on my activities as best I can. I shall require the exclusive use of this room, as well as that drafty sewer which you call the library. I want no one to come in or out while I am in this room.

STANLEY. What do you mean, sir?

MRS. STANLEY (*stunned*). But we have to go up the stairs to get to our rooms, Mr. Whiteside.

WHITESIDE. Isn't there a back entrance?

MRS. STANLEY. Why—yes.

WHITESIDE. Then use that. I shall also require a room for my secretary, Miss Cutler. I shall have a great many incoming and outgoing calls, so please use the telephone as little as possible. I sleep until noon and require quiet through the house until that hour. There will be five for lunch today. Where is the cook?

STANLEY. Mr. Whiteside, if I may interrupt for a moment—

WHITESIDE. You may not, sir. . . . Will you take your clammy hand off my chair? (*This last to the nurse*) . . . And now will you all leave quietly, or must I ask Miss Cutler to pass among you with a baseball bat? (MRS. DEXTER *and* MRS. MC CUTCHEON *are beating a hasty retreat, their gifts still in hand.*)

MRS. MC CUTCHEON. Well—good-bye, Daisy. We'll call you— Oh, no, we mustn't use the phone. Well—we'll see you. (*And they are gone.*)

STANLEY (*boldly*). Now look here, Mr. Whiteside—

WHITESIDE. There is nothing to discuss, sir. Considering the damage I have suffered at your hands, I am asking very little. Good day.

STANLEY (*controlling himself*). I'll call you from the office later, Daisy.

WHITESIDE. Not on this phone, please.

(STANLEY *gives him a look, but goes.*)

WHITESIDE. Here is the menu for lunch. (*He extends a slip of paper to* MRS. STANLEY.)

MRS. STANLEY. But—I've already ordered lunch.

WHITESIDE. It will be sent up to you on a tray. I am using the dining room for my guests. . . . Where are those cigarettes?

MRS. STANLEY. Why—my son went for them. I don't know why he— here, Sarah. (*She hands* SARAH *the luncheon slip*) I'll—have mine up-stairs on a tray. (SARAH *and* JOHN *depart.*)

WHITESIDE (*to* JUNE, *who has been posed on the landing during all this*). Young lady, will you either go up those stairs or come down them? I cannot stand indecision.

(JUNE *is about to speak, decides against it, and ascends the stairs with a good deal of spirit.* MRS. STANLEY *is hovering uncertainly on the steps as* RICHARD *returns with the cigarettes.*)

RICHARD. Oh, good morning. I'm sorry I was so long—I had to go to three different stores.

WHITESIDE. How did you travel? By ox-cart?

(RICHARD *is considerably taken aback. His eyes go to his mother, who motions to him to come up the stairs. They disappear together, their eyes unsteadily on* WHITESIDE.)

WHITESIDE. Is there a man in the world who suffers as I do from the gross inadequacies of the human race? (*To the* NURSE, *who is fussing around the chair again*) Take those canal boats away from me! (*She obeys, hastily*) Go in and read the life of Florence Nightingale and learn how unfitted you are for your chosen profession. (MISS PREEN *glares at him, but goes.*)

DR. BRADLEY (*heartily*). Well, I think I can safely leave you in Miss Cutler's capable hands. Shall I look in again this afternoon?

WHITESIDE. If you do, I shall spit right in your eye.

DR. BRADLEY. What a sense of humor you writers have! By the way, it isn't really worth mentioning, but—I've been doing a little writing my-self. About my medical experiences.

WHITESIDE (*quietly*). Am I to be spared nothing?

DR. BRADLEY. Would it be too much to ask you to—glance over it while you're here?

WHITESIDE (*eyes half closed, as though the pain were too exquisite to bear*). Trapped.

DR. BRADLEY (*delving into his bag*). I just happen to have a copy with me. (*He brings out a tremendous manuscript*) "Forty Years an Ohio Doctor. The Story of a Humble Practitioner."

WHITESIDE. I shall drop everything.

DR. BRADLEY. Much obliged, and I hope you like it. Well, see you on the morrow. Keep that hip quiet and don't forget those little pills. (*He goes.*)

WHITESIDE (*handing the manuscript to* MAGGIE). Maggie, will you take *Forty Years Below the Navel* or whatever it's called?

MAGGIE (*surveying him*). I must say you have certainly behaved with all of your accustomed grace and charm.

WHITESIDE. Look here, Puss—I am in no mood to discuss my behavior good or bad.

MAGGIE. These people have done everything in their power to make you comfortable. And they happen, God knows why, to look upon you with a certain wonder and admiration.

WHITESIDE. If they had looked a little more carefully at their doorstep I would not be troubling them now. I did not wish to cross their cheerless threshold. I was hounded and badgered into it. I now find myself, after two weeks of racking pain, accused of behaving without charm. What would you have me do? Kiss them?

MAGGIE (*giving up*). Very well, Sherry. After ten years I should have known better than to try to do anything about your manners. But when I finally give up this job I may write a book about it all. *Cavalcade of Insult*, or *Through the Years with Prince Charming*.

WHITESIDE. Listen, Repulsive, you are tied to me with an umbilical cord made of piano wire. And now if we may dismiss the subject of my charm, for which, incidentally, I receive fifteen hundred dollars per appearance, possibly we can go to work . . .

Howard Lindsay and
Russel Crouse

A Scene from Act II of
"Life With Father"

[Wherein Father (who never has been baptized) tries to teach his wife Vinnie (who never has learned double-entry bookkeeping) how to be an efficient housewife. *Father has turned his attention to the household accounts. He picks up one bill and emits a cry of rage.*]

FATHER. Oh, God! (*His son* CLARENCE *retreats.* FATHER *rises and holds the bill in question between thumb and forefinger as though it were too repulsive to touch.* VINNIE *comes rushing down the stairs.*)

VINNIE. What's the matter, Clare? What's wrong?

FATHER. I will *not* send this person a check!

(VINNIE *looks at it.*)

VINNIE. Why, Clare, that's the only hat I've bought since March and it was reduced from forty dollars.

FATHER. I don't question your buying the hat or what you paid for it, but the person from whom you bought it—this Mademoiselle Mimi—isn't fit to be in the hat business or any other.

VINNIE. I never went there before, but it's a very nice place and I don't see why you object to it.

FATHER (*exasperated*). I object to it because this confounded person doesn't put her name on her bills! Mimi what? Mimi O'Brien? Mimi Jones? Mimi Weinstein?

VINNIE. How do I know? It's just Mimi.

FATHER. It isn't just Mimi. She must have some other name, damn it! Now, I wouldn't make out a check payable to Charley or to Jimmy, and I won't make out a check payable to Mimi. Find out what her last name is, and I'll pay her the money.

VINNIE. All right. All right. (*She starts out.*)

FATHER. Just a minute, Vinnie, that isn't all.

VINNIE. But Cora will be leaving any minute, Clare, and it isn't polite for me—

FATHER. Never mind Cora. Sit down. (CLARENCE *goes into the hall, looks upstairs, wanders up and down the hall restlessly.* VINNIE *reluctantly sits down opposite* FATHER *at the table*) Vinnie, you know I like to live well, and I want my family to live well. But this house must be run on a business basis. I must know how much money I'm spending and what for. For instance, if you recall, two weeks ago I gave you six dollars to buy a new coffeepot—

VINNIE. Yes, because you broke the old one. You threw it right on the floor.

FATHER. I'm not talking about that. I'm simply endeavoring—

VINNIE. But it was so silly to break that nice coffeepot, Clare, and there was nothing the matter with the coffee that morning. It was made just the same as always.

FATHER. It was not! It was made in a damned barbaric manner!

VINNIE. I couldn't get another imported one. That little shop has stopped selling them. They said the tariff wouldn't let them. And that's your fault, Clare, because you're always voting to raise the tariff.

FATHER. The tariff protects America against cheap foreign labor. (*He sounds as though he is quoting*) Now I find that—

VINNIE. The tariff does nothing but put up the prices and that's hard on everybody, especially the farmer. (*She sounds as though she is quoting back.*)

FATHER (*annoyed*). I wish to God you wouldn't talk about matters you don't know a damn thing about!

VINNIE. I do too know about them. Miss Gulick says every intelligent woman should have some opinion—

FATHER. Who, may I ask, is Miss Gulick?

VINNIE. Why, she's that current-events woman I told you about and the tickets are a dollar every Tuesday.

FATHER. Do you mean to tell me that a pack of idle minded females pay a dollar apiece to hear another female gabble about the events of the day? Listen to me if you want to know anything about the events of the day!

VINNIE. But you get so excited, Clare, and besides, Miss Gulick says that our President, whom you're always belittling, prays to God for guidance and—

FATHER (*having had enough of Miss Gulick*). Vinnie, what happened to that six dollars?

VINNIE. What six dollars?

FATHER. I gave you six dollars to buy a new coffeepot and now I find that you apparently got one at Lewis & Conger's and charged it. Here's their bill: "One coffeepot—five dollars."

VINNIE. So you owe me a dollar and you can hand it right over. (*She holds out her hand for it.*)

FATHER. I'll do nothing of the kind! What did you do with that six dollars?

VINNIE. Why, Clare, I can't tell you now, dear. Why didn't you ask me at the time?

FATHER. Oh, my God!

VINNIE. Wait a moment! I spent four dollars and a half for that new umbrella I told you I wanted and you said I didn't need, but I did, very much.

(FATHER *takes his pencil and writes in the account book.*)

FATHER. Now we're getting somewhere. One umbrella—four dollars and a half.

VINNIE. And that must have been the week I paid Mrs. Tobin for two extra days' washing.

FATHER (*entering the item*). Mrs. Tobin.

VINNIE. So that was two dollars more.

FATHER. Two dollars.

VINNIE. That makes six dollars and fifty cents. And that's another fifty cents you owe me.

FATHER. I don't owe you anything. (*Stung by* VINNIE's *tactics into a determination to pin her butterfly mind down*) What you owe me is an explanation of where my money's gone! We're going over this account book item by item. (*Starts to sort the bills for the purposes of cross-examination, but the butterfly takes wing again.*)

VINNIE. I do the very best I can to keep down expenses. And you know yourself that Cousin Phoebe spends twice as much as we do.

FATHER. Damn Cousin Phoebe!—I don't wish to be told how she throws her money around.

VINNIE. Oh, Clare, how can you? And I thought you were so fond of Cousin Phoebe.

FATHER. All right, I am fond of Cousin Phoebe, but I can get along without hearing so much about her.

VINNIE. You talk about your own relatives enough.

FATHER (*hurt*). That's not fair, Vinnie. When I talk about my relatives I criticize them.

VINNIE. If I can't even speak of Cousin Phoebe—

FATHER. You can speak of her all you want to—but I won't have Cousin Phoebe or anyone else dictating to me how to run my house. Now this month's total—

VINNIE (*righteously*). I didn't say a word about her dictating, Clare—she isn't that kind!

FATHER (*dazed*). I don't know what you said, now. You never stick to the point. I endeavor to show you how to run this house on a business basis and you wind up by jibbering and jabbering about everything under the sun. If you'll just explain to me—(*Finally cornered,* VINNIE *realizes the time has come for tears. Quietly she turns them on.*)

VINNIE. I don't know what you expect of me. I tire myself out chasing up and down those stairs all day long—trying to look after your comfort—to bring up our children—I do the mending and the marketing and as if that isn't enough, you want me to be an expert bookkeeper, too.

FATHER (*touched where* VINNIE *has hoped to touch him*). Vinnie, I want to be reasonable; but can't you understand?—I'm doing all this for your own good. (VINNIE *rises with a moan.* FATHER *sighs with resignation*) I suppose I'll have to go ahead just paying the bills and hoping I've got money enough in the bank to meet them. But it's all very discouraging.

VINNIE. I'll try to do better, Clare. (FATHER *looks up into her tearful face and melts.*)

FATHER. That's all I'm asking. (*She goes to him and puts her arm around his shoulder*) I'll go down and make out the checks and sign them. (VINNIE *doesn't seem entirely consoled, so he attempts a lighter note to cheer her up*) Oh, Vinnie, maybe I haven't any right to sign those checks, since in the sight of the Lord I haven't any name at all. Do you suppose the bank will feel that way about it too—or do you think they'll take a chance? (*He should not have said this.*)

VINNIE. That's right! Clare, to make those checks good you'll have to be baptized right away.

FATHER (*retreating angrily*). Vinnie, the bank doesn't care whether I've been baptized or not!

VINNIE. Well, I care! And no matter what Dr. Lloyd says, I'm not sure we're really married.

FATHER. Damn it, Vinnie, we have four children! If we're not married now we never will be!

VINNIE. Oh, Clare, don't you see how serious this is? You've got to do something about it.

FATHER. Well, just now I've got to do something about these damn bills you've run up. (*Sternly*) I'm going downstairs.

VINNIE. Not before you give me that dollar and a half!

FATHER. What dollar and a half?

VINNIE. The dollar and a half you owe me!

FATHER (*thoroughly enraged*). I don't owe you any dollar and a half! I gave you money to buy a coffeepot for me and somehow it turned into an umbrella for you.

VINNIE. Clarence Day, what kind of a man are you? Quibbling about a dollar and a half when your immortal soul is in danger! And what's more—

FATHER. All right. All right. All right. (*He takes the dollar and a half from his change purse and gives it to her.*)

VINNIE. (*smiling*). Thank you, Clare. (VINNIE *turns and leaves the room. Her progress upstairs is a one-woman march of triumph.* FATHER *puts his purse back, gathers up his papers and his dignity, and starts out.* CLARENCE *waylays him in the arch.*)

CLARENCE. Father—you never did tell me—can I have a new suit of clothes?

FATHER. No, Clarence! I'm sorry, but I have to be firm with you, too! (*He stalks off.*)

Two Famous Radio "Feuds"

The comedy of insult predominates in radio and television. Think back to all the programs you have listened to yourself, and see how many of them earned their laughs through the device of a central character who was insulted continuously by his supporting cast. Indifferently done, this sort of thing quickly palls, but when such masters of timing and delivery as Jack Benny, Fred Allen, Edgar Bergen, and the late W. C. Fields took a hand in the proceedings, it was another story entirely.

Be sure to bear in mind that the two "feuds" described in the paragraphs following were contrived for laughs exclusively; the parties involved were firm good friends before, during, and after!

BENNY vs. ALLEN

IN JANUARY 1937, a boy violinist on Fred Allen's radio program played "The Flight of the Bumblebee." At its conclusion, he announced that he was only ten years old, prompting Allen's delighted ad-lib, "Jack Benny ought to be ashamed of himself."

On *his* next program, Benny struck back. In his native Waukegan, Illinois, he reminded Allen, he *too* had mastered "The Bumblebee" on his fiddle by the time he was ten. He had played it so often, and faithfully, in fact, that he had come down with the hives. Audiences, furthermore, cheerfully had *paid* for the privilege of listening to him.

Nonsense, thundered Allen, and produced a character who claimed to have been mayor of Waukegan at the time specified. Benny's theatre, proclaimed His Honor, had been located so deep in the woods that the ticket-taker was a bear. When he had heard Benny massacre "The Bumblebee," he had paid him off in honey.

Jack Benny now announced a new ruling: anybody working for him could listen to Allen but mustn't enjoy him. "I want you to know," he told Mary Livingston, "that I played 'The Bumblebee' long before I knew a thing about strawberry, cherry, orange, or lime Jello." "You left out raspberry," reminded the sponsor. "I'll bet the audience didn't," wired Allen.

The editor wishes to thank Jack Benny for help in preparing this material.

Fred observed at this point that Jack was growing so nervous over the feud that he had to buy himself a new set of false teeth. "They're so loose," added Fred, "that every time he takes a step they click. He called 'Hello' to me in the lobby of the Palmer House the other morning and three elevators started upstairs."

Benny finally rendered "The Bumblebee" on his own program (he plays the violin quite well, as a matter of fact; those dreadful mistakes are made deliberately). "What are you trying to do?" demanded Mary. "What do you think this thing is under my chin?" countered Jack. "Another chin?" hazarded Mary. After the number she added, "They ought to rename a town in Forida for you: Offkey West!"

The next day Jack's mother-in-law got into the act. "Speaking of of 'The Bee,'" she wired, "please send me a check for two hundred dollars."

By this time "The Flight of the Bumblebee" had buzzed its way so deep into the hearts of the public that it made the Hit Parade. "The feud had reached such proportions," writes Jack Benny, "that we kept it going for years and made it the excuse for innumerable guest shot appearances on each other's programs. There's only one reason we ever stopped. We went to work for rival cigarettes!"

W. C. FIELDS *vs.* CHARLIE McCARTHY

(Charlie, of course, is the famous wooden dummy created by ventriloquist—and humorist—Edgar Bergen)

FIELDS: *(FADE IN—SINGING)* "When you wore a tulip
                                And I drank mint julep
                                And I got a big red nose."

BERGEN: Why, W. C. Fields!
             (APPLAUSE)

CHARLIE: What an ad for black coffee. Well, if it isn't W. C., the original half-man half-nose.

FIELDS: Well, Charlie McCarthy. The woodpecker's pin-up boy. Charles, I hear you got married and raised yourself a cord of kids.

CHARLIE: I fear that isn't quite true, sir.

FIELDS: You fear. . . . Anything I hate is a polite kid.

The editor wishes to thank Edgar Bergen for permission to reprint this material.

BERGEN: Bill, it's good to see you again. How true that old proverb is, "Old friends, like old wines, are best."

FIELDS: Yes indeed, Edgar . . . especially the wine.

BERGEN: Bill, I was going to bring you a basket of fruit, but I decided to ask you what you liked best and have it sent out.

FIELDS: Brandied peaches are very nourishing—I like them squeezed. Which reminds me, somebody get me a sedative with an olive in it.

CHARLIE: Mr. Fields, is that your nose, or are you eating a tomato?

FIELDS: Very good, my little chum. You know, Charles, many's the time I've wished you could be here to fill a terrible vacancy.

CHARLIE: In your heart?

FIELDS: No. In my fireplace.

BERGEN: Mr. Fields, what does make your nose so red?

FIELDS: Edgar, my scarlet proboscis is a result of an unfortunate accident in my youth.

CHARLIE: What did you do, fall off a wagon?

FIELDS: Very funny. Tell me, Charles, is it true your father was a gate-leg table?

CHARLIE: If it is—your father was under it.

FIELDS: Why, you stunted spruce—I'll throw a Japanese beetle on you.

CHARLIE: Why, you bar fly—I'll stick a wick in your mouth and use you for an alcohol lamp.

FIELDS: Yes . . . Well, the stuff is really hard to get nowadays.

BERGEN: Well, you see, Bill, alcohol is very important to the war. They're using it in ammunition.

FIELDS: Well, praise the Lord and pass the ammunition.

BERGEN: I just read where there are two ounces of alcohol in a bullet and ten ounces of alcohol in a hand grenade.

FIELDS: Well, shake hands with an old blockbuster.

CHARLIE: I have no sympathy for a man who's intoxicated all the time.

FIELDS: A man who's intoxicated all the time doesn't need sympathy.

BERGEN: Gentlemen, please!

FIELDS: One more crack out of you, Charlie, and I'll nail some runners on your stomach and use you for a sled.

CHARLIE: Oh, you *sleigh* me.

FIELDS: Charles, if you were sawdust on a bar-room floor I'd walk eight blocks for a chocolate soda. I've never had a kid irritate me so much since the day I was born.

CHARLIE: You weren't born. . . . You were squeezed out of a bar rag. (And so on . . . indefinitely.)

John Crosby

EXCERPTS FROM *OUT OF THE BLUE*

THE EASTER PARADE

N. B. C.'s broadcast of the 1947 Easter parade on Fifth Avenue ought to serve as a warning to anyone who yearns to be an announcer. Stay out of radio, bub, or you might wind up in the same fix that confronted Ben Grauer last Sunday. Mr. Grauer was in an open car ornamented with one thousand tulips and Maggi McNellis, both, according to Mr. Grauer, spectacularly beautiful. Shortly after the broadcast started, the car turned right on Fifth Avenue, which Mr. Grauer described as the "most famous avenue in the world," a phrase which took quite a kicking around all day.

"Oh, it's a beautiful day!" shouted Mr. Grauer happily. "Here we are plumb in the center of Fifth Avenue." For a few moments he spoke feelingly of the colorful crowds. He described Miss McNellis's hat with some assistance from Miss McNellis, who last year was voted the best-dressed woman in radio.

Then things started to go wrong. "No, please lady!" A note of alarm was evident in his voice. "Yes, thanks but . . . We're having a riot here." I'm not entirely sure what was going on, but I gathered that a number of ladies were busily plucking the tulips from Mr. Grauer's car. "I'm sorry, madam. . . . No, no, you can't. No, please! Driver would you go along, please?"

It was too late, I gathered. Herb Sheldon, a fellow announcer who came along to help describe the parade, said: "Well, we lost our thousand tulips in about three seconds."

"Thousands of people wanted our lovely tulips," said Miss McNellis brightly.

Then Mr. Grauer and the N. B. C. car ran into a traffic block. "Inspector," said Mr. Grauer, summoning up all his charm, "could we go ahead there? We're from N. B. C. . . . What? . . . Oh! . . . Oh, thank you, inspector, thank you."

There was a hapless pause. "That was the voice of a high police official you just heard," said Mr. Grauer bitterly. "We have now turned off Fifth Avenue—at the request of the Police Department. I hope I'm still smiling."

The car proceeded east on Fifty-second Street, which Mr. Grauer, for lack of anything else to do, described in considerable detail. "We're now in an eddy of the Easter parade. The inspector—and all remember him lovingly this Eastertide—suggested we take our N. B. C. car down a side street."

Soon the car was sailing down Madison Avenue. "We're now behind St. Patrick's Cathedral," said Mr. Grauer helplessly. He gave a vivid description of the rear of St. Patrick's. Miss McNellis chimed in with a few historical notes about the old Whitelaw Reid house across Madison from St. Patrick's. Mr. Grauer suggested that it was a nice day. Miss McNellis, who sounded restive, described a beautiful blonde climbing into a taxi.

"She isn't wearing an Easter bonnet," said the best-dressed lady in radio, who had been brought along especially to describe Easter bonnets. "In fact, she isn't wearing a hat at all."

"Maggi," said Mr. Grauer in desperation. "See that nice policeman with the nice Easter smile? Well, smile back at him and see if he'll open that lane for us."

I could visualize Maggi smiling prettily and determinedly at the cop. "We're trying to get back to Fifth Avenue," Mr. Grauer explained to his unseen audience. He needn't have bothered. By this time we had forgotten all about the Easter parade and were caught up in the drama of the thing. Would Mr. Grauer get back to Fifth Avenue? Would Miss McNellis get a chance to describe a hat?

Apparently the cop yielded to Miss McNellis, for a moment later Mr. Grauer shouted: "Now we're heading west on Fiftieth Street. People are waving at us. Now we're back on Fifth Avenue, right in the heart of Fifth Avenue." He sounded like Ronald Colman when he finally got back to Shangri-La.

It was a brilliant but short-lived triumph because the fifteen minutes were up. "This has been a broadcast of the Fifth Avenue Easter parade," said the announcer, stretching a point. "This is Ben Grauer returning you to N. B. C., the National Broadcasting Company."

Oh, well, you can hear a description of the Easter parade any year. This one was different.

THE COMPULSIVE DRINKER

A BUNCH of the boys were whooping it up in Bleeck's saloon the other night drinking more than was good for them and singing old folk songs and some of the more recent ones. About midnight the quartet, a seedy but determined bunch of singers, began, as is their custom at that hour, that old English chantey which goes:

> "It's delicious yum yum yum.
> "It's delightful. Order some.
> "Now demand it. What's the name?
> "Piel's light beer of Broadway fame."

After they finished, Fogarty, the red-headed bass of this outfit, said mournfully: "They don't write songs like in the old days." It's a complaint familiar to most of the drinkers there, especially after midnight. "Now," he continued pugnaciously, "you take a grand old number like 'Pepsi-Cola Hits the Spot.' Nobody is writing songs like that any more." He began singing a snatch:

"Nickel, nickel, nickel, nickel."

"They took that out," Roberts, the tenor, reminded him. "It isn't a nickel any more. It's six cents."

"Inflation," said Fogarty sadly. "It's even ruining the old songs. And the new songs you can't sing at all. Now you take a song like this song I heard yesterday." He sang in his watery bass:

> "When the values go up, up, up
> "And the prices come down, down, down
> "Robert Hall this season
> "Will tell you the reason.
> "Low overhead, low overhead."

He broke off in disgust. "What sort of song is that, I ask you?

'Low overhead, low overhead.' Sir William Gilbert would turn over in his grave. Man can't open his mouth on these new lyrics."

Roberts, a dreamy and timid little drunk, spoke up. "There's another one going the rounds that's even harder." He sang it.

> "Don't be afraid to look at your hands
> "When you get through scouring pots and pans.
> "Use Ajax, new miracle cleanser
> "With exclusive foaming action."

Everyone agreed that last line foamed in the wrong places. I watched Roberts closely after that one because he is a strange little guy, what the psychiatrists call a compulsive drinker. In fact, he suffers from a lot of funny compulsions, a pushover for an advertising man. Sure enough, he started looking at his hands guiltily. He probably never scoured a pot or pan in his life but the thought had been put in his mind that he was afraid to look at his hands. I bet anything he scurried around to the grocery store the next day and bought some of that miracle cleanser.

Every one of those songs that demanded you do something, Roberts went and did it, simply because he didn't believe in taking any chances. "Don't be half safe. Don't be half safe. Don't be half safe," was his philosophy, sung to the tune of "The Volga Boatman."

I feel sorry for this little guy because I think singing commercials have wrecked his life. I remember the night we were all sitting around the back room at Bleeck's, singing. Roberts had this girl with him and Roberts, for no special reason, began singing—all by himself because no one else knew the words—that splendid old ballad:

> "You can say yes to romance.
> "Be dainty and don't take a chance.
> "Soft as a lover's caress
> "Vote for happiness."

Well, sir, this girl followed instructions to the letter; the following week she said yes to romance, married poor Roberts and has made his life miserable ever since. There's only one of these songs that ever did Roberts any good. That's the one that goes:

> "Today is Tuesday. Today is Tuesday.
> "Time for Adam, candy coated gum."

Up until the time that one got on the air, Roberts used to wander around all day Tuesday thinking in his confused way that it was

Thursday. Now he's hep to the day of the week but, come to think of it, I don't know what good that does him either.

Just then the subject of these speculations spoke up: "I got to get home. Just one more, fellows." And he began and we all joined in on that rollicking little number:

> "Kasco! Kasco! Dogs all love it so.
> "What a meaty treat is Kasco
> "K-A-S-C-O.
> "Oh where, oh where has my little dog gone?
> "He's heading for the kitchen and his
> "K-A-S-C-O."

Dr. Kronkhite

A VAUDEVILLE CLASSIC

DR. KRONKHITE and his only living patient, Mr. Dubious, last appeared in public for an extended run in 1952, when Judy Garland brought big-time vaudeville back to the Palace Theatre on Broadway. For twenty weeks Kronkhite and Dubious—in real life Joe Smith and Charlie Dale, of the old Avon Comedy Four—convulsed a new generation with exactly the same material that had earned them stardom over forty years before.

Aaron Fishman, in his forthcoming life story of Smith and Dale, entitled *Stage Struck*, sets the origin of their comedy classic in 1906. Joe Smith developed the character of Mr. Dubious for the principal purpose of asking a departing patient, "What does the doctor charge for a visit?" The patient answered, "Five dollars for the first visit, three dollars for the second, and one dollar for the third." When Charlie Dale, as Dr. Kronkhite, appeared, Smith greeted him with the now famous line, "Well, Doctor, here I am again!" (And Kronkhite answered, "Take the same medicine I prescribed last time.")

In 1914, Sime Silverman, the wizard of V*ariety*, advised Smith and Dale that their doctor bit could easily be developed into a complete act. How right he was! George Jean Nathan has described the resultant skit as "the champion vest-button buster in the theatre." Fellow performers have come to know the lines by heart, and they recite them along with Smith and Dale as they stand in the wings, laughing and applauding with the audiences out front.

Incidental lines in "Dr. Kronkhite" are changed from time to time, but this is now approximately the standard version:

PATIENT: (*Enters doctor's office*)

NURSE: How do you do.

PATIENT: This is doctor Kronkhite's office, no?

NURSE: Yes. I'm his nurse.

PATIENT: Is the doctor sick too?

NURSE: No. I'm a trained nurse.

PATIENT: Oh. You do tricks. . . . Is the doctor in?

NURSE: Yes, but he's very busy.

PATIENT: I'll wait.

NURSE: Take a chair please.

PATIENT: Thank you. I'll take it on my way out . . . what's the doctor's office hours?

NURSE: They're from 12 to 3 . . . 3 to 6 . . . 6 to 9 . . . 9 to 12 . . . and 12 to 3.

PATIENT: He gives good odds, he must be a horse doctor.

NURSE: Those are his hours.

PATIENT: Is that A.M. or F.M.

NURSE: That's T.V.

PATIENT: Oh, Tuesday or Vendsday. Is the doctor a good doctor?

NURSE: He'll do you good.

Voice: (*Off stage we hear loud groans*) Oh you butcher!

PATIENT: I'm cured. (*Starts to leave but nurse stops him*)

NURSE: Where are you going?

PATIENT: I'm going home. I forgot something.

NURSE: What did you forget?

PATIENT: I forgot to stay home.

NURSE: You mustn't run out on the doctor.

PATIENT: Better than being carried out!
(*Nurse exits*)

DOCTOR: (*Enters. Skips over to patient*) How do you do sir.

PATIENT: (*A bit skeptical*) Are you a doctor?

DOCTOR: Yes.

PATIENT: I'm dubious.

DOCTOR: How do you do Mr. Dubious. Sit down Mr. Dubious. By the way, who recommended you?

PATIENT: A Mr. Vladamer Sonavitch.

DOCTOR: Sonavitch? I had a Sonavitch that owed me twenty-five dollars.

PATIENT: Maybe that's another Sonavitch, but this Sonavitch is a married man and home he's got three little Sonavitches. You should see the three of them, a boy and a girl.

DOCTOR: Three, a boy and a girl? What's the other one?

PATIENT: It's so young, who can tell?

DOCTOR: Mr. Dubious, are you married?

PATIENT: Yes, and no.

DOCTOR: What do you mean, yes and no.

PATIENT: I am, but I wish I wasn't . . . you see I'm my wife's stephusband. He stepped out, and I stepped in.

DOCTOR: You carry any insurance?

PATIENT: Not one penny.

DOCTOR: If you should kick the bucket, what'll your wife bury you with?

PATIENT: With pleasure.

DOCTOR: Well, that's that. Now, what's the matter with you?

PATIENT: I'm as sick as a dog.

DOCTOR: You came to the right place. I'm also a veterinarian.

PATIENT: Where did you practice?

DOCTOR: I practiced in Cairo.

PATIENT: A chiropracticer too . . . which are you going to practice on me?

DOCTOR: What's your complaint?

PATIENT: Every time I eat a heavy meal I don't feel so hungry after.

DOCTOR: Maybe you're not eating the right kind of vitaminnies. What kind of dishes do you eat?

PATIENT: Dishes? what am I a crockadile?

DOCTOR: What do you do for exercise?

PATIENT: I ride horseback every midnight.

DOCTOR: Why do you pick such an hour?

PATIENT: In the daytime the crook who owns the horse wants six dollars an hour.

DOCTOR: What does he charge at night?

PATIENT: He isn't there.

DOCTOR: What kind of meats do you eat?

PATIENT: Weal I eat.

DOCTOR: I don't ask you will you eat, I said what do you eat?

PATIENT: I told you weal. (*Spells*) We-he-hay-hell. Weal.

DOCTOR: You should say we with a v instead of a woo. Now, how do you like your veal well to do?

PATIENT: It could be medium on one side and optional on the other.

DOCTOR: So far so good. Now when you are drinking drinks what kind of beverage drinks you are drinking?

PATIENT: You mean like coffee, milk, or chocolate?

DOCTOR: Yes.

PATIENT: I drink tea. And strong tea is my weakness.

DOCTOR: You drink Ceylion tea?

PATIENT: No. Orange Peconeeze. Ouch!

DOCTOR: What troubles you?

PATIENT: Bursitis and it's on the back of my neck. That's a bad place.

DOCTOR: Where would you want a better place than on the back of your neck?

PATIENT: On the back of your neck . . . and I got a corn on the bottom of my foot. That's a bad spot, no?

DOCTOR: Yes it's a good spot because nobody can step on it but you. Now, regarding your bursitis you should go to Mount Clemmons.

PATIENT: Is that a good place for bursitis?

DOCTOR: The best place in the country.

PATIENT: How do you know?

DOCTOR: That's where I got mine . . . or you can go to Switzerland.

PATIENT: What can I do in Switzerland?

DOCTOR: Just sit there and switz . . . now, take off the coat my boy I want to diogenes the case.

PATIENT: (*Removes coat puts it across the chair*)

DOCTOR: (*Sings while he takes out his stethoscope . . . he blows his breath on the handles and rubs it with his bandana 'ker-chief*)

PATIENT: Doctor. What are you doing?

DOCTOR: I'm sterlizing the instrument. (*He places the stethoscope to the patient's chest*) Now. Don't breathe . . . I would like to see you inhale . . . (*Listens*) Inhale! I would like to see you.

PATIENT: (*Surprised*) Inhale I would like to see YOU!

DOCTOR: Now, keep your mouth open and say, FISH.

PATIENT: (*With open mouth*) Herring.

DOCTOR: Stick out your tongue.

PATIENT: (*Does so*)

DOCTOR: More! more!

PATIENT: I can't, it's tied on the back.

DOCTOR: (*Looks at it*)

PATIENT: Well?

DOCTOR: I've seen better tongues hanging in a delicatessen window. Now, how do you sleep?

PATIENT: (*Closes eyes and crosses arms*) Like this.

DOCTOR: You don't get me.

PATIENT: I don't want you.

DOCTOR: (*Jumps up and down*) Please! Don't aggravate me. I got no patience.

PATIENT: I shouldn't be here either.

DOCTOR: I asked you how do you sleep at night?

PATIENT: At night I can't sleep. I walk around all night.

DOCTOR: Oh. You're a sonnambulance.

PATIENT: No. I'm a night watchman.

DOCTOR: Now sit down, close your eyes, and throw out your face.

PATIENT: (*Puzzled*) Throw it out?

DOCTOR: Throw out your face!

PATIENT: Did you ever take a good look at *your* face?

DOCTOR: (*Jumps up and down*) For pity sake! You are crazy!

PATIENT: I'm crazy for coming here and don't take advantage of me because I'm sick.

DOCTOR: You got sick. I didn't send for you . . . now, look me in the face.

PATIENT: I got my own troubles.

DOCTOR: Alright you can put your coat on.

PATIENT: You understand the whole case.

DOCTOR: Yes. The trouble with you is you need eyeglasses.

PATIENT: What do I owe you?

DOCTOR: Ten dollars.

PATIENT: For what?

DOCTOR: Ten dollars for my advice.

PATIENT: Here's two dollars. Take it doctor. That's my advice.

DOCTOR: You're nothing but a cheap low-down addlepated first-class insignificant . . .

PATIENT: (*Still holding the bills in front of the doctor*) One more word from you and you'll only get a dollar.

DOCTOR: YOU . . .

PATIENT: That's the word. Here's the dollar . . . Good-by.

Bennett Cerf

SHOW CASES

WHAT this country needs is a new show for the Marx Brothers. It's all very well to recall their patter of years gone by, and chuckle reminiscently over it, but something fresh along the lines of "The Coconuts" or "Animal Crackers" would give Broadway an unbelievable fillip. The funniest lines usually fell to Groucho. He revived on the radio the other night his "I never forget a face—but I'm willing to make an exception in your case."

One of his funniest routines concerned his African hunting trip which began with "Did I ever tell you how I shot a wild elephant in my pajamas? How he got into my pajamas I'll never know. Getting his tusks off was quite a problem. In Alabama the Tuscaloosa." He came home in a rickshaw. The meter registered $11.40. "Confound it," he roared to the driver. "Didn't I *tell* you not to go through India?"

Then there was the skit where Groucho and Chico served as opposing lawyers. Chico became tongue-tied when it was his turn to question the witness. The judge thundered, "Well, ask your witness some questions." "All-a-right," said Chico. "What's a big-a da animal wid four legs an' a trunk in da front?" "That's irrelevant," screamed Groucho. "Dat's a right," agreed Chico. Groucho crossed the stage, planted his portfolio on the judge's bench, and declared, "I rest my case."

And the time when Groucho proposed to that wonderful foil, Mrs. Rittenhouse. "Your eyes shine," he told her, "like the seat of my blue serge pants." "But you'll have to get out of that house you're living in," he added. "I don't like Junior crossing the tracks. In fact, come to think of it, I don't like Junior."

The weak sister of the Four Marx Brothers on the stage was Zeppo, but when he quit the grease paint and became an agent, he ended with more pelf than the other three put together. Harpo, who never says a word on the stage, is the wittiest conversationalist in private life, and was one of Alexander Woollcott's favorite companions. Harpo once flew all the way from Hollywood to Bomoseen, Vermont, for a week end, to surprise Woollcott. He painted himself from head to foot with hideous hues, paddled to the Island, and howled like a banshee. Nobody was frightened, however. In fact, nobody was on the Island. Another time, Harpo appeared in a broken-down Model-T Ford. "What on earth do you call that?" scoffed Woollcott. "This is my town car," said Harpo grandly. "Yes," answered Woollcott, "and the town is Pompeii."

Chico's wife invited an elderly relative to spend a few weeks at his house one time. The visitor was very charming, but her English was on the sketchy side. When Irving Thalberg and his wife, Norma Shearer, were coming for dinner, Chico took the old lady aside. "When Mr. Thalberg says 'pleased to meet you,'" he instructed her, "all you have to do is answer with one word: 'likewise.'" The old lady repeated the word several times, and swore that she would uphold her end without mishap. The Thalbergs arrived. "Pleased to meet you," said Thalberg as expected. The old lady beamed at him. "Wise guy," she said.

The Marx Brothers once became the managers of a prize fighter. He was a lumbering giant named Cohen, and richly earned the nickname of "Canvasback" by an invariable custom of getting himself knocked cold in Round One of every fight. The boys had a great time with Canvasback Cohen until one day, according to legend, Groucho knocked him out in a gymnasium workout. That was too much. Harpo claims that Canvasback started as a lightweight, but was hit so many times that he swelled out into a heavy.

As long as I have rambled on this far about the Marx Brothers, I'd better quote a few other of their more famous lines, if only to avoid the wrath of thousands of enthusiasts who remember their dialogues almost word for word and are ready to fight at the drop of a wisecrack. In "Horse Feathers," Groucho informed his son, "I'd horsewhip you— if I had a horse."

His secretary interrupted him to announce, "Jennings has been waiting to see you for hours, and he is waxing wroth." Groucho's reply to this was, "Tell Roth to wax Jennings for a change."

When Chico entered the scene, Groucho commented, "Hey, you look a lot like a guy I know by the name of Ravelli." "I am Ravelli," declared Chico. "Aha," said Groucho, "that accounts for the resemblance."

In "Monkey Business" Groucho discovered a large automatic pistol and near it a few small pearl-handled revolvers. "This gat," announced Groucho, "had gittens." Almost immediately after that deduction, the ship's captain hove into view. "I've got a complaint," roared Groucho. "What is it?" said the captain testily. "Last night when I was in bed in my cabin, who do you think came tiptoeing along the corridor and tapped on my door?" The captain said he didn't know. "Nobody did," declared Groucho, "and that's my complaint."

Marx Brothers addicts will never forget their burlesque of Madame Du Barry. Groucho, essaying the role of high minister, was feverishly embracing Du Barry when Chico came charging into the scene. "Who are you?" snarled Groucho. "King of France," averred Chico. "What?" said Groucho. "You the king? And I the prime minister? France is certainly in one hell of a fix!"

* * * * *

One of Ed Wynn's funniest acts found him dressed as a huntsman, rifle in hand, horn slung over his shoulder, ready to go out and bag his prey. Just before he sallied forth, he took a look at himself in a pocket mirror, and gasped, "Thank the Lord I'm not in season."

In the same show he was operating a pretzel stand when a cop informed him, "Hey, fella, you can't sell those pretzels here without a license." Wynn answered, "I knew there was some reason I couldn't sell them, but thanks for telling me what it was."

In "Manhattan Mary," Wynn played a waiter (Ona Munson was Mary) and told a patron who ordered caviar, "Here's some tapioca pudding and a pair of smoked glasses." Somebody else grumbled, "I don't like all the flies in here." "Point out the ones you don't like," suggested Wynn, "and I'll evict them." A third customer demanded lamb chops au gratin. Wynn shouted to the kitchen, "Cheese it, the chops."

When a patron said, "I'm so hungry I could eat a horse," Wynn led a live nag on to the stage. Then he sold it to the customer. "This horse has only one peculiarity," he told the befuddled buyer. "He loves to sit on potatoes. Remember that!" The man made off with his horse, but was back a moment later. "You fraud," he screamed, "I no sooner got that horse to the bridge down the road, when he bolted out of my control and jumped over the bridge into the river." "Oh, I forgot to tell you," said the contrite Wynn. "That horse loves to sit on fish, too!"

In another scene, Wynn was busy painting a ship. An old dowager entered and asserted, "Mr. Wynn, I have decided to commission you to paint my ancestors." "Oh, I couldn't do that," he protested. "I'm just a ship painter." "Nevertheless," insisted the dowager, "you are the man I want for the job." "But I tell you," he wailed, "I only paint ships." "The question is closed," she announced. "You, and you alone, are going to paint my ancestors." "All right," agreed Wynn finally. "I'll paint your darn ancestors. But I want to warn you now: they're going to look like ships!"

* * * * *

Bobby Clark, one of the greatest comedians of our time, would like to revive the lion act he did in burlesque with his old partner McCullough. It is a project that should be encouraged, if necessary, by a special grant from Congress.

The manager of a side show offered Clark a dollar to wrestle with a lion. When Clark demurred, the manager assured him, "Our real lion has escaped. This fellow (McCullough) will wear a lion skin and the suckers will never know the difference." Clark, of course, perked up at once when he heard this. And the real lion, of course, walked into the cage behind his back while he told the audience what he was going to do to the "king of beasts."

The next ten minutes provided more belly laughs than any other act I can remember. Clark whacked the lion with his cane, kicked it in the rump, played leap frog with it, and waved a flashlight in its eyes. When the lion roared, he would cry, "That's great! You sure are fooling the audience." Occasionally he'd sniff and declare, "What a performance! You even *smell* like a lion."

For the pay-off, the lion would start chasing Clark around the cage. The manager yelled, "Hey, I've been trying to tell you! That's the *real lion* in there with you!" Clark's final speech was, "This is a hell of a time to tell me!"

* * * * *

Charles W. Couldock was a distinguished stage star some years ago. He was noted both for his excellence as an actor and for his personal irascibility. In one of his plays, the opening scene was between himself, another actor, and a third actor, who played Mr. Couldock's elderly father. One night the actor playing the elderly father didn't show up. The stage manager hastily put a long white beard on a super and seated him on a chair at the fireplace, telling him just to sit there and that he, the stage manager, would speak the lines from off stage through the fireplace. There was time only to tell Mr. Couldock that there was to be a different actor playing his father and to assure him that everything would be all right.

The stage manager rang up the curtain, then hurried down below the stage to reach the fireplace on the other side of the set. In his haste he ran into a beam and knocked himself unconscious. Over his head, the play progressed to the point where Couldock was asked how old his father was. Couldock answered: "I don't know exactly. I shall ask him." He went over to the bearded super and said, "Father, how old are you?" There was no answer. Couldock stared at him, ad-libbed a line about father's being a little deaf, kicked the super in the shins, swore at him under his breath and repeated the question, "Father, how old are you?" Again the answer was complete silence.

Couldock marched down to the footlights and addressed the audience. "Ladies and gentlemen, my father is so goddam old he can't even talk."

* * * * *

Frank Case, amiable Boniface of the Algonquin Hotel, told the story of the day the late DeWolf Hopper protested to him that nowhere in New York could he find his favorite dessert, brown betty, on the menu. "I'd have it here for you," Case said, "if I thought there would be a reasonable demand for it." "You put it on your menu tomorrow night," proposed Hopper, "and I'll see to it personally that the demand develops." The next night brown betty was duly added to the Algonquin bill of fare, and Hopper, much gratified, made a personal tour of every table in the dining room. "I am DeWolf Hopper," he announced to the surprised patrons, "and I personally urge you to sample the brown betty this evening. It's delicious!" Hopper then repaired to his own table, toyed with a beefsteak, and summoned his waiter. "Now," he said, rubbing his hands in anticipation. "I'll have a double order of brown betty." "I'm very sorry, sir," said the waiter. "It's all gone."

* * * * *

When an author has determined to be dissatisfied and depressed, there is nothing in the world that can make him change his mind. Take the case of the late George M. Cohan as an example. The last years of his life were embittered by the thought that the parade had passed him by, and that lines and devices for which people had cheered him in happier days were now regarded as "corny" and obvious. A succession of failures sharpened his resentment. Then came "Ah, Wilderness!" and a chance to star in a sure-fire hit. Cohan appeared in another author's play for the first time in years. The first-night audience gave him an ovation, and the critics sang his praises to the sky.

Was Cohan happy? He was not! When a friend said, "Well, George, this is something like again, isn't it?" Cohan shook his head dejectedly and grumbled, "Imagine my reciting lines by Eugene O'Neill! Why, he ought to be on the stage reciting lines by *me!*"

Irving Berlin made another classic remark—but he was only kidding. He had been turning out a string of smash hits, besides coining a fortune from the revival of his old stand-bys in pictures. Congratulated on his great run of luck, Berlin thought for a moment and then said, "Oh, I don't know, I've only sold 'Mandy' once this year!"

At one of the first performances of *Annie Get Your Gun,* Dick Rodgers, the producer, stood in the lobby during the intermission with Berlin, composer of the hit-studded score. Berlin moved away, and a stout lady standing nearby obviously recognized him. She nudged her husband, and Dick heard her say wonderingly, "Sam, to look at him who would think?"

* * * * *

Howard Cullman, the play backer, hired a new butler recently, named Jenkins, whose deportment on his first morning proclaimed him a gem. Cullman's clothes were laid out beautifully, breakfast was served in the best manner, and as he was leaving, Jenkins handed him his hat and neatly folded newspaper. There was a short flight of stairs to descend, and unfortunately, Cullman tripped over something on the top step. When he tripped again the following morning at the same spot, he became suspicious. The third morning he caught Jenkins red-handed, or red-footed, slyly preparing to trip him deliberately again.

Cullman figured that the butler needed a psychiatrist more than an employer, so he fired him. A week later, Dick Rodgers got Cullman on the telephone. "I've been interviewing a butler named Jenkins," he said. "He's given you as a reference." "He's a fine butler," Cullman answered him, "but I warn you: he'll trip you up. I think he's nuts." Rodgers laughed indulgently and hung up.

A few days later Rodgers met Cullman at the Ritz Grill. The composer had a black eye and a bruised lip. "You guessed it, Howard," he told Cullman. "I hired your butler."

* * * * *

The wonderful saga of Two-Top Gruskin, the two-headed pitcher, is the brain child of Ed Gardner, the incomparable Archie of Duffy's Tavern radio program. It goes something like this:

Duffy's Irish Yankees have mechanical perfection, but no color. "This guy, Athos and Porthos McGinnes, may be your dish," says Dugan, the shortstop, to the disconsolate Duffy. "They call him Two-Top Gruskin for short, I guess, on account of him having two heads."

"A pitcher with two heads?" says Duffy dubiously. "You think it'd be a novelty?"

"What if it ain't?" points out Dugan. "Who else could watch first and third base at the same time? Besides, he's a great guy to pitch double-headers."

So Two-Top is summoned from his home (Walla Walla, of course) and arrives to sign his contract in a dress suit. "What are all you guys staring at?" he asks sourly. "Ain't none of you seen a tuxedo before?"

"Two-Top," says Duffy, "I'm a man of few words. Report tomorrow. There's a uniform and two caps waiting for you. Waiter, bring my new pitcher two beers."

Two-Top wins a masquerade that very night by disguising himself as a pair of book ends with a copy of *My Son, My Son* between the two heads. The next afternoon Duffy introduces him to his catcher, Gorilla Hogan, who measures 6 foot 14 inches and squats standing up. "Most people," says Duffy proudly, "calls Gorilla a monstrosity, and I agree with them—a swell guy." Gorilla soon gets into trouble with Two-Top, however. He signals for a high fast one. Two-Top nods "yes" with one head, but shakes the other one "no." Confused and mortified, Gorilla hurls off his mask and yells to Duffy, "Duffy, you such-and-such, I am sick and tired of two-headed pitchers around this place."

"Take it easy," soothes Duffy. "Talk it over with the guy. After all, three heads is better than one."

But the Gorilla says, "It's no use, Duffy. I got a feeling that the guy ain't normal. Besides, you notice how he's always got those two heads together? Maybe he's cooking up a strike around here. No, sir, one of us will have to go, Duffy—and don't forget who owns the baseball."

Well, that's the end of Two-Top Gruskin's baseball career. For a while he watches tennis matches for the News of the Day. Then the Army gets him. The doctor takes his chart to the colonel. "Lemme see," says the colonel. "Eyes—blue and brown. Hair, blond and brunette. Mustache: yes and no. This guy sounds as if he's got two heads." "He has," says the doc. "Oh," says the colonel.

Two-Top will be a big success in the Army as soon as he can make up his mind which head to salute.

* * * * *

A famous producer we will call Darryl Selznick hadn't found a story that suited him for six years and had reached a point where he was ready to listen to all comers. An unknown aspirant was ushered into his august presence one day. "They tell me you have a play," said the producer, with a reassuring wave of his hand. "Go ahead and read it to me."

This was more than the author had expected. Furthermore, he had been a victim of severe stuttering since he first learned to talk. The chance was too good to miss, however, so he sat down and read his whole play, scene by scene. When he had finished, Darryl Selznick shouted for his secretary.

"Sign this guy up at once," he cried. "He's got a new twist that'll have them rolling in the aisles. Every character in his play stutters."

* * * * *

Harry Brand, super-publicist of Twentieth Century-Fox, collected a black eye recently. He says he ran into an open door. At any rate, he had himself photographed with the black eye showing prominently, and sent a copy to his friend Sid Skolsky with this inscription: "Nobody can talk that way about you when I'm around!"

* * * * *

Gene Fowler sends along a story about a Hollywood mogul who met a young eyeful on Wilshire Boulevard and gushed, "Golly, it's good to see you again. It so happens there's going to be a marvelous party tonight, and I want you to come to it. I won't take no for an answer." "Where's it to be?" asked the girl. "At my house, darling. And I think it will be an all-time high for fun. Lots of liquor, music, sex, and nobody knows when it ever will break up." "Sounds great," said the girl eagerly. "Who's going to be there?" "Oh," replied the prospective host, "just you and me."

* * * * *

Two agents sat together watching a preview of an important picture. One happened to be the agent for the male star of the piece, the other for the female lead. They sat silently while several reels were unwound, and then one nudged the other in the ribs. "Look at those two hams up there," he said with some disgust, "getting eighty per cent of our dough."

* * * * *

Another agent story concerns a flourishing coast agency named Feitlebaum & Garfinkel. One morning Feitlebaum came to Garfinkel and explained that he was sick and tired of his cumbersome and harsh-sounding name. "With your permission," he explained, "I have changed my name this morning to O'Brien." Garfinkel said nothing, but a few mornings later he came to his partner with the declaration that he too was tired of the name he had been bearing all his life. "With your permission," he said, "I have also changed my name to O'Brien." Thereupon, the old sign was taken down and a resplendent new one, reading "O'Brien and O'Brien" was put up in its place. A few mornings later the telpehone rang and a voice demanded to be connected with Mr. O'Brien. "Very good, sir," said the cheery-voiced operator, "but which Mr. O'Brien do you want: Feitlebaum or Garfinkel?"

* * * * *

A third agent, usually very chipper, sat despondently at the soda counter of Schwab's Pharmacy. "Whassamatter?" asked a friend anxiously. "It's that new client I'm representing," groaned the agent. "Sings like Lanza, fights like Flynn, and acts like Victor Mature." "So why do you worry," laughed the friend. "You'll make a million out of this guy." "Guy nothing, you dope," cried the agent. "It's a *girl!*"

* * * * *

Ghost writers are in great demand these days in Hollywood—but the great men who require their services are exacting taskmasters.

One producer, for instance, hired a college professor to write a learned paper for him defending the morals of the community and flaying critics who declared his pictures were a sorry sort of advertisement for the American way in foreign countries. He read a draft of the proposed article with furrowed brow, and then told the professor, "It's all right, but I want you to take out those fancy words. I want to know what I'm talking about."

Another magnate fired a new ghost writer because, he explained, "He doesn't understand my style of writing as well as the last fellow I had."

Then there was the day the old friend of a famous comedian passed away, and the comedian was asked to say a few words at the funeral. He called up his gag writer and said, "I've got to make a speech at a cemetery tomorrow. Rush me over a page of funeral jokes."

* * * * *

A favorite picture star who married well—and often—found it expedient to get a divorce in a hurry a few months ago. Her lawyer suggested Mexico. "But I don't speak Spanish," she protested. "That's all right," said the lawyer. "Whenever there's a pause, all you have to do is say 'si, si.'"

The star created a sensation in the little Mexican village, and when she appeared in court, the whole town turned out to witness the event. There was a great deal of emoting and bowing, and the star said "si, si" very firmly on numerous occasions. Suddenly the crowd gave a great cheer. "Well, I guess I'm divorced," she said complacently. "Divorced, my eye," cried her perspiring attorney. "You've married the mayor!"

XI. GROWING PAINS

Robert Benchley

ONE LEGEND LESS

LITTLE children, climbing over my knee and into my hair, often address me as follows:

"Tell us, praeceptor—what were the origins of some of our better-known legends?"

"Do you mean the woollen legends you put on when you go out in the snow?" I ask, hiding my face so that they shall not see the tell-tale twinkle in my eye—and also so that they shall not hit the bridge of my nose.

"It seems incredible," they reply, "that a man of your size should think it funny to confuse legends with leggings, but since such is your pleasure let us call the whole thing off."

And they slide down from my lap, leaving me alone to my reveries—which was exactly my idea in the first place.

But sometimes I am forced to go into the thing, either to appease the curiosity of some new member of the group or to show the others that I have my serious side (usually the left side, which the afternoon sun doesn't strike), and then it is that I tell them of Theseus and the Minotaur and how the story ever happened to take its place in legendary history. As if I knew!

The original of Theseus was a mythical Greek hero named Mnamnos, son of the god Pylon and a young woman from Thrace. Mnamnos himself was really a later embodiment of an even more mythical Greek character named Thyroid, who preceded him by about eight years. His ancestor, Monad, was the one who founded the legend, later attributed to Mnamnos and still later to Theseus. Today Richard Halliburton sometimes gets credit for it.

Mnamnos, or Monad, is supposed to have gone to the Island of Clecos and there to have slew—slain—slown—a fabulous monster named Boracicacidopulous—half bull, one-quarter rabbit and one-quarter tree-toad, with a dash of angostura—which breathed fire at one minute before noon each day and was known to the natives as "Old Faithful," or sometimes just plain "Benny." He didn't have a friend in the world.

In slaying this monster Mnamnos started a legend which, when the earliest Greeks got sick of it, was carried into other countries, where it was considered hot stuff for a while and then discarded or passed on. In each country Mnamnos was called by a different name and we find the Romans calling him "Lethargus," the Visigoths "Glovis," the Picts "Funny-Face," and so on (and so forth).

But it always was the same story (Alexander Woollcott told it a little differently over the radio, making it an account submitted to him by a correspondent from Nîmes, France, in which the monster turned out to be already dead when the modern Mnamnos arrived, holding under his outstretched paw a *note written by the young man himself to a German prisoner when a member of the* A. E. F. *in 1918!*) and the supposition is that it never really happened at all.

By this time, as you may well imagine, the kiddies are off my knee and downtown at some night club, but I am so fascinated with the story myself that I sometimes begin it all over again and tell it to myself. This is why there is some talk of sending me up-State for a while, where I can get lots of fresh air and plain food, and a marble game to get my mind off business.

F. Scott Fitzgerald

THE BABY PARTY

WHEN John Andros felt old he found solace in the thought of life continuing through his child. The dark trumpets of oblivion were less loud at the patter of his child's feet or at the sound of his child's voice babbling mad non sequiturs to him over the telephone. The latter incident occurred every afternoon at three when his wife called the office from the country, and he came to look forward to it as one of the vivid minutes of his day.

He was not physically old, but his life had been a series of struggles up a series of rugged hills, and here at thirty-eight having won his battles against ill-health and poverty he cherished less than the usual number of illusions. Even his feeling about his little girl was qualified. She had interrupted his rather intense love affair with his wife, and she was the reason for their living in a suburban town, where they paid for country air with endless servant troubles and the weary merry-go-round of the commuting train.

It was little Ede as a definite piece of youth that chiefly interested him. He liked to take her on his lap and examine minutely her fragrant, downy scalp and her eyes with their irises of morning blue. Having paid this homage John was content that the nurse should take her away. After ten minutes the very vitality of the child irritated him; he was inclined to lose his temper when things were broken, and one Sunday afternoon when she had disrupted a bridge game by permanently hiding up the ace of spades, he had made a scene that had reduced his wife to tears.

This was absurd and John was ashamed of himself. It was inevitable that such things would happen, and it was impossible that little Ede should spend all her indoor hours in the nursery upstairs when she was becoming, as her mother said, more nearly a "real person" every day.

She was two and a half, and this afternoon, for instance, she was going to a baby party. Grown-up Edith, her mother, had telephoned the information to the office, and little Ede had confirmed the business by shouting "I yam going to a *pantry!*" into John's unsuspecting left ear.

"Drop in at the Markeys' when you get home, won't you, dear?" resumed her mother. "It'll be funny. Ede's going to be all dressed up in her new pink dress——"

The conversation terminated abruptly with a squawk which indicated that the telephone had been pulled violently to the floor. John laughed and decided to get an early train out; the prospect of a baby party in some one else's house amused him.

"What a peach of a mess!" he thought humorously. "A dozen mothers, and each one looking at nothing but her own child. All the babies breaking things and grabbing at the cake, and each mamma going home thinking about the subtle superiority of her own child to every other child there."

He was in a good humor today—all the things in his life were going better than they had ever gone before. When he got off the train at his station he shook his head at an importunate taxi man, and began to walk up the long hill toward his house through the crisp December twilight. It was only six o'clock but the moon was out, shining with proud brilliance on the thin sugary snow that lay over the lawns.

As he walked along drawing his lungs full of cold air his happiness increased, and the idea of a baby party appealed to him more and more. He began to wonder how Ede compared to other children of her own age, and if the pink dress she was to wear was something radical and mature. Increasing his gait he came in sight of his own house, where the lights of a defunct Christmas tree still blossomed in the window, but he continued on past the walk. The party was at the Markeys' next door.

As he mounted the brick step and rang the bell he became aware of voices inside, and he was glad he was not too late. Then he raised his head and listened—the voices were not children's voices, but they were loud and pitched high with anger; there were at least three of them and one, which rose as he listened to a hysterical sob, he recognized immediately as his wife's.

"There's been some trouble," he thought quickly.

Trying the door, he found it unlocked and pushed it open.

The baby party began at half past four, but Edith Andros, calculating shrewdly that the new dress would stand out more sensationally against vestments already rumpled, planned the arrival of herself and little Ede for five. When they appeared it was already a flourishing affair. Four baby girls and nine baby boys, each one curled and washed and dressed with all the care of a proud and jealous heart, were dancing to the music of a phonograph. Never more than two or three were dancing at once, but as all were continually in motion running to and from their mothers for encouragement, the general effect was the same.

As Edith and her daughter entered, the music was temporarily drowned out by a sustained chorus, consisting largely of the word *cute* and directed toward little Ede, who stood looking timidly about and fingering the edges of her pink dress. She was not kissed—this is the sanitary age—but she was passed along a row of mammas each one of whom said "cu-u-ute" to her and held her pink little hand before passing her on to the next. After some encouragement and a few mild pushes she was absorbed into the dance, and became an active member of the party.

Edith stood near the door talking to Mrs. Markey, and keeping one eye on the tiny figure in the pink dress. She did not care for Mrs. Markey; she considered her both snippy and common, but John and Joe Markey were congenial and went in together on the commuting train every morning, so the two women kept up an elaborate pretense of warm amity. They were always reproaching each other for "not coming to see me," and they were always planning the kind of parties that began with "You'll have to come to dinner with us soon, and we'll go in to the theatre," but never matured further.

"Little Ede looks perfectly darling," said Mrs. Markey, smiling and moistening her lips in a way that Edith found particularly repulsive. "So *grown-up*—I can't *believe* it!"

Edith wondered if "little Ede" referred to the fact that Billy Markey, though several months younger, weighed almost five pounds more. Accepting a cup of tea she took a seat with two other ladies on a divan and launched into the real business of the afternoon, which of course lay in relating the recent accomplishments and insouciances of her child.

An hour passed. Dancing palled and the babies took to sterner sport. They ran into the dining-room, rounded the big table, and essayed the kitchen door, from which they were rescued by an expeditionary force of mothers. Having been rounded up they immediately broke loose, and rushing back to the dining-room tried the familiar swinging door again. The word "overheated" began to be used, and small white brows were dried with small white handkerchiefs. A general attempt to make the babies sit down began, but the babies squirmed off laps with peremptory cries of "Down! Down!" and the rush into the fascinating dining-room began anew.

This phase of the party came to an end with the arrival of refreshments, a large cake with two candles, and saucers of vanilla ice cream. Billy Markey, a stout laughing baby with red hair and legs somewhat bowed, blew out the candles, and placed an experimental thumb on the white frosting. The refreshments were distributed, and the children ate, greedily but without confusion—they had behaved remarkably well all afternoon. They were modern babies who ate and slept at regular hours, so their dispositions were good, and their faces healthy and pink—such a peaceful party would not have been possible thirty years ago.

After the refreshments a gradual exodus began. Edith glanced anxiously at her watch—it was almost six, and John had not arrived. She wanted him to see Ede with the other children—to see how dignified and polite and intelligent she was, and how the only ice-cream spot on her dress was some that had dropped from her chin when she was joggled from behind.

"You're a darling," she whispered to her child, drawing her suddenly against her knee. "Do you know you're a darling? Do you *know* you're a darling?"

Ede laughed. "Bow-wow," she said suddenly.

"Bow-wow?" Edith looked around. "There isn't any bow-wow."

"Bow-wow," repeated Ede. "I want a bow-wow."

Edith followed the small pointing finger.

"That isn't a bow-wow, dearest, that's a teddy-bear."

"Bear?"

"Yes, that's a teddy-bear, and it belongs to Billy Markey. You don't want Billy Markey's teddy-bear, do you?"

Ede did want it.

She broke away from her mother and approached Billy Markey, who held the toy closely in his arms. Ede stood regarding him with inscrutable eyes, and Billy laughed.

Grown-up Edith looked at her watch again, this time impatiently.

The party had dwindled until, besides Ede and Billy, there were only two babies remaining—and one of the two remained only by virtue of having hidden himself under the dining-room table. It was selfish of John not to come. It showed so little pride in the child. Other fathers had come, half a dozen of them, to call for their wives, and they had stayed for a while and looked on.

There was a sudden wail. Ede had obtained Billy's teddy-bear by pulling it forcibly from his arms, and on Billy's attempt to recover it, she had pushed him casually to the floor.

"Why, Ede!" cried her mother, repressing an inclination to laugh.

Joe Markey, a handsome, broad-shouldered man of thirty-five, picked up his son and set him on his feet. "You're a fine fellow," he said jovially. "Let a girl knock you over! You're a fine fellow."

"Did he bump his head?" Mrs. Markey returned anxiously from bowing the next to last remaining mother out the door.

"No-o-o-o," exclaimed Markey. "He bumped something else, didn't you, Billy? He bumped something else."

Billy had so far forgotten the bump that he was already making an attempt to recover his property. He seized a leg of the bear which projected from Ede's enveloping arms and tugged at it but without success.

"No," said Ede emphatically.

Suddenly, encouraged by the success of her former half-accidental manœuvre, Ede dropped the teddy-bear, placed her hands on Billy's shoulders and pushed him backward off his feet.

This time he landed less harmlessly; his head hit the bare floor just off the rug with a dull hollow sound, whereupon he drew in his breath and delivered an agonized yell.

Immediately the room was in confusion. With an exclamation Markey hurried to his son, but his wife was first to reach the injured baby and catch him up into her arms.

"Oh, *Billy*," she cried, "what a terrible bump! She ought to be spanked."

Edith, who had rushed immediately to her daughter, heard this remark, and her lips came sharply together.

"Why, Ede," she whispered perfunctorily, "you bad girl!"

Ede put back her little head suddenly and laughed. It was a loud laugh, a triumphant laugh with victory in it and challenge and contempt. Unfortunately it was also an infectious laugh. Before her mother realized the delicacy of the situation, she too had laughed, an audible, distinct laugh not unlike the baby's, and partaking of the same overtones.

Then, as suddenly, she stopped.

Mrs. Markey's face had grown red with anger, and Markey, who had been feeling the back of the baby's head with one finger, looked at her, frowning.

"It's swollen already," he said with a note of reproof in his voice. "I'll get some witch-hazel."

But Mrs. Markey had lost her temper. "I don't see anything funny about a child being hurt!" she said in a trembling voice.

Little Ede meanwhile had been looking at her mother curiously. She noted that her own laugh had produced her mother's, and she wondered if the same cause would always produce the same effect. So she chose this moment to throw back her head and laugh again.

To her mother the additional mirth added the final touch of hysteria to the situation. Pressing her handkerchief to her mouth she giggled irrepressibly. It was more than nervousness—she felt that in a peculiar way she was laughing with her child—they were laughing together.

It was in a way a defiance—those two against the world.

While Markey rushed upstairs to the bathroom for ointment, his wife was walking up and down rocking the yelling boy in her arms.

"Please go home!" she broke out suddenly. "The child's badly hurt, and if you haven't the decency to be quiet, you'd better go home."

"Very well," said Edith, her own temper rising. "I've never seen any one make such a mountain out of——"

"Get out!" cried Mrs. Markey frantically. "There's the door, get out—I never want to see you in our house again. You or your brat either!"

Edith had taken her daughter's hand and was moving quickly toward the door, but at this remark she stopped and turned around, her face contracting with indignation.

"Don't you dare call her that!"

Mrs. Markey did not answer but continued walking up and down, muttering to herself and to Billy in an inaudible voice.

Edith began to cry.

"I will get out!" she sobbed, "I've never heard anybody so rude and c-common in my life. I'm glad your baby did get pushed down—he's nothing but a f-fat little fool anyhow."

Joe Markey reached the foot of the stairs just in time to hear this remark.

"Why, Mrs. Andros," he said sharply, "can't you see the child's hurt? You really ought to control yourself."

"Control m-myself!" exclaimed Edith brokenly. "You better ask her to c-control herself. I've never heard anybody so c-common in my life."

"She's insulting me!" Mrs. Markey was now livid with rage. "Did you hear what she said, Joe? I wish you'd put her out. If she won't go, just take her by the shoulders and put her out!"

"Don't you dare touch me!" cried Edith. "I'm going just as quick as I can find my c-coat!"

Blind with tears she took a step toward the hall. It was just at this moment that the door opened and John Andros walked anxiously in.

"John!" cried Edith, and fled to him wildly.

"What's the matter? Why, what's the matter?"

"They're—they're putting me out!" she wailed, collapsing against him. "He'd just started to take me by the shoulders and put me out. I want my coat!"

"That's not true," objected Markey hurriedly. "Nobody's going to put you out." He turned to John. "Nobody's going to put her out," he repeated. "She's——"

"What do you mean 'put her out'?" demanded John abruptly. "What's all this talk, anyhow?"

"Oh, let's go!" cried Edith. "I want to go. They're so *common*, John!"

"Look here!" Markey's face darkened. "You've said that about enough. You're acting sort of crazy."

"They called Ede a brat!"

For the second time that afternoon little Ede expressed emotion at an inopportune moment. Confused and frightened at the shouting voices, she began to cry, and her tears had the effect of conveying that she felt the insult in her heart.

"What's the idea of this?" broke out John. "Do you insult your guests in your own house?"

"It seems to me it's your wife that's done the insulting!" answered Markey crisply. "In fact, your baby there started all the trouble."

John gave a contemptuous snort. "Are you calling names at a little baby?" he inquired. "That's a fine manly business!"

"Don't talk to him, John," insisted Edith. "Find my coat!"

"You must be in a bad way," went on John angrily, "if you have to take out your temper on a helpless little baby."

"I never heard anything so damn twisted in my life," shouted Markey. "If that wife of yours would shut her mouth for a minute——"

"Wait a minute! You're not talking to a woman and child now——"

There was an incidental interruption. Edith had been fumbling on a chair for her coat, and Mrs. Markey had been watching her with hot, angry eyes. Suddenly she laid Billy down on the sofa, where he immediately stopped crying and pulled himself upright, and coming into the hall she quickly found Edith's coat and handed it to her without a word. Then she went back to the sofa, picked up Billy, and rocking him in her arms looked again at Edith with hot, angry eyes. The interruption had taken less than half a minute.

"Your wife comes in here and begins shouting around about how common we are!" burst out Markey violently. "Well, if we're so damn common, you'd better stay away! And, what's more, you'd better get out now!"

Again John gave a short, contemptuous laugh.

"You're not only common," he returned, "you're evidently an awful bully—when there's any helpless women and children around." He felt for the knob and swung the door open. "Come on, Edith."

Taking up her daughter in her arms, his wife stepped outside and John, still looking contemptuously at Markey, started to follow.

"Wait a minute!" Markey took a step forward; he was trembling slightly, and two large veins on his temple were suddenly full of blood. "You don't think you can get away with that, do you? With me?"

Without a word John walked out the door, leaving it open.

Edith, still weeping, had started for home. After following her with his eyes until she reached her own walk, John turned back toward the lighted doorway where Markey was slowly coming down the slippery steps. He took off his overcoat and hat, tossed them off the path onto the snow. Then, sliding a little on the iced walk, he took a step forward.

At the first blow, they both slipped and fell heavily to the sidewalk, half rising then, and again pulling each other to the ground. They found a better foothold in the thin snow to the side of the walk and rushed at each other, both swinging wildly and pressing out the snow into a pasty mud underfoot.

The street was deserted, and except for their short tired gasps and the padded sound as one or the other slipped down into the slushy mud, they fought in silence, clearly defined to each other by the full moonlight as well as by the amber glow that shone out of the open door. Several times they both slipped down together, and then for a while the conflict threshed about wildly on the lawn.

For ten, fifteen, twenty minutes they fought there senselessly in the moonlight. They had both taken off coats and vests at some silently agreed upon interval and now their shirts dripped from their backs in wet pulpy shreds. Both were torn and bleeding and so exhausted that they could stand only when by their position they mutually supported each other—the impact, the mere effort of a blow, would send them both to their hands and knees.

But it was not weariness that ended the business, and the very meaninglessness of the fight was a reason for not stopping. They stopped because once when they were straining at each other on the ground, they heard a man's footsteps coming along the sidewalk. They had rolled somehow into the shadow, and when they heard these footsteps they stopped fighting, stopped moving, stopped breathing, lay huddled together like two boys playing Indian until the footsteps had passed. Then, staggering to their feet, they looked at each other like two drunken men.

"I'll be damned if I'm going on with this thing any more," cried Markey thickly.

"I'm not going on any more either," said John Andros. "I've had enough of this thing."

Again they looked at each other, sulkily this time, as if each suspected the other of urging him to a renewal of the fight. Markey spat out a mouthful of blood from a cut lip; then he cursed softly, and picking up his coat and vest, shook off the snow from them in a surprised way, as if their comparative dampness was his only worry in the world.

"Want to come in and wash up?" he asked suddenly.

"No, thanks," said John. "I ought to be going home—my wife'll be worried."

He too picked up his coat and vest and then his overcoat and hat. Soaking wet and dripping with perspiration, it seemed absurd that less than half an hour ago he had been wearing all these clothes.

"Well—good night," he said hesitantly.

Suddenly they both walked toward each other and shook hands. It was no perfunctory hand-shake: John Andros's arm went around Markey's shoulder, and he patted him softly on the back for a little while.

"No harm done," he said brokenly.

"No—you?"

"No, no harm done."

"Well," said John Andros after a minute, "I guess I'll say good night."

"Good night."

Limping slightly and with his clothes over his arm, John Andros turned away. The moonlight was still bright as he left the dark patch of trampled ground and walked over the intervening lawn. Down at the station, half a mile away, he could hear the rumble of the seven o'clock train.

"But you must have been crazy," cried Edith brokenly. "I thought you were going to fix it all up there and shake hands. That's why I went away."

"Did you want us to fix it up?"

"Of course not, I never want to see them again. But I thought of course that was what you were going to do." She was touching the bruises on his neck and back with iodine as he sat placidly in a hot bath. "I'm going to get the doctor," she said insistently. "You may be hurt internally."

He shook his head. "Not a chance," he answered. "I don't want this to get all over town."

"I don't understand yet how it all happened."

"Neither do I." He smiled grimly. "I guess these baby parties are pretty rough affairs."

"Well, one thing—" suggested Edith hopefully, "I'm certainly glad we have beefsteak in the house for tomorrow's dinner."

"Why?"

"For your eye, of course. Do you know I came within an ace of ordering veal? Wasn't that the luckiest thing?"

Half an hour later, dressed except that his neck would accommodate no collar, John moved his limbs experimentally before the glass. "I believe I'll get myself in better shape," he said thoughtfully. "I must be getting old."

"You mean so that next time you can beat him?"

"I did beat him," he announced. "At least, I beat him as much as he beat me. And there isn't going to be any next time. Don't you go calling people common any more. If you get in any trouble, you just take your coat and go home. Understand?"

"Yes, dear," she said meekly. "I was very foolish and now I understand."

Out in the hall, he paused abruptly by the baby's door.

"Is she asleep?"

"Sound asleep. But you can go in and peek at her—just to say good night."

They tiptoed in and bent together over the bed. Little Ede, her cheeks flushed with health, her pink hands clasped tight together, was sleeping soundly in the cool, dark room. John reached over the railing of the bed and passed his hand lightly over the silken hair.

"She's asleep," he murmured in a puzzled way.

"Naturally, after such an afternoon."

"Miz Andros," the colored maid's stage whisper floated in from the hall, "Mr. and Miz Markey downstairs an' want to see you. Mr. Markey he's all cut up in pieces, ma'am. His face look like a roast beef. An' Miz Markey she 'pear mighty mad."

"Why, what incomparable nerve!" exclaimed Edith. "Just tell them we're not home. I wouldn't go down for anything in the world."

"You most certainly will." John's voice was hard and set.

"What?"

"You'll go down right now, and, what's more, whatever that other woman does, you'll apologize for what you said this afternoon. After that you don't ever have to see her again."

"Why—John, I can't."

"You've got to. And just remember that she probably hated to come over here just twice as much as you hate to go downstairs."

"Aren't you coming? Do I have to go alone?"

"I'll be down—in just a minute."

John Andros waited until she had closed the door behind her; then he reached over into the bed, and picking up his daughter, blankets and all, sat down in the rocking-chair holding her tightly in his arms. She moved a little, and he held his breath, but she was sleeping soundly, and in a moment she was resting quietly in the hollow of his elbow. Slowly he bent his head until his cheek was against her bright hair. "Dear little girl," he whispered. "Dear little girl, dear little girl."

John Andros knew at length what it was he had fought for so savagely that evening. He had it now, he possessed it forever, and for some time he sat there rocking very slowly to and fro in the darkness.

Milt Gross

EXCERPTS FROM NIZE BABY

[EDITOR'S NOTE: *The characters created by the late Milt Gross for* Nize Baby *dwelled in a walk-up apartment house in the Bronx, where most conversations, apparently, were conducted by residents leaning out of front windows, and neighborhood tidbits were acquired by astute eavesdropping in the vicinity of the dumbwaiter shaft.*

Exchanges between residents on the first and second floor went something like this:]

Second Floor. Sotch a intresting hotticle wot I was ridding lest night in de noosepaper, Mrs. Feitlebaum!!!!

First Floor. Wot was??

Second Floor. Hm!! Wot was? It was stending dere in de paper a hotticle about a meelionaire from Pittsboig—a men wot he's woit maybe from seexty meelion dollars——

First Floor. Seexty meelion dollars!!! Yi yi yi yi yi—from wot did he made all dot money??

Second Floor. From fish!

First Floor. From FISH!!!!

Second Floor. Yeh—from fish. He got it in Pittsboig from refining smelts——

First Floor. Yi yi yi yi. De tings wot dey paying money for in dis country!!

Second Floor. So he hed it a dudder—a beautiful goil—so diss dudder she eloped mit a collision!

First Floor. Mitt a collision!!!

Second Floor. Yeh! A collision! A soffermore from Yale College!! Look it's stending in de paper "Rich hearess elopes mitt a welty collision!" "Britegroom, a welty sign of a noble family—married to dudder of nutted steel magnet" by Jostice from de Peas merrige was wit—yi yi yi! De crazy tings wot dem sosiety pipple doing!

First Floor. Wot is??

Second Floor. Wid a hydrant dey got married!!!

First Floor. Wid a HYDRANT?!!

Second Floor. Yeh, yeh, look it's sending here "De wadding took place mitt de pomp end——"

[*On the third floor, an irate father usually could be heard upbraiding his young son, punctuating his orations with well-aimed and resounding wallops. For instance:*]

So, Isidor . . . Again you was by dot bum in de houze (SMACK) You shouldn't go (SMACK) by dot bum (SMACK) in de houze (SMACK!!). Weendows you break, ha? (SMACK!) Wot I gotta (SMACK) pay for it (SMACK). A baseball fighter you'll grow opp, maybe (SMACK). I'll tich you (SMACK) a lesson (SMACK!). (Morris! Morris!! sh-h! sh!! It's a shame for de neighbors.) SHARROP!! I'll geeve him (SMACK). Dot bum (SMACK!). Dot he'll grow opp (SMACK) a respectable poison!!!

[*Or, on another occasion:*]

Third Floor. (SMACK)!!!!!! So, Isidor, a "D" on de reputt card you gatting, ha? (SMACK!) Mobbles you'll play all day, ha? (SMACK!) Instad (SMACK) wot you should be stoddying (SMACK) de lassons! (SMACK) Did I was sotch a dope, ha? (SMACK) Did MINE FODDER was sotch a dope, ha? (SMACK) Benjos (SMACK) mitt yookellellys (SMACK) mitt jezz-time (SMACK) you know all about it, ha! But de heestry (SMACK) mitt jometry (SMACK) mitt pheezics (SMACK) you don't know it, ha? (SMACK) Is diss a system? (SMACK)

[*It was the fourth floor, however, that produced the character on which Gross' fame as a humorist securely—and deservedly—rests. A young mother, conning her "nize baby" into "eating opp all de oatmill," retold in her own wonderful vernacular some of the world's best fairy stories. Following are a few classic examples:*]

POCAHANTAS WITT KEPTAIN JOHN SMEET

Oohoo, Nize baby, itt opp all de shradded whit, so momma'll gonna tell you a sturry from Pocahantas witt Keptain John Smeet. Wance oppon a time was a Hindian Chiff from a whole tripe from Hindians, wot he hed it a dudder wot her name was Pocahantas! Hm! Sotch a byooty wot she was, witt a grazeful forum witt a feegure witt raving bleck hair, witt a holive skeen witt fleshing heyes—mmmmmm—a ragular pitch!! (Nize baby, take annodder spoon shradded whit.) So in de minntime, it came over from Hingland a band from oily tsettlers wot dey called dem columnists. So de lidder from de columnists was a Ganeral from a name Keptain John Smeet.

So one hefternoon he was taking a leedle strull in de woots, so it was lurching dere in a hambush dem doidy Hindians so, so soon wot he pessed by dey gave queeck a yell, "Hends opp!—odder we'll cot you off de scallop wid a tommyhuck." So he saw wot it was against him de hodds so he compiled gredually witt de requast!!!

So dey brut him in de front from de tripe so de chiff witt de Sockems from de tripe held a mitting, wot should be from him. So de chiff sad, "Wot kind beezness you in?" So he replite, "I'm a columnist wot we tsettling de colonizz!!!" So de chiff sad, "Hm! Trapezing on priwate property, ha?? So for diss, we'll gonna chop you off de had!!" So jost dey leefted opp de hexes it should chop him off de had——it jomped opp gredually Pocahantas, wot she sad, "Ciss!!!"

So de chiff sad, "Wot's de rizzon we should ciss?"

So Pocahantas sad, "I dun't want wot you should do diss didd!!"

So de chiff sad, "Somebody esked you for a hopinion?? Why you don't want??"

So Pocahantas sad, "Jost bickuss!!!"

So de chiff sad, "Aha! You took already maybe a lightning to diss goot-for-notting, ha?? Hm! Sotch hideas! Is here a whole tripe from brave witt nubble worriers wot itch one it would make a idill hosband so you got to fall yat for a dope wot he billives wot Sitting Bull is a cow's hosband!! I tink wot I'll make him run yet a gimlet foist!"

So Pocahantas sad, "I luff him."

So de chiff sad, "Hm! A son-in-law I nidd yat wot he wears a monologue in de heye!! Go beck queeck in de weeckwam und don't meex opp in mine beezness odder you'll gat from me wid a strep."

So Pocahantas sad, "If you'll wouldn't lat him go I'll tell momma wot it was going on lest night in de Hell Fay Clob witt you witt dop wemp from a Minnie-Ha-Ha!! Hm, you gatting pale, ha?? Noo, so wot'll gonna be? Queeck!"

So de chiff sad, "Blast you, mine cheeldren!!!"

So dey gradually got married so in a shut time de chiff was a grenpapa from a leedle caboose! (Hm!! Sotch a dollink baby ate opp all de shradded whit!!)

DE FERRY TAIL FROM KEENG MITAS

Oohoo, nize baby, itt opp all de Cheeken Zoop so mamma'll gonna tell you a Ferry-Tail from Keeng Mitas. Wance oppon a time was a werry, werry reech Keeng from de name from Keeng Mitas. Sotch a welt wot he hed!—wot it would make J. P. Morgan witt Hanry Fudd witt John D. Rockefeller dey should look like puppers. (Nize baby, take anodder spoon cheeken zoop——.)

So instat from bing setisfite witt contempted—he becrutched yat averybody helse wot dey possassed, und he was only trying how he could incriss yat wot he had (mmmm—dot griddy ting). So a whole time he was hudding opp de moneh witt glutting yat from it like a miser. So wan day he was wukking opp witt don in de godden so he was tinking so, "Hm—wot could I do, dot I should hev it ivvin more yat from wot I got?" (mmm—dot salfish critchure). So he was interropted by a leedle Ferry wot it was stending in de front from him witt a Magic Want.

So de Ferry sad, "You Keeng Mitas???"

So de Keeng sad, "So wot is??"

So de Ferry sad, "I'm a Ferry wot I could grent you wot annyting wot you'll weesh so'll be foolfeeled de weesh!!!" So de Keeng sad, "Wot kind bunco-steerage game you call dees, ha? You got maybe some goot-for-notting Hoil Stocks wot you want to sell it, ha, maybe? Odder a petent carpet-swipper, odder maybe a phuny Gold mine yat, ha!! Try batter by Old Keeng Cole, not by me—Goot hefternoon!!"

So de Ferry sad, "Hm—you a werry septical poison, ha? Soppose wot you geeve me a hopportunity I should conweence you!"

So de Keeng sad, "Ho K, I weesh wot averyting wot I toch it, it should toin into gold."

So he was holding in de hand a spectre, so de Ferry gave him a tree times a tep witt de megic want—so he gave a look—so it was by him a solit gold spectre in de hend!!—Noo, noo!—So don't esk!!!

So de Keeng was dencing witt jomping witt lipping witt bonding witt prencing from joy. You should see wot he was deshing hitter witt titter—opp witt don, high witt low—beck witt futt, too witt frau,—wot he was toching averyting on wheech he put on de hends. So his Wessel sad, "Is goot now?" So de Keeng sad, "Yeh, is goot bot look a hincome-tax I'll gonna have und'll be mine lock yat wot I'll gat maybe to-morrow roomateezum in de hends." (MMMmmm—dot apparitious ting.)

So it came gredually deener-time so de Keeng was werry hongry so he set don he should itt opp a hoyster. So so soon wot he toched de hoyster it became solid gold!! So he sad, "Hm—Wot's dees??" So he tried he should ketch in queek a potato in de mout no one should see, so so soon wot he stodded he should chew it, it became solid gold wot it broke him two teet witt a cron witt a heff from de breedge—woik yat besites wot it was werry hot so it made him yat a bleesters on de tong!!

So he sad—"Hm!—Is a seerous preposition. It simms wot I'll have to employ stragedy." So he sad to de Wessel, "I'll gonna stend witt de mout open—So you'll put in a binn-shooter a hepple, wot you'll shoot it, it should go in mine mout wot I'll swallow it queeck it shouldn't toch me." So de Wessel compiled gredually witt de requast, bot he was a werry poor mox-man, so instat from de Keeng's mout it went in de had wot it became immiditly gold wot it gave him sotch a knock wot he hed almost conclusion from de brain.

So was a werry cricketal situation—wot de Keeng sad, "Hm, so it rimmains wot I'll gonna hev to leeve maybe a whole life on gold-feesh, Ha!!" So it was gredually all kind from trobbles!! It came de night so he stodded in he should ondrass so it was dere by him a pair from 18 carrot Bivvy Dizz wot de wessels had to ondrass him yat witt a can-uppener. So one day he was wukking opp witt don so it came ronning over to heem his leedle dudder—Hm, deed she was a switt child!! So he was so epsom minded, dot dope, wot he put on her head de hend he should toch her so she became solit gold. Yi yi yi yi—So you should see a griff from a remuss wot it was by de Keeng—mmm!!! Deed he was sowry!!! witt meeserable witt don-hotted—witt rependant—wot he was wipping beeterly.

So it gredually appeared in de front from him de Ferry wit de Megic Want so he sad, "Goot Monnink, Keeng, How is by you de Gold Rosh??? So de Keeng gave sotch a grun from meesery wot it toched de Ferry's hott—so he sad, "You'll gonna be steengy witt griddy wit salfish anny more?"

So de Keeng sad, "NO."

"You'll gonna dunnate maybe itch year someting to de Meelk Fond?"

"Yeh."

"Wid de Selwation Ommy?"

"Yeh."

"Widd de Ufffan's Home?"

"Yeh."

"So you'll gonna refumm, ha?"

"Yeh."

"In odder woids you'll gonna be from now on a deeference indiwijial halltogadder?"

"Cruss mine hott!"

So de Ferry gave him tree times a tep witt de Megic Want so dere it was stending in de front from him de leedle dudder jost like new, wot dey leeved happily hever hefter.

(Hm—Sotch a dollink baby—ate opp all de cheeken Zoop!)

JECK WITT DE BINN-STUCK

Oohoo, nize baby, itt opp all de Chucklitt Putting, so momma'll gonna tell you a Ferry-Tail from Jeck witt de Binn-stuck. Wance oppon a time, was leeving a werry, werry poor weedow witt a son from de name from Jeck. Hm!—sotch a lazy sheeftless goot for notting wot he was. A whole day henging arond witt de loafers in de front from de poolroom instat wot he should look for a dissint job. So dey hed it one seengle cow wot he became gredually werry skinny from lack from narrishment, so dey decited wot dey'll gonna sell de cow. (Nize baby, take anodder spoon Chucklitt Putting.)

So Jeck was motching witt de cow to de mocket he should sell de cow so he mat gredually in de rote a man wot he was kerrying a beg from binns. So he sad: "Goot monnink, gimme a binn." So de man sad, "A binn you want, ha, you frash keed. Hm!—sotch a crost witt a noive wot dem keeds got nowadays. Dees is werry wellyible binns. From one binn you could make at list a gellon binn-zoop. Eef you'll geeve me de cow—I'll geeve you de whole beg from binns." So Jeck, dot dope, sad: "Ho K. De dill is on!!" So dey made a trait.

So he arrifed home so de modder sad, "Hm—you socker!! De lendlor we'll gonna pay de rant maybe witt binns, ha? Hm—sotch a boop! Woister ivvin from you fodder!"

So Jeck sad, "Never mind! I'll gonna plent de binns in de yod!"

So she sad, "A Looter Boibank you became yat also, ha? Trow away de binns and look opp batter de Halp Wanted Hads!"

So de naxt monnink dey gave a look in de yod—so was growing dere a beeg beeg binnstuck!! Hm! sotch a hide wot it riched opp to, higher ivvin from de clouts. So Jeck sad, "Hm, I teenk wot I'll gonna inwastigate!! So he gave gredually a jomp witt a spreeng witt a lipp wot he climbed opp de binnstuck.

So on de top from de binnstuck was a kestle in wheech it leeved a hogre wot he ate opp pipple. So Jeck gave a knock on de door so it uppened de door de hogre's wife. So Jeck sad:

"Goot monnink, Meessus Hogre!!"

So she sad, "Who you??"

So he sad: "Hm—I'm from de Gezz Company—wot I should ridd de mitter."

So she sad, "Hm—mine hosband'll gonna itt you opp. Hite batter in de hoven."

So he hit in de hoven. So it came in gredually de hogre wot he gave a sneef so he sad:

"FEE, FOOY, FOOY, FROM!"
 I smell de blood from a Human Bing!
 Be he alife odder be he dat—
 I'll make from heem a corn-biff sanawich!!"

So de wife sad: "Hm—dun't be non sensible! Was here to-day de plumber wot you smelling heem. Go itt batter you sopper."

So de hogre set don by de taple on wheech it was dere a whole cow—witt seextinn docks witt fife geeze—witt a will-berrell full from cebbidges—witt a heff from a peeg yat, witt a whole kag from tsider. So he sad, "Hm, wot's de metter—sotch a skeempy sopper—you gatting econominal maybe, odder you teenk is by me a honger-strike—odder a dite, I should redooze wot I should bicome pale witt inimic yat, ha? Go queeck fatch me a copple dozzen helephants knockles." So he ate opp wit one golp de sopper.

So den he called over a han wot it was a megic han wot it lait only golden haggs. So den he sad: "Breeng me mine hop!!" So she brutt in

de hop. So de hogre gave a yell: "Play!" So was a megic hop wot it
stodded to play from its own occurd. "Yookillily Lady" witt "Ho Ket-
trinna." So de hogre fell aslipp so Jeck snickked out from de hoven
so he grebbed queeck de hop witt de han witt de haggs he should
ron away so de hop wot it was like a wentreeloquist gave a yell:
"HALP! HALP!—is stilling me a tiff wit a keednepper! Halp!!" So
de hogre gave a jomp opp witt a rur from rage. Bot Jeck gave queeck
a jomp out from de weendow wot he ren fest like a strick from lightning to de binnstuck so he sleet don—so he grebbed queeck a hex wot
he chopped don de binnstuck so de hogre wot he was in de meedle
from de binnstuck came tombling don in a hipp wot it keeled him so
he was dat. So Jeck witt de momma leeved heppily hever hefter."

(Hm—sotch a dollink baby—ate opp all de Chucklitt Putting!)

Elledin witt de Wanderful Lemp

Oohoo, nize baby, zipp opp all de horange-jooze, so momma'll
gonna tell you a ferry tail from Elledin Witt de Wanderful Lemp.
Wance oppon a time was leeving in China a werry, werry poor weedow
wot she hed it a son from de name from Elledin. So he was a goot-
for-notting, wot de whole day he was playing Ma Jonk instat wot he
should attent to de lundry. So it stodded in to complain de costomers
wot dey sad so: "Hm—de teeckets you meexing opp und de collars
we sanding you wot you should iron dem, so instat you shoppening
dem. Und de Bivvy Dizz you stotching opp yat!! Is diss a system???"

(Nize baby, take anodder zip horange-jooze.)

So it went leedle by leedle to de dugs de beezness besites wot it
uppened opp yat gredually a rifle acruss de stritt. So hall in hall—
Elledin became don witt out.

So wan day he was seeting, wot he was playing a song on a man-
darin, so it came along a men wot he sad he was a lung-lust huncle
witt a beeg botter-und-agg men. (Of cuss, he deedn't rilly was; he
was rilly a doidy crook from a mageecian witt a susser.) So he gritted
Elledin werry cudgelly wot he sad: "Mmmm mm, hollo, naffew dollink!! Sotch a beeg handsome shick you grew opp. How's de momma?
C'mon, lat's we'll gonna knock over a bowl rize!!"

So Elledin went witt heem so dey arrifed gredually in a plaze so de
huncle made a mysteerous notion witt de hends wot it uppened opp
in de grond a hole. So de huncle sad: "Naffew dollink, go don stess

so you'll see henging dere a lemp so you'll breeng me opp de lemp like a goot boy!!"

So Elledin was extrimmingly souprise witt dezzled witt bewilted, so he compiled gredually witt de requast so he fond de lemp so he stodded in he should come opp so de huncle sad:

"Gimme foist de lemp."

So Elledin sad, "Lat me foist I should come opp."

So de huncle reppitted, "Gimme foist de lemp!!"

So Elledin sad, "Lat me foist I should come opp!!"

So de huncle sad, "Gimme foist de lemp, you frash keed."

So Elledin sad, "In you hat!!"

So de huncle sad, "Hm! beck-tuk, witt smot-crecks, ha?? Wait, I'll geeve you!! You teenk wot I'm you huncle, ha? Dope! So I'm rilly Pincus de Megeecian!! Hm, you gatting pale, ha? Wait yat!!" So he gave gredually a yell, "Huckuss Puckuss!!!"—wot it closed opp de hole so he ren away. (Mm-mm, dot doidy ting!)

So don't esk!! So it sizzed Elledin sotch a penic witt a fright wot he was sheevering witt shaking like a aspirin leaf. So in de minntime he gave accidentally a rob witt de helbow de lemp so it appeared in de front from heem a Ginny wot he sad: "Yassar, wot you weesh, sar?"

So Elledin esked, "Who you?"

So de Ginny sad: "Any one wot he geeves a rob de lemp so wotever he weeshes so I foolfeel heem de weesh!! Wot you'll gonna have!!"

So Elledin sad: "Hm—lat's see . . . Breeng me a cheecken chommain witt a plate boid's nast zoop, witt yom dom, witt bemboo chutes, witt a pot from hoolong tea, und breeng batter a hextra pair chopsteecks!!"

So efter dees he went gredually home wot he robbed a whole day lung de lemp wot he, witt de momma, hed it everyting wot dey weeshed. So he married gredually de Soltan's dudder. Und de megeecian, dot crook, he hed to seet yat in preeson.

(Hm! Sotch a dollink baby—zipped opp all de horange-jooze!)

Margaret Millar

EXCERPTS FROM
IT'S ALL IN THE FAMILY

A Problem in Economics

AT SEVEN o'clock on Saturday morning the golden hours began. As soon as she opened her eyes Priscilla could feel in her bones that it was Saturday. The air smelled different, and it seemed to quiver with anticipation. The pink wallpaper roses were pinker, and the hump under the covers of the other twin bed was not just the Becky whom she had to drag to school with her every week day, it was the Saturday Becky, co-partner in all kinds of dashing schemes. She herself was the Saturday Priscilla, and when she peered into the mirror (before putting up the blind and letting in the light) she looked mysterious and shadowy, like a famous singer, in her nightgown-evening dress, or a mermaid with her seaweed hair, or the Lady of Shalott floating down to Camelot. Float, float, float. She floated into her clothes and through the hall and down the stairs into the kitchen, where Edna compressed her beautiful seaweed hair into tight and unromantic braids, and remarked that the Lady of Shalott's neck was dirty.

"Grandpa says a little dirt never hurt anybody," Priscilla said. "Anyway we all have to eat fifteen pounds of dirt before we die."

"Who says so?" Edna asked suspiciously.

"Nobody said so. It's just a rule."

"It don't sound like much of a rule to me."

"Well, ask anybody. Ask God."

"Fiddlesticks," said Edna.

Edna was always cross in the morning before she had taken her hot water and lemon to tone up her complexion and system in general. It had rained during the night and Edna's marcel had come out. Her short dark hair stood up straight on her head and she moved around the kitchen on her short legs like a ferocious pygmy.

"Now you go up and get washed," Edna said, "and don't stand around pesting."

"I didn't even open my mouth."

"You were going to."

"I was not, I was just standing here thinking."

"Tra la," said Edna. She squeezed the juice of a lemon into a cup of hot water, and sipped it. She felt her complexion improving on the spot and her system in general toning itself up.

"I was thinking," Priscilla said, "how nice I felt fifteen minutes ago."

"Indeedy?"

"Then I remembered something like a bolt from the blue. I need a dime."

"A dime? I ask you, where would I get a dime? Anyway your ma said not to give you kids any more money. She said to let you and Becky work things out for yourselves."

"Becky's a miser," Priscilla said darkly. "Personally, she'd sell her soul to the devil for two dollars."

Priscilla would not have objected to such a transaction except that she considered it highly improbable that Becky could be persuaded to part with any of the two dollars received.

"The way you talk," Edna said, scowling. "My land, it don't sound ladylike. Selling souls to the devil. Wait'll your ma hears about that."

"Edna?"

"No dime, no sirreee!"

"It's a mere trifling matter of lending me the money," Priscilla said haughtily. "It isn't like I was asking you to *give* it to me."

"It's six of one and a half a dozen of the other if you ask me," Edna said. "And when *I* was eleven and wanted ten cents I went out and got me a ten-cent task to do."

"I can't think of any ten-cent task except just plain being good."

"In this world you don't get paid for being good. Now go away and don't pester me. I got to make breakfast."

"You have a heart like lead," Priscilla said. With this parting shot she wandered back upstairs in search of her next best source of supply, her brother, Paul.

Paul was in the bathroom. He had been in the bathroom now for nearly half an hour, and Priscilla suspected that he was shaving. Paul was sixteen and he was supposed to shave only once a week, on Sunday mornings before church, but he sometimes shaved on Saturdays too, to stimulate his whiskers. Paul had several whiskers, and by commenting on their rapid growth Priscilla was occasionally able to extract a nickel or a dime from him.

Putting her mouth to the keyhole of the bathroom door, Priscilla whispered, "I bet I know what you're doing."

"Aw, beat it," said Paul in the tight tense voice which indicated that he had reached the most delicate part of his work, the upper lip. Here the growth was sparse, and each hair had to be tracked and mowed down individually.

"I bet you're shaving."

"Oh yeah?"

"I bet you had to. I saw with my own eyes last night, your whiskers are getting like Father's."

This was the perfect approach and it might even have worked if Father himself had not come striding out of his room. Father's whiskers had grown during the night and he looked very fierce and dark and handsome, like Black Douglas.

"What the devil is he doing in there?" Father said, pounding on the bathroom door with his fist. "Paul! Paul!"

"Well, gosh almighty," Paul said. "Holy catsoup, can't a fellow spend a couple of minutes in the bathroom without everybody yelling at him?"

"A couple of minutes," Father said. "Allie! Do you hear that, Allie?"

"I hear it," Mother replied. She came out into the hall with her light hair flowing down her back. Some of the more fashionable ladies of Woodlawn Avenue had had their hair shingled and mother was forced to think up new reasons nearly every day to justify her lack of stylishness. She told Father that bobbed hair was unwomanly, and that no lady should enter a barbershop. She informed Edna that bobbed hair was a passing fad, and she reminded the girls, Becky and Priscilla, that she could sit on her hair (at the risk of putting her neck out of joint). But the real reason why Mother didn't get her hair cut off was that it kept her neck and shoulders warm in bed in the wintertime.

It wasn't winter any more but it was still cold. Mother draped her hair around her throat like a scarf and said, "Hurry up, Paul. Your father's going to be late to the office and you know how upset he gets."

"Well, all right, all right," Paul muttered. "Keep your shirts on, I'm coming."

"Upset?" Father repeated. "Who's upset?"

"Did I say upset?" Mother smiled in a vague kindly way. "I only meant perturbed. You know, excited."

"Hysterical," said Priscilla, who was always willing to help people express themselves. "Opposite of calm. We had opposites in school last week and the teacher asked what was the opposite of calm and I put my hand up and said hysterical, and the teacher said that was very clever but wrong. She said you couldn't say, the lake is very hysterical today. But I asked Grandpa and Grandpa said you could *so* say the lake is very hysterical today. He said he's seen *lots* of hysterical lakes, and that's that. Grandpa knows."

"All right, all right," Father said, looking fiercer and darker than ever. "You've proved it. I'm convinced. I'm hysterical. The subject is closed. Though I may add this point, that anybody who expects justice in this house is certainly hysterical. Justice, do you hear, Allie? That's all I ask. One bathroom and seven people, and *I'm* the *seventh*."

"Oh, I don't think so," Mother said mildly and drifted back into the bedroom.

Face to face with Black Douglas, Priscilla did not flinch.

"Mrs. Barton's brother is the seventh son of a seventh son and he could tell the future if he wasn't dead. He died when he was a baby before he could talk so he never told anyone the future."

"Is that a fact?" Father said.

"You know what? We could get *two* bathrooms. Then there'd be three and one half people for each one. Grandpa and Edna and I could have one and you and Mother and Paul could have the other one and Becky could half the time use ours and half the time use yours. Becky's such a mere child she only counts as a half anyway."

Priscilla's reference to Becky was necessarily bitter. Becky could have solved her financial problem in a minute if she wanted to and if Priscilla didn't already owe her seventeen cents and eight gumdrops. Becky always managed to save money out of her allowance. She was not exactly stingy, but she had a way with money. All over the house were secret caches of dimes and nickels, in pockets, in the toes of shoes, in the corners of drawers, on the slats of beds and in the toy cupboard camouflaged with plasticine. These caches gave Becky, otherwise an insignificant creature of seven, a great power. When Priscilla, impoverished as usual, felt that she absolutely could not go on living without an Eskimo Pie, she appealed to Becky for a nickel.

Becky had established a ritual for granting such appeals. Priscilla was compelled to say, "Your Royal Highness, I am but a humble starving dairymaid"—or woodcutter, spinner of flax, garbage collector, butcher, or whichever profession Becky considered lowliest at the time. After this Becky, wearing an inscrutable and majestic smile, would lock Priscilla in the cedar closet in the upstairs hall while she fished the necessary amount from one of her secret caches. Becky's mind wandered at times, and she occasionally left Priscilla in the cedar closet for as long as half an hour.

"Bathrooms," said Father, "cost money."

"It's ghastly to be a pauper, isn't it?"

"I hardly think we can be classified as paupers."

"I meant I am a pauper and it's ghastly," Priscilla said, looking wistful by widening her eyes and letting her mouth droop at the corners just like Clara Bow. It was one of her most effective expressions, perfected after long practice in front of her bureau mirror, but as usual it was wasted on Father.

"You had your allowance last Wednesday," Father said, banging on the bathroom door again. "What did you do with it?"

"I don't remember exactly. I *may* have *lost* some of it, say a dime or so maybe."

"So you want a dime or so maybe. What for?"

Father liked straight answers to straight questions, so Priscilla obliged. "There's a special morning movie at the Star, a Jackie Coogan feature and a Chester Conklin funny, all for ten cents. Becky's going, because she still has her allowance left."

"If Becky has her allowance left and you haven't, it seems to me she has more sense than you have."

Priscilla was wounded to the core by this remark. "How can she have more sense than I have when I'm eleven going on twelve and she's merely a trifling seven? She's stingy, that's all. It's not hard to save money when you're stingy. When you're stingy you're not even *tempted* in the wrong direction. I'm tempted all the time."

"Then you'll have to build up some resistance," Father said, "because the answer is no. You must learn the value of money some time, you may as well begin when you're young."

"Oh, cows," said Priscilla.

Her father's attitude caused her great anguish, for the fact was that no one the whole length and breadth of Woodlawn Avenue knew the value of money as well as she did. For ten cents you could buy exactly 69 licorice allsorts at Bowman's if Mrs. Bowman weighed them, and 73 if Mr. Bowman weighed them. You could get 3 cream buns at Ingersoll's, 8 pieces of Turkish Delight at Burdick's, 4 two-for-a-nickel ice cream cones from the ice cream man, and 20 aggies at Dodie's Department Store.

"And don't say 'cows,'" Father said. "It doesn't make sense."

"Well, sometimes you say Jesus Q. Murphy."

"That's an entirely different matter."

Paul emerged from the bathroom with the lower half of his face swathed in a towel to hide the nicks. Paul's face was always liberally scarred after a battle with Father's straight razor.

"You weren't supposed to shave until tomorrow," Father said rather grimly, since his razor usually suffered as much as Paul's face from the ordeal.

"Well, gosh almighty," Paul said, "you can't expect a fellow to go around with a heavy beard, can you? Gosh almighty, it's Saturday. I got to look decent."

"You have a peculiar way of going about it," Father said. He locked himself in the bathroom.

Paul had lost considerable blood in the cause of looking decent and he was in no mood to give anybody anything except a swift kick in the slats.

"Well, Jesus Q. Murphy, you don't have to be so mean about it," Priscilla said, deeply wounded. "I never saw such a mean family in my life. The way I'm treated around this house you'd think I was an orphan from the storm."

The idea of being an orphan from the storm appealed to Priscilla's dramatic instincts. Before going down to breakfast she dropped in to her room to see if she bore any resemblance to Oliver Twist. She carefully ignored Becky, who was sitting on the floor tying the shoelaces of her second-best Oxfords. Becky, however, never knew when she was being ignored, so Priscilla was forced to draw it to her attention.

"I'm not even speaking to you," she said loftily. "And you can't even tie shoelaces, you baby."

"I can, too," Becky said. "If I set my mind I can tie shoelaces better than anybody in the whole world."

"I bet you can't. I bet a dime."

Becky thought this proposition over for some time. "I can't bet," she said finally, "'count of my Sunday School teacher says it's against the Bible and maybe I wouldn't win."

"You do other things against the Bible."

Becky was surprised. "Do I?"

"You bury your talents, talents being money."

"Oh, I never did bury any talents. Just dead things like birds and dolls and caterpillars."

Priscilla flung her pride to the winds. "Well, the least you can do is *lend* me a dime and when I get to be a famous movie actress I'll pay you back with fur coats and diamonds, etc."

"How many fur coats?" Becky asked cautiously.

"Lots and lots of them, with muffs to match and fur hats, too."

Becky was very fond of furry things like cats and dogs and squirrels and fur coats, owing to their softness, and for a whole minute she was tempted in the wrong direction. The prospect of the fur coats was enchanting but it was also rather dim, and there was the immediate matter of the seventeen cents and the eight gumdrops already owing to her.

"Ten plus seventeen equals twenty-seven," Becky said thoughtfully. "That's a lot of talents, plus the gumdrops."

"You'll never get a fur coat at all if I don't get to the movies so I can learn to be a famous actress."

"You can't go to the movies anyway," Becky pointed out. "You're being punished 'count of last night."

"Oh, God!" Priscilla said in an agonized voice.

In the excitement of chasing the dime, she had forgotten that last night she had broken one of Mother's germ-rules.

Mother's mind was inclined to vagueness, and partly to compensate for this and partly because she liked making up rules anyway, Mother had strict and definite rules covering nearly everything. Most of these rules were never enforced but the mere fact that they were there gave Mother a pleasant feeling of competence. Mother's most stringent rules concerned germs, a subject worthy of her mettle. Germs were everywhere and in her attempt to outwit them; Mother had devised a long and involved set of rules. Several of them necessarily applied to the dog, Skipper. Though Mother loyally claimed that Skipper was the cleanest dog in town, she was compelled to recognize his fondness for decaying vegetable and animal matter, and so she had laid down a law that he was to be kissed on only two occasions, immediately after his bath and on his deathbed.

It was naturally a great shock to Mother when the night before she had come upon Priscilla eating out of Skipper's dish.

Pressed for reasons, Priscilla found several. "I was *only* trying to show him I loved him and that he's *just* as good as *I* am. And also I *only* wanted to see how it tasted and how it felt to be a dog."

Father was curious. "Well, how does it feel?"

"Frederick, how can you treat it so lightly?" Mother cried. "Think of all those germs in her system."

Mother prepared a gargle of sodium perborate and meted out justice. Priscilla was to stay home from the Saturday morning matinée, partly as a punishment, but mostly because a system so loaded with germs should not be exposed to any more germs.

"My, I bet you're full of germs," Becky said with admiration. "Maybe you'll *get* something."

"I don't care if I do. I *hope* I do." She saw herself lying in a white satin coffin, very pale and dead with plenty of flowers around her. Grandpa and Mother and Becky and Edna and Paul and Father were all crying their eyes out and offering her dimes and silver dollars and shin plasters and five-dollar gold pieces, which, alas, her poor little dead hand couldn't reach out and take.

This was such a weepy thought that real tears stung her eyelids. So young to die. Cut off in her youth by the grim reaper. Rest in peace.

"My, I wish I could get something, too," Becky said. It was a great sorrow to Becky that all her friends had had some form of distinction like mumps or whooping cough and all she ever got was a cold in the nose. "Maybe if you get something I can catch it from you and we would have a big red sign on the front door and be guaranteed."

"*Quaranteed*," Priscilla said, frowning. "Grandpa says you murder the King's English. He says you get it from Edna."

Becky squinted up her eyes stubbornly and talked back, inside her head: *Guar*anteed, *guar*anteed, *guar*anteed. I want to be *guar*anteed with a big red sign on the front door.

Then, setting her mind, she tied the shoelaces of her second-best Oxfords. Now that her moment of weakness and temptation in the wrong direction had passed, she felt kindly disposed toward her sister.

"I will tell you all about the movie," Becky said. "I will even keep my eyes open at the bad parts."

"I hope I get galloping consumption and everybody will be sorry when I die," Priscilla said bitterly and went down to breakfast.

Edna was timing the eggs with her own special egg-timer, a tiny hourglass filled with red sand.

"Did you get your dime?"

"No."

"Well, we all got our troubles," Edna said brusquely. "Take you, it's money, and take me, it's Harry and Delbert and my goiter. We just got to bear our crosses nobly."

Nobility was an attitude that Priscilla hadn't tried for at least two days. Flinging back her shoulders and holding her head high, Priscilla bore her crosses and ate three eggs.

THE PERILS OF LILYBELLE

SUNDAY, while not Priscilla's favorite day of the week owing to Sunday School, was usually lively and strenuous, for it was the day the clan gathered. All Mother's relatives and all Father's relatives except the aged, the infirm and the distant, met for the purposes of eating, drinking and comparing children. In the summertime these meetings took the form of picnics and were enjoyed by all except Grandpa, who said he hated nature as the gates of Hell.

At other times of the year the family gathered for the afternoon and evening occasionally at Aunt Marnie's or Uncle Bruce's house but usually at Mother's. Since Uncle Bruce was a widower and Aunt Marnie lived fifteen miles out in the country, it was Mother who took the burden of the feeding and entertaining. This was simple justice, Aunt Marnie claimed, since Mother was the only one who had a big house and a hired girl.

Aunt Marnie was Mother's older sister. She had married beneath her, it was said, in a number of ways. Her husband, Edward, was a short dreamy man who carved bedposts and table legs in a furniture factory. As a sideline Uncle Ed scorched designs on pieces of velvet, and all over his house, on tables and pillows and chairs and walls, there were odds and ends of velvet scorched with roses and bunches of grapes and Greek frets and Abraham Lincoln. Priscilla and Becky owned several pieces of Uncle Ed's handiwork. A blue pillow cover decorated with curlicues and "Sleep Sweet For God is Nigh," twin dresses with roses at the bosom, and a handkerchief case bearing half a dozen plums (or large cherries).

Uncle Ed took more pleasure in the Sunday meetings than anyone else, for he loved to talk and he loved to eat. He had a big appetite for his size, and his enjoyment of Mother's fine suppers was marred only by the fact that he was deathly afraid of dogs, even very small dogs or very old ones without teeth.

Skipper had discovered this peculiarity of Uncle Ed's right away and he used it to amuse himself. No matter how many people arrived at the house simultaneously, Skipper would single out Uncle Ed for special attention, plant his paws on Uncle Ed's shoulders and lick his ears or whatever portion of his anatomy he could reach. Skipper looked forward to these demonstrations all week, and early Sunday morning he would take up his position at the front door, rolling his eyes in anticipation.

"It's amazing the things that dog knows," Mother said fondly. "Just look at him. He *knows* it's Sunday."

"Naturally he does," Father said rather irritably because Edna had put too much starch in his high Sunday collar. "He sees me choking to death in this damned collar, and he's commiserating, as one male to another."

This may have been partly true, but Skipper had other and better reasons for believing it was Sunday. Priscilla and Becky were very clean, for one thing, and did not smell interesting. They wore identical blue satin dresses that stank of rose water and had no flavorsome spots to lick. Also they refused to play with him and treated him like a leper if he so much as offered to shake hands. Sunday would have been a sad day indeed for Skipper if he hadn't had Uncle Ed to look forward to.

At two o'clock his vigilance was rewarded by the sound of Uncle Ed's old Graydort in the driveway and Lilybelle's shrieks of delight over her imminent meeting with her arch-enemy and cousin, Priscilla.

"Take the dog out, Paul," Mother said, hurrying into the hall. "You know how Uncle Ed is about dogs."

"Here, Skipper," Paul called lazily. "Here, old boy. Come on, go for a run."

Skipper rose and stretched dreamily. Giving Paul a contemptuous glance he chose the spot, about six feet away from the door, from which he could, with the most ease, spring at Uncle Ed.

Mother always got over-excited at the arrival of Aunt Marnie who was inclined to be critical not only of Mother's housekeeping, but of her children and husband and dog as well. Mother gave the hall-rack a last minute swipe with her handkerchief and shouted orders to everyone in the house at the same time.

"Take his collar, Paul. Frederick, where are you? They're here! Priscilla, Becky, come downstairs. For goodness' sake, Paul, take his *collar*."

Paul took hold of Skipper's collar, which made springing more difficult but not impossible. Skipper ignored Lilybelle and Aunt Marnie who came in first, and with a delighted roar, he lunged at Uncle Ed.

Uncle Ed supported himself by clinging to the door.

"Down," he whispered. "Down, fellow. Down."

"It seems a funny thing to me you don't take that dog out when you know how Ed feels about dogs," said Aunt Marnie. "Say hello to your Aunt Allie, Lilybelle."

"Hello," said Lilybelle. "Where's Priscilla?"

"Down," said Uncle Ed, stiff with fright. "That's a good fellow. Down, fellow."

"He's only showing you how much he loves you," Mother said, making a futile grab at Skipper's tail. "Look, he just adores you."

"Get him away," Uncle Ed said. "I don't want him to adore me."

Skipper finally accomplished what he had been trying to do for several months. Ignoring the pressure on his collar and his tail, he licked Uncle Ed square on the mouth.

Lilybelle saved the situation by squealing with delight and attracting Skipper's attention. The momentary lull allowed Uncle Ed time to squeeze out through the front door and shut it firmly behind him. Paul and Mother then dragged Skipper through the house to the back door and pushed him outside. Paul whistled an all-clear signal, Uncle Ed bolted back into the house via the front door, and the gathering of the clan had officially begun.

Lilybelle disappeared in search of Priscilla, with a number of bones to pick and scores to settle.

"Now remember, no quarreling," Aunt Marnie called after her. "And say your piece over to yourself a couple of times so you won't forget it."

"I know it perfect," Lilybelle screamed back.

Mother's heart sank somewhat at this news. Lilybelle was taking elocution lessons and the Sunday family meeting provided a suitable, if unresponsive, audience to practise on. Neither self-consciousness nor loss of memory, let alone hell or high water, could prevent Lilybelle from elocuting.

"How is she coming along with her lessons?" Mother asked with hollow politeness.

"Just wonderfully. That child's memory . . ."

"Got a memory like an elephant," Uncle Ed put in proudly. "She got a new piece last week, the longest one yet, and she doesn't forget a word."

Mother smiled rather anxiously. "I remember 'The Cattle Thief' was pretty long, the one she recited last Sunday."

"This one is twice as long," Aunt Marnie said.

Father appeared and he and Uncle Ed went into the living room. It was Uncle Ed's opinion that the furniture business (and the coal business as well) was going to pot, and to protect himself against the coming ruin he had taken up sculpting. Since he carved furniture and scorched velvet, sculpting was second nature to him. He had already finished three small cherubs, two with wings and one without wings, and his next task was a bust of Lilybelle (who had also inspired the cherubs). By the merest chance Uncle Ed had happened to bring the wingless cherub with him, and he went back to the hall to get it out of his overcoat pocket.

Aunt Marnie and Mother were in the midst of a consultation about the rib roast of beef, and Grandpa was hobbling down the steps carrying a book under one arm.

The book was a very bad sign, for it meant that Grandpa had had his door open and had overheard the conversation about Lilybelle's elocution lessons. Grandpa had been a great elocutionist in his day, having a loud clear voice charged with emotion, and it was one of his gravest disappointments that Priscilla, his favorite granddaughter, hadn't followed in his steps. He had spent long hours coaching her but Priscilla lapsed easily into amnesia. Eventually she had learned one piece, with a great deal of repetition in it, called the "Sands of Dee."

Aunt Marnie kissed Grandpa and told him he was looking much better.

"I feel fine," Grandpa said. "Where's Priscilla?"

"I don't know," Mother replied in haste. "She's playing somewhere with Lilybelle. I hate to disturb them."

Grandpa switched the book from his right arm to his left arm in order to shake hands with Uncle Ed, who had to switch the wingless cherub in order to shake hands with Grandpa. During this maneuver Mother was able to see the title of the book, *Shorter Poems*, and her worst fears were realized. Grandpa had resurrected the "Sands of Dee."

Uncle Ed unveiled his cherub and explained the reason for his new work.

"These are bad times we're living in, bad times. The world is going to pot. In a few years I predict that every businessman in the country will be sorry he was born. But the artist—now that's a different matter. He at least will have his Art."

Uncle Ed whisked the cherub away into the living room and set it on the mantel.

Mother was feeling very depressed because of the world going to pot and the "Sands of Dee" and the fact that she had no art.

"Oh, Frederick," she said, and Father understood immediately and kissed her on the cheek to cheer her up.

"You two lovebirds," Aunt Marnie said with a touch of envy. "You act like a couple of kids."

Uncle Ed predicted that in a few years they wouldn't be acting like a couple of kids, no siree. Aunt Marnie shut him up by reminding him that no matter what happened to the world, no matter if they had to eat hay and beet-tops, Lilybelle was going to have her chances and continue with her elocution lessons.

Grandpa lowered himself into the platform rocker. It was Grandpa's opinion that these Sunday meetings were a barbarous custom. Families should get together no oftener than once a year, preferably at Christmas time when everyone was feeling good anyway. His children, Alice, Marnetta and Bruce, were individually all right, but they had an unfortunate effect on each other.

"Plato," Grandpa said suddenly, "was right."

Everyone waited in respectful silence for Grandpa to elucidate this statement but he merely opened his book and read a number of poems to himself, half-aloud.

Grandpa was embittered by the fact that not one of his children could read Latin and Greek with any ease. Marnetta had once shown signs of becoming a scholar, but Alice had interfered with that by marrying Frederick when she was quite young. Marnetta, older and less attractive than Alice, had promptly accepted the first man who proposed to her and married him over Grandpa's dead body. Marriage or no marriage, Marnetta had not escaped spinsterhood, and each year she grew more acid and more envious.

Though Alice was by no means dull, she had never shown any signs of becoming anything other than a satisfactory woman. As for the youngest, Bruce, he had from birth been an incurable optimist. He had ambled through the *Iliad*, toyed with Livy, mooned over Catullus, and ended up by owning a bowling alley and becoming the champion bowler of the county. Grandpa had reached the conclusion that children, being uncivilized and perverse, automatically shied away from the occupations their parents chose for them.

His own children had failed him badly, and of his grandchildren, Lilybelle, Priscilla, Becky, Paul, and Bruce's two boys, Jim and Willie, only Priscilla had what Grandpa called "the spark." In his attempts to fan this spark into a flame, Grandpa was sometimes forced to be quite firm with Priscilla.

Grandpa turned to the "Sands of Dee" and muttered, "Oh, Mary, go and call the cattle home." He was damned if a scatterbrained snippet like Lilybelle was going to outdo Priscilla.

Mother heard the familiar first line and with a hurried excuse she went to look for Priscilla and give her fair warning.

Lilybelle and Priscilla exchanged cold appraising smiles by way of greeting. Priscilla had the advantage because she was wearing Edna's gunmetal pumps and a trace of lipstick. Also she had just finished examining her profile in the mirror and decided it compared favorably with Colleen Moore's.

"Hello," said Lilybelle.

"Hello."

"Let's play hide and seek."

"No."

"I'll tell your mother if you don't."

"Tattletale baby."

Lilybelle always wanted to play hide and seek because it was the one game she was sure of winning. She was as old as Priscilla but very tiny for her age and could hide in places inaccessible even to Becky.

"I want to play hide and seek too," Becky said.

"Well, play by yourselves, you two babies," Priscilla said, lifting one foot to admire it in the mirror.

"It's no fun with only two," Lilybelle complained, "and I'm going right down and tell your mother. When you've got company you're supposed to do what the company wants to do, and I think you're the meanest thing that ever lived."

"I am not."

"You are too."

"Blabbermouth tattletale."

"Stinkweed."

This brisk exchange of epithets cleared the air a little. The fact was that Priscilla had intended to play hide and seek all along, partly because she had never played it with high heels on and she liked to try new experiences, and partly because she always had a faint hope of beating Lilybelle.

"I bore to be it," said Lilybelle and began counting to two hundred by fives before anyone could dispute her claim.

Priscilla and Becky made a dash for the attic, where Becky attempted to climb inside a drawer in the old green bureau. She managed to get everything in but her head which stuck out quite noticeably.

"Put your head in," said Priscilla from under the brass bed.

"I can't."

"You've got to, it's as plain as day."

"There isn't any room for my head," said Becky.

"Then cover it up with something, camaflouge it."

Though Becky camouflaged her head with one of Father's cast-off union suits, Lilybelle spotted it right away.

"One two three for Becky," said Lilybelle, and Becky was it.

Becky couldn't count by fives very well, so she didn't count at all. She stood and stared pensively into space until quietness reigned in the attic and she knew everyone was hidden. She found Priscilla wedged behind Mother's old dressmaker's dummy.

Mother had inherited the dummy from Grandma. It was no longer used for fitting dresses, having an hourglass figure with a huge platform bosom and flowering hips. It came in handy at Halloween, however. Given a black robe, a broomstick and a Jack O'lantern head, it became a creditable witch. It was also useful when Priscilla gave a show in the garage. She had a special act wherein she stood on a box behind the dummy lending it her own head and arms. She would then sing a number of songs, with suitable gestures and grimaces, a performance that brought down the house and always gave Becky laughing-pains in her side or the hiccups.

"Let's give a show," Becky said. "I would like to give a show, if you ask *me*."

Priscilla stepped out from behind the dummy and polished the gunmetal pumps with a little spit on her handkerchief.

"It's too much trouble," she said. "I do all the work and what do I get out of it? Nothing."

"We could make people pay *real money*."

"Mother wouldn't let us."

"Just a penny and maybe she'd let us."

"Well, I don't know."

"I'd love to get laughing-pains," Becky said wistfully. "I haven't had laughing-pains for six years."

"Oh, you fibber, you had them at Christmas time."

"It feels to me like six years."

"If we had a show we'd have to let Lilybelle be in it and she'd want to be the whole cheese."

"I forgot all about Lilybelle," said Becky and cast a half-hearted glance around the attic in the vague hope of spotting a left-over limb or a piece of Lilybelle's dress or head. "I bet she's in some place special and I will never ever find her."

"We'll both hunt," Priscilla offered.

Lilybelle was not in any drawers, trunks, closets or suitcases, or behind the blackboard or under the brass bed. She was not in the attic at all, although Becky distinctly remembered hearing her go up the stairs. Or else down the stairs.

"She is certainly a good hider," Priscilla said grudgingly. "I give her credit for that."

A search of all the bedrooms on the second floor failed to reveal Lilybelle, although they heard her distant ghostly voice challenging them to find her.

"I bet she's not hiding at all," Becky said. "I bet she just quit playing and went down to talk to the grownups."

Mother appeared at this point and Priscilla asked her if Lilybelle had come downstairs.

"No, she didn't," Mother said. "And if you know what's good for you, you won't come downstairs either for a while."

Priscilla made a quick mental review of her current transgressions but could find none deserving of these harsh words. "Why not?"

"Grandpa wants you to recite."

"Oh, cows," Priscilla groaned. "Oh, cows, cows."

"There's no use carrying on about it. Do you remember it?"

Priscilla shook her head.

"You must remember *some* of it," Mother said nervously. " 'Oh Mary, go and call the cattle home.' "

" 'Oh Mary, go and call the cattle home.' "

" 'Across the sands of Dee,' " Mother prompted.

" 'Across the sands of Dee.' "

"Don't forget to repeat 'And call the cattle home' twice before 'across the sands of Dee.' "

"I'll try not to."

"All right. 'The western wind was wild and dank with foam and all alone went she.' "

" 'The western wind was wild and dank with foam,' " Priscilla said. "Dank is one of my most favorite words. 'And all alone went she.' "

"Can't catch a flea," came Lilybelle's faint derisive chant. "Can't catch a flea!"

"Now the second stanza. Do you remember how it starts?"

"No."

"If one of us could just remember the first line, or figure it out, the rest would be repetition. It's right on the tip of my tongue but I can't for the life of me— It *must* have something to do with cattle again."

"Can't catch a flea," cried Lilybelle. "Can't catch a— Mama! Mama!"

"Good heavens," said Mother, who had a keen nose for disaster. "You don't suppose she—oh, she couldn't, she wouldn't . . ."

But Lilybelle could and had. In her desire to outwit her cousins Lilybelle had incautiously chosen the small ledge of the laundry chute as her hiding place.

The chute ran from the attic to the cellar with little doors opening on each floor of the house. Inside each door was a ledge presumably to prevent children from falling through to the laundry basket in the cellar.

Mother dashed up to the first landing of the attic steps and opened the door of the chute. Lilybelle's head and hands were visible as she clung to the ledge, but her feet pointed inexorably toward the cellar. She was screaming blue murder, not without justification, since the laundry chute had been intended only for laundry and the wood had never been sand-papered.

Mother thrust herself as far into the little doorway as she could, took hold of Lilybelle's wrists, and pulled.

"Help help help help help!" Lilybelle shrieked. Her face was contorted with anguish, for while she was thin she was not thin enough for the laundry chute, and the only effect Mother's pulling had was to force several more slivers into Lilybelle's tender skin.

"Oh, my God," Mother said, letting go of Lilybelle's wrists. "Frederick! Paul! Do something! Help!"

The acoustics of the laundry chute were deceiving, and as Mother's voice and Lilybelle's shrieks appeared to be coming from the cellar everyone rushed down there and then had to rush back up again, which added considerably to the confusion.

Aunt Marnie, half-fainting from fright and from running up and down steps so fast, could do nothing but yell: "Hang on, Lilybelle! Hang on, my darling, hang on! Mother's here, hang on!"

Lilybelle couldn't very well do anything else but hang on unless she wanted to drop straight through to the cellar, an alternative suggested by Grandpa.

Grandpa had taken the situation in at a glance and it was his suggestion that since Lilybelle couldn't be pulled out she be allowed to drop. The close fit of the laundry chute would help to offset the force of gravity, or in case it didn't, the laundry basket in the cellar could be padded with pillows and the eiderdowns off all the beds, to break Lilybelle's fall.

This speech sent Aunt Marnie into genuine hysterics. She kept shrieking, "Gravity, gravity, gravity," over and over again and Grandpa had to raise his voice to be heard at all.

"Can't let her hang there all night," he said. "She'll keep me awake."

After two more unsuccessful attempts to pull Lilybelle out, Father agreed to Grandpa's suggestion but in a modified form. Gravity couldn't be depended upon, so it was decided to cut down the clothesline in the backyard, tie it around Lilybelle under her arms and lower her gently into the cellar.

While Paul was cutting the clothesline Uncle Ed calmed Lilybelle by promising her a pound of chocolates, as many pickles as she could eat at suppertime, a new doll, crayons, and immunity from Sunday School for three months. He was on the point of raising the ante to six months, on Lilybelle's demand, when Paul arrived with the rope. Father tied it as well as he could around Lilybelle, then he and Paul and Uncle Ed took firm hold of the rope and the descent began.

"Heave ho," said Grandpa pleasantly.

Becky and Priscilla dashed down to the cellar in order to be the first to greet Lilybelle after her trip. Mother and Aunt Marnie waited at the second-floor door of the chute until Lilybelle's legs appeared, and finally Lilybelle's face.

"Are you all right?" Aunt Marnie said, her voice worn down to a hoarse whisper. "Are you all right, Lilybelle? Speak to me."

Lilybelle, no longer faced with certain death and buoyed up by her father's promises, was fine but she had too much discretion to admit it. She merely smiled wanly as her head disappeared.

"The darling, the brave darling," said Aunt Marnie and sprinted for the first floor where she addressed Lilybelle's dangling legs. "Only a bit more to go, Lilybelle. Be brave, my brave girl."

The last lap of Lilybelle's journey was much pleasanter, since the inside of the chute had been more or less smoothed by the more frequent passage of laundry from kitchen to cellar.

"She's coming!" Becky shrieked. "She's coming! I see her legs!"

Lilybelle's reception committee was large. It now included Edna and Delbert who had just arrived. It was sure a shame, Delbert said, that he hadn't come sooner. He could have torn out the ledge with his bare hands and rescued Lilybelle in the twinkling of an eye.

Lilybelle emerged, suffering slightly from shock and slivers. Some of the slivers were removed with Edna's eyebrow tweezers. For the shock, Lilybelle was given hot coffee, several large dill pickles and two chocolate raisin cookies.

Emotions ran high. Aunt Marnie hugged and kissed Lilybelle repeatedly while at the same time blaming Mother for having in the house such traps as laundry chutes to lure innocent children to destruction. She also blamed Becky and Priscilla for enticing Lilybelle into the chute in the first place, and Grandpa for his brutal callousness in wanting to trust Lilybelle to gravity.

"Gravity," said Aunt Marnie bitterly. "Gravity. I *ask* you."

"I will never forget this day," Uncle Ed said, regarding Lilybelle with awe. "Never will I forget it, the day Lilybelle almost lost her life."

In order to make sure he didn't forget it, he put the clothesline in his overcoat pocket as a souvenir. Since tomorrow was washday and it was the only clothesline Mother had, she made a futile attempt to hang onto it by trying to persuade Uncle Ed that it was much better to forget such grim incidents. Uncle Ed disagreed. He intended to coil the rope, shellac it and keep it as a souvenir for Lilybelle's children and grandchildren.

On this solemn thought everyone had some more coffee and Lilybelle helped herself to another dill pickle to ward off the aftermath of shock.

Shirley Jackson

CHARLES

THE day my son Laurie started kindergarten he renounced corduroy overalls with bibs and began wearing blue jeans with a belt; I watched him go off the first morning with the older girl next door, seeing clearly that an era of my life was ended, my sweet-voiced nursery-school tot replaced by a long-trousered, swaggering character who forgot to stop at the corner and wave good-bye to me.

He came home the same way, the front door slamming open, his cap on the floor, and the voice suddenly become raucous shouting, "Isn't anybody *here?*"

At lunch he spoke insolently to his father, spilled his baby sister's milk, and remarked that his teacher said we were not to take the name of the Lord in vain.

"How *was* school today?" I asked, elaborately casual.

"All right," he said.

"Did you learn anything?" his father asked.

Laurie regarded his father coldly. "I didn't learn nothing," he said.

"Anything," I said. "Didn't learn anything."

"The teacher spanked a boy, though," Laurie said, addressing his bread and butter. "For being fresh," he added, with his mouth full.

"What did he do?" I asked. "Who was it?"

Laurie thought. "It was Charles," he said. "He was fresh. The teacher spanked him and made him stand in a corner. He was awfully fresh."

"What did he do?" I asked again, but Laurie slid off his chair, took a cookie, and left, while his father was still saying, "See here, young man."

The next day Laurie remarked at lunch, as soon as he sat down, "Well, Charles was bad again today." He grinned enormously and said, "Today Charles hit the teacher."

"Good heavens," I said, mindful of the Lord's name, "I suppose he got spanked again?"

"He sure did," Laurie said. "Look up," he said to his father.

"What?" his father said, looking up.

"Look down," Laurie said. "Look at my thumb. Gee, you're dumb." He began to laugh insanely.

"Why did Charles hit the teacher?" I asked quickly.

"Because she tried to make him color with red crayons," Laurie said. "Charles wanted to color with green crayons so he hit the teacher and she spanked him and said nobody play with Charles but everybody did."

The third day—it was Wednesday of the first week—Charles bounced a see-saw on to the head of a little girl and made her bleed, and the teacher made him stay inside all during recess. Thursday Charles had to stand in a corner during story-time because he kept pounding his feet on the floor. Friday Charles was deprived of blackboard privileges because he threw chalk.

On Saturday I remarked to my husband, "Do you think kindergarten is too unsettling for Laurie? All his toughness, and bad grammar, and this Charles boy sounds like such a bad influence."

"It'll be all right," my husband said reassuringly. "Bound to be people like Charles in the world. Might as well meet them now as later."

On Monday Laurie came home late, full of news. "Charles," he shouted as he came up the hill; I was waiting anxiously on the front steps. "Charles," Laurie yelled all the way up the hill, "Charles was bad again."

"Come right in," I said, as soon as he came close enough. "Lunch is waiting."

"You know what Charles did?" he demanded, following me through the door. "Charles yelled so in school they sent a boy in from first grade to tell the teacher she had to make Charles keep quiet, and so Charles had to stay after school. And so all the children stayed to watch him."

"What did he do?" I asked.

"He just sat there," Laurie said, climbing into his chair at the table. "Hi, Pop, y'old dust mop."

"Charles had to stay after school today," I told my husband. "Everyone stayed with him."

"What does this Charles look like?" my husband asked Laurie. "What's his other name?"

"He's bigger than me," Laurie said. "And he doesn't have any rubbers and he doesn't ever wear a jacket."

Monday night was the first Parent-Teachers meeting, and only the fact that the baby had a cold kept me from going; I wanted passionately to meet Charles's mother. On Tuesday Laurie remarked suddenly, "Our teacher had a friend come to see her in school today."

"Charles's mother?" my husband and I asked simultaneously.

"Naaah," Laurie said scornfully. "It was a man who came and made us do exercises, we had to touch our toes. Look." He climbed down from his chair and squatted down and touched his toes. "Like this," he said. He got solemnly back into his chair and said, picking up his fork, "Charles didn't even *do* exercises."

"That's fine," I said heartily. "Didn't Charles want to do exercises?"

"Naaah," Laurie said. "Charles was so fresh to the teacher's friend he wasn't *let* do exercises."

"Fresh again?" I said.

"He kicked the teacher's friend," Laurie said. "The teacher's friend told Charles to touch his toes like I just did and Charles kicked him."

"What are they going to do about Charles, do you suppose?" Laurie's father asked him.

Laurie shrugged elaborately. "Throw him out of school, I guess," he said.

Wednesday and Thursday were routine; Charles yelled during story hour and hit a boy in the stomach and made him cry. On Friday Charles stayed after school again and so did all the other children.

With the third week of kindergarten Charles was an institution in our family; the baby was being a Charles when she cried all afternoon; Laurie did a Charles when he filled his wagon full of mud and pulled it through the kitchen; even my husband, when he caught his elbow in the telephone cord and pulled telephone, ashtray, and a bowl of flowers off the table, said, after the first minute, "Looks like Charles."

During the third and fourth weeks it looked like a reformation in Charles; Laurie reported grimly at lunch on Thursday of the third week, "Charles was so good today the teacher gave him an apple."

"What?" I said, and my husband added warily, "You mean Charles?"

"Charles," Laurie said. "He gave the crayons around and he picked up the books afterward and the teacher said he was her helper."

"What happened?" I asked incredulously.

"He was her helper, that's all," Laurie said, and shrugged.

"Can this be true, about Charles?" I asked my husband that night. "Can something like this happen?"

"Wait and see," my husband said cynically. "When you've got a Charles to deal with, this may mean he's only plotting."

He seemed to be wrong. For over a week Charles was the teacher's helper; each day he handed things out and he picked things up; no one had to stay after school.

"The P.T.A. meeting's next week again," I told my husband one evening. "I'm going to find Charles's mother there."

"Ask her what happened to Charles," my husband said. "I'd like to know."

"I'd like to know myself," I said.

On Friday of that week things were back to normal. "You know what Charles did today?" Laurie demanded at the lunch table, in a voice slightly awed. "He told a little girl to say a word and she said it and the teacher washed her mouth out with soap and Charles laughed."

"What word?" his father asked unwisely, and Laurie said, "I'll have to whisper it to you, it's so bad." He got down off his chair and went around to his father. His father bent his head down and Laurie whispered joyfully. His father's eyes widened.

"Did Charles tell the little girl to say *that?*" he asked respectfully.

"She said it *twice,*" Laurie said. "Charles told her to say it *twice.*"

"What happened to Charles?" my husband asked.

"Nothing," Laurie said. "He was passing out the crayons."

Monday morning Charles abandoned the little girl and said the evil word himself three or four times, getting his mouth washed out with soap each time. He also threw chalk.

My husband came to the door with me that evening as I set out for the P.T.A. meeting. "Invite her over for a cup of tea after the meeting," he said. "I want to get a look at her."

"If only she's there," I said prayerfully.

"She'll be there," my husband said. "I don't see how they could hold a P.T.A. meeting without Charles's mother."

At the meeting I sat restlessly, scanning each comfortable matronly face, trying to determine which one hid the secret of Charles. None of them looked to me haggard enough. No one stood up in the meeting and apologized for the way her son had been acting. No one mentioned Charles.

After the meeting I identified and sought out Laurie's kindergarten teacher. She had a plate with a cup of tea and a piece of chocolate cake; I had a plate with a cup of tea and a piece of marshmallow cake. We maneuvered up to one another cautiously, and smiled.

"I've been so anxious to meet you," I said. "I'm Laurie's mother."

"We're all so interested in Laurie," she said.

"Well, he certainly likes kindergarten," I said. "He talks about it all the time."

"We had a little trouble adjusting, the first week or so," she said primly, "but now he's a fine little helper. With occasional lapses, of course."

"Laurie usually adjusts very quickly," I said. "I suppose this time it's Charles's influence."

"Charles?"

"Yes," I said, laughing, "you must have your hands full in that kindergarten, with Charles."

"Charles?" she said. "We don't have any Charles in the kindergarten."

Ruth McKenney

AN EXCERPT FROM *MY SISTER EILEEN*

A Loud Sneer for our Feathered Friends

FROM childhood, my sister and I have had a well-grounded dislike for our friends the birds. We came to hate them when she was ten and I was eleven. We had been exiled by what we considered an unfeeling family to one of those loathsome girls' camps where Indian lore is rife and the management puts up neatly lettered signs reminding the clients to be Good Sports. From the moment Eileen and I arrived at dismal old Camp Hi-Wah, we were Bad Sports, and we liked it.

We refused to get out of bed when the bugle blew in the morning, we fought against scrubbing our teeth in public to music, we sneered when the flag was ceremoniously lowered at sunset, we avoided doing a good deed a day, we complained loudly about the food, which was terrible, and we bought some chalk once and wrote all over the Recreation Cabin, "We hate Camp Hi-Wah." It made a wonderful scandal, although unfortunately we were immediately accused of the crime. All the other little campers *loved* dear old Camp Hi-Wah, which shows you what kind of people they were.

The first two weeks Eileen and I were at Camp Hi-Wah, we sat in our cabin grinding our teeth at our councilor and writing letters to distant relatives. These letters were, if I say so myself, real masterpieces of double dealing and heartless chicanery. In our childish and, we hoped, appealing scrawl, we explained to Great-Aunt Mary Farrel and Second Cousin Joe Murphy that we were having such fun at dear Camp Hi-Wah making Indian pocketbooks.

"We would simply L-O-V-E to make you a pocketbook, dear Aunt Mary," we wrote, "only the leather costs $1 for a small pocketbook or $1.67 for a large size pocketbook, which is much nicer because you can carry more things in it, and the rawhide you sew it up with, just exactly the way the Indians did, costs 40 cents more. We burn pictures on the leather but that doesn't cost anything. If we O-N-L-Y had $1 or $1.67 and 40 cents for the rawhide, we could make you the s-w-e-l-l-e-s-t pocketbook."

As soon as we had enough orders for Indian pocketbooks with pictures burnt on them, we planned to abscond with the funds sent by our trusting relatives and run away to New York City, where, as we used to explain dramatically to our cabin-mates, we intended to live a life of sin. After a few days, our exciting plans for our immediate future were bruited all over the camp, and admirers came from as far away as Cabin Minnehaha, which was way down at the end of Hiawatha Alley, just to hear us tell about New York and sin.

Fame had its price, however. One of the sweet little girls who lived in our cabin turned out to be such a Good Citizen ("Camp Hi-Wah Girls Learn to Be Good Citizens") that she told our dreadful secret to our councilor. Our mail was impounded for weeks, and worst of all, we actually had to make several Indian pocketbooks with pictures burnt on them. My pictures were all supposed to be snakes, although they were pretty blurred. Eileen specialized in what she believed to be the likeness of a werewolf, but Cousin Joe, who had generously ordered three pocketbooks, wrote a nice letter thanking Eileen for his pretty pocketbooks with the pretty pictures of Abraham Lincoln on them. We were terribly disgusted by the whole thing.

It was in this mood that we turned to birds. The handicraft hour at Camp Hi-Wah, heralded by the ten-thirty A.M. bugle, competed for popularity with the bird walks at the same hour. You could, as Eileen had already somewhat precociously learned how to say, name your own poison. After three weeks of burning pictures on leather, we were ready for anything, even our feathered friends.

So one hot morning in July, the two McKenney sisters, big and bad and fierce for their age, answered the bird-walk bugle call, leaving the Indian-pocketbook teacher to mourn her two most backward pupils. We were dressed, somewhat reluctantly, to be sure, in the required heavy stockings for poison ivy and brambles, and carried, each of us, in our dirty hands a copy of a guide to bird lore called *Bird Life for Children*.

Bird Life for Children was a volume that all the Good Citizens in Camp Hi-Wah pretended to find engrossing. Eileen and I thought it was stupefyingly dull. Our favorite literary character at the time was Dumas' Marguerite de Valois, who took her decapitated lover's head home in a big handkerchief for old times' sake. Eileen, in those days, was always going to name her first girl child Marguerite de Valois.

Bird Life for Children was full of horrid pictures in full color of robins and pigeons and redbirds. Under each picture was a loathsomely whimsical paragraph describing how the bird in question spent his spare time, what he ate, and why children should love him. Eileen and I hated the book so, we were quite prepared to despise birds when we started off that morning on our first bird walk, but we had no idea of what we were going to suffer, that whole awful summer, because of our feathered friends. In the first place, since we had started off making leather pocketbooks, we were three weeks behind the rest of the Hi-Wah bird-lovers. They had been tramping through blackberry bushes for days and days and had already got the hang of the more ordinary bird life around camp, whereas the only bird I could identify at the time was the vulture. Cousin Joe took me to a zoo once, and there was a fine vulture there, a big, fat one. They fed him six live rats every day in lieu of human flesh. I kept a sharp eye out for a vulture all summer, but one never turned up at Camp Hi-Wah. Nothing interesting ever happened around that place.

On that first bird walk, Eileen and I trotted anxiously along behind the little band of serious-minded bird-lovers, trying desperately to see, or at least hear, even one bird, even one robin. But alas, while other bird-walkers saw, or pretended to see—for Eileen and I never believed them for a moment—all kinds of hummingbirds and hawks and owls and whatnot, we never saw or heard a single, solitary feathered friend, not one.

By the time we staggered into camp for lunch, with stubbed toes, scratched faces, and tangled hair, Eileen and I were soured for life on birds. Our bird logs, which we carried strapped to our belts along with the *Guide*, were still chaste and bare, while all the other little bird-lovers had fulsome entries, such as "Saw and heard redbird at 10:37 A.M. Molting."

Still, for the next three days we stayed honest and suffered. For three terrible mornings we endured being dolts among bird-walkers, the laughing-stock of Camp Hi-Wah. After six incredibly tiresome hours, our bird logs were still blank. Then we cracked under the strain. The fourth morning we got up feeling grim but determined. We sharpened our pencils before we started off on the now-familiar trail through the second-growth forest.

When we got well into the woods and Mary Mahoney, the premier bird-walker of Camp Hi-Wah, had already spotted and logged her first redbird of the morning, Eileen suddenly stopped dead in her tracks.

"Hark!" she cried. She had read that somewhere in a book. "Quiet!" I echoed instantly.

The bird-walkers drew to a halt respectfully and stood in silence. They stood and stood. It was not good form even to whisper while fellow bird-walkers were logging a victim, but after quite a long time the Leader, whose feet were flat and often hurt her, whispered impatiently, "Haven't you got him logged yet?"

"You drove him away," Eileen replied sternly. "It was a yellow-billed cuckoo."

"A yellow-billed cuckoo?" cried the Leader incredulously.

"Well," Eileen said modestly, "at least *I* think it was." Then, with many a pretty hesitation and thoughtful pause, she recited the leading features of the yellow-billed cuckoo, as recorded in *Bird Life for Children*.

The Leader was terribly impressed. Later on that morning I logged a kingfisher, a red-headed woodpecker, and a yellow-bellied sapsucker, which was all I could remember at the moment. Each time, I kept the bird-walkers standing around for an interminable period, gaping into blank space and listening desperately to the rustle of the wind in the trees and the creak of their shoes as they went from one foot to another.

In a few days Eileen and I were the apple of our Leader's eye, the modest heroes of the Camp Hi-Wah bird walks. Naturally, there were base children around camp, former leading bird-walkers, who spread foul rumors up and down Hiawatha Alley that Eileen and I were frauds. We soon stopped this ugly talk, however. Eileen was the pitcher, and a very good one, too, of the Red Bird ball team and I was the first base. When Elouise Pritchard, the worst gossip in Cabin Sitting Bull, came up to bat, she got a pitched ball right in the stomach. Of course it was only a soft ball, but Eileen could throw it pretty hard. To vary this routine, I tagged Mary Mahoney, former head bird-walker, out at first base, and Mary had a bruise on her thigh for weeks. The rumors stopped abruptly.

We had begun to get pretty bored with logging rare birds when the game took on a new angle. Mary Mahoney and several other bird-walkers began to see the same birds we did on our morning jaunts into the forest. This made us pretty mad, but there wasn't much we could do about it. Next, Mary Mahoney began to see birds we weren't logging. The third week after we joined the Camp Hi-Wah Bird Study Circle, everybody except the poor, dumb Leader and a few backward but honest bird-lovers was logging the rarest birds seen around Camp

Hi-Wah in twenty years. Bird walks developed into a race to see who could shout "Hark!" first and keep the rest of the little party in fidgety silence for the next five minutes.

The poor bird-walk Leader was in agony. Her reputation as a bird-lover was in shreds. Her talented pupils were seeing rare birds right and left, while the best she could log for herself would be a few crummy old redbirds and a robin or so. At last our Leader's morale collapsed. It was the day when nearly everybody in the study circle swore that she saw and heard a bona-fide nightingale.

"Where?" cried our Leader desperately, after the fourth nightingale had been triumphantly logged in the short space of five minutes. Heartless fingers pointed to a vague bush. The Leader strained her honest eyes. No notion of our duplicity crossed her innocent, unworldly mind.

"I can't see any nightingale," our Leader cried, and burst into tears. Then, full of shame, she sped back to camp, leaving the Camp Hi-Wah bird-lovers to their nightingales and guilty thoughts.

Eileen and I ate a hearty lunch that noon because we thought we would need it. Then we strolled down Hiawatha Alley and hunted up Mary Mahoney.

"We will put the Iron Cross on you if you tell," Eileen started off, as soon as we found Mary.

"What's the Iron Cross?" Mary squeaked, startled out of her usual haughty poise.

"Never mind," I growled. "You'll find out if you tell."

We walked past Cabin Sitting Bull, past the flagpole, into the tall grass beyond the ball field.

"She'll tell," Eileen said finally.

"What'll we do?" I replied mournfully. "They'll try us at campfire tonight."

They did, too. It was terrible. We denied everything, but the Head of Camp, a mean old lady who wore middy blouses and pleated serge bloomers, sentenced us to no desserts and eight-o'clock bedtime for two weeks. We thought over what to do to Mary Mahoney for four whole days. Nothing seemed sufficiently frightful, but in the end we put the wart curse on her. The wart curse was simple but horrible. We dropped around to Cabin Sitting Bull one evening and in the presence of Mary and her allies we drew ourselves up to our full height and said solemnly in unison, "We put the wart curse on you, Mary Mahoney." Then we stalked away.

We didn't believe for a moment in the wart curse, but we hoped

Mary would. At first she was openly contemptuous, but to our delight, on the fourth evening she developed a horrible sty in her eye. We told everybody a sty was a kind of a wart and that we had Mary in our power. The next day Mary broke down and came around to our cabin and apologized in choked accents. She gave Eileen her best hair ribbon and me a little barrel that had a picture of Niagara Falls inside it, if you looked hard enough. We were satisfied.

John Mason Brown

HAPPY BIRTHDAY

MY WIFE had planned it carefully. Before that Saturday was over, we were to learn the afternoon was to take far more than careful planning.

"Movies in the front hall here?" I had asked, thinking back to those earlier birthday parties when, with a borrowed machine and six chairs of Baby Bear size, we had quieted the young until suppertime with rented films of Mickey Mouse and Felix the Cat.

"Dear me, no. At nine? They're much too old for that. He's asking them here for lunch, not supper this year. Eight of them. Then, I thought we'd take them to the Rodeo."

"The Rodeo?" I gasped, looking tired already.

"Of course. They'll love it. Besides, it'll get them out of the apartment."

I knew what she meant. Any parent would know. So would any houseowner who was not a professional wrecker. I remembered the growing damage of those earlier parties as gradually the puréed peas and scrambled eggs had given way to meat balls and peas unpuréed. Although less and less milk had been sloshed on the table, the noise and debris had swelled each year as the first conversational goo-goos had changed into the constant roar of simulated ack-ack. The wide-open spaces of Madison Square Garden were an inspiration.

"A wonderful idea," said I. "I'll get the tickets today."

They were asked for twelve-thirty. This meant, of course, that most of them came at twelve. The doorbell began ringing then with a violence grownups are unable to muster. They arrived when my wife and I, as exiles from the dining room, were still gobbling a quick lunch on trays in the living room.

Illness had taken a lighter toll than usual. Only one of the eight was missing. The others turned out to be either classmates in school or Park friends since the buggy-pushing days of long ago. Some of them wore short trousers under their blue jackets, some long—their first long pants. Although those so encased resembled pygmies seen through the wrong end of opera glasses, they felt superior. You sensed this the moment they appeared. They sported the happy look of the recently promoted. They were burdened by the same self-consciousness, too.

Four were deposited by their nurses; three by their mothers. "When can we expect him home?" each nurse or mother invariably demanded. "Not until five-thirty or so," my wife or I would say. Thereupon the faces of these women changed imperceptibly. A telltale suggestion of relief—or was it gratitude?—brightened their eyes. As a storm signal, this should have been warning enough.

The first fifteen minutes were occupied with the presentation and inspection of presents. Every time the bell rang, the birthday-boy would scamper down the hall, accompanied by his four-year-old brother. The latter, because of having been included in such venerable company, could not have been prouder had he met Eisenhower.

"Hi, Alfred!" "Hi, David!" Or "Hi, Harold!" the two boys would call, with arms outstretched. Before any answers could be given, and the prepared speech regretfully made, the presents were snatched from the bestowing hand, and a race started to the nine-year-old's bedroom.

My wife and I stayed in the living room as a rather unwelcome welcoming committee. Everything seemed to be going satisfactorily back in his room, until the air was atomized by sudden shrieks.

"I wanna come in! I wanna come in!"

It was the little fellow's voice. He was bawling, his heart broken. After a few minutes I could stand neither his agony nor my own. Following Ford's example, I went on a peace mission.

"What's the matter?" I demanded, pushing past him and hard against a stoutly defended door. When the door at last gave way, I was confronted by a room filled with dropped wrapping paper, disordered ribbons, shiny toys, screams of delight, little boys, the rat-tat-

tat of a machine gun, and the smells of a new chemistry set already in use.

"We told him he could stay out there and stand guard," said one of the bigger boys, amazed that anyone should not find joy in such an assignment.

"Let him in right this minute," said I, "and no more foolishness." Then I hastily retreated. Partly because I had just been hit in the face by a paper wad released from a slingshot. But mainly because I realized that my tones had been scarcely those which, as a host, I employed for adult guests.

A few minutes later his nurse appeared at the living room door. Already she had a tattered look. "Please come," she said, "they are shooting at people in the street."

I dashed back to find the window open and three of the little boys leaning out of it, peppering passers-by with their slingshots.

Once again, I'm afraid, my voice got out of control. "Put them down this instant," I ordered. To my astonishment I saw that even those who were not leaning out of the window had upraised slingshots in their hands.

"The next person who takes a slingshot out of his pocket will be sent home at once without lunch," I thundered charmingly. The boys eyed me angrily but uncowed. "Without ice cream!" I added. Two slingshots came down. "And he won't go to the Rodeo at all!" Every slingshot slunk into a protecting pocket.

"Where's Richard?" I asked, trying to remind them that I could be a considerate host.

"He's not here," my son muttered.

This time, when I left the room, a chorus of voices followed me. "I tell you what, let's gang up on Richard."—"Say, that's neat."—"When he comes, let's all get guns and hide in the front hall and attack him."

At that moment the doorbell rang. And Richard appeared with his mother. There was a brief armistice for company manners. During it I could have sworn I saw small figures at the far end of the hall creeping behind corners into imaginary pillboxes. They proved to be wily strategists, these juvenile commandos. They waited. A deceptive quiet settled on the apartment until Richard's mother left, and Richard started back with my sons, supposedly to the older boy's bedroom. H-hour struck halfway down the hall. An H-hour as much Comanche as it was Krupp.

"Stop it," I cried, "that's no way to treat Richard." But Richard didn't seem to mind at all. As an invading force, he was letting out a bombardment calculated to neutralize all shore defenses.

"I wonder when lunch will be ready," my wife asked. It was the tenth time she had asked this same question during the past quarter hour.

"I was just about to ask you again," said I.

Finally, however, lunch was ready. After the inevitable last minute trips to the bathroom, they trooped into the dining room.

No party our friends had ever come to proved as noisily conversational as this one. Few bachelor dinners have ever so shaken the chandeliers.

My wife and I appeared only at moments of climax, which meant that we came in fairly often. Sudden summits of sound gave us our entrance cues. These came whenever favors were being hurled across the table, paper hats were being exchanged without consent, or when two guests were delightedly spitting in each other's faces. In comparison, the pop of snappers seemed to us as gentle as a lullaby. Although there was a good deal of simultaneous soliloquizing, there was little small talk. The conversation, when distinguishable from a barrage, consisted chiefly of fragrant descriptions of rival schools or discussions of figures in the comics utterly unknown to us. It ranged from sudden booms, followed by "Say, listen to that atomic bomb," to boastful inquiries as to how many times this or that boy had been to the Rodeo.

At last, after a good deal of coaxing and commanding, the main course was finished, and the ice cream served. Then came the great moment, the moment blissful and friendly, when the lighted cake flickered at the pantry door as the signal for cease firing and the singing of "Happy Birthday." When the wish was made, the candles blown out, and the cake sliced, one little boy screamed, "No cake for me. I hate it."

By then, the Wild West was calling. It was time to get going, which meant going to the bathroom once again on a community plan.

It's appalling how children can make scoutmasters of us all. My wife and I suddenly heard ourselves clapping our hands peremptorily and saying, without so much as a blush, "Now we will divide into teams. You're on my team, Harold. You're on my team, David."

When this sheep and goat separation was finally effected, and the right coats, caps, and gloves had been claimed by and put on the right boys, our two groups started for the elevator.

Just when its doors opened, one boy shoved another in play. He picked the wrong one. Every group of kids seems to include one who has taken boxing lessons. He functions like a tank among archers. The pushed boy had not put on his gloves in vain. He felt he had been exposed to a sneak attack. He retaliated in kind, waging war without declaring it in the best Japanese tradition. His right arm swung out, administering near the left eye of his friend a sock of which Cashel Byron would have been proud. The howls which followed were natural and instantaneous. So was the confusion. I found myself in the midst of the ring, a referee taking sides. I refused to admit the pugilist into my taxi. This meant another regrouping, and another slight delay.

When the two taxis were loaded, they proved noisier than calliopes. I remember only two things about the ride down. One was vigorously applying my handkerchief to the running eye of the bruised boy. The other was the moment when the noise in the cab became so great that the driver stopped the car to say, "Listen, you kids, either shut up or get out!"

Upon reaching the Garden, our car emptied like the Trojan horse. The Rodeo, when seen alone, is wearing enough. When seen in the company of seven little boys, it is downright exhausting. You not only watch the bucking broncos; you are surrounded by them.

The performance in the ring that afternoon is blurred in my mind. I didn't get to see much of it. I spent most of my time in the men's room. I functioned more as a shepherd than as a spectator.

I soon reached the conclusion that Aristotle must have had a rodeo rather than a tragedy in mind, when he spoke of the purgation of emotions through pity and fear. At least seven times during the afternoon I climbed over the people either behind me or around me, to lead little boys on private missions. Once I had all seven of them with me, including the four-year-old. By this time the others were completely at home on the range. He, however, was paying his first visit. Although there are pleasanter places than the men's room at the Garden, he thought it charming. No toreador could have been happier. With a look of excitement on his face he took a deep inhale, and said, so that everyone could hear him, "Oh, Daddy, smell the bulls!"

Even when not convoying the young, I could not give my full attention to the ring. For one thing, I never realized that people could ask so many questions, or such questions, in voices so loud. "What's a steer?" demanded one little fellow, while every adult head in the row in front of me turned around to await the answer.

Then, there were the vendors. Being astute psychologists, they sized up my predicament in a moment, and hovered around me like planes returning to a carrier. Popcorn, peanuts, spun candy, Coca-Cola, ice-cream—these were simple enough; inexpensive, too. I didn't mind them. The real hazards were the men who came by screaming, "Want a cowboy belt?" "Want a Roy Rogers pistol?" "Want a Western whip?"

"Will you buy me one?" asked each little boy, in spite of the fact that the prices ranged from fifty cents to a dollar and a half.

"No!" I would say firmly. "No!"

"Oh, Daddy!!" my nine-year-old would snarl, not only indignant but ashamed. And six other sneering faces would pivot toward me. From them I learned something I had never before suspected. A Bronx cheer can be silent.

Just before the time came to leave, I was cowardly enough to surrender. I began to wonder what these boys would say to their fathers about my son's father. Accordingly, I bought each boy at fifty cents apiece chameleons or turtles that I knew could be purchased for ten cents three blocks away.

The leaving was not without its difficulties. My wife and I desired to get out before the crowd. Our guests desired to stay until after the crowd had left. We won, however, although not without a struggle.

Then, once again, we divided into teams. Once again with our teams we crawled into separate taxis. Our last job was to deposit each boy at his respective doorstep.

When we got home, and our boy had had his supper, he said, his eyes still glistening, "Wasn't it a wonderful birthday!" Then he went to bed. So did we. At once.

Sally Benson

AN EXCERPT FROM *JUNIOR MISS*

DADDY DEAR

ALTHOUGH the picture starring a child actress had been shown in New York at various theatres for almost a year, Judy Graves didn't see it until it reached the small playhouse in her own neighborhood. It was about the hysterical devotion of a curly-haired little girl for her father, a whimsical Englishman who had been lost in the shuffle during the Boer War and had been found again through the untiring efforts of his little daughter and the dignified acquiescence of Queen Victoria. Judy attended the heartbreaking performance on a Saturday afternoon with her best friend, Fuffy Adams, who thought the whole thing bilge and said so. Fuffy was almost thirteen, five months older than Judy, and the years had taken their toll. Judy walked up the aisle of the threatre behind her friend, so that she could compose herself before being exposed to the daylight.

In the lobby, Fuffy turned to her. "I'm gagging," she said.

"Me, too." July drew in her breath and swallowed the lump in her throat.

"Did you ever," Fuffy asked, "see anything so absolutely *saccharine*?"

"Revolting," Judy answered. The memory of the child star danced before her eyes; she could see her brave little smile, the blind faith that shone in her face, the cunning way she saluted her father, a soldier of the Queen; Judy could also see her enchanting dresses with their dainty ruffles and the touching mannerisms that softened the heart of every male in the cast.

The two girls left the theatre and walked toward the drugstore on the corner. Fuffy scuffed her feet on the sidewalk in disgust. "The little stinker certainly made a monkey of her old man," she commented.

This was too much for Judy. "Really, Fuff," she said, "you shouldn't be so sophisticated. After all, things were different in the olden days. I must say you act awfully hardboiled sometimes."

Fuffy tilted her beret, which bore the emblem of the Charlton School on it, down over one eye. "Well, my old man's a right guy, but if I acted that way around him, he'd slough me."

They hoisted themselves up on the stools in front of the soda counter. They were tall for their twelve years and substantially built. "Make mine a double vanilla with hot fudge," Judy told the man.

"Ditto," Fuffy ordered.

"And no whipped cream on mine," Judy added virtuously.

"I'll have the works."

Seeing that her reproof had sent Fuffy clean off, Judy spoke pacifically. "You've got to admit she acted like a good egg when they put her out of her lovely room at school and made her sleep in the garret."

"Well, yes."

"And she really did find her father, even when everyone thought he was dead."

"Granted," Fuffy said.

Judy took a large spoonful of ice cream. "My father was in the World War," she said thoughtfully, "but he wasn't lost that I know of. Think how you'd feel if we got into another war and your father had to go and was maybe lost somewhere."

"That would be kind of awful," Fuffy agreed.

"So you see how talking the way you do *sounds*," Judy persisted.

"O.K., you win," Fuffy said.

They walked out of the store happily, filled with a pleasing sense of impending disaster. At the entrance to the apartment house where Fuffy lived, Judy gave her an affectionate squeeze. "'Bye, now," she said.

"Be seeing you," Fuffy responded.

Freed from the chill of Fuffy's skepticism, Judy started toward home. She thought of the careless, almost indifferent way she treated her own father, and her heart melted for him. She remembered how Lois, her fifteen-year-old sister, bossed him, and when she considered the tenderness he had never had from his two daughters, she felt ashamed. Her eyes lighted with a fanatic resolve, and she turned over a new leaf. Elated over the prospect of a future in which she and her father wandered forever hand in hand, she began to skip. Her full cheeks bounced as her feet hit hard on the pavement, and passers-by, seeing her approach, gave her a clear path.

Her thoughts were so filled with a blurred image of her father, who had obligingly donned the uniform of a British officer, that it was rather startling to find him actually sitting in the living room reading a paper when she got home. She walked softly over to his chair and shook her head at him playfully. Her hair hung in a thick, straight line to her shoulders, and no soft curls bobbed about at the movement. "Good evening, Daddy dear," she said.

Mr. Graves lifted his eyes. "Oh, hello there, Lois—Judy," he answered.

She moved closer to him and sat down on the arm of the chair.

"Here, watch what you're doing," he said. He pulled his paper to one side.

"Aren't you home early, Daddy?" she asked.

"Look out now, Judy," he said. "You'll have the arm of the chair off in another minute."

"I've had *such* a lovely day, Daddy. I hope you have, too." She threw a solid little arm around his neck.

"Ouch!" he exclaimed. "Have a heart! Go play with Lois. She's around here somewhere."

"Daddy," she asked, "are you and Mommy going to stay home tonight?"

"Nope," he answered. "And that reminds me that I've got to dress." He gave her a friendly whack. "Get up."

She pulled herself to her feet and shook her head at him again. "Will you come and say goodbye to me before you go?" In her own mind she was already lying in a small bed in a frilly, old-fashioned nightgown, lifting up her arms for a good-night kiss.

"What do you keep shaking your head for?" he demanded. "Have you got something in your ear?"

For a minute she looked at him scornfully. "No," she said. It was an effort to skip toward the door and turn to blow him a kiss.

Mr. Graves walked slowly into the bedroom he shared with his wife. His voice, when he spoke to her, was puzzled. "Listen, Grace, what's got into Judy?"

"Judy?" Mrs. Graves repeated, as though the name were foreign to her.

"Yes," he said. "She acts funny. Nothing you can put your finger on, but just funny."

"You'd better hurry and get dressed or we'll be late," Mrs. Graves told him.

Judy was waiting in the living room when they were ready to leave. She had changed from the sweater and skirt she had been wearing into a last summer's dress of red-and-white dotted swiss with cherry-colored ribbons. It was limp from hanging in the closet and she had had trouble tying the bows, but it had a ruffle around the bottom of the skirt. When she saw her father, she sprang toward him with such enthusiasm that she almost threw him. "How *nice* you look!" she cried.

"Judy!" Mrs. Graves said sternly. "How many times have I told you not to make fun of your father. It's time you girls showed him a little respect."

"Make *fun* of him," Judy repeated in amazement.

"I think he looks very nice," Mrs. Graves said. "Now, say good night to him and tell Lois ten-thirty and *no later*. And nine-thirty for you." She leaned toward Judy and kissed her lightly on the cheek.

Judy caught at her father's arm. "Daddy dear, what are you going to do tomorrow?"

"I'm going to sleep, for one thing."

"All day?"

"All day," he said positively.

"If you should happen to wake up, we might go to the Park." Her dark eyes, as she looked at him, were pleading, and he felt flattered and uncomfortable.

"We'll see," he told her.

Going down in the elevator, Mrs. Graves turned to him. "I think Judy was trying to make amends for poking fun at you," she said. "And I don't think it would hurt you to take her to the Park."

"Tomorrow," Mr. Graves said, "is another day."

The next morning, which was Sunday, Mr. Graves awoke earlier than he had hoped. It was a bright, cold day, and the sun seemed to shine on him reproachfully at he sat in the big chair by the window after breakfast. Judy had been sitting there when he came into the room and had got up to give him her place. Now she lay curled up on the couch across the room and every time he looked at her she gave him a quick, anxious smile.

"Pardon me for interrupting," she said at last, "but if this country goes into the war, would you have to go?"

"I hope not," he answered.

"Oh, I hope so, too. On the other hand, you couldn't very well *not* go, could you? I mean if your regiment went."

"What are you talking about?" he asked crossly. "I don't belong to any regiment."

"You did once."

"Well, *once* I did. And once was enough."

Judy, remembering the gallant way the English father had answered the call to colors, found it hard to answer, "You know best, Daddy dear."

Mr. Graves was conscious of her disapproval and spoke pleasantly. "What time is it?"

She turned her head to see the clock on the mantel. "Almost eleven," she answered.

He rose to his feet. "Well, how about that walk in the Park you promised me?"

"Oh, you *sweet* daddy!" Judy exclaimed. "Wait till I get my things and I'll be with you in a sec. I'll run quick, like a bunny."

Mr. Graves' face, as he took his coat and hat from the hall closet, was a picture.

Although it was very cold, the Park was filled with people; babies looking pink and stuffed sat in their carriages blinking in the sunlight, dogs strained at their leashes and seemed about to choke. Judy clung to her father's arm and skipped by his side.

"Too bad Lois couldn't come," he said. He was remembering the neat way Lois walked.

"Oh, *her*," Judy scoffed. "She went to church."

"That's a very lovely thing for Lois to do. You should have gone with her."

Judy squeezed his arm so hard that he winced. "I'd love to go to church, Daddy, if you would go with me. Shall we?"

"Someday," he said.

As they strolled, Judy talked. "It must be *too* marv to work downtown," she said. "But it must have seemed dull to you at first. I mean, after."

"After?"

"After the war. Tell me about the war."

During the next hour, Mr. Graves was thoroughly and not too artfully drawn out. It seemed to him that he had never noticed before how much Judy bounced as she walked or how clumsy she was on her feet. There were times when he was afraid she would fall flat on her face, and he warned her about it. "You'll land on your puss if you're not careful," he said.

They walked all the way around the reservoir. Mr. Graves' arm grew stiff with the weight of Judy's body as she swung on it. By the time they reached the Fifth Avenue exit, he felt as though his side must be worn raw where she had bumped against it. As they stood on the corner waiting for the lights to change, he shook her off. "Stop wiggling, for Christ's sake, and *light!*" he exclaimed. "And step on it, because I'd like to have time to snatch a drink before dinner."

Judy dropped his arm and they started across the street. She stopped skipping and her feet, in their brown oxfords, dragged heavily. It was not usual for her father to mix drinks before Sunday dinner, and the the soldier-father in the picture certainly hadn't reached for a bottle after a brief session with his idolized little daughter. As she stumped along, keeping step with her own father, she decided that it was not easy to become the apple of someone's eye. A wave of sadness swept over her, which was immediately followed by a stronger, more familiar sensation. It was a sensation that always made her yawn pleasantly.

Her father looked down at her and smiled. "Well, well," he said. "That must mean somebody's hungry."

Al Capp

MEMORIES OF MISS MANDELBAUM

RECENTLY a man from Santa Barbara, California, wrote to a weekly news magazine to complain that I am overpaid for the pictures I draw, in contrast to what other people get for doing something useful. Well, I may be overpaid now, but I wasn't when I started out in the world as a professional artist, which was when I was eleven years old and in the seventh grade of P.S. 62, in Brooklyn. I was paid ten cents a picture then, and risked being clapped into the reformatory every time I drew one. Today, thanks to the willingness of the average American to laugh at a group of characters even more bedeviled than he is (a necessarily fictitious group, of course), my price has risen somewhat and I now risk nothing more than having my income disapproved of by people who live in places I can't afford to live in.

My career as a professional artist started during the year we lived in the teeming hot-pastrami and block-gang-warfare jungle of the

Brownsville (or Murder, Inc.) section of Brooklyn. My father had moved us (my mother, my two younger brothers, and sister) there from the serenity of New Haven, Connecticut, because he had just gone bankrupt in a new business.

My father's new businesses never lasted long enough to become old ones. These businesses were based on my father's ever-new ideas (part of which, always, was to move his family to a new community, a new city, a new state even—where we would find a new and glorious life). My father was a gifted artist and a brilliant idea man. He should have used his ideas in a comic strip, like I do, in which he could create a world he could manage, like I can. But there weren't enough comic strips in the early 1900's, and so my father's ideas had to be tried in an inferior, unmanageable real world. These business ideas would have worked out perfectly in a comic strip, for they all had just the right touch of fantasy, but they inevitably ended in a disaster in real life. For events in a comic strip can be controlled to follow reason and sanity; the characters in one can be made to behave with kindness, humor, and faith. But in uncontrollable reality, unreasonable misfortunes overtook my father's brilliant ideas (nobody bought his stuff) and the characters he dealt with behaved unspeakably (they wanted their money) and so we were constantly moving out of used-up communities and into bright, new El Dorados, and my father was constantly going out of new businesses and into even newer ones, with new ideas, and new, romantic backers.

And so, in 1920, we came to Brooklyn, and I was enrolled at P.S. 62, a huge, barren, penitentiary-like structure, bursting with a brawling horde of children of all races, presided over by a senile, dipsomaniacal political appointee, and staffed by frantic, overworked, and bad-tempered teachers, as unlike the Connecticut type as vodka is from milk.

It was my luck to enter P.S. 62 at the time when Mr. Lawless was organizing his Experimental Class. When I tell you that a few months later the Experimental Class was discontinued because Mr. Lawless himself was hauled off to an insane asylum (where he spent the rest of his days) you may get some idea of the thinking behind the experiment itself, and, indeed, of that of the School Authorities, which permitted this project.

Mr. Lawless' idea was that if you combined twenty of the school's worst boys (subnormals, petty thieves, rapists, and thugs) with twenty of its best boys, association with the good kids would make the bad kids better. What actually happened, of course, was that the good kids were so enchanted with the bad kids that, from the first day on, we tried to be like them, and, in some cases, so spectacularly surpassed them that, in the end, they were hard put to it to be as lousy as we were.

You'll notice that, by using the word "we," I include myself among the good kids. This was never officially established. I just supposed I was, and always have.

One fact about me did get established immediately. I was the "best drawrer" in the class. I was always the "best drawrer" in every class (for there is seldom more than one kid who can draw decently at all, in any class). In Connecticut, this had given me about twenty minutes of distinction once a week, for in a school curriculum sanely designed to prepare kids for life, this was all the drawing considered necessary. But in Mr. Lawless' Experimental Class, drawing became increasingly important as the experiment became increasingly disordered. In fact, drawing became a lifesaver. For instance, when Mr. Lawless would announce a quiz, based on reading presumably done at home the night before, the Smart Kids (who had done their reading) would settle back and yawn. They knew that Mr. Lawless wouldn't call on them, because he knew they'd done their homework. (By the way, as this sort of thing went on, the Smart Kids stopped doing any homework. They were smart enough to realize that Mr. Lawless would always believe they had). But the Bad Kids would stiffen up, alert, rebellious, and ready for trouble. They knew they'd get called on, because Mr. Lawless knew they never did their homework the night before, if for no other reason than that they never went home nights.

These quizzes would begin with the clouding of Mr. Lawless' face and the clenching of his teeth. He'd start getting mad at the answers he knew he'd get before he had asked the first question. For the first answer would, inevitably, be a request to repeat the first question. Mr. Lawless' face would then get darker, his jaw muscles would twitch violently, and he would repeat the question. This, in itself, was a victory for Badness over Authority, and the other Bad 'Uns, knowing what was coming, would titter, with a few of the weak-willed Good 'Uns, even, joining in. The question having been repeated (which Mr. Lawless knew very well the Bad 'Un had clearly heard in the first place—and which the Bad 'Un knew Mr. Lawless knew he'd heard), the formula for the destruction of Mr. Lawless' control went relentlessly on.

It was a simple formula. You just answered a question by asking another question, until Mr. Lawless exploded. Like this:—

"Who was the first president of the United States?"

"I didn't getcha, sir. Would you please repeat th' question?"

"Who — was — the — first — president — of — the — United — States?"

"Of the United States?"

"Yes. The United States."

"Oh. I getcha." Then you sat down, with the air of one to whom everything had been made clear, and was now satisfied.

This accomplished the first stage of the destruction of Mr. Lawless' control. His jaw muscles would twitch more violently. He would clench and unclench his fists, and he would rise behind his desk.

"GET UP!" His voice would have the hint of a scream in it. "You haven't answered my question!!!"

You arose, and asked, "What question?"

"The question about the first president."

"I toldja. He was the first president of the United States."

"Who was??"—and now Mr. Lawless was screaming. You pretty nearly had him. You just had to keep answering his questions by asking him questions.

The answer to "WHO was?" was, of course, "Who was WHAT?" Any moron in the class knew that, and knew too that, any minute now, Mr. Lawless' control would snap and he'd call you a sonofabitch and you could say, "You got no right to call me no sonofabitch, sir," and the poor dazed man would realize that somehow he'd been maneuvered into being in the wrong, that he was licked again, give the whole thing up, and announce a drawing class. These drawing classes became, as I said, lifesavers. The passing out of "drawring paper" and crayons and the borrowing of rulers and erasers gave legality to the jabbering and conviviality that always went on anyhow.

Mr. Lawless pretended to himself that these drawing classes weren't just outs from hopeless situations, but, rather, shrewd psychological probes, by announcing "Themes" for each drawing. Like "What I Would Like to Do Tonight When I Get Out of School." Announcements like these caused a great deal of foul merriment among the subnormal. They were stupid, all right, but not stupid enough to confess what THEY'D like to do that night when they got out of school.

The "What I Would Like to Be When I Am a Man" theme first indicated to the Bad Kids that my drawing, which up to then was merely admired and envied, could be put to some practical use. Most of them wanted to be gunmen, bookies, and thieves when they grew up, but these hopes and dreams they preferred to keep sacred. For Mr. Lawless' eyes, they represented themselves as yearning to become policemen, firemen, and senators. Now policeman, fireman, and senator uniforms are not easy to draw, if you are subnormal, and so they began to drift over to my desk for help with their idiot scratchings.

I extended myself for them. Being slowed up by having lost my left leg at nine, I couldn't win the respect of such heroes as Cowboy Scalenzo, Six-Toe Tanglebaum, or Crooksie Rattigan in the ordinary way—namely, by attacking my classmates from behind, and running off with their possessions before they could scramble up.

At first, all I got for my efforts, and all I wanted, was respect. This is how money came into it, and after that, Miss Mandelbaum.

One day Cowboy Scalenzo came into class with a black eye and many purple bruises on his face. He didn't offer to tell us how badly moidered the other two or three guys were and so we knew these were not the scars of victory, but something that the Cowboy preferred not to discuss. The drawing session came early that day when Six-Toe Tanglebaum wittily replied to a statement by Mr. Lawless that if he (Six-Toe) was a little rat then he (Mr. Lawless) must be a big rat. The theme that day was "My Greatest Ambition."

After I had drawn Crooksie Rattigan as a G-Man and Jackson Jackson, a colored boy, being inaugurated President of the United States, Cowboy Scalenzo came over with his usual request—to draw him like a cowboy. As always he would fascinatedly watch me draw his pinched, swarthy little face in a huge Stetson, and then put a kerchief, star-studded Western vest, boots, and spurs on his drawn-much-healthier-than-life body. As always he would offer no suggestions with these technicalities of costume, but just breathe harder as his image became like a cowboy. It was never until I reached the drawing of the gun and holster that the cowboy ever spoke. At that point, he would carefully describe just what kind of gun he was carrying that day, how the gun barrels were shaped, exactly how the handle was curved. He was very particular about these things. You had the feeling that up to that time we were in fantasy and artistic license was tolerated, but when we came to the gun, we had come down to business and that had to be right. On this day, however, the little bruised, bitter face said, "I ain't only holdin' the gun, see—I'm shootin' it."

I drew him shooting it.

The Cowboy looked at the billows of smoke coming from the nozzle with grim satisfaction.

"Got room for anudder guy?" he asked.

There was room.

"I'm shootin' it at my brudder. Drawr the bullet goin' right into him."

"What does your brother look like?" I asked.

"His name is Angelo. He's older than me. He looks lousy."

With this description, it was the work of only a few minutes to draw Angelo accurately, a look of anguish on his face, a bullet going right into him, and his legs kicking wildly in the air.

The Cowboy studied the drawing with pleasure meanwhile tenderly rubbing his blackened eye and bruised jaw.

He didn't turn the drawing in. He continued to study it at his desk the rest of the day, seeming to forget the pain of his injuries in the joy of his revenge on Angelo.

When school was over, he laid two pennies on my desk. "You done good," he said.

And that's how I became a merchant of dreams. For all my little subnormal classmates had their little subnormal dreams which were, generally, of assault and battery on those larger than themselves. At first I was glad to draw their dreamings for free, for their respect. But, then, my commissions became so many and so intricate, and I, with my increasing importance, became such a prima donna, that the shrewder little morons began offering me pennies, then nickels, and finally, a dime apiece to do theirs first.

That dime a drawing cut the number of requests down, but there still came in more than I could comfortably handle, and I was looking around for an assistant. I had read in *The Book of Knowledge* how Peter Paul Rubens, an artist of another age but with practically the same problem as I, had hired assistants to help him with detail, and I had my eye on a comer in the third grade, when Miss Mandelbaum appeared and all hell broke loose.

Miss Mandelbaum taught drawing, and was the first female teacher (in fact, the first female of any kind) to enter our classroom. Miss Mandelbaum was new and young and no one had told her. She had simply noticed that the quality of drawings coming from Mr. Lawless' class (mostly done by me) was pretty high for a class composed mainly of morons.

It quickly became apparent to Miss Mandelbaum that I was the Talent, and she showed a great interest in my work, coming in every day, bending over my desk to watch me draw, and (nothing is more distracting or destructive to the artist) coaching me as I went along. My classmates showed a great interest in Miss Mandelbaum's coaching, mainly because of what happened to her neckline when she bent over to coach me.

Their respectful crowding around Miss Mandelbaum during her

daily visit to my desk, and their silent, rapt attention, delighted Miss Mandelbaum and gave poor Mr. Lawless his first glimmer of hope that the Experiment was stimulating those little subnormal minds. He was right. After Miss Mandelbaum, my commissions changed.

For the first time, Cowboy Scalenzo didn't order a murder. "Drawr me Miss Mandelbaum wit' a one-piece bathin' suit on," he said. In the early 1920's, the one-piece bathing suit was no more than a mad rumor then appearing in the more sensational press. No one had ever actually seen anyone wearing one, and even the most advanced and hopeful among us doubted that anyone ever would. I was a little hazy about the arrangement of a plump lady teacher with a one-piece bathing suit on, but the Cowboy helped me with details. He was visibly pleased by the drawing, gave me a dime, and took it to his desk to study it.

After a while, he came back. I was busy drawing Miss Mandelbaum in a one-piece bathing suit (the idea had caught on) for Six-Toe Tanglebaum, who had canceled his order for a picture of him knifing Cowboy Scalenzo in the back (I played no favorites).

"Can that one," proposed Cowboy Scalenzo, "and I'll make it a quarter if ya finish this one." He laid on my desk the original One-Piece Bathing Suit Miss Mandelbaum.

"Finish it?" I asked, perplexed. "Didn't I draw everything you told me was there?"

"Sure you did, Al," said the Cowboy, "but I want you to draw me lookin' at her."

I drew Cowboy Scalenzo, in a cowboy suit, looking at Miss Mandelbaum in a one-piece bathing suit.

This caught on.

I then drew Tanglebaum looking at HIS Miss Mandelbaum.

Before the end of that day I had drawn dozens of Portraits of Young Morons Looking at Miss Mandelbaums. It had been my biggest day, at the new rate of two bits a Portrait, and I was loaded with commissions for the next day. I took some of the more urgent jobs home with me, and felt that I could no longer delay my talk with that comer in the third grade. Rubens was right.

The next day Fourfingers Bastardo came over to my desk.

"You finish that pitcher o' me an' Miss Mandelbaum yet?" he asked.

"Not yet, Fourf, I'm still kinda working it up," I replied in a lying tone that was, in later years, to become familiar to deadline-worried syndicate editors.

"That means you ain't started on it yet," said Fourfingers, who even as a twelve-year-old subnormal was a better judge of my character than syndicate editors, "an' that's okay, because I don't want you should do it."

"Well, that's okay with me, Fourf," I replied, confident that this wouldn't become a trend. "I've got plenty o' others I can—"

"I don't want you to work on no others," said my patron. "I don't want you should drawr me simply LOOKIN' at Miss Mandelbaum." He bent over and whispered, "I'll give you a extra dime if you drawr Miss Mandelbaum in that one-piece bathin' suit and me in a policeman's uniform, and she's sittin' in my lap."

I followed his instructions, putting everything down very lightly, so that I wouldn't have to erase if I made any mistakes. It was all very complicated, and terribly engrossing, and before we realized it, Miss Mandelbaum had slipped into the room and was bending over my desk.

"Doing a wrestling scene, I see," she remarked brightly. "But the penciling is so light, so timid—as if you weren't sure of the anatomical details." She beamed at me, and picked up my pencil. "The only way out—to bring out the real meaning—is to *emphasize* all the main construction lines, with good, *bold* strokes!!"

She proceeded to do this, penciling vigorously over my light lines. Fourfingers' face emerged, and then the positions of both figures. It wasn't until she put in the few good bold strokes that brought out her own lightly, but accurately, sketched-in face that she realized what she was doing. She screamed a terrible scream of anguish and betrayal, dropped the pencil as though it were red-hot, and ran out of the room. She never came back. My father's business failed, we moved to Massachusetts, and my career as a professional artist didn't get going again for ten years.

Hildegarde Dolson

AN EXCERPT FROM
WE SHOOK THE FAMILY TREE

How Beautiful With Mud

PERHAPS the surest way to tell when a female goes over the boundary from childhood into meaningful adolescence is to watch how long it takes her to get to bed at night. My own cross-over, which could be summed up in our family as "What on earth is Hildegarde *doing* in the bathroom?" must have occurred when I was a freshman in high school. Until then, I fell into bed dog-tired each night, after the briefest possible bout with toothbrush and washcloth. But once I'd become aware of the Body Beautiful, as portrayed in advertisements in women's magazines, my absorption was complete and my attitude highly optimistic. I too would be beautiful. I would also be Flower-Fresh, Fastidious and Dainty—a triple-threat virtue obviously prized above pearls by the entire male sex, as depicted in the *Ladies' Home Journal*.

Somehow, out of my dollar a week allowance, I managed to buy Mum, Odorono, Listerine and something called Nipso, the latter guaranteed to remove excess hair from arms and legs, and make a man think, "Oooo, what a flawless surface." It's true that I had no men, nor was I a particularly hairy child, having only a light yellow down on my angular appendages. Nevertheless, I applied the Nipso painstakingly in the bathroom one night with Sally as my interested audience. I had noticed the stuff had a rather overpowering, sickish sweet scent, but this was a very minor drawback, considering the goal I had in mind. After Sally had been watching me for a few minutes, she began holding her nose. Finally she asked me to unlock the door and let her out. "Don't you want to see me wash it off?" I asked, rather hurt.

"No," Sally said. "It smells funny."

In the next hour, as my father, mother and brothers followed their noses to the upstairs hall, there were far more detailed descriptions of just how Nipso affected the olfactory senses. Jimmy, being a simple child, merely said "Pugh" and went away. My father thought it was most like the odor of rotten eggs, but Bobby said No, it was more like a mouse that's been dead quite a while. Mother was more tactful, only remarking that Nipso obviously wasn't meant to be applied in a house people lived in. Since it certainly wasn't meant to be applied in a wooded dell, either, I was prevailed upon to throw the rest of the tube away.

I didn't mind too much, because I already had my eye on something that sounded far more fascinating than Nipso. This was a miraculous substance called Beauty Clay, and every time I read about it in a magazine advertisement, the words enveloped me in rapture. Even the story of its discovery was a masterpiece in lyrical prose. Seems this girl was traveling in an obscure European country (name on request) and ran out of those things ladies always run out of at the wrong time, such as powder and make-up lotion. The worst part was that the girl really *needed* such artifices to cover up bumps. Through some intuitive process which escapes me at the moment, she had the presence of mind to go to a near-by hamlet, pick up a handful of mud, and plaster it on her face. Then she lay dozing in the sun, by a brook. When she came to, washed the claylike mud off her face, and looked at her reflection in the brook, she knew she had hit the jackpot. Boy, was she beautiful. Looking at the Before-and-After pictures, I could see that *this* beauty was more than skin-deep, having benefited even her nose, eyes and hair.

After pondering all this, I could well understand why a jar of the imported Beauty Clay cost $4.98. In fact, it was dirt cheap at the price, and my only problem was how to lay my hands on $4.98. Certainly I had no intention of enlisting financial support from my parents. For one thing, it was too much money, and for another thing, parents ask too many questions. Far better, I thought, to let the transformation of their oldest daughter come as a dazzling surprise.

Due to the fact that I had such important things as Beauty Clay on my mind, it was understandable that my monthly marks in algebra should cause even more distress than usual in the bosom of my family. Each month, the high-school honor roll, consisting of the names of the ten highest students in each class, was published in the *Franklin News-Herald*. (The *Herald*, as I'd known it on Armistice Day, had been taken over by the *News*.) And each month, my own name was prominently absent. Appeals to my better nature, my pride, and the honor of the Dolsons did no good. I honestly meant well, and I even went so far as to carry books home from school and carry them back again the next morning. But freshman algebra, implying as it did that X equals Y, was simply beyond me. Finally my father said that if I got on the Honor Roll he'd give me five dollars. Wobbly as I was in Mathematics, it took me only a flash to realize this sum was approximately equal to $4.98, or the piddling price of the Beauty Clay. From there on in, I was straining every muscle. When I say that I got 89 in algebra and climbed to the bottom rung of the Honor Roll, I am stating a miracle simply. What is more important, I got the five bucks.

My father said that if I liked, he'd put most of it in my savings account. Bobby said, with even more enthusiasm, that he knew where I could get a bargain in a second-hand pistol. I declined both offers, marveling at the things men could think of to do with money, and made my way, on foot, to Riesenman's drugstore. When Mr. Riesenman said he had no Beauty Clay, I was grieved. When he said he'd never even heard of the stuff, I was appalled. It took three trips to convince him that he must order it immediately, money on the line.

Then I went home and waited. With admirable restraint, I waited five days. After that, I made daily inquiries on my way home from school. If I was with friends, I'd say I had to do an errand for Mother and would catch up to them later. They must often have wondered, in the next thirty days, at the number of unobtainable items my mother demanded of a drugstore. Finally came the wonderful afternoon when Mr. Riesenman said, "Here you are, Hildegarde." His jovial air may have been due to the fact that he was rid of me at last. My own joy was primitive and unconfined. At last I'd got hold of a rainbow.

It took a week more before I could achieve the needed privacy for my quick-change act. Mother was taking Jimmy and Sally down town to get new shoes, Bobby was going skiing, and my father, as usual, would be at the office. I got home to the empty house at twenty minutes of four, and made a bee-line for the Beauty Clay. According to the directions, I then washed off all make-up, which in my own case was a faint dash of powder on my nose, and wrapped myself in a sheet "To protect that pretty frock," or, more accurately, my blue-serge middy blouse. Then I took a small wooden spatula the manufacturer had thoughtfully provided, and dug into the jar.

The Beauty Clay was a rather peculiar shade of grayish-green, and I spread this all over my face and neck—"even to the hairline where tell-tale wrinkles hide." The directions also urged me not to talk or smile during the twenty minutes it would take the clay to dry. The last thing in the world I wanted to do was talk or smile. That could come later. For now, a reverent silence would suffice. In fact, as the thick green clay dried firmly in place, it had to suffice. Even though my face and neck felt as if they'd been cast in cement, the very sensation reassured me. Obviously, something was happening. I sat bolt upright in a chair and let it happen.

After fifteen minutes of this, the doorbell rang. I decided to ignore it. The doorbell rang again and again, jangling at my conscience. Nobody at our house ever ignored doorbells, and I was relieved when it stopped. In my eagerness to see who had been calling on us, I ran to my window, opened it, and leaned out. The departing guest was only the man who brought us country butter each week, I was glad to note. Hearing the sound of the window opening above him, he looked up. When he saw me leaning out, his mouth dropped open and he let out a hoarse, awful sound. Then he turned and ran down the steep hill at incredible speed. I couldn't imagine what had struck him, to act so foolish.

It wasn't until I'd remembered the clay and went to look in a mirror that I understood. Swathed in a sheet, and with every visible millimeter of skin a sickly gray-green, I scared even myself.

According to the clock, the Beauty Clay had been on the required twenty minutes, and was now ready to be washed off. It occurred to me that if twenty minutes was enough to make me beautiful, thirty minutes or even forty minutes would make me twice as beautiful. Besides, it would give me more lovely moments of anticipation, and Mother wouldn't be home till after five.

By the time my face was so rigid that even my eyeballs felt yanked from their sockets, I knew I must be done, on both sides. As I started back to the bathroom, I heard Bobby's voice downstairs yelling "Mom!" With the haste born of horror I ran back and just managed to bolt myself inside the bathroom as Bobby leaped up the stairs and came down the hall toward his room. Then I turned on the faucet and set to work. The directions had particularly warned "Use only gentle splashes to remove the mask—No rubbing or washcloth." It took several minutes of gentle splashing to make me realize this was getting me nowhere fast. Indeed, it was like splashing playfully at the Rock of Gibraltar. I decided that maybe it wouldn't hurt if I rubbed the beauty mask just a little, with a nailbrush. This hurt only the nailbrush. I myself remained embedded in Beauty Clay.

By this time, I was getting worried. Mother would be home very soon and I needed a face—even any old face. Suddenly it occurred to me that a silver knife would be a big help, although I wasn't sure just how. When I heard Bobby moving around in his room, I yelled at him to bring me a knife from the dining-room sideboard. Rather, that's what I intended to yell, but my facial muscles were still cast in stone, and the most I could do was grunt. In desperation, I ran down to the sideboard, tripping over my sheet as I went, and got the knife. Unfortunately, just as I was coming back through the dusky upstairs hall, Bobby walked out of his room and met me, face to face. The mental impact, on Bobby, was terrific. To do him justice, he realized almost instantly that this was his own sister, and not, as he at first imagined, a sea monster. But even this realization was not too reassuring.

I had often imagined how my family would look at me after the Beauty Clay had taken effect. Now it had taken effect—or even permanent possession of me—and Bobby was certainly reacting, but not quite as I'd pictured it.

"Wh—what?" he finally managed to croak, pointing at my face.

His concern was so obvious and even comforting that I tried to explain what had happened. The sounds that came out alarmed him even more.

Not having the time or the necessary freedom of speech to explain any further, I dashed into the bathroom and began hitting the handle of the knife against my rocky visage. To my heavenly relief, it began to crack. After repeated blows, which made me a little groggy, the stuff had broken up enough to allow me to wriggle my jaw. Meanwhile, Bobby stood at the door watching, completely bemused.

Taking advantage of the cracks in my surface, I dug the blade of the knife in, and by scraping, gouging, digging and prying, I got part of my face clear. As soon as I could talk, I turned on Bobby. "If you tell anybody about this, I'll kill you," I said fiercely.

Whether it was the intensity of my threat or a latent chivalry aroused by seeing a lady tortured before his very eyes, I still don't know, but Bobby said, "Cross my heart and hope to die."

He then pointed out that spots of the gray-green stuff were still very much with me. As I grabbed up the nailbrush again, to tackle these remnants, he asked in a hushed voice, "But what *is* it?"

"Beauty Clay," I said. "I sent away for it."

Bobby looked as though he couldn't understand why anyone would deliberately send away for such punishment, when there was already enough trouble in the world. However, for the first time in a long, hideous half hour, I remembered why I'd gone through this ordeal, and I now looked into the mirror expecting to see results that would wipe out all memory of suffering. The reflection that met my eye was certainly changed all right, varying as it did between an angry scarlet where the skin had been rubbed off, to the greenish splotches still clinging.

Maybe if I got it all off, I thought. When it was all off, except those portions wedded to my hair, I gazed at myself wearily, all hope abandoned. My face was my own—but raw. Instead of the Body Beautiful I looked like the Body Boiled. Even worse, my illusions had been cracked wide open, and not by a silver knife.

"You look awfully red," Bobby said. I did indeed. To add to my troubles, we could now hear the family assembling downstairs, and Mother's voice came up, "Hildegarde, will you come set the table right away, dear?"

I moved numbly.

"You'd better take off the sheet," Bobby said.

I took off the sheet.

Just as I reached the stairs, he whispered, "Why don't you say you were frostbitten and rubbed yourself with snow?"

I looked at him with limp gratitude.

When Mother saw my scarlet, splotched face, she exclaimed in concern. "Why, Hildegarde, are you feverish?" She made a move as if to feel my forehead, but I backed away. I was burning up, but not with fever.

"I'm all right," I said, applying myself to setting the table. With my face half in the china cupboard, I mumbled that I'd been frostbitten and had rubbed myself with snow.

"Oh, Cliff," Mother called. "Little Hildegarde was frostbitten."

My Father immediately came out to the kitchen. "How could she be frostbitten?" he asked reasonably. "It's thirty-four above zero."

"But her ears still look white," Mother said.

They probably did, too, compared to the rest of my face. By some oversight, I had neglected to put Beauty Clay on my ears. "I'm all right," I insisted again. "I rubbed hard to get the circulation going."

This at least was true. Anyone could tell at a glance that my circulation was going full blast, from the neck up.

Bobby had followed me out to the kitchen to see how the frostbite story went over. As Mother kept exclaiming over my condition he now said staunchly, "Sure she's all right. Let her alone."

My father and mother both stared at him, in this new role of Big Brother Galahad. In fact, my father reacted rather cynically. "Bobby, did you and your friends knock Hildegarde down and rub her face with snow?" he asked.

"Me?" Bobby squeaked. He gave me a dirty look, as if to say, "You'd better talk fast."

I denied hotly that Bobby had done any such thing. In fact, I proceeded to build him up as my sole rescuer, a great big St. Bernard of a brother who had come bounding through the snowdrifts to bring me life and hope.

Bobby looked so gratified at what he'd been through in my story that I knew my secret was safe.

Sally, always an affectionate child, began to sob. "She might have died. Bobby saved her from freezing."

My father and mother remained dry-eyed. Against this new set-up of Brother Loves Sister they were suspicious, but inclined to do nothing.

And in a way I *had* been frostbitten, to the quick. Lying in bed that night, still smarting, I tried to think up ways to get even. It wasn't clear to me exactly whom or what I had to get even with. All I knew was that I was sore and unbeautiful, and mulcted of five dollars. With the hot and cold fury of a woman stung, I suddenly conceived my plan for revenge. It was so simple and logical and yet brilliant that my mind relaxed at last. Some day I, too, would write advertisements.

XII. BEYOND THE
TWELVE-MILE LIMIT

Anita Loos

EXCERPTS FROM
GENTLEMEN PREFER BLONDES

[*Pages from the diary of Lorelei Lee, who coined the immortal phrase, "Diamonds are a girl's best friends."*]

March 16th:

A GENTLEMAN friend and I were dining at the Ritz last evening and he said that if I took a pencil and a paper and put down all of my thoughts it would make a book. This almost made me smile as what it would really make would be a whole row of encyclopediacs. I mean I seem to be thinking practically all of the time. I mean it is my favorite recreation and sometimes I sit for hours and do not seem to do anything else but think. So this gentleman said a girl with brains ought to do something else with them besides think. And he said he ought to know brains when he sees them, because he is in the senate and he spends quite a great deal of time in Washington, d. c., and when he comes into contract with brains he always notices it. So it might have all blown over but this morning he sent me a book. And so when my maid brought it to me, I said to her, "Well, Lulu, here is another book and we have not read half the ones we have got yet." But when I opened it and saw that it was all a blank I remembered what my gentleman acquaintance said, and so then I realized that it was a diary. So here I am writing a book instead of reading one.

But now it is the 16th of March and of course it is to late to begin with January, but it does not matter as my gentleman friend, Mr. Eisman, was in town practically all of January and February, and when he is in town one day seems to be practically the same as the next day.

I mean Mr. Eisman is in the wholesale button profession in Chicago and he is the gentleman who is known practically all over Chicago as Gus Eisman the Button King. And he is the gentleman who is interested in educating me, so of course he is always coming down to New York to see how my brains have improved since the last time. But when Mr. Eisman is in New York we always seem to do the same thing and if I wrote down one day in my diary, all I would have to do would be to put quotation marks for all other days. I mean we always seem to have dinner at the Colony and see a show and go to the Trocadero and then Mr. Eisman shows me to my apartment. So of course when a gentleman is interested in educating a girl, he likes to stay and talk about the topics of the day until quite late, so I am quite fatigued the next day and I do not really get up until it is time to dress for dinner at the Colony.

It would be strange if I turn out to be an authoress. I mean at my home near Little Rock, Arkansas, my family all wanted me to do something about my music. Because all of my friends said I had talent and they all kept after me and kept after me about practising. But some way I never seemed to care so much about practising. I mean I simply could not sit for hours and hours at a time practising just for the sake of a career. So one day I got quite tempermental and threw the old mandolin clear across the room and I have really never touched it since. But writing is different because you do not have to learn or practise and it is more tempermental because practising seems to take all the temperment out of me. So now I really almost have to smile because I have just noticed that I have written clear across two pages onto March 18th, so this will do for today and tomorrow. And it just shows how tempermental I am when I get started.

March 19th:

Well last evening Dorothy called up and Dorothy said she has met a gentleman who gave himself an introduction to her in the lobby of the Ritz. So then they went to luncheon and tea and dinner and then they went to a show and then they went to the Trocadero. So Dorothy said his name was Lord Cooksleigh but what she really calls him is Coocoo. So Dorothy said why don't you and I and Coocoo go to the Follies tonight and bring Gus along if he is in town? So then Dorothy and I had quite a little quarrel because every time that Dorothy mentions the subject of Mr. Eisman she calls Mr. Eisman by his first name, and she does not seem to realize that when a gentleman who is as important as Mr. Eisman, spends quite a lot of money educating a girl, it really does not show reverance to call a gentleman by his first name. I mean I never even think of calling Mr. Eisman by his first name, but if I want to call him anything at all, I call him "Daddy" and I do not even call him "Daddy" if a place seems to be public. So I told Dorothy that Mr. Eisman would not be in town until day after tomorrow. So then Dorothy and Coocoo came up and we went to the Follies.

So this morning Coocoo called up and he wanted me to luncheon at the Ritz. I mean these foreigners really have quite a nerve. Just because Coocoo is an Englishman and a Lord he thinks a girl can waste hours on him just for a luncheon at the Ritz, when all he does is talk about some exposition he went on to a place called Tibet and after talking for hours I found out that all they were was a lot of Chinamen. So I will be quite glad to see Mr. Eisman when he gets in. Because he always has something quite interesting to talk about, as for instants the last time he was here he presented me with quite a beautiful emerald bracelet. So next week is my birthday and he always has some delightful surprise on holidays.

I did intend to luncheon at the Ritz with Dorothy today and of course Coocoo had to spoil it, as I told him that I could not luncheon with him today, because my brother was in town on business and had the mumps, so I really could not leave him alone. Because of course if I went to the Ritz now I would bump into Coocoo. But I sometimes almost have to smile at my own imagination, because of course I have not got any brother and I have not even thought of the mumps for years. I mean it is no wonder that I can write.

So the reason I thought I would take luncheon at the Ritz was because Mr. Chaplin is at the Ritz and I always like to renew old acquaintances, because I met Mr. Chaplin once when we were both working on the same lot in Hollywood and I am sure he would remember me. Gentlemen always seem to remember blondes. I mean the only career I would like to be besides an authoress is a cinema star and I was doing quite well in the cinema when Mr. Eisman made me give it all up. Because of course when a gentleman takes such a friendly interest in educating a girl as Mr. Eisman does, you like to show that you appreciate it, and he is against a girl being in the cinema because his mother is authrodox.

March 20th:

Mr. Eisman gets in tomorrow to be here in time for my birthday. So I thought it would really be delightful to have at least one good time before Mr. Eisman got in, so last evening I had some literary gentlemen in to spend the evening because Mr. Eisman always likes me to have literary people in and out of the apartment. I mean he is quite anxious for a girl to improve her mind and his greatest interest in me is because I always seem to want to improve my mind and not waste any time. And Mr. Eisman likes me to have what the French people call a "salo" which means that people all get together in the evening and improve their minds. So I invited all of the brainy gentlemen I could think up. So I thought up a gentleman who is the proffessor of all of the economics up at Columbia College, and the editor who is the famous editor of the New York Transcript and another gentleman who is a famous playright who writes very, very famous plays that are all about Life. I mean anybody would recognize his name but it always seems to slip my memory because all of we real friends of his only call him Sam. So Sam asked if he could bring a gentleman who writes novels from England, so I said yes, so he brought him. And then we all got together and I called up Gloria and Dorothy and the gentleman brought their own liquor. So of course the place was a wreck this morning and Lulu and I worked like proverbial dogs to get it cleaned up, but Heaven knows how long it will take to get the chandelier fixed.

April 7th:

Well Mr. Eisman arrived this morning and he and I had quite a long talk, and after all I think he is right. Because here is the first real opportunity I have ever really had. I mean to go to Paris and broaden out and improve my writing. So I am sailing for France and London on Tuesday and taking Dorothy with me and Mr. Eisman says that he will see us there later. So Dorothy knows all of the ropes and she can get along in Paris just as though she knew French and besides she knows a French gentleman who was born and raised there, who speaks it like a native and knows Paris like a book. And Dorothy says that when we get to London nearly everybody speaks English anyway. So Mr. Eisman gave me quite a nice string of pearls and he gave Dorothy a diamond pin and we all went to the Colony for dinner and we all went to a show and supper at the Trocadero and we all spent quite a pleasant evening.

April 27th:

Paris is devine. I mean Dorothy and I got to Paris yesterday, and it really is devine. Because the French are devine. Because when we were coming off the boat, and we were coming through the customs, it was quite hot and it seemed to smell quite a lot and all the French gentlemen in the customs, were squealing quite a lot. So I looked around and I picked out a French gentleman who was really in a very gorgeous uniform and he seemed to be a very, very important gentleman and I gave him twenty francs worth of French money and he was very very gallant and he knocked everybody else down and took our bags right through the custom. Because I really think that twenty Francs is quite cheap for a gentleman that has got on at least $100 worth of gold braid on his coat alone, to speak nothing of his trousers.

I mean the French gentlemen always seem to be squealing quite a lot, especially taxi drivers when they only get a small size yellow dime called a 'fifty santeems' for a tip. But the good thing about French gentlemen is that every time a French gentleman starts in to squeal, you can always stop him with five francs, no matter who he is. I mean it is so refreshing to listen to a French gentleman stop squeaking, that it would really be quite a bargain even for ten francs.

And when a girl walks around and reads all of the signs with all of the famous historical names it really makes you hold your breath. Because when Dorothy and I went on a walk, we only walked a few blocks but in only a few blocks we read all of the famous historical names, like Coty and Cartier and I knew we were seeing something educational at last and our whole trip was not a failure. I mean I really try to make Dorothy get educated and have reverance. So when we stood at the corner of a place called the Place Vandome, if you turn your back on a monument they have in the middle and look up, you can see none other than Coty's sign. So I said to Dorothy, does it not really give you a thrill to realize that that is the historical spot where Mr. Coty makes all the perfume? So then Dorothy said that she supposed Mr. Coty came to Paris and he smelled Paris and he realized that something had to be done. So Dorothy will really never have any reverance.

May 17th:

So now we are on an oriental express and everything seems to be quite unusual. I mean Dorothy and I got up this morning and we looked out of the window of our compartment and it was really quite unusual. Because it was farms, and we saw quite a lot of girls who seemed to be putting small size hay stacks onto large size hay stacks while their husbands seemed to sit at a table under quite a shady tree and drink beer. Or else their husbands seemed to sit on a fence and smoke their pipe and watch them. So Dorothy and I looked at two girls who seemed to be ploughing up all of the ground with only the aid of a cow and Dorothy said, "I think we girls have gone one step to far away from New York, because it begins to look to me as if the Central of Europe is no country for we girls." So we both became quite worried. I mean I became quite depressed because if this is what Mr. Eisman thinks we American girls ought to learn I really think it is quite depressing. So I do not think we care to meet any gentlemen who have been born and raised in the Central of Europe. I mean the more I travel and the more I seem to see other gentlemen the more I seem to think of American gentlemen.

So now I am going to get dressed and go to the dining car and look for some American gentleman and hold a conversation, because I really feel so depressed. I mean Dorothy keeps trying to depress me because she keeps saying that I will probably end up in a farm in the Central of Europe doing a sister act with a plough. Because Dorothy's jokes are really very unrefined and I think that I will feel much better if I go to the dining car and have some luncheon.

Well I went to the dining car and I met a gentleman who was quite a delightful American gentleman. I mean it was quite a co-instance, because we girls have always heard about Henry Spoffard and it was really nobody else but the famous Henry Spoffard, who is the famous Spoffard family, who is a very very fine old family who is very very wealthy. I mean Mr. Spoffard is one of the most famous familys in New York and he is not like most gentlemen who are wealthy, but he works all of the time for the good of the others. I mean he is the gentleman who always gets his picture in all of the newspapers because he is always senshuring all of the plays that are not good for peoples morals. And all of we girls remember the time when he was in the Ritz for luncheon and he met a gentleman friend of his and the gentleman friend had Peggy Hopkins Joyce to luncheon and he introduced Peggy Hopkins Joyce to Mr. Spoffard and Mr. Spoffard turned on his heels and walked away. Because Mr. Spoffard is a very very famous Prespyterian and he is really much to Prespyterian to meet Peggy Hopkins Joyce. I mean it is unusual to see a gentleman who is such a young gentleman as Mr. Spoffard be so Prespyterian, because when most gentlemen are 35 years of age their minds nearly always seem to be on something else.

So when I saw no one else but the famous Mr. Spoffard I really became quite thrilled. Because all of we girls have tried very hard to have an introduction to Henry Spoffard and it was quite unusual to be shut up on a train in the Central of Europe with him. So I thought it would be quite unusual for a girl like I to have a friendship with a gentleman like Mr. Spoffard, who really does not even look at a girl unless she at least looks like a Prespyterian. And I mean our family in Little Rock were really not so Prespyterian.

So I thought I would sit at his table. So then I had to ask him about all of the money because all of the money they use in the Central of Europe has not even got so much sense to it as the kind of franks they use in Paris. Because it seems to be called kronens and it seems to take quite a lot of them because it takes 50,000 of them to even buy a small size package of cigarettes and Dorothy says if the cigarettes had tobacco in them, we couldn't lift enough kronens over a counter to pay for a package. So this morning Dorothy and I asked the porter to bring us a bottle of champagne and we really did not know what to give him for a tip. So Dorothy said for me to take one of the things called a one million kronens and she would take one of them called a one million kronens and I would give him mine first and if he gave me quite a dirty look, she would give him hers. So after we paid for the bottle of champagne I gave him my one million kronens and before we could do anything else he started in to grabbing my hand and kissing my hand and getting down on his knees. So we finally had to push him right out of the compartment. So one million kronens seemed to be enough. So I told Mr. Spoffard how we did not know what to give the porter when he brought us our bottle of minral water. So then I asked him to tell me all about all of the money because I told him I always seem to think that a penny earned was a penny saved. So it really was quite unusual because Mr. Spoffard said that that was his favorite motto.

Donald Ogden Stewart

EXCERPTS FROM
MR. AND MRS. HADDOCK ABROAD

MR. AND MRS. HADDOCK were very excited about going abroad. It was the first time either of them had ever been abroad to Europe, although Mr. Haddock had been to Chicago eight times, Kansas City five times, Kansas City (Kan.) five times, St. Louis four times, Denver four times, and New York City twice, but it had rained four days out of five.

Mrs. Haddock had been to St. Louis once and Chicago twice, in Pullman cars, named, respectively, Edgar Allen Poe, Sweet Juniper, and Spauldingopolis. She had not slept very well the first two times and the third time she had not slept at all. She slept very well at home, though, mostly on her back and left side. Her mother's maiden name had been Quetch.

Mr. and Mrs. Haddock had been married twenty-four odd years and their grandparents were all dead on both sides. So they were quite alone in the world except for Mr. Haddock's father and mother and Mrs. Haddock's father and mother, who were, however, quite old, their combined ages totalling 439 or several score years.

They also had a son, Frank Haddock, but he wasn't going abroad, although he could have gone abroad if he had wanted to, but he didn't want to, and they also had a young daughter Mildred.

That ought to give you a pretty fair idea of the city in which Mr. and Mrs. Haddock lived. It was called Legion, being named after an old Indian squaw called Legion, who was said to have been buried there originally.

When Mr. Haddock and Mrs. Haddock had been first married he had said to a lot of their best friends:

"You may sneer at us now for only going to the Mammoth Cave, Kentucky, on our wedding journey but some day you will sneer out of the other side of your mouth."

And with that he had hit his horse a terrific slash and driven away, and he and she had sworn that very day that before they were forty they would show everybody and go abroad. Mr. Haddock was now fifty-one and Mrs. Haddock was forty-nine and so their prophecy had come true. They were going abroad.

"Do you think the silver will be safe?" had been Mrs. Haddock's anxious question each year when Mr. Haddock had proposed a trip to Europe, and Mr. Haddock each year had sadly shaken his head and said "No."

But this year, instead of answering "No" he had replied:

"We could put it in a safe deposit box in some bank," and so that problem had been finally solved.

There were, however, other problems which confronted the prospective travellers.

There was, first of all, the problem of Mildred. Mildred was Mr. and Mrs. Haddock's ten year old daughter who had come to them late in life but was having her teeth straightened by Dr. Hawley.

"This trip abroad will be so wonderful for Mildred," said Mrs. Haddock.

"And for the people with whom she comes in contact," added a voice, but Mrs. Haddock had gone. It was Mr. Marsden, Mildred's Sunday School teacher, so that on his otherwise pleasant face was no mean snarl.

Then there was the age old problem of where to go.

"Paris?" suggested Mr. Haddock, a little hopefully.

"The Dickens' country," said Mrs. Haddock, who liked all of Dickens except "Bleak House" and parts of "Great Expectations," "Barnaby Rudge," "Oliver Twist," and "Vanity Fair."

The very next day Mr. Haddock had another idea:

"I tell you where let's go," he said, "Paris."

"We can't speak French," replied Mrs. Haddock, "but of course we ought to go to Paris. Won't it be wonderful to really see Notre Dame."

"And the Sewers," said Mr. Haddock. "And, besides, Mildred can speak French."

"Beautifully," added Mrs. Haddock. "You ought to hear what Miss Spencer says, Will."

A few days later Mr. Haddock said "Rome."

"The Catacombs," said Mrs. Haddock.

"Venice," said Mr. Haddock.

"Gondolas," said Mrs. Haddock. "Will, I think you had really better take your heavy overcoat."

And so one by one the more important problems were disposed of.
"I think I ought to get a note book," said Mrs. Haddock.

So she made a note on a piece of paper, "Get note book," and lost
the piece of paper but got the note book at Bromfield's where they had
had an account for many years.

"We are going abroad," she said to the clerk.

"My," said the clerk, "I certainly envy you."

So the note book was called "My Trip Abroad" and in front were a
number of interesting pages devoted to the population of cities (1900)
and how to change from Fahrenheit to Centigrade and back again
when it was hot, and what the different Storm and Distress signals
were in International Navigation. It also had a useful Comparative
Money Table for Travellers which showed that one German mark was
worth a little over 24 cents in American money.

"It says here, Will," said Mrs. Haddock, "that one German mark is
worth a little over 24 cents in American money."

"Does it?" replied Mr. Haddock and that was all that was ever said
about the German mark.

Then too "My Trip Abroad" had a large folded map of the World
on which was a black cross showing the exact spot where the "Titanic"
had sunk. One night Mrs. Haddock blotted out that cross so that no
one could tell what it was for, unless little Mildred told them. Little
Mildred always told them.

"That blot," said little Mildred, "is where the 'Titanic' sank. There
used to be a cross there but mother blotted it out. Two thousand three
hundred and fifty-eight lives were lost."

It was very difficult to fool little Mildred about anything.

In another part of Mrs. Haddock's note book were several blank
pages entitled "Places Visited and Interesting People Met," and there
was one whole page for the "Captain's Signature."

"I can hardly wait until we get on the boat," said Mrs. Haddock,
and she filled both her fountain pens very full of ink and got most of
it off her fingers by using the pumice stone in the upstairs bathroom.

* * *

"New York!" called the conductor confidently, and it *was* New
York, because the conductor had been with the road forty-two years.

"A taxi cab," said Mr. Haddock to the Red Cap who grabbed his
bag.

"I can carry this all right," said Mrs. Haddock, drawing away.

"Nonsense, dear," said Mr. Haddock. "Give him your bag. It's only a dime." So Mrs. Haddock surrendered her bag to the nice patronizing negro.

"Do you really think we need to take a taxi cab?" she asked her husband.

"Certainly, dear," said Mr. Haddock, who had been to New York before. "And which color would you choose?"

They walked along in silence for several minutes, and finally Mrs. Haddock said:

"Pink."

"A pink taxi cab," said Mr. Haddock to the porter.

"All out of pink," said the porter, and Mrs. Haddock bit her lip in vexation.

"Well—lavender then," she finally said, "light lavender."

"All out of lavender," said the porter.

"Oh dear!" said Mrs. Haddock.

"Black and white, black and white checker, yellow, yellow checker, green—hey Frank!" he called to a nearby cab starter.

"Wot?" replied Frank.

"Any more green?"

"Naw," replied Frank.

"No more green," said the Red Cap. "Hurry up, lady."

"Well, I'll take yellow—no—black and white—no—yellow," said Mrs. Haddock. "But Will, don't you take it just because I did."

"No, I really wanted yellow," said Mr. Haddock.

"Honestly?" asked Mrs. Haddock.

"Yes, honestly," said Mr. Haddock, smiling at her reassuringly.

"A yellow for three," he said to the porter; "and the check, please— we're in a hurry."

By the time they had got into the cab all were smiling again and Mr. Haddock insisted that he would ride backward on the little seat.

After they had sat there expectantly for some time without moving, the taxi driver leaned around, opened the door and said "Well where do youse want to go?"

"Oh," said Mr. Haddock, "I forgot. Why—we want to go to a good hotel. Do you know the name of any?"

"I would say the Ritz," replied the taxi driver, "if I hadn't heard lately that the cuisine had fallen off a bit. There really aren't any good hotels in New York any more."

"Is it near Grant's Tomb?" asked Mrs. Haddock. "I want to see Grant's Tomb this afternoon."

"How about the Waldorf?" asked Mr. Haddock.

The taxi driver shrugged his shoulders.

"I'll take you there, of course, if you want to go," he said, "but——"

"Maybe that gentleman could help us," said Mr. Haddock, indicating a white clad Street Cleaner who was busily plying his trade nearby.

"Oh Mr. Perkins," called the taxi driver, and the Street Cleaner laid down his cigarette, stroked his moustache once or twice, and came up to the cab.

"Mr. Perkins," said the taxi driver, "this is my friend Mr.——"

"Haddock," said Mr. Haddock; "and this is Mrs. Haddock and my daughter Mildred."

"How do you do?" said Mr. Perkins, removing his white hat and one white glove and bowing politely. "Not the Boston Haddocks?"

"No," said Mr. Haddock. "We're from the middle west."

"Ah, yes," said Mr. Perkins. "I see." And the tone of his voice became somewhat more reserved.

"My grandfather came from Boston though," asserted Mrs. Haddock proudly.

"Of course," said Mr. Perkins. "Of course. And this is your first visit to our city, Mr. Haddock?"

"No indeed," said Mr. Haddock quickly. "I have been here twice before—once for three days and once for two."

"Charming place, don't you think?" said Mr. Perkins. "But probably you don't like it—most strangers don't at first. Mrs. Perkins and I are very fond of New York—and it's really the best summer resort in America, too. We wouldn't go anywhere else for the world. Are you here for long, Mrs. Haddock?"

"We sail for Europe to-morrow," said Mrs. Haddock.

"Ah yes," said Mr. Perkins. "On the Aquitania?"

"No," said Mr. Haddock, after an embarrassing pause.

"We couldn't get passage," added Mrs. Haddock quickly.

"I see," said Mr. Perkins, stroking his moustache with a slight smile. "Well, well—I certainly envy you. Paris, I suppose?"

"Yes," said Mr. Haddock.

"Ah—Paris, Paris," said Mr. Perkins, and leaning on his broom handle he smiled reflectively. "I suppose Berry Wall and the Princesse de Lorme are still holding forth at Longchamps. You *must* go to Longchamps for the races."

"Are you fond of horses?" asked Mrs. Haddock sympathetically.

"I detest horses," said Mr. Perkins with a sudden convulsive grasp of his broom handle.

*   *   *

"Well, I guess we're off," said Mr. Haddock with just the shadow of a doubt in his voice, but as the boat swung around into the river and moved down past the Woolworth building and the Battery, his doubts gradually became a little dissipated.

"There's the Statue of Liberty," whispered Mrs. Haddock, who was really very excited.

"Look, Mildred!" said Mr. Haddock, "there's the Statue of Liberty."

"I'm hungry," said Mildred, and so he knew they were really off for Europe.

When they went down to their stateroom to wash for lunch they were surprised and delighted to find seven baskets and eleven boxes, containing among other things 103 oranges, 67 bunches of hot-house grapes, 241 fresh figs, 119 cured figs, and 141 prunes.

"This one is from Mrs. Gueminder," said Mrs. Haddock, reading a card.

"I wonder how she knew I was so constipated," mused Mr. Haddock, but delighted, just the same, with the timely gift.

Mrs. Haddock began folding up the tissue paper and string in order to save them for some occasion in their travels when they might be terribly in need of tissue paper and string, while Mr. Haddock took out a pencil and began figuring on the back of an envelope.

"Dear," he said at last, "I may be a fraction of a decimal off, either plus or minus, but in round numbers I figure that if we concentrate all our efforts and cut out theaters and sleep we can just finish the last of this fruit before we get to France."

"Oh, dear!" said Mrs. Haddock, "what *will* we do with it all?"

"Eat it!" said Mr. Haddock. "Now, for the first three days I have alloted you 165 grapes, 68 figs, 54 prunes, and 49 oranges."

"But I don't like oranges," said Mrs. Haddock.

"That doesn't matter," said Mr. Haddock severely. "In a crisis like this we must forget our petty individual likes or dislikes and work only for the good of the whole."

*   *   *

Mr. Haddock was awakened the next morning by some one knocking on the door.

"Your bath is ready, sir," called a voice. Mr. Haddock rubbed his eyes and looked at his watch.

"What bath?" he said, perplexedly trying to think of all the baths he had known, but without success.

"*Your* bath," replied the steward.

"All right," he finally said, and he got out of bed.

Mrs. Haddock and Mildred had gone, leaving what seemed to Mr. Haddock a great many women's clothes all over the stateroom.

"This way, sir," said the bath steward.

"Are we on time?" asked Mr. Haddock, yawning.

"We lost twenty minutes in the night," said the steward. "The captain fell overboard."

"Well, well," said Mr. Haddock. "He'd better watch out."

"He's very unhappy about it," replied the steward.

"Steward!" yelled a voice.

"Yours is the fifth door down this corridor," said the steward. "Coming, sir!" and he left in the other direction.

"The fifth," said Mr. Haddock. "Thank you." And when he had reached the fourth door down the corridor he opened it and went in.

"Oh, I beg your pardon," he said.

"Why, Will Haddock!" exclaimed the lady who was taking a bath. "Think of seeing *you* here."

"Well, if it isn't Nellie Fisher," said Mr. Haddock. "Well, well, this *is* a surprise."

"You're just in time, Will," said Nellie. "My soap slipped under the tub."

"With the greatest of pleasure," said Mr. Haddock, and he stooped down and felt under the tub until he had recovered the recalcitrant soap, which he handed to Nellie with a magnificent bow and a sweep of his arm.

* * *

"Read me the news, Mildred," said Mr. Haddock, "while I shave"; and so, as he was lathering his face, Mildred opened the front page of the newspaper, which was published on board ship every day, just like a regular newspaper, and read:

"Pipe Smoking a Favorite Diversion of Many Kings."

"Is that this morning's paper?" asked Mr. Haddock. Mildred looked at the date and nodded affirmatively.

"Maybe that's only the home edition," suggested Mrs. Haddock. "Go on, Mildred."

"New York, June 14." Mildred read: "The growing popularity of pipe smoking in London in recent years recalls the interesting fact that many kings have been enthusiastic followers of this practice, and the collection of pipes of the late Edward VII is said to have been valued at several thousand pounds."

"They must have gotten that by radio," said Mr. Haddock. "Try something else."

"Here's a list of famous London fogs," said Mildred, "starting with 1649."

"When was the last one?" asked Mr. Haddock, deftly cutting his chin with his safety razor.

"December 5, 1906," said Mildred.

"Just in time for this edition," said Mr. Haddock, putting cold water on the cut, and then he added, thoughtfully, "What would our grandfathers and great grandfathers have said if some one had told them that every morning on a ship in the middle of the ocean you could get the very latest news of all that was happening on two continents?"

"It used to take three days," said little Mildred, "to go from New York to Philadelphia, Pennsylvania."

"And now, in three days," said Mr. Haddock, "we are—" and he looked out of the stateroom porthole. "Well, it's kind of hard to tell just where we are. The water keeps moving so."

"I don't see how that makes any difference," said Mrs. Haddock, and then she added: "Aren't you almost finished, Will?"

"Just finished," he said, and after he had put on his collar and necktie and coat Mrs. Haddock and Mildred went out on the deck to walk, and Mr. Haddock went in to breakfast.

Mark Twain

A NIGHT OF TERROR

WHEN we got back to the German hotel I wound and set the pedometer and put it in my pocket, for I was to carry it next day and keep record of the miles we made. The work which we had given the instrument to do during the day which had just closed, had not fatigued it perceptibly.

From A Tramp Abroad. Reprinted by permission of Harper & Brothers.

We were in bed by ten, for we wanted to be up and away on our tramp homeward with the dawn. I hung fire, but Harris went to sleep at once. I hate a man who goes to sleep at once; there is a sort of indefinable something about it which is not exactly an insult, and yet is an insolence; and one which is hard to bear, too. I lay there fretting over this injury, and trying to go to sleep; but the harder I tried, the wider awake I grew. I got to feeling very lonely in the dark, with no company but an undigested dinner. My mind got a start by and by, and began to consider the beginning of every subject which has ever been thought of; but it never went further than the beginning; it was touch and go; it fled from topic to topic with a frantic speed. At the end of an hour my head was in a perfect whirl and I was dead tired, fagged out.

The fatigue was so great that it presently began to make some head against the nervous excitement; while imagining myself wide awake, I would really doze into momentary unconsciousness, and come suddenly out of them with a physical jerk which nearly wrenched my joints apart,—the delusion of the instant being that I was tumbling backwards over a precipice. After I had fallen over eight or nine precipices and thus found out that one half of my brain had been asleep eight or nine times without the wide-awake, hard-working other half suspecting it, the periodical unconsciousnesses began to extend their spell gradually over more of my brain-territory, and at last I sank into a drowse which grew deeper and deeper and was doubtless just on the very point of becoming a solid, blessed, dreamless stupor, when,— what was that?

My dulled faculties dragged themselves partly back to life and took a receptive attitude. Now out of an immense, a limitless distance, came a something which grew and grew, and approached, and presently was recognizable as a sound,—it had rather seemed to be a feeling, before. This sound was a mile away, now—perhaps it was the murmur of a storm; and now it was nearer,—not a quarter of a mile away; was it the muffled rasping and grinding of distant machinery? No, it came still nearer; was it the measured tramp of a marching troop? But it came nearer still, and still nearer,—and at last it was right in the room: it was merely a mouse gnawing the wood-work. So I had held my breath all that time for such a trifle.

Well, what was done could not be helped; I would go to sleep at once and make up the lost time. That was a thoughtless thought. Without intending it,—hardly knowing it,—I fell to listening intently to that sound, and even unconsciously counting the strokes of the mouse's nutmeg-grater. Presently I was deriving exquisite suffering from this employment, yet maybe I could have endured it if the mouse had attended steadily to his work; but he did not do that, he stopped every now and then, and I suffered more while waiting and listening for him to begin again than I did while he was gnawing. Along at first I was mentally offering a reward of five,—six,—seven,—ten—dollars for that mouse; but toward the last I was offering rewards which were entirely beyond my means. I close-reefed my ears,—that is to say, I bent the flaps of them down and furled them into five or six folds, and pressed them against the hearing-orifice,—but it did no good: the faculty was so sharpened by nervous excitement that it was become a microphone and could hear through the overlays without trouble.

My anger grew to a frenzy. I finally did what all persons before me have done, clear back to Adam,—resolved to throw something. I reached down and got my walking shoes, then sat up in bed and listened, in order to exactly locate the noise. But I couldn't do it; it was as unlocatable as a cricket's noise; and where one thinks that that is, is always the very place where it isn't. So I presently hurled a shoe at random, and with a vicious vigor. It struck the wall over Harris's head and fell down on him; I had not imagined I could throw so far. It woke Harris, and I was glad of it until I found he was not angry; then I was sorry. He soon went to sleep again, which pleased me; but straightway the mouse began again, which roused my temper once more. I did not want to wake Harris a second time, but the gnawing continued until I was compelled to throw the other shoe. This time I broke a mirror,—there were two in the room,—I got the largest one, of course. Harris woke again, but did not complain, and I was sorrier than ever. I resolved that I would suffer all possible torture before I would disturb him a third time.

The mouse eventually retired, and by and by I was sinking to sleep, when a clock began to strike; I counted, till it was done, and was about to drowse again when another clock began; I counted; then the two great Rathaus clock angels began to send forth soft, rich, melodious blasts from their long trumpets. I had never heard anything that was so lovely, or weird, or mysterious,—but when they got to blowing the quarter-hours, they seemed to me to be overdoing the thing. Every time I dropped off for a moment, a new noise woke me. Each time I woke I missed my coverlet, and had to reach down to the floor and get it again.

At last all sleepiness forsook me. I recognized the fact that I was hopelessly and permanently wide awake. Wide awake, and feverish and thirsty. When I had lain tossing there as long as I could endure it, it occurred to me that it would be a good idea to dress and go out in the great square and take a refreshing wash in the fountain, and smoke and reflect there until the remnant of the night was gone.

I believed I could dress in the dark without waking Harris. I had banished my shoes after the mouse, but my slippers would do for a summer night. So I rose softly, and gradually got on everything,—down to one sock. I couldn't seem to get on the track of that sock, any way I could fix it. But I had to have it; so I went down on my hands and knees, with one slipper on and the other in my hand, and began to paw gently around and rake the floor, but with no success. I enlarged my circle, and went on pawing and raking. With every pressure of my knee, how the floor creaked! and every time I chanced to rake against any article, it seemed to give out thirty-five or thirty-six times more noise than it would have done in the daytime. In those cases I always stopped and held my breath till I was sure Harris had not awakened,—then I crept along again. I moved on and on, but I could not find the sock; I could not seem to find anything but furniture. I could not remember that there was much furniture in the room when I went to bed, but the place was alive with it now,—especially chairs,—chairs everywhere,—had a couple of families moved in, in the meantime? And I never could seem to *glance* on one of those chairs, but always struck it full and square with my head. My temper rose, by steady and sure degrees, and as I pawed on and on, I fell to making vicious comments under my breath.

Finally, with a venomous access of irritation, I said I would leave without the sock; so I rose up and made straight for the door,—as I supposed,—and suddenly confronted my dim spectral image in the unbroken mirror. It startled the breath out of me, for an instant; it also showed me that I was lost, and had no sort of idea where I was. When I realized this, I was so angry that I had to sit down on the floor and take hold of something to keep from lifting the roof off with an explosion of opinion. If there had been only one mirror, it might possibly have helped to locate me; but there were two, and two were as bad as a thousand; besides these were on opposite sides of the room. I could see the dim blur of the windows, but in my turned-around condition they were exactly where they ought not to be, and so they only confused me instead of helping me.

I started to get up, and knocked down an umbrella; it made a noise like a pistol-shot when it struck that hard, slick carpetless floor; I grated my teeth and held my breath,—Harris did not stir. I set the umbrella slowly and carefully on end against the wall, but as soon as I took my hand away, its heel slipped from under it, and down it came again with another bang. I shrunk together and listened a moment in silent fury,—no harm done, everything quiet. With the most pains-taking care and nicety I stood the umbrella up once more, took my hand away, and down it came again.

I have been strictly reared, but if it had not been so dark and sol-emn and awful there in that lonely vast room, I do believe I should have said something then which could not be put into a Sunday School book without injuring the sale of it. If my reasoning powers had not been already sapped dry by my harassments, I would have known better than to try to set an umbrella on end on one of those glassy German floors in the dark; it can't be done in the daytime with-out four failures to one success. I had one comfort, though,—Harris was yet still and silent,—he had not stirred.

The umbrella could not locate me,—there were four standing around the room, and all alike. I thought I would feel along the wall and find the door in that way. I rose up and began this operation, but raked down a picture. It was not a large one, but it made noise enough for a panorama. Harris gave out no sound, but I felt that if I experi-mented any further with the pictures I should be sure to wake him. Better give up trying to get out. Yes, I would find King Arthur's Round Table once more,—I had already found it several times,—and use it for a base of departure on an exploring tour for my bed; if I could find my bed I could then find my water pitcher; I would quench my raging thirst and turn in. So I started on my hands and knees, because I could go faster that way, and with more confidence, too, and not knock down things. By and by I found the table,—with my head,—rubbed the bruise a little, then rose up and started, with hands abroad and fingers spread, to balance myself. I found a chair; then the wall; then another chair; then a sofa; then an alpenstock; then another sofa; this con-founded me, for I had thought there was only one sofa. I hunted up the table again and took a fresh start; found some more chairs.

It occurred to me, now, as it ought to have done before, that as the table was round, it was therefore of no value as a base to aim from; so I moved off once more, and at random among the wilderness of chairs and sofas,—wandered off into unfamiliar regions, and presently knocked a candlestick off a mantel-piece; grabbed at the candlestick and knocked off a lamp; grabbed at the lamp and knocked off a water-pitcher with a rattling crash, and thought to myself, "I've found you at last,—I judged I was close upon you." Harris shouted "murder," and "thieves," and finished with "I'm absolutely drowned."

The crash had roused the house. Mr. X. pranced in, in his long night garment, with a candle, young Z. after him with another candle; a procession swept in at another door, with candles and lanterns,—landlord and two German guests in their nightgowns, and a chambermaid in hers.

I looked around; I was at Harris's bed, a Sabbath day's journey from my own. There was only one sofa; it was against the wall; there was only one chair where a body could get at it,—I had been revolving around it like a planet, and colliding with it like a comet half the night.

I explained how I had been employing myself, and why. Then the landlord's party left, and the rest of us set about our preparations for breakfast, for the dawn was ready to break. I glanced furtively at my pedometer, and found I had made 47 miles. But I did not care, for I had come out for a pedestrian tour anyway.

Donald Moffat

GENDARMES AND THE MAN

ROSY was a second-hand Renault of eleven horsepower, a nice friendly machine, partly covered with second-hand paint and adorned with a high tonneau or bustle, like the poop of a galleon. Although really quite fond of Rosy, Mr. Mott, a sensitive man, didn't quite like to leave her hanging round outside the Hotel Crillon, as he felt that the contrast between her out-moded raiment and that of her smartly dressed sisters might cause her (and him) mental anguish. She was perfectly at home in front of Mr. Mott's own hôtel, however, and was undeniably an object of pride to Pierre, the combined valet, concierge, and chasseur, who loved to stand outside in his striped

From *A Villa in Brittany*, copyright, 1929, 1930, 1931, by Donald Moffat. Reprinted by permission of Doubleday & Company, Inc. Originally in *The New Yorker*.

apron and felt slippers, with one hand resting affectionately on the fender, and open the door for the Motts and smile them out of sight.

Mr. Mott's first act after taking Rosy over from an Englishman named Wrightstoneham, her most recent protector, was to drive her the two blocks from her little *rez-de-chaussée*, or garage, to the hôtel, proudly honking the squeaky little horn all the way like a real Parisian. There he left her by the sidewalk, and went upstairs for as long as it takes a man to recite 'The Wreck of the Hesperus,' and came down again with a song on his lips and a bright smile for Célie, known in the hotel as the maid-of-all-work because she did all the work. '*Monsieur va faire un petit tour?*' Ah-ha! Wasn't he just—and monsieur skipped out the door.

And immediately ceased being Monsieur.

A sinister figure in blue and red was leaning over Rosy. In his hand was a notebook, and he was moistening a pencil at his lips. Rosy looked furtive, as if this sort of thing had happened to her before, *en faisant le trottoir*.

Mr. Mott murmured: 'What is it that it has, Mr. the Agent? She is to me, the carriage.'

He turned his attention from Rosy. 'Ha!' he stated. 'She is to you, the carriage. Then!' Mr. Mott thought he had seldom seen a more unpleasant face.

'One has, maybe, committed a fault of which one is ignorant?'

'Evidently!'

'May one be permitted to inquire the nature of this fault?'

'Ha!' stated the gendarme again. 'One has placed the carriage at the bad side of the street; see you, how can other carriages circulate in these old ways so contracted? Thus, if all the world pleases but himself without consideration of no matter what other voyagers, what *tohubohu* does not then arrive, by example?'

Mr. Mott brightened. 'But yesterday,' he said, 'I observed the carriage of the merchant of wine and carbon at the same side, here.' A mistake.

'Yesterday! But yesterday is not today, figure to yourself.'

Mr. Mott bowed, with dignity.

'Show me then the gray card,' the gendarme demanded sternly.

Mr. Mott unbuckled his portfolio of licenses and dealt a hand from the top of the deck. The gendarme sorted them skillfully and discarded onto the front seat, keeping only the gray registration card and the pink driving license. He read them attentively, then looked at the nickel plaque on Rosy's instrument board, which the law requires to be inscribed with the owner's name and address, and gave a sudden start.

'Then!' he thundered, pointing dramatically to the plaque. 'The name on the gray card is not in rapport with the one on the plaque, evidently! That is your name engraved on the dashboard.' And so it came about that Mr. Mott was known as Monsieur Vrrigstonhonh throughout the subsequent proceedings.

Mr. Mott tried to deny it, with some confidence at first. 'But no, monsieur. That is the name of the old proprietor. I am the proprietor since fifteen days, and was even now on road to the graver for my proper plaque, already commanded.'

'Make no histories,' the gendarme ordered darkly. 'I can read, I.'

At this point the investigating committee was swelled by the arrival of a bicycle bearing another and more potent gendarme, and on his heels a little group consisting of a stubby patriarch with a long yellow beard, part of a bowler hat, and one half of a pair of suspenders; an old and respectable female in black, with a figure, who had been washing out a bit of flannel in the fresh current of the gutter; and a man-child with long bare legs, a downy beard, and serious tonsil trouble.

The committee rose long enough for the ranking gendarme to suggest politely to this trio that possibly it had, then, other affairs to claim its attention than breathing on the foreign sir, a suggestion for which the prisoner was grateful. They drifted on a few yards, and the committee took up the minutes.

Mr. Mott's man said: 'The carriage of this sir rests, evidently, at the bad side of the street. He pretends, too, that the carriage is to him, when see you, my sergeant, the name of another, a Monsieur Mott, is inscribed on the gray card.'

The true owner of the name opened his mouth to take exception to this use of the word 'pretend,' but was interrupted by the sergeant, a tall, lean man with an apoplectic face who, like all his rank, believed in action: 'Get the hell over there on the other side of the street where you belong, then we'll take up the paper work,' and Mr. Mott, glad of something to do besides being talked at, sprang in, started the motor, and in order to turn round as quickly as possible, backed Rosy up.

Instantly he heard a gentle crashing, crumpling sound from behind, then two bellows, or screams, one hoarse and low, the other shrill and vibrant, which Mr. Mott traced quickly to the two gendarmes. He stopped and looked over the side, more in curiosity than apprehension . . .

A bicycle had been left leaning against the curb behind Rosy.

One had backed Rosy over the bicycle.

To whom was the bicycle?

The bicycle was to the tall gendarme with the hoarse voice.

What says the tall gendarme?

The words of the tall gendarme would have no meaning except to another Frenchman.

The tall gendarme angers himself of it, *hein*?

Yes, he angers himself of it formidably.

And the companion of the tall one, he, too, has choler not badly.

For the bicycle of the tall gendarme lies by the ground, riven by the foreign sir.

Eventually the filibuster, with gestures, began to simmer down, and Mr. Mott began to get his first tips on Paris traffic regulations; he learned, for instance, about the crime of backing up, with or without destruction of police bicycles. And there was something mysterious and obviously childish said about parking on the odd and even sides of the street, to the undisguised interest of the little group of assorted bystanders who had, it was apparent, nothing better to do that day after all than to breathe upon the foreign sir.

The gendarmes collared all Mr. Mott's documents, told him to follow in the car, and started to walk away, carrying the injured bicycle. This brought up what Mr. Mott considered a nice point of behavior.

He bleated: 'How, then, is one to follow, since it is forbidden to recoil and the way is too narrow to make a turn?'

'Drive round the block,' they snarled over their shoulders, as who should say: Go take a running dive off the Eiffel Tower. 'One awaits your return here.'

Rosy and Mr. Mott obediently scuttled off down the street, took the first left, and instantly heard a whistle. They stopped, shuddering with emotion. A stout gendarme with a red beard and pince-nez was approaching with deliberate tread. He leaned affectionately over Rosy's shoulder.

'Attend, my little,' he said indulgently. 'Is it that one knows not how to read?' He pointed to a red disk high up on the corner building: '*Sens interdit.*'—One-way Street.

'My God!' thought Mr. Mott.

The gendarme said: 'Let me see your gray card.'

'Mr. the Agent,' Mr. Mott replied, 'I come from being arrested by two other agents of high rank who have taken all my papers and even now await my return from this voyage round the block. I now find that it is forbidden to advance further; nor can I retreat, as that, too, is forbidden. Must one then rest here forever, a mute inglorious warning to all other foreign conductors?'

The gendarme roared with dignified laughter. 'Recoil, then, my old,' adding to himself, Mr. Mott felt sure, 'and may Heaven protect thee.'

Mr. Mott backed up, or recoiled, while the gendarme held up three swiftly converging streams of taxis whose drivers honked their horns and bellowed personal remarks, and drove slowly back to his original captors. They were looking suggestively at their watches.

Mr. Mott followed them round the corner to the police station and left Rosy behind a taxi which Heaven had sent to be his guide in the still mysterious matter of parking. He entered the building and, closely attended by his guards, approached the desk. A squat man with one evil eye and a face slashed with old scars examined his papers and listened to the sergeant's story of his crimes. When the commissioner asked him his true name, then, he rashly reached across the desk to point it out on the gray card which the commissioner held in his hand. This proved to be an error. The commissioner shouted 'Halte!' snatched the card away, and glared. The gendarmes each seized one of Mr. Mott's arms, and glared; a huge black cat that had been sleeping quietly on the desk sprang to its feet, humped its back, glared, *and* spat at him. Mr. Mott waited, in terror, to be searched for arms.

Finally, after a prolonged discussion in which he took no part, as his French had utterly deserted him in the stress of emotion, Mr. Mott's true identity was established with the help of his passport, it was decided that he had an honest face, that very likely he had not actually stolen the car, and that he might be treated with indulgence on account of his ignorance of the ways of a civilized country. The parking mystery was not further explained. Nor was any mention made of the smashed bicycle. Mr. Mott learned why in the corridor outside, when the owner whispered that he had not mentioned it to the commissioner because he counted on Mr. Mott to make private reparation, and that fifty francs would be just about the right amount.

Mr. Mott paid the fifty francs, and after shaking hands all round they parted, the gendarmes on their wheels—the damage to the bicycle had apparently been exaggerated—and Mr. Mott to return Rosy temporarily to her garage, draw a deep breath or two, and hasten for something to restore his injured nerve tissues at the nearest café—a rather pleasant feature of Paris life which I won't go into just now because I think something has already been written on the subject.

Art Buchwald
SOME HEADY PHRASES ON WINE

THE problem of besting your friends at wine talk becomes increasingly difficult. It isn't enongh to drink wines—you must be able to talk about them, if not intelligently, at least at length. Alexis Lichine, who wrote a book called "Wines of France," and who is up to his neck in the wine business, has given us some provocative phrases that can be used at the dinner table, either in your own home or as a guest in the home of a friend.

* * *

If you're serving wine in your own home Mr. Lichine advises you to be very modest. When the bottle is put on the table, apologize to your guests. "I'll have to beg your pardon," you might say, "but this is a small, red wine, inconsequential, with hardly any character." If your guests don't contradict you, start building slowly. After tasting it, remark to some one, "In spite of everything, I do believe it has some breed, even if it hasn't hit its pinnacle." If no one takes the bait, go a peg higher. "You know something, I believe this wine is declaring itself. Why yes, it certainly is. It does have manifestations of greatness at that." By this time, if your remarks still go unheeded, let out all stops. "The French consider this wine as one of their most magnificent sovereigns. They laughingly call it the Napoleon of Burgundies. It's a pity it has to be wasted on such clods."

Drinking wine in some one else's home is a much easier problem. The host is always looking for compliments and if you're not careful, some of the sillier people at the table may start giving them.

* * *

The thing to remember is always be polite. After tasting the wine a comment like this might be used, "Yes, it does have a pleasing shimmer. Isn't it too bad the nose doesn't live up to the color for it could have been a big, stout boy." Don't let up just because you've won the first engagement. You could continue by saying, "How sad it didn't come from noble soil, because I'm sure it might have taken on a prestige of its own. Yes, I've seen it happen, time and time again, with underprivileged wines." Or if you wish, "It's provocative, I'm sure, but I wouldn't dare put it up against a Haut Brion." Or, "What a delightful name. It almost tastes domestic in flavor."

* * *

When speaking of vintages, never refer to a wine as 1935 or 1936. Always drop the nineteen and refer to them as thirty-fours, thirty-fives, thirty-nines, etc. Learn the names of a few rare wines and throw them around as much as you can. If you can associate them with a good French restaurant, it always helps. For example, never say, "I like a Margaux." It's much better to reminisce, "I remember a Margaux I once had at the Grand Vefour in forty-six. What a noble lunch that was."

Never refer to "wine, woman and song" in front of connoisseurs. Next to wine, the other two are so inferior they should not be mentioned in the same breath.

It may be useful when talking about wine to know that Bordeaux comes in slim bottles and Burgundy in squat ones. This always impresses.

* * *

When ordering wines in restaurants, study the card for a long time even if you don't understand what you're reading. Cluck occasionally, and then turn to the sommelier and ask him to advise you on what to order. Never accept his first suggestion. He is testing you, and you don't want to lose face.

Always carry a vintage chart with you. If you're not sure of the best wine years, take the wine card to the washroom and check it against your vintage chart.

When drinking champagne, always make a remark about the bubbles. You can either take the side that you like the bubbles, or that you're against them. Our favorite line on this subject is, "I like champagne—because it always tastes like my foot's asleep."

Art Buchwald
OTHER VOICES, OTHER WINES

IN preceding pages we discussed wine phrases which one should use when he wishes to show off his knowledge of French wines. But from Vienna comes word from another wine connoisseur, Herr Alex Kendrick, the thrice-decorated member of the International Food Patrol, and a gastronomic soldier of fortune.

Mr. Kendrick makes the point that there is a difference between the wine conversation in the East and the West. In French wine-drinking countries one might describe a Burgundy like this: "The French consider this one of their most magnificent sovereigns, the Napoleon of Burgundies. Its nobility has gone unquestioned for ages." But Mr. Kendrick says if you're invited into an Austrian home, the conversation may go something like this:

"Got a real treat for you tonight. I have some new wine and the treat is I stamped on the grapes this morning myself. Now this stuff might not hit you right at first, but after the second or third shot you won't know if you're coming or going. And if you get tired of drinking it, just rub some of it on your chest. I don't know anything better for this except maybe bear fat.

*   *   *

Mr. Kendrick also points out that in the Eastern countries less attention is paid to vintage. "In these countries," he says, "a good wine needs no vintage. In Austria, for instance, nobody ever heard of vintages except for horse-radish. There are only two kinds of wines . . . this year's wine and last year's wine. If you must discuss vintages you either say 'This year's wine is better than last year's' or 'Last year's wine was better than this year's.' A year is mentioned in connection with wine only when you are trying to place an important event such as: 'Yes, poor Kaiser Franz-Josef died in 1916, and I can remember the wine was really sour.'"

*   *   *

Bottles also do not have the importance in Austria that they do in

France and it is said around the Cafe Mozart that a good wine does not need a bottle, and needs no wine glasses either. In Vienna the people prefer to drink it out of water glasses.

When discussing Austrian wine, Mr. Kendrick says, the Austrians can hold their own with the French. He tape-recorded a conversation between two Austrian wine lovers, without their knowledge. The conversation went like this:

"Ahhhhhhhhhhh! Gut, ja?"

"Jawohl! Aber Gut!"

"Gesundheit!"

"Gesundheit!"

"Ahhhhhhhhhhh! Gut!"

Even Americans who visit Austria are able to discuss Austrian wines intelligently. Mr. Kendrick made a tape-recording of two American students in a Viennese restaurant.

"Goes down easy, huh?"

"Why it's just like water. I didn't realize wine drinking was so easy. Let's get another liter."

"Now, wait a minute, Willie, take it easy. This stuff is dynamite and it's liable to blow your head off."

"Ah, who are you kiddin'? It's just like water. Waiter, another liter."

Mr. Kendrick reported that after two more liters his tape-recording machine was destroyed. Willie's head really blew off.

*   *   *

The International Food Patrolman took issue with Mr. Lichine on his knowledge of wines and his ability to toss them around in conversation.

He wrote: "Mr. Lichine's name-dropping is sheer snobbery. Has he ever heard, for example, of a Yugoslav wine named Dingach? Does he know of a Turkish white wine called Kimizi (named after the Turkish word for chemistry)? What about a Bulgarian wine called Flodiv, or a Hungarian wine called Badacsyoni?

"Probably the only Hungarian wine Lichine has heard of is Tokay. Does he know there hasn't been any genuine Tokay since 1939? And has he ever tasted Steer Blood, another Hungarian masterpiece? Has he sampled Greek Retsina? If he tells you it tastes like paint, he's lying—it tastes like paint remover.

"You see there is a lot about wine that Mr. Lichine doesn't know and there are many other countries besides France that grow wine. In these vast areas no one looks at the labels, because there are no labels; but in the end good wines as well as bad, old wines as well as young ones, imported wines as well as domestic wines, all produce the same effect—bad livers. Why doesn't Mr. Lichine talk about that?"

Robert Benchley

CARNIVAL WEEK IN SUNNY LAS LOS

YOU have all doubtless wanted to know, at one time or another, a few of the quaint customs which residents of the continent of Europe seem to feel called upon to perpetuate from one century to another. You may know about a few of them already, such as child-bearing (which has been taken up on this continent to such an alarming extent) and others of the more common variety of folk man-nerisms, but I am very proud and happy to be able to tell you today of some of the less generally known customs of the inhabitants of that medieval Spanish province Las Los (or Los Las, as it was formerly called, either way meaning "The The" *pl.*) where I have had the extremely bad fortune to be spending the summer.

Las Los, nestling, as it does, in the intercostal nooks of the Pyrenees, makes up into one of the nicest little plague-spots on the continent of Europe. Europe has often claimed that Las Los was *not* a part of it, and in 1356 Spain began a long and costly war with France, the loser to take Los Las and two outfielders. France won and Spain built an extension onto the Pyrenees in which to hide Los Las. They succeeded in hiding it from view, but there was one thing about Los Las that they forgot; so you always know that it is there.

It was in this little out-of-the-way corner of the world, then, that I set up my easel and began painting my fingers and wrists. I soon made friends with the natives (all of whom were named Pedro) and it was not long before they were bringing me their best Sunday knives and sticking them in my back for me to try and tell which was which. And such laughter would go up when I guessed the wrong one! All Lat-ins, after all, are just children at heart.

But I am not here to tell you of the many merry days I myself spent in Las Los, but of some of the native customs which I was privileged to see, and, once in a while, take part in. They rather resent an outsider taking part in most of them, however, for there is an old saying in Las Los that "when an outsider takes part, rain will surely dart" (meaning "dart" from the clouds, you see) and above all things rain is abhorred in that section of the country, as rain has a tendency to cleanse whatever it touches, and, as another old proverb has it, "clean things, dead things"—which isn't exactly accurate, but appeals to these simple, childish people, to whom cleanliness is next to a broken hip.

First of all, then, let us tiptoe up on the natives of Las Los during their carnival time. The carnival week comes during the last week in July, just when it is hottest. This makes it really ideal for the Los Lasians, for extreme heat, added to everything else, renders their charming little town practically unbearable. This week was chosen many hundreds of years ago and is supposed to mark the anniversary of the marriage of old Don Pedro's daughter to a thunderbolt, a union which was so unsatisfactory to the young lady that she left her husband in two days and married a boy named Carlos, who sold tortillas. This so enraged the thunderbolt that he swore never to come to Los Las again, and, from that day to this (so the saying goes, I know not whether it be true or not) that region has never had any locusts. (This would almost make it seem that the repulsed bridegroom had been a locust, but the natives, on being questioned, explain that the *patois* for "Thunderbolt" [*enjuejoz*] is very much like the *patois* for "locust" [*enjuejoz*] and that the thunder god, in giving his order for the future of Los Las, put the accent on the wrong syllable and cut them off from locusts instead of thunderstorms). This may, or may not, be the truth, but, as I said to the old man who told me "Who the hell cares?" The first day of the Carnival of the Absence of Locusts (just why they should be so cocky about having no locusts is not clear. Locusts would be a god-send compared to some of the things they *have* got) is spent in bed, storing up strength for the festival. On this day all the shops, except those selling wine, are closed. This means that a little shop down by the river which sells sieves is closed. People lie in bed and send out to the wine-shops for the native drink, which is known as *wheero*. All that is necessary to do with this drink is to place it in an open saucer on the window sill and inhale deeply from across the room. In about eight seconds the top of the inhaler's head rises slowly and in a dignified manner until it reaches the ceiling where it floats, bumping gently up and down. The teeth then drop out and arrange themselves on the floor to spell "Portage High School, 1930," the eyes roll upward and backward, and a strange odor of burning rubber fills the room. This is followed by an unaccountable feeling of intense lassitude.

Thus we may expect nothing from the natives for the first two days of the carnival, for the second day is spent in looking for bits of head and teeth, and in general moaning. (A sorry carnival, you will say—and I will say, too.) But later on, things will brighten up.

On the third day the inhabitants emerge, walking very carefully in order not to jar off their ears, and get into a lot of decorated ox carts. They are not very crazy about getting into these ox carts, but it is more or less expected of them at carnival time. Pictures are taken of them riding about and are sent to the London illustrated papers, and if they were to pass up one year without riding in decorated ox carts, it wouldn't seem like carnival week to the readers of the London illustrated papers. You can hardly blame a man with a *wheero* hangover, however, for not wanting to bump around over cobblestones in an old two-wheeled cart, even if it has got paper flowers strung all over it. One of the saddest sights in the world is to see a native, all dressed up in red and yellow, with a garland of orange roses around his neck, jolting and jouncing along over hard stone bumps with a girl on his knee, and trying to simulate that famous Spanish smile and gay abandon, all the time feeling that one more bump and away goes that meal he ate several days ago, along with his legs and arms and portions of his lower jaw. No wonder Spaniards look worried.

However, there is a great deal of shouting and cawing among those who can open their mouths, and occasionally someone hits a tambourine. This is usually frowned upon by the person standing next to the tambourine-hitter and a remark, in Spanish, is made which could roughly be translated as: "For the love of God, shut up that incessant banging!"

The carnival, which is known as *Romeria*, is supposed to be a festival of the picnic type combined with a religious pilgrimage to some sort of shrine. This shrine, however, is never reached, as along about noon of the third day some desperate guy, with a hangover no longer to be borne, evolves a cure on the "hair of the dog that bit you" theory, and the *wheero* is brought out again. The village watering trough is filled with it and a sort of native dance is held around the trough, everyone inhaling deeply. Those who are still unable to inhale are carried to the edge of the trough and a little *wheero* is rubbed on their upper-lips, just under the nose. Then it is "good-night all, and a merry, merry trip to Blanket Bay," for the festive villagers, and the carnival is shot to hell. A week later business is quietly resumed.

On the fifth day of the carnival there is supposed to be a bull chase through the streets. The principle of the thing is that a bull is let loose and everyone chases it, or vice versa. As, however, there was nobody fit to chase a butterfly, much less a bull, on the fifth day of this carnival, I had to take care of the bull myself. The two of us sat all alone in the public square among the cadavers drinking a sort of lemon squash together.

"A dash of *wheero?*" I asked the bull.

Well, you should have heard him laugh! After that, I got up on his back and rode all around the town, visiting the points of interest and climbing several of the better-looking mountains. Pretty soon we were in Turkey, where we saw many interesting sights and then, swinging around through the Balkans, I got back just in time for me to scramble into bed. I must have hit my head on the footboard while pulling up the sheet, for the next morning (or whenever it was) when I awoke, I had quite a bad headache. Thank heaven I knew enough to lay off that *wheero*, however. I'm no fool.

S. J. Perelman
THE IDOL'S EYE

I HAD been week-ending with Gabriel Snubbers at his villa, "The Acacias," on the edge of the Downs. Gabriel isn't seen about as much as he used to be; one hears that an eccentric aunt left him a tidy little sum and the lazy beggar refuses to leave his native haunts. Four of us had cycled down from London together: Gossip Gabrilowitsch, the Polish pianist; Downey Couch, the Irish tenor; Frank Falcovsky, the Jewish prowler, and myself, Clay Modelling. Snubbers, his face beaming, met us at the keeper's lodge. His eyes were set in deep rolls of fat for our arrival, and I couldn't help thinking how well they looked. I wondered whether it was because his daring farce, *Mrs. Stebbins' Step-Ins*, had been doing so well at the Haymarket.

"Deuced decent of you chaps to make this filthy trip," he told us, leading us up the great avenue of two stately alms toward the house. "Rum place, this." A surprise awaited us when we reached the house, for the entire left wing had just burned down. Snubbers, poor fellow, stared at it a bit ruefully, I thought.

"Just as well. It was only a plague-spot," sympathized Falcovsky. Snubbers was thoughtful.

"D'ye know, you chaps," he said suddenly, "I could swear an aunt of mine was staying in that wing." Falcovsky stirred the ashes with his stick and uncovered a pair of knitting needles and a half-charred corset.

"No, it must have been the other wing," dismissed Snubbers. "How about a spot of whisky and soda?" We entered and Littlejohn, Snubbers' man, brought in a spot of whisky on a piece of paper which we all examined with interest. A splendid fire was already roaring in the middle of the floor to drive out the warmth.

"Soda?" offered Snubbers. I took it to please him, for Gabriel's cellar was reputedly excellent. A second later I wished that I had drunk the cellar instead. Baking soda is hardly the thing after a three-hour bicycle trip.

"You drank that like a little soldier," he complimented, his little button eyes fastened on me. I was about to remark that I had never drunk a little soldier, when I noticed Littlejohn hovering in the doorway.

"Yes, that will be all," Snubbers waved, "and, oh, by the way, send up to London tomorrow for a new wing, will you?" Littlejohn bowed and left, silently, sleekly Oriental.

"Queer cove, Littlejohn," commented Snubbers. "Shall I tell you a story?" He did, and it was one of the dullest I have ever heard. At the end of it Falcovsky grunted. Snubbers surveyed him suspiciously.

"Why, what's up, old man?" he queried.

"What's up? Nothing's up," snarled Falcovsky. "Can't a man grunt in front of an open fire if he wants to?"

"But. . ." began Snubbers.

"But nothing," Falcovsky grated. "You haven't lived till you've grunted in front of an open fire. Just for that—grunt, grunt, grunt," and he grunted several times out of sheer spite. The baking soda was beginning to tell on Snubbers.

"Remarkable thing happened the other day," he began. "I was pottering about in the garden . . ."

"Why must one always potter around in a garden?" demanded Couch. "Can't you potter around in an armchair just as well?"

"I did once," confessed Snubbers moodily, revealing a whitish scar on his chin. "Gad, sir, what a wildcat she was!" He chewed his wad of carbon paper reminiscently. "Oh, well, never mind. But as I was saying—I was going through some of my great-grandfather's things the other day . . ."

"What things?" demanded Falcovsky.

"His bones, if you must know," Snubbers said coldly. "You know, Great-grandfather died under strange circumstances. He opened a vein in his bath."

"I never knew baths had veins," protested Gabrilowitsch.

"I never knew his great-grandfather had a ba—" began Falcovsky derisively. With a shout Snubbers threw himself on Falcovsky. It was the signal for Pandemonium, the upstairs girl, to enter and throw herself with a shout on Couch. The outcome of the necking bee was as follows: Canadians 12, Visitors 9. Krebs and Vronsky played footie, subbing for Gerber and Weinwald, who were disabled by flying antipasto.

We were silent after Snubbers had spoken; men who have wandered in far places have an innate delicacy about their great-grandfathers' bones. Snubbers' face was a mask, his voice a harsh whip of pain in the stillness when he spoke again.

"I fancy none of you knew my great-grandfather," he said slowly. "Before your time, I daresay. A rare giant of a man with quizzical eyes and a great shock of wiry red hair, he had come through the Peninsular Wars without a scratch. Women loved this impetual Irish adventurer who would rather fight than eat and vice versa. The wars over, he turned toward cookery, planning to devote his failing years to the perfection of the welsh rarebit, a dish he loved. One night he was chafing at The Bit, a tavern in Portsmouth, when he overheard a chance remark from a brawny gunner's mate in his cups. In Calcutta the man had heard native tales of a mysterious idol, whose single eye was a flawless ruby.

" 'Topscuttle my bamberger, it's the size of a bloomin' pigeon's egg!' spat the salt, shifting his quid to his other cheek. 'A bloomin' rajah's ransom and ye may lay to that, mateys!'

"The following morning the *Maid of Hull*, a frigate of the line mounting thirty-six guns, out of Bath and into bed in a twinkling, dropped downstream on the tide, bound out for Bombay, object matrimony. On her as passenger went my great-grandfather, an extra pair of nankeen pants and a dirk his only baggage. Fifty-three days later in Poona, he was heading for the interior of one of the Northern states. Living almost entirely on cameo brooches and the few ptarmigan which fell to the ptrigger of his pfowlingpiece, he at last sighted the towers of Ishpeming, the Holy City of the Surds and Cosines, fanatic Mohammedan warrior sects. He disguised himself as a beggar and entered the gates.

"For weeks my great-grandfather awaited his chance to enter the temple of the idol. They were changing the guard one evening when he saw it. One of the native janissaries dropped his knife. My great-grandfather leaped forward with cringing servility and returned it to him, in the small of his back. Donning the soldier's turban, he quickly slipped into his place. Midnight found him within ten feet of his prize. Now came the final test. He furtively drew from the folds of his robes a plate of curry, a dish much prized by Indians, and set it in a far corner. The guards rushed upon it with bulging squeals of delight. A twist of his wrist and the gem was his. With an elaborately stifled yawn, my great-grandfather left under pretense of going out for a glass of water. The soldiers winked slyly but when he did not return after two hours, their suspicions were aroused. They hastily made a canvass of the places where water was served and their worst fears were realized. The ruby in his burnoose, Great-grandfather was escaping by fast elephant over the Khyber Pass. Dockside loungers in Yarmouth forty days later stared curiously at a mammoth of a man with flaming red hair striding toward the Bull and Bloater Tavern. Under his belt, did they but only know it, lay the Ruby Eye.

"Ten years to that night had passed, and my great-grandfather, in seclusion under this very roof, had almost forgotten his daring escapade. Smoking by the fireplace, he listened to the roar of the wind and reviewed his campaigns. Suddenly he leaped to his feet—a dark face had vanished from the window. Too late my great-grandfather snatched up powder and ball and sent a charge hurtling into the night. The note pinned to the window drained the blood from his face.

"It was the first of a series. Overnight his hair turned from rose-red to snow-white. And finally, when it seemed as though madness were to rob them of their revenge, *they came*."

Snubbers stopped, his eyes those of a man who had looked beyond life and had seen things best left hidden from mortal orbs. Falcovsky's hand was trembling as he pressed a pinch of snuff against his gums.

"You—you mean?" he quavelled.

"Yes." Snubbers' voice had sunk to a whisper. "He fought with the strength of nine devils, but the movers took away his piano. You see," he added very gently, "Great-grandfather had missed the last four instalments." Gabrilowitsch sighed deeply and arose, his eyes fixed intently on Snubbers.

"And—and the ruby?" he asked softly, his delicate fingers closing around the fire-tongs.

"Oh, *that*," shrugged Snubbers, "I just threw that in to make it interesting."

We bashed in his conk and left him to the vultures.

Wolcott Gibbs

CURE

MR. AND MRS. GRAVES, who had come on the cruise because Mr. Graves had taken to whimpering in his sleep, were the first at the table. Mr. Graves saw instantly that something was up. Instead of the regular menu cards, there were great creamy folders with pictures of Bermuda on their covers. There were six snappers—those explosive paper cylinders, containing mottoes and "favors," that ornament children's parties—and a cardboard hat, with S. S. Kursvaal printed on it, beside each place. Mr. Graves picked up his hat and looked under it. There was nothing there. He had rather expected a cobra.

"*Now* what the hell?" he said.

"It's the last night out," said Mrs. Graves. "They always have a party then."

"Oh," said Mr. Graves.

"Perhaps you'd better put on your hat," she said gently. "Everybody seems to be doing it."

Looking around, Mr. Graves saw that this was true. The dining-room was about half full, and all the guests were wearing cardboard hats. It was, he felt, one of those occasions when it is best to conform. Mrs. Graves laughed.

"You look like the iceman's horse," she said.

By this time pandemonium had descended on the room. After putting on their hats, the guests had begun to apply themselves happily to their snappers. The air was full of tiny explosions and the soft squealing of ladies, deliciously terrified. The snappers contained whistles and rattles and a sort of paper snake that unrolled with a whinny when you blew into it. Mr. Graves pulled one of his snappers, and found a wooden pig with a whistle in its back. There was also a slip of paper that said: "There'll be a hot time in the old town tonight," instead of the usual scrap of inspirational verse. This seemed grimly prophetic to Mr. Graves. He gathered up the five remaining snappers and let them fall quietly under the table. Mr. and Mrs. Tyler, who confessed that they did a lot to keep Milwaukee on its toes socially, dropped into their seats across from the Graves.

"Hello, folks," said Mr. Tyler.

He had on a mess jacket, but he did not look especially like Clifton Webb. He put on a cardboard hat, and so did Mrs. Tyler, who was a large woman, rather casually assembled. Mrs. Tyler exploded one of her snappers and found a collapsible wooden rattle that spread madness and desolation when put together and swung. She swung it with spirit. Mr. Tyler got a small tin whistle, but did better with it than might have been expected.

Miss Polly Canopy and the three Yale men appeared next and sat down, completing the table. The three Yale men had pursued Miss Canopy relentlessly throughout the cruise—catching her, Mrs. Tyler had remarked cynically, more often than not. One of the Yale men found a brass ring in his snapper and put it on Miss Canopy's finger.

"Make an honest woman of you," he said with a leer. Miss Canopy shrieked with rapture, but Mrs. Tyler only looked down her nose.

Somewhere near the end of the room, the orchestra blared into the "cruise song," the text of which appeared on a small card by each plate.

> "Of all the ships that sail the sea,
> The Kursvaal is the ship for me.
> Though she's not an ocean liner,
> Not a ship that's built's built finer,"

thundered the passengers.

There was a lot more, ending in a nightmare of discords:

"On the oooooold Kursvaaaal."

Dishes began to appear before Mr. Graves. They were rich in color and eccentric in design, and he wondered vaguely if they were edible, although he had neither the spirit nor the appetite to find out. He would scarcely have had time in any case, because the steward was lit with the strange ecstasy of the occasion and put them down and took them away with great rapidity. For some reason he had on a high black hat with a capital "R" in white on both sides.

Miss Canopy and the Yale men yielded gaily to much champagne, and pelted each other with innuendoes which made it appear that Mrs. Tyler had underestimated Miss Canopy's activities, if anything. Mr. Tyler yearned toward Mr. Graves with a story about a policy he had sold to, by God, the toughest man in Wisconsin. Mrs. Tyler swung her grim rattle. Mrs. Graves, pink and beautiful, ate salted peanuts. From time to time everybody sang about the Kursvaal. Mr. Graves wished he were dead.

At a quarter to nine, one of the Yale men insulted Mrs. Tyler. She was, he said, staring at Miss Canopy like an odalisque.

"You're drunk," said Mrs. Tyler fiercely. "That girl, too. All four of you."

"Never mind, Mother," said Mr. Tyler, who would have made five if his wife had cared to be precise. "I'm going to smash somebody."

He had indeed risen to smash somebody when, without warning, the main lights in the room went out, leaving only a small, dim lamp on each table. In the half-light, strange things began to happen. The steward loomed suddenly beside Mr. Graves with a dish bearing a great damp block which gave off a frail and unearthly radiance.

"What's that?" demanded Mr. Graves uneasily.

"Ize-krim," said the steward.

Mr. Graves looked again, and indeed it was ice cream.

"Is ilictric lights inside," said the steward, thinking him still incredulous.

"Oh," said Mr. Graves. He declined the luminous ice cream, although Mr. and Mrs. Tyler and the undergraduates ate it without apparent discomfort. There was, by this time, such torment on Mr. Graves's face that his wife patted his knee under the table.

"Never mind, lamb," she said. "It's almost over. They certainly can't think of anything *more* to do to you."

"Oh, can't they?" said Mr. Graves darkly, and his pessimism was almost instantly justified. All the lights went out now, and in the darkness the orchestra burst once more into the cruise song. Suddenly across the room a row of fiery letters staggered into sight. They were large letters, suspended about six feet in the air, and although they wavered and blinked a good deal, it was soon apparent that they spelled KURSVAAL. The letters began a slow, bobbing circuit of the room, advancing implacably upon Mr. Graves.

"It's only the stewards," whispered Mrs. Graves, feeling her husband stiffen beside her as the fiery march approached. "They've got electric lights in their hats. Like the ice cream."

When the line came abreast of the table, he saw that this was true. In some manner electric lights had been installed inside the stewards' hats, and shone brightly through the transparent letters.

The fact that there was a reasonable explanation for the marching lights, however, did little to console Mr. Graves. It was too late. He knew miserably that they, and the illuminated ice cream, and the snappers, and even Miss Canopy and the Tylers, had already joined the long procession of disturbing images which came to torment his dreams. He would see them all many times at night, strangely illuminated from within and marching to that preposterous song, and he would still whimper.

"Come on," he said. "Let's get out of this."

Thomas Heggen

THE BIRTHMARK

(From His Famous World-War II Novel, "Mr. Roberts")

THE ANCHORING of the Naval Auxiliary "U.S.S. Reluctant" was accomplished without incident. The anchor chain banged and rattled in the hawse pipes and the ship shuddered as it stampeded out. The word, 'Secure the special sea detail,' was blatted over the

P.A. system and five seconds later the engine room called the bridge for permission to secure the main engines. The Captain made the appropriate reply, 'Goddamit, they'll secure when I get good and ready to let them secure,' but he did it without enthusiasm, and he only muttered for perhaps two minutes about those bastards down there who sit on their tails waiting to secure. It was a very hot, sweaty day, about three in the afternoon, and it seemed just another island: so nobody's heart beat very much faster at being anchored.

The port routine commenced, a matter of loosening the ship's belt a notch or two. The gun watches stayed on, but the lookouts were secured and ran below to find the crap game. A boat was lowered to go over and get the mail. Back on number four hatch the canvas screen was rigged for the night's movie. Stuyzuiski, a seaman in the third division who wouldn't get out of his clothes under way, took a bath; and at chow everyone remarked on how much better he smelled. Ensign Pulver mixed himself what he called a Manhattan—a third of a water-glass of brandy, a splash of vermouth, and a couple of ice cubes —and lay in his bunk and sipped it admiringly. The crew leaned on the rail and looked around incuriously at the little bay and the naval base ashore. Becker, a seaman received on board in the last draft, was moved to remark to Dowdy: 'This ain't a bad place, you know it?' Dowdy said something obscene without even turning his head. Becker bumbled on: 'No, I mean it ain't as bad as most of the places we been to. It's kind of pretty.'

Becker was right, though; it *was* kind of pretty; it was really a rather lovely little bay. The water off the reef was terribly blue, a showy light-ink blue. The bay was enclosed by a chain of islands, and instead of the usual flat barren coral these were green with lush and heavy foliage, and on two sides of the anchorage they ran up to impressive hills that were remote and purpling in the late afternoon sun. And the channel at the end of the bay wound away into the deep shadow between the islands and reappeared flashing in the secret and smoky distance. The crew, lined along the rail, began to feel obscurely good at being here; and even Dowdy was probably aware that, aesthetically, this was quite a superior place.

Its intrinsic and most spectacular virtue fell to Sam Insigna to discover. (Although if Sam hadn't found it one of the other signalmen would have soon enough.) Sam was a little monkey of a man, not quite five feet tall, long-armed and bow-legged like a monkey, with a monkey's grinning, wizened face, who had achieved considerable fame aboard the ship by once attacking, unprovoked and with the inten-

tion of doing physical violence, a six-foot-four-inch marine. Sam was
up on the flying bridge with the other signalmen and he was idly
scanning the beach through the ship's telescope, a large, mounted glass
of thirty-two power. The ship was anchored perhaps two hundred
yards from the beach, and just off the starboard bow, the way she was
heading now, there was a base hospital. The hospital flag was flying
over three rows of Quonset huts; there was well-trimmed grass between
the huts, and straight neat coral paths that looked like sidewalks. Farther off to the right was the rest of the naval base; clapboard buildings and Quonsets scattered between coconut palms, and down at the
waterfront there was a long wooden dock where a Liberty ship was unloading. Dead ahead, right on the point, was the interesting thing,
though, the really amazing thing. It was a house, easily identifiable as
a house; an authentic civilian house. It was a wooden, two-story house,
painted yellow; long and low, with a veranda running the entire
length. There was a swing on the veranda and several cane chairs, there
was a fine green lawn running down to the beach, and there were two
green wooden benches on the lawn under the trees. It was an old
house, obviously long antedating American occupation of the island;
it was a formless, bleak, and even ugly house; yet, in these surroundings, in the middle of the Pacific, it seemed to the signalmen a thing
of great magnificence.

'It must have been the Governor's house,' Schlemmer explained.

Sam swung the telescope around to have a look at this. At first he
trained it carelessly around the grounds, then he turned it on the
house. For perhaps a full minute nothing happened, and then it did.
Sam had been leaning with one elbow on the windshield; all of a sudden he jerked upright, sucked in his breath and grabbed at the glass
as if he were falling. The idea flashed through the mind of Schlemmer,
standing beside him, that Sam had been hit by a sniper.

'Holy Christ!' Sam said. He seemed to have difficulty in speaking.

'What is it?' Schlemmer said, and he grabbed for a long-glass.

There was only reverence in Sam's voice. 'Holy Christ! She's bare-
assed!'

One of the many anomalies of our ponderous Navy is its ability
to move fast, to strike the swift, telling blow at the precise moment it
is needed. There were accessible in the wheelhouse and charthouse
seven pairs of binoculars; on the flying bridge were two spyglasses and
two long-glasses, and the ship's telescope; and on a platform above was
the range-finder, an instrument of powerful magnification. Within a
commendably brief time after Sam had sounded the alarm, some-

where between fifteen and twenty seconds, there were manned six pairs of binoculars, two spyglasses, two long-glasses, of course the ship's telescope, and the range-finder. The glasses were all on the target right away, but the range-finder took a little longer, that instrument being a large unwieldy affair which required considerable frantic cranking and adjusting by two men in order to focus on a target. Through a rather surprising sense of delicacy, considering that two quartermasters and the talker were left without, one pair of binoculars remained untouched: the ones clearly labeled 'Captain.' In future scrutinies, it was found necessary to press all glasses into service, exempting none.

Sam's discovery was basically simple, natural, reasonable. He had discovered that nurses lived in the long, yellow house. He had discovered two large windows in the middle of the second-story front, and that these windows had none but shade curtains, retracted. He had discovered (the telescope is a powerful glass and the room was well illumined by sunlight) that the windows belonged to the bathroom. It is, of course, redundant to say that he had also discovered a nurse in the shower stall in the far left-hand corner of the room. All of this would seem to be a model of logic, of sweet reasonableness: what could possibly be more logical than that there be a hospital at this base, that there be nurses attached to this hospital, that these nurses lived in a house, that this house have a bathroom, that this bathroom have windows, that these nurses bathe? Nothing, you would think. And yet to these signalmen and quartermasters (who had last seen a white woman, probably fat, certainly fully clothed, perhaps fourteen months ago) this vision was literally that, a vision, and a miracle, and not a very small miracle, either. Like Sam, they were stricken with reverence in its presence, and like Sam, their remarks were reverent; those who could speak at all. 'Holy Christ!' a few of them managed to breathe, and 'Son-of-a-bitch!' That was all. Those are the only legitimate things a man can say when suddenly confronted with the imponderable.

The word spread fast, although how it is difficult to say: certainly no one left the bridge. The four-to-eight signal watch, Niesen and Canappa, never known to relieve before the stroke of the hour, appeared at three-thirty and met an equally incredible thing; a watch that refused to be relieved. 'Get the hell out of here,' Sam told the newcomers. 'We're staying up here till chow.' There was some bitterness and much indignant insistence by the oncoming pair of their *right* to relieve the watch, but the old watch, firmly entrenched at the glasses, stayed by them until chow was piped. There was a splendid run of bathers. The shore station blinked for half an hour trying to rouse this ship, a bare two hundred yards away; and, finally succeeding, sent out a nasty message about keeping a more alert signal watch. Accordingly, the glass of the striker Mannion was taken away from him and he was detailed to watch for signals. It seemed that Sam had just gone below for supper when he was back again, demanding and getting his telescope. He and the rest of the watch stayed on until after sunset, when lights went on in the bathroom and the curtains were pulled chastely down for the night; all the way down, leaving not the merest crack.

That first day was chaotic, comparable perhaps to the establishing of a beachhead. It was ill-organized; there was duplication and wasted effort. The next day went much better. A system and a pattern appeared. The curtain was raised at 0745 and was witnessed by Sam, Schlemmer, Canappa, Mannion, Morris, Niesen, three quartermasters, and the officer-of-the-deck. For perhaps forty-five minutes there was a dazzling crowd of early-morning bathers; almost a surfeit of them, sometimes three or four at a time. Then there was a long slack period (no one in the room) that extended to ten o'clock. Sam organized for the slack period. It is fatiguing to stand squinting through an eyepiece for long periods, so Sam arranged that one man, by turns, keep the lookout during the off-hours and give the word when action developed. But he refused to let Mannion take a turn. "That son-of-a-bitch watched one strip down yesterday and didn't open his mouth,' he accused.

It was possible by this time to establish the routine of the house. After the big early-morning rush there was only an occasional and accidental visitor until around ten, when the night watch would begin to get up. From ten to eleven was fairly good, and eleven until noon was very good. From lunch until two was quiet, but from two until two-forty-five there was the same rich procession as in the morning. After four, things dropped off sharply and weren't really much good again for the rest of the day. It was shrewdly observed and duly noted that watches at the hospital evidently changed at eight in the morning and three in the afternoon. All glasses were manned during those periods; pathetic little two-power opera glasses made their appearance then, and the windshield and splintershields of the flying bridge presented a solid wall of variously magnified eyeballs.

By this time, also, the watch—as it came to be known—assumed a routine of its own. The assignment and ownership of glasses came to be understood. Three pairs of binoculars belonged down below for the officer-of-the-deck and two quartermasters. The other four pairs of binoculars, the spyglasses and the long-glasses, belonged to the signalmen; to use themselves or lend to radiomen, storekeepers, and cooks in return for future favors. The range-finder came to be recognized as officer property and was almost continually manned by a rotating team of two officers; Lieutenant Carney and Ensign Moulton being the most constant. The big telescope, of course, was a prize. It magnified thirty-two times. There was a box of Lux soap sitting on a shelf on the far wall of the bathroom, and with the telescope Sam could make out with ease the big letters 'LUX' and below them, in smaller letters, the word 'Thrifty.' He could even almost make out the much smaller words in the lower left-hand corner of the box. The long-glass could barely make out the word 'Thrifty' and couldn't begin to make out the words in the corner. The spyglasses and the binoculars couldn't even make out the word 'Thrifty.'

From the first, Sam's right to the telescope had been strangely unchallenged, perhaps in intuitive recognition of his zeal. Turncliffe, the first-class signalman, gave him a brief argument once—more of a token argument, really, than anything else—and then retired to the long-glass. For quite a while Sam was indisputably on the telescope; then one morning Lieutenant (jg) Billings chanced on the bridge. Lieutenant Billings was the communication officer and Sam's boss, and he relieved Sam briefly on the telescope. That was all right the first time; Sam was good-natured in yielding; he liked Mr. Billings. But then Mr. Billings began to chance on the bridge frequently and regularly, and every time he would relieve Sam. Not only that, he had an uncanny talent for arriving at the most propitious moment. Sam got pretty sore over the whole business. As he complained to his friend Schlemmer: 'Sure, he's an officer. All right. If we was in a chow line together, sure, he could go in ahead of me. All right. But I sure can't see where that gives him the right to take a man's glass away from him!' To Sam, a man's glass was an inviolable thing.

By the third day personalities began to emerge from the amorphous group that flitted past the bathroom windows. Despite the fact that the light was usually bad up around the face, thus eliminating facial identifications as a method, the boys were able to distinguish one nurse from another with considerable accuracy. There appeared to be nine consistent users of this particular bathroom. Canappa insisted there were only eight, but then he denied the validity of the two-blonde theory. The two-blonde theory was Sam's and it was supported by the consensus. Canappa pointed out that the two had never been seen together; but this was rather a foolish argument, as both had been examined separately from the same angle, which happened to be a telling one. Canappa, who had not seen both from this angle, stuck to his discredited opinion. Undeniably, there were grounds for confusion. Both girls were young, both were pretty (although, as mentioned before, facial characteristics were inexact), and both wore red-and-white striped bathrobes—or maybe even the same bathrobe. That is no doubt what threw Canappa off. Because, actually, there was conclusive evidence of their separate identity; evidence of the most distinctive sort which one of the girls carried.

As Mannion put it, looking up from his glass: 'What the hell is that she's got?'

Sam *didn't* look up from his glass. 'You dumb bastard, that's a birth-mark.'

Mannion was convinced, but he was irritated by Sam's tone. 'Birth-mark!' he said scornfully. 'Who the hell ever heard of a birthmark down there? That's paint; she's gotten into some paint. Or else it's a burn. That's what it is—it's a burn!'

Sam's rebuttal was simple and unanswerable: 'Who the hell ever heard of a burn down there?' It routed Mannion satisfactorily, and after a moment Sam disclosed: 'Why, Christ, I had an uncle once who had a birthmark . . .' He went on to tell where his uncle's birthmark was situated. He described it in some detail.

The two blondes were the real stars: as the result of comparison the other girls came to be regarded as rather run-of-the-mill and were observed with condescension and even some small degree of indifference. There was one, rather old and quite fat, who absolutely disgusted Schlemmer. Whenever she put in an appearance, he would leave his glass and indignantly exhort the rest of the watch to do the same. 'Don't look at her,' he would say. 'She's nausorating!' He got quite angry when he was ignored.

With the emergence of personalities came the recognition of personal habits. The tall skinny brunette always let the shower water run for several minutes before a bath. The stubby little brunette with the yellow bathrobe always used the bathtub; would sit in the tub and drink what looked like coffee, but might have been tea. The girl with high, piled-up hair would fuss for an hour extracting hairpins, and then take a shampoo in the washbasin by the window without removing her robe. 'That's a stupid goddamn way to take a shampoo,' Sam commented.

But by far the most notable idiosyncrasy belonged to the blonde

with the birthmark. It was one which endeared her to all the watchers
and drove Morris to rapturously announce: 'I'm going to marry that
gal!' Like everything about the place it was plausible, normal, and
really not at all remarkable. It occurred before every bath and consisted simply of shedding the red-and-white striped bathrobe and
standing for several minutes (discreetly withdrawn from the window),
looking out over the bay. Undoubtedly, this was a girl who loved
beauty, and certainly the view was a fine one. The bay in the afternoon was shiny blue plate glass, really perfect except where the wake
of a lazily paddled native canoe flawed the illusion. The tall coconut palms along the beach were as poetically motionless as sculpture.
A little way out from the bay was the thin white line of the surf at
the reef, and far, far out was the scary, almost indistinguishable line
of the horizon. Perhaps the girl's thoughts, as she stood admiring all
that beatitude, ran something like this: 'What peace! There is no effort anywhere. See the canoe drifting lazily across the bay. Observe the
trees with not a leaf stirring, and the ship riding peacefully at anchor,
her men justly resting after the arduous days at sea. What utter tran-
quillity!' From there she could not hear the cranking of the range-
finder.

There was one ghastly afternoon when not a soul, not a single soul,
came in for a bath. The watchers were bewildered and resentful; and,
finally, disgusted. Sam probably spoke for all when he said: 'Christ,
and they call themselves nurses! They're nothing but a goddamn
bunch of filthy pigs. A nurse would at least take a bath once in a
while. Jesus, I pity those poor sick bastards over there who have to let
those filthy pigs handle them!'

But that only happened once, and by and large it could not fairly
be said that the nurses were disappointing. In fact, Sam himself was
once moved to observe: 'This is too good to last.' It was one of the
most prophetic things Sam ever said.

Lieutenant (jg) Langston, the gunnery officer, had been having a
good bit of trouble with his eyes. He wasn't at all satisfied with his
glasses. One day he had a splitting headache and the next morning he
went over to the base hospital to have his eyes refracted. They were
very nice over there. The Doctor was very nice, and there was a pleas-
ant-faced nurse who helped, and she also was very nice. It took only
about an hour and a half to find just the right lenses, and while he
was waiting for his pupils to contract, Langston began talking with the
nurse. In a very short time it came out that she was from a town not

twenty miles from Youngstown, Ohio, where he lived. Langston felt that a certain bond was established, and on the strength of it he invited the nurse, whose name was Miss Williamson, to dinner on the ship that night. It is well known that shipboard food is several cuts above shore-based food, and this consideration was perhaps a factor in Miss Williamson's ready acceptance. She did add one clause, though: she asked if she could bring a friend, 'a terribly cute girl.' Langston, a personable if rather courtly young man, of course said yes, and mentioned that he would assign her to a friend of his, an Ensign Pulver, whom he described as a 'very handsome young man.' Everything was most friendly.

When the girls came aboard that night, escorted by the two officers, the entire crew was massed along the rail and on the bridges. As the white-stockinged legs tripped up the gangway, one great, composite, heartfelt whistle rose to the heavens and hung there. Ensign Pulver's girl, Miss Girard, had turned out to be a knockout. At dinner in the wardroom he could scarcely keep his eyes off her, and no more could the other officers, who feigned eating and made self-conscious conversation. Miss Girard had lovely soft blond hair which she wore in bangs, wide blue innocent eyes, and the pertest nose there ever was. The total effect was that of radiant innocence; innocence triumphant. Only Ensign Pulver noted that when she smiled her eyes screwed up shrewdly and her mouth curved knowingly; but then only Ensign Pulver would. For Langston, it was enough to have what he felt to be the envious admiration of his messmates; but there began to grow in the mind of Ensign Pulver, himself a young man of deceptively guileless appearance, visions of a greater reward. Once in a while he would catch and hold Miss Girard's glance, and when he did he thought he detected interest there.

After dinner, when the party repaired to his room for further polite conversation, he felt more and more sure of it. There were only two chairs in the room and so he and Miss Girard sat together on the edge of the bottom bunk. That gave a certain intimacy, he thought; a certain tie of shared experience. He was moved to break out the quart of Old Overholt, four-fifths full, which he had kept hidden for two months in the little recess under the drawer of his bunk. With Coca-Cola which Langston provided it made a nice drink. Ensign Pulver was then emboldened to tell what he privately called his 'test story,' the decisively off-color tale of 'ze black chapeau.' Miss Girard's response was excellent; she laughed delightedly. Then, craftily aware of the impressiveness of the unfamiliar, he proposed a tour of the ship, and both girls enthusiastically approved. The plan now began to shape itself in Pulver's mind: after the tour, a few more drinks; then a little dancing in the wardroom; then a few more drinks; then get Langston to take the other one off somewhere. As they started out, Miss Girard gave him her small hand.

First they toured the main deck, the offices and the galley and sick bay. Then they dropped down into the cavernous engine room, and Pulver, who was an engineering officer, talked casually of the massive turbines and terrifying boilers. The girls were very much impressed. From the engine room they went up to the bridge, through the wheelhouse, through the charthouse, through the radio room, and on up to the flying bridge. That was a thoughtless thing for the two officers to do, but fortunately an alert quartermaster had preceded them. The inspection party found the signalmen clustered in an innocent group under the canvas awning, and the telescope trained at an angle of ninety degrees from the yellow house. The signalmen presented a curious sight. They were absolutely speechless; they seemed welded to the deck with awe. The two nurses giggled a little, no doubt over the prospect of these men so obviously dumbfounded at seeing a woman that they could only gape. Ensign Pulver later claimed that he felt something ominous in that group, but whether or not he actually did is unimportant.

Langston led the party to the forward splintershield, where it could look down the sheer drop to the main deck, and the even more scary distance to the very bottom of number three hatch. The girls were *really* impressed with that. When they started to walk around behind the funnel, Ensign Pulver noticed that Sam Insigna was trailing them. He was a little annoyed, but, being a young man of poise, he made a sort of introduction. 'This is Sam,' he said, 'one of the signalmen.'

Miss Girard smiled at Sam. 'How do you do, Sam,' she said graciously. Sam was evidently too shy and flustered to speak; he just stood there and grinned foolishly. When they had gone on, Miss Girard squeezed her escort's hand and whispered, 'He's darling.' Pulver nodded dubiously. They took a turn around the funnel, came forward again, and went over to the port wing to look at the twenty-millimeters. By this time the signalmen had gotten their tongues back and were having a bitter and quite vocal argument under the awning. It was obvious that they were trying to keep their voices guarded, but, as often happens, the restraint only intensified them. Sam's voice in particular carried well. 'Goddamit,' the party heard him say, 'I'll bet you one hundred bucks!' Lieutenant (jg) Langston nodded his head in the direction of the signalmen, smiled superiorly, and said to the nurses: 'Seems to be an argument.' Then Sam's voice came to them again. That voice was several things: it was shrill, it was combative, it was angry; but most of all it was audible. There have been few more audible voices, before or since. It traveled out from under the awning in an unfaltering parabola, fell on the ears of the inspection party, and broke into words of simple eloquence.

'You stupid son-of-a-bitch, I tell you that's her! I got one hundred bucks that says that's the one with the birthmark on her ass! Now put up or shut up!'

Sam may have been right, at that. No one ever knew; no one on the ship ever saw that birthmark again. The curtains of the two middle upstairs windows were not raised next morning, and when the ship sailed three days later they were still down. It was three weeks before a sizable membership of the crew would speak to Sam except to curse him, and it was longer than that before Ensign Pulver would speak to him at all.

Guy Gilpatric

MARY, QUEEN OF SCOTS

THE *Inchcliffe Castle*, Para to Naples, stuck her rusty snout around the bend of Andalucia and ambled into sheltered waters across which sprawled the purple shadow of Gibraltar. Behind the Rock the sun had climbed an hour high; but Britannia's Lion, in its towering majesty, shut off all save a few ambitious rays which leaked around its edges, and framed it in a pinkly glowing aureole.

The full moon, on the other hand—it would have been your left—swung over the white houses of Algeciras, in Spain, and sinking lower, paved a baleful pathway beyond Trafalgar for the wandering footsteps of Admiral Nelson's unquiet, lovesick ghost.

In this strange and lovely moment of borning day and dying night, the *Inchcliffe Castle's* anchor let go with a shocking clatter of chains, a vulgar display of sparks, much profanity from the fo'c'sle head and even more from the bridge. The profanity was that of religious men, which is the kind that blisters paint.

The anchor caught in the mud, jerked loose once or twice, stirred up many bubbles and an evil smell, and finally hooked a fluke. Mr. Montgomery, hanging over the bow and seeing the chain stretch taut, waved his hands with the weary yet triumphant gesture of an orchestra leader bringing the Ninth Symphony to a glorious close.

Captain Ball, on the bridge, heaved a stertorous sigh. "Ring off the engines," he directed; and somewhere down below, the telegraph jingled. Suddenly, disturbingly, the decks ceased to throb and the stanchions to tremble. After eighteen pulsing days the ship seemed no longer to be alive. Silence, torrents of silence, poured in from all sides. And just then the sun, conquering the traditionally-unconquerable, scaled Gibraltar's heights and sent the night, its moon, and its lovely mystery scurrying away into Africa.

"Hell's bones!" remarked Captain Ball, unbottoning his overcoat and taking a cigar from his night-shirt pocket, "What a trip *that* was!" Resting his elbows on the bridge rail, his eye travelled aft over the battered gear and salt-streaked superstructure which told of a rough and troublous passage.

Mr. Glencannon, the Chief Engineer, appeared on the deck below. At the heels of his oil-soaked carpet slippers toddled a jet black female Scottish terrier with barrel chest, stump legs, and whiskers such as one associates with natives of Aberdeen. Mr. Glencannon strolled to the rail, spat copiously over it, and considered Gibraltar at length—meanwhile wiping his face with a handful of greasy cottonwaste. Then he lifted the dog in his arms, and placed her forepaws on the rail.

"Mary," he said, "this is Geebraltar, an heestoric port. I'll first deerect your attention to the street which runs peerpindicular to yon wharf. If ye'll note the fourth—no, the fufth building on the left, ye'll be notin' a pub whuch sells the finest whusky South of the Firth o' Clyde. And then, on the nuxt street, over toward the naval coal docks, ye'll see a sma' house wi' a red roof. That's a pub called 'The Royal Oak,' after an old ancient freegate ship whuch . . . oh, a vurra gude morning to you, Captain Ball!"

"Good morning, Mr. Glencannon," and the Captain nodded over the canvas dodger. "How are you and Mary this morning—fit?"

Mr. Glencannon shook his head dolefully. "As fur my ain puir health, the less said the better. But Mary, the little lass, is ailin' sore. I was aboot to crave yer kind permeesion, Sir, to tak' her ashoor to a vetereenary, and get him to preescribe."

"Right-o," agreed the Captain cheerfully.

"Thanks kindly, Captain Ball," said Mr. Glencannon, setting Mary on the deck and deftly brushing up her coat. "The lass and I are grateful. We are indeed. Come on, Sweetheart—we'll ha' a bit o' brukfust, we will, and then Papa'll put on his new uneefurrm, and dress his ain little lass in her tartan collar, and hoot! ashore for a romp we'll go!"

"Oh, now, my eye!" exploded Mr. Montgomery, the mate, who had joined Captain Ball upon the bridge. "Did you ever 'ear such blithering tosh in all your life, Sir?—Mr. Glencannon mykes a bit of an arss of 'imself over that dog when 'e sets 'is mind to it, 'e does!"

Captain Ball crinkled the corners of his eyes as do men who weren't born yesterday. "Well, I'll tell you, Mr. Montgomery, it's like this. I know as well as you do that he's going ashore to get drunk. Mr. Glencannon has his weaknesses, as who of us does not? Scripture says that 'To sin is human,' and though Mr. Glencannon drinks a full quart of whisky every day, and be damned if I haven't seen him drink five quarts, we must remember to let he without sin cast the first stone.— Particularly when he's the only Engineer on the high seas who can handle our rusty old tubercular junk pile of a blank-blanked engine."

"Well, all I can say is, God 'elp the Rock of Gibraltar!" grunted Mr. Montgomery, only half convinced. " 'Ere 'e comes now."

Mr. Glencannon, brave in his best white cap, the four gold stripes of his rank, and the medal awarded him for saving a German's life by mistake, stood at the foot of the gangway and invited bids from the yammering bumboatmen to take him ashore. He cut the lowest bid in half, kicked the chin of the nearest competitor, who had sought to seize his arm, and made the trip to the Commercial Wharf for thruppence. With Mary frisking at his heels, he passed through cobbled streets lined with whitewashed houses labelled, for example, "*Sgt. Major Alfred Hoskins, 67th Rgt. R.G.A.*," and "*Non-Com. Married Quarters—No Loitering.*" The latter sign he felt to be distinctly offensive in its insinuation. "Ha' no fear!" he muttered toward it. "I've better to do than loiter aboot with the she-beef o' the Royal Garrison Arteelery!" And forthwith he turned into an establishment the window of which displayed a spirited lithograph of the Relief of Lucknow, depicting several bottles of MacCrimmon's Very Old Liqueur Whisky being put to good use by the beleaguered defenders in the foreground.

He found MacCrimmon's Very Old to be distinctly creditable stuff—as good, in some respects, as The Laird's Selected Relics, Clammarty Royal Tartan Blend and Dunleven Particularly Choice. But none of them, of course, could compare with Duggan's Dew of Kirkintilloch—most gorgeous of all liquids that ever dripped golden from the nozzle of a still to mingle its perfume with that of the heather in the cold Highland mists.

Now, like Duggan's Dew, Mr. Glencannon hailed from the town of Kirkintilloch, in Dumbartonshire; and the picture on the label made him first happy, then sentimental, and finally homesick. A great grief overcame him; tears coursed his cheeks as he contemplated that label, and he was weeping copiously when he finished the bottle. "Look," he sobbed, hoisting Mary to the table, "Gaze, Lass, upon the dear fameeliar scenes o' your childhood! 'Tis there that our Mothers live. Ye played there as a bairn, and so, alas, did I. . . ." And Mary, falling into the spirit of the occasion, tilted back her head and gave vent to piercing wails. Mr. Glencannon purchased six cases of the whisky, ordered five to be delivered aboard the ship and the sixth to be stowed in a cab. The cab proved to be a spidery victoria driven by a Spaniard in straw hat, short jacket and baggy trousers. Mr. Glencannon and Mary scrambled aboard with the God-speed of the publican and some assistance from the by-standers.

"Where to, Capitan?" inquired the Spaniard.

"How in the hell shud I know?" replied Mr. Glencannon. "Must I act as guide to ye, on ye're ain native heath?"

"But I come from La Linea, Senor," protested the Spaniard.

"Vurra weel—let's go there, then," and with Mary perched on the seat beside him, Mr. Glencannon dropped off to sleep.

They had clip-clopped out of the streets of the town and were well in sight of the Neutral Strip—a barb-wired belt of land which separates Spain from the Crown Colony of Gibraltar—when the driver reined in his nag. Mr. Glencannon, opening his eyes, saw that they were halted at a house before which paced a sentry in the uniform of the Royal Garrison Artillery. A sign on the place read "H.Q. *Frontier Guard. Passes for Spain.*" Across the road, under the flat face of the Rock, stretched a field filled with hurdles, water-jumps, cricket greens, polo goal posts, and aeroplane hangars. Upon this field, troops were playing football.

The driver dismounted, entered the house, and shortly emerged with a little green slip which read "North front. Permit until first evening gunfire. John Cochrane, Chief of Frontier Police."

Mr. Glencannon was considering this suspiciously, and was just about to ask Mary what country they were in, when a disturbing sound came from the distance. At first he thought he only imagined it, and instinctively he glanced at Mary for confirmation. But, yes—her ears were cocked, her tail was wagging, and she was craning her neck around the side of the carriage. It was the sound of bagpipes; and they were playing "Piobair o' Lochaber."

"Foosh!" exclaimed Mr. Glencannon, lurching to his feet. "Why, it's the Argyll and Dumbarton Highlanders!" Mary showed her front teeth in a broad smile and then her entire perfect set in a series of joyous barks. Her little hairy forepaws pattered on the cushions, and she wriggled with excitement. For there, down the long white road, was the head of the approaching column—kilts and sporans swinging to the time, white gaiters slogging up and down, tartan ribbons aflutter on the pipes, and the bass-drummer with his leopard-skin apron whirling his sticks cross-armed, overhead, and behind him in the wild inimitable Highland manner!—It was the Dumbartons, beyond a doot —and Mr. Glencannon's own Cousin Douglas was a Sergeant of the Regiment!

Nearer and nearer they came—the shrill chant and basso drone of the pipes leaping into the air and echoing against the great grey face of the Rock above the plain. Then came the muffled *clump* of sixteen hundred hobnailed boots, the rhythmic swish of eight hundred tartan kilts! The Dumbartons—the great and glorious Dumbartons!—were marching by! Wheeling smartly before his very carriage, they deployed into the field.

They were going to play football, and so they weren't carrying their rifles. Numerous sporting Majors, Captains and Subalterns had turned out with the team, and they swung along with their walking sticks beneath their arms and banter upon their lips. And over all, there was a friendly, comfortable smell of venerable Scotch whisky upon the soft Iberian air. . . .

Mr. Glencannon was sniffing deep when suddenly he and Mary beheld a sight which transfixed them. It was the regimental mascot— the handsomest, whiskeriest Scottish terrier in the whole wide world —a rakish, swashbuckling lad wearing a tiny Highland bonnet cocked over one ear, the silver-and-cairngorm badge of the Dumbartons pinned to the side of it. And he toddled along with a man who stood full seven feet high—a giant with a chest the size of the *Inchcliffe Castle's* main boiler, and great hairy knees like the oak trees worshipped by

the Druids of antiquity. This giant—there could be no mistaking him!
—was Mr. Glencannon's own Cousin Douglas.

Mary cast virginal modesty to the winds, and shrilly yapped her
admiration. Cousin Douglas, spotting Mr. Glencannon, gave vent to a
joyous "Hoot!" and promptly fell out of the ranks. Mr. Glencannon,
not to be outdone, promptly fell out of the carriage.

"Heigh-nanny, lass!" said the terrier with the bonnet, swaggering up
to Mary and kissing her full upon her luscious black lips without so
much as a by-your-leave. "I'm Jock o' the Dumbartons, senior dog o'
the reegiment. Welcome to Geebraltar!" Mary stood blushing, eyes
downcast but heart throbbing wildly. . . . Mr. Glencannon and
Cousin Douglas were slapping each other on the back, saying "Weel,
weel, weel, I'll be domned!" and repeating it over and over again.

"Foosh, Cousin Colin, and it's gude to see you!" roared the giant
at length. "Why, ye domned old ghoul, ye, when did we meet, the
last?"

"Let me think, let me think," said Mr. Glencannon, closing his eyes
and grasping the carriage lamp for support. "Why, o' course!—it was
Nineteen-fufteen, when I was Second on the transpoort takin' ye oot
to G'llipoli."

"Thirteen years ago—eh, to think of it!" sighed Cousin Douglas,
and the sigh was as the sound of a locomotive plunging into a tunnel.
"Weel,"—and he wrinkled his nose, smacked his lips, and cast his eye
on the case of whisky partly concealed by the carriage rug, "Weel, it's
customarra in such happy ceercumstances . . ."

"—I was aboot to suggest it!" hastened Mr. Glencannon. "Coachman, I'll thank ye for the loan o' a corkscrew."

"Dinna trouble yersel'," said Cousin Douglas, seizing a bottle and
smiting it so lustily against his palm that the cork leapt out as from
the choicer vintages of Rheims. "Come, Cousin Colin, do we mount
yon carriage the twa o' us, an' go see the bullfight over in Spanish
Town. 'Twull be better than the futball. But feerst, let us drink a
drap to our happy meeting. Here—I'll open another bottle so we'll
both have one." . . . He tilted his own quart beneath his bristly red
moustache; and when he took it down again, lo, it was only a pint.

"Haw!" he snorted, closing his eyes ecstatically and holding the
bottle at arm's length, " 'Tis the Dew o' Kirkintilloch! I dinna ha' to
look at the label—I recognize the way it treeckles doon an' cozeys
my sluggish liver! 'Tis a happy meetin', Cousin Colin—a happy
meetin' indeed!"

He climbed aboard the carriage, which groaned in every joint and took an alarming list to starboard as he settled into the seat. Mr. Glencannon was about to join him, when he saw Mary and the mascot joyfully gambolling across the troop-filled field.

"'Tis a-richt, peerfectly a-richt," Cousin Douglas assured him, "Let the little tykes frusk aboot while the lads are playin' futball. I'll tell MacPheerson and MacColquhoun to keep an eye on them, and leave them with Corporal MacClintoch at the Frontier guard house.—Ye see," he explained, "We're off juty today to play the 67th Arteelery—attendance optional. My time's my ain till evening gun. So, carra on, coachman!"

The driver beat several clouds of dust out of the hide of his nag, and headed for the border. At the British side they were halted by a Highlander who blanched perceptibly as he recognized Sergeant Douglas Glencannon.

"I'll thank ye for a look at your passes, gentlemen," he said, saluting.

"Tak' a gude look at this, Corporal MacClintoch!" replied Cousin Douglas, extending a fist the size of a hoof, and quivering it threateningly beneath the guardian's nose. "Tak' a verra gude look, while ye're still alive to see it!"

"Thank ye," said Corporal MacClintoch, backing up a trifle, and saluting again, "Yere passes are sateesfactorra."

They jogged across the Neutral Strip—a stretch of meadow in which the kine of Castile and Britain browsed in sisterly contentment—and paused again, for inspection at the Spanish Customs. The *aduanero* was a fat gentleman in a blue uniform and a sword left over from the American War. "Have you tobacco or spirits?" he asked in perfect English.

"I dinna ken your lingo," replied Cousin Douglas, smacking a fresh bottle against his palm, and watching the cork sail into a roadside cactus. "Drive on, gilly!"

The coachman was plainly troubled. "Tell heem you have no the tobacco, no the alcohol," he whispered.

Without removing his feet from the opposite cushions, Cousin Douglas leaned halfway across the road and seized the *aduanero* by the throat. Dragging him to the side of the carriage he shook him playfully.

"Pass!" gurgled the guard, retreating into his hut and swallowing diligently—"*Vaya con Dios!*" The driver clucked to his horse, and five minutes later they turned into the main street of La Linea de la Concepcion, headed for the bull ring. Evidently, from the cheering, the *corrida* was already in progress.

Arrived at the Plaza, Mr. Glencannon dismounted first. "Do ye please tak' charge o' the refreshments, Cousin Dooglas, while I pay for the cab," he said, handing the driver a counterfeit Costa Rican *colon* and three brass Chinese coins with holes in them. The Spaniard raised his voice in protest, whereupon Cousin Douglas, standing in the carriage with the case of whisky under his arm, jumped into the air thrice and so mightily that the vehicle broke into two distinct halves. As he stood triumphant in the splintered wreck of the rear section, the terrified horse, the driver and the front wheels vanished in a dust-cloud down the street.

A crowd collected, and through it five cocked-hatted policemen shouldered their way. They took one look at Cousin Douglas, and shouldered their way out again.

Mr. Glencannon placed a shilling on the ledge of the ticket booth. "Twa!" he ordered, holding up two fingers. The Spaniard shook his head and pointed at the scale of prices. "*Dos duros, Senores,*" he said. "Twa duros!" snorted Cousin Douglas, "Why, 'tis rank extortion! Dinna submeet to it, Cousin Colin, dinna submeet!" Seizing the ticket booth by one of its upper corners, he rocked it back and forth so violently that the Spaniard, the cash-till and two chairs went rattling about the interior like peas in a withered pod. Then, reaching through the window, he seized a sheaf of tickets and led the way through the cool shadowy tunnel which gave access to the seats.

They entered the first vacant box and were about to sit down when the audience burst into a storm of frenzied "*vivas!*" Ortiz, the Seville Sticker, had manoeuvred his bull into a perfect *pase de la firma,* and dispatched him with a masterly thrust. "*Oreja! Oreja!*" screamed the crowd; and at a sign from the President of the *corrida,* a man sliced an ear off the bull and handed it—the highest of honors—to the *matador.*

Ortiz, in his heelless slippers, strutted bowing around the *sombra* side of the arena, amid a shower of hats, fans and flowers.

"Oh!" exclaimed Mr. Glencannon, "Look, Cousin Dooglas—you can throw things! Foosh! what fun!" And falling wholeheartedly into the spirit of it all, he tossed a chair over the barrier and knocked the *matador* flat.

In that instant the cheers turned into the menacing roar of a mob whose idol has been desecrated. Wheeling about, Cousin Douglas saw a thousand Spaniards descending upon them with murder in their eyes. His bottle was almost empty; so hesitating only to empty it completely, he hurled it into the front rank with withering effect. Four chairs were handy, and he flung them with unerring aim. A policeman appeared with drawn sword. Cousin Douglas seized the sword, spanked him with it, and grasped him by the belt and threw him across seven tiers of seats. The seats were vacant—in fact by this time they had an entire section of the arena to themselves.

"Weel," he said, languidly, settling himself beside Mr. Glencannon, who had been busy uncorking bottles, "We can better enjoy the speectacle noo, without the fumes o' garlic from yon feelthy Spaniards."

"Ye're richt," agreed Mr. Glencannon, impatiently viewing the group which bore Ortiz from the arena on a stretcher, "But if they dinna proceed with their domned bull-sticking soon, I shall deemand our money back."

"A verra reasonable and tolerant deecision, Cousin Colin! We're being imposed upon by these swundling foreigners, and it's time we asseerted oursel's!"

Grasping the captured sword, he was about to go out and complain to the management when a fanfare of trumpets gave him pause. A herald appeared upon the bloody sand below.

"Hoot!" applauded Mr. Glencannon, pounding his bottle on the ledge of the box, "He's aboot to eloqute! Lusten closely, Cousin Dooglas!"

Choosing his words according to the conventions of the *Corrida*, the herald announced that El Vaquerito, the thrice-eminent *espada* from Bilbao, would match wits with a bull "*con buenos adornos en la pensadora*"—which meant a most intelligent bull indeed. The bull, he went on to say, was none other than El *Maquinista*. . . .

"L. MacKinister!" exclaimed Mr. Glencannon, "Did ye hear that name, Cousin Dooglas?"

"I canna believe my ears! Why, he must be a MacKinister o' Kirkintilloch! A Scottish bull!"

Mr. Glencannon grasped him by the arm. "Cousin Dooglas," he hissed, "We canna permeet it!"

"Ye're domned richt we canna!" boomed Cousin Douglas, seizing his sword, shoving the two remaining bottles into his sporan, and rising to his full seven feet, "Come, Cousin Colin—the Glencannons are gaein' to the wars!"

They vaulted the rail of the box and clambered over the barrier into the arena. Three thousand Spaniards shouted, but only twenty interfered. Cousin Douglas attended to fourteen, and Mr. Glencannon disposed of six. " 'Twas dry and theersty work," observed Mr. Glencannon, surveying the scene of carnage,—"Thank ye, Cousin Dooglas—I ha' a bottle o' my ain."

Occupied as they were, neither of them saw El Maquinista as he rushed snorting into the sunlight. Spotting Cousin Douglas's flaming scarlet kilt from afar, he thundered toward it. A mighty shout came from the audience.

"Lusten to them, Cousin Dooglas—why, I do believe they're giving us a cheer!" Mr. Glencannon raised his cap in a graceful gesture of acknowledgment, and Cousin Douglas made a courtly bow. As he did so, El Maquinista's horn very neatly removed his kilt, and left him with nothing below the waist save gaiters, shoes and stockings.

"Oh, shame, shame, Cousin Dooglas!" cried Mr. Glencannon, "Quick, lad—do ye stand in back o' me and pull down your sporan!"

" 'Twull be inadeequate," announced Cousin Douglas, "Look yonder, Colin—that domned bull has trompled my kilt all to nowt!"

A great rage came upon him. Despite Mr. Glencannon's scandalised protests, he strode across the arena and addressed the bewildered bull.

"Ye lout, ye!" he shouted, shaking his fist in the animal's face, "Ye ruddy garlic-eating impostor, ye! Ye're no Scot—ye're a feelthy, treecherous, back-knifing Spaniard, that's what ye are!"

El Maquinista bellowed, put down his head, and charged. Cousin Douglas stood his ground and met the charge with a right to the nose and a left jab to the eye. Stepping in, he landed blow after blow, every one of which jolted the bull from stem to stern.

"I'll knock ye oot, ye big booby, ye!" panted Cousin Douglas, "Another minute, and I'll uncoork the uppercut that made me Champion o' the Breetish Army."

Mr. Glencannon took out his watch, and stood solemnly by, ready to time the count. El Maquinista, both eyes closed and bleeding at the nose, was groggy on his feet when the bullfighters intervened. As they drove the bull out of the arena Cousin Douglas knocked out a couple of *toreros* for good measure. "Quick, Cousin Colin!" he shouted, "Help me borrow their troosers!" Together they had yanked most of the clothing off the limp Spaniards, when they saw five *picadores* galloping toward them, lances couched.

"Run for yere life, Cousin Dooglas—here comes the cavalry!" warned Mr. Glencannon; and dropping most of their spoils, they sprinted for the runway down which El Maquinista had vanished. He was standing just within the entrance, but he hastily stood aside when he recognized Cousin Douglas.

Climbing over the wall of the runway, they plunged into the labyrinthian foundations of the stadium. In the distance, they heard the hue and cry raised after them. Groping on their way, they came to a hole in the wall, and they crawled through it to find themselves in the back yard of a wine-shop.

"Foosh!" said Mr. Glencannon. "What a happy coeencidence! Let us gae in, Cousin Dooglas, and subdue the proprieter."

The *tabernero* was alone among his wine barrels, so Cousin Douglas imprisoned him within one, and sat upon it. "Oh, deary me, but I've a theerst on me!" he said, "Mak' haste, Cousin Colin, and let us quaff our fill."

"Verra weel," agreed Mr. Glencannon, inspecting the rows of bottles on the shelf, "I canna read any o' them, so we'll ha' to sample them all."

At this point things became curiously garbled. It seemed that a great deal was transpiring over a long period of time, but Mr. Glencannon's next really definite impression was of a splitting headache. He lay with eyes closed, his very soul cringing as white hot twinges of migraine surged through his brain.

Opening his eyes, he found that he was in his own room aboard the *Inchcliffe Castle*, and that he was wearing the green velvet jacket of a Spanish *matador*. Painfully hoisting himself to a sitting posture, he saw Mary Queen of Scots upon the floor, contentedly chewing a bull's ear.

"Bless me, I remember noo!" he chuckled, "Daddy brought it hame to his lass as a souvenir of Spain."

Mary wagged her tail and continued chewing.

"Weel," sighed Mr. Glencannon, lurching to his feet, "I wonder if we've coaled yet. Why! I do believe we're at sea!" He peered through the port at a blue expanse of Mediterranean across which trailed a long black smudge from the *Inchcliffe Castle's* funnel. He opened the port and gratefully gulped down the fresh, cool breeze. In the corner of his room were piled the five new cases of the Dew of Kirkintilloch, and uncorking a bottle, he poured himself a brimming tumblerful.

"Thur's no cure for dog-bite like the hair of the dog that bit ye!" he remarked to Mary, tossing it off and smacking his lips. Then, donning his working clothes, he made his way to the engine room—head clear, step brisk, and hand steady.

"Strike me ruddy, but the Chief's a wonder!" observed Mr. Swales, the Second Mate. "To look at 'im, this arfternoon, you'd think 'e was the H'Archbishop of Canterb'ry!"

" 'Is recuperating powers are remarkable," agreed Mr. Montgomery. "I 'ad 'Ell's own time gettin' 'im out of the tender larst night. There was 'im and another wild man—a non-com. 'Ighlander nine foot tall, with nothing on below the wyste but one of them 'airy Scotch tobacco-pouches, like. Singin' '*Scots wha hae wi' Wallace bled,*' they were, and drinking out of bottles. They 'ad another of them black tykes with 'em, syme as Mary—wearing a little Scotch bonnet, 'e was."

"Well, the Scotch are a mad race," said Mr. Swales.

"Mad as 'Ell," agreed Mr. Montgomery, "And Mr. Glencannon's the maddest of the lot. But despite 'is quart a day, not counting 'olidays, he's a great engineer, Mr. Swales, a great engineer."

Some weeks later, though (they had called at Naples, gone to Cattaro, thence to Odessa, and were westward bound in the Sea of Candia) Mr. Glencannon's madness took a disquieting form. He became preoccupied, morose. He spent long hours in his room with Mary. His appetite dwindled.

At first there was only a rumor. Then the rumor spread throughout the ship's company until it was discussed incredulously from fo'c'sle to engine room. *Mr. Glencannon had sworn off liquor!*

"The thing is serious," declared Captain Ball, shaking his head ominously. "A man who has drank all his life like Mr. Glencannon has drank, can't shut down on it all at once."

" 'E can't indeed!" said Mr. Montgomery, "But are you sure 'e 'as really sworn orff, Sir!"

"Yes. Last night I asked him if he'd lend me the loan of a little whisky to rub on my corns. He said 'Take all I've got and welcome, Captain—I'm quit o' the feelthy stuff!' "

"H'm," mused the Mate, "That looks bad, Sir.—Specially, offering you all 'e's got, 'im being of the Scottish persuasion, as you might say."

"Exactly! And he went moping off to his room saying he had to fix some medicine for Mary. She's sick or something, too."

"Sick my aunt, Sir! It's only the way 'e pampers the poor tyke! Meanwhile, 'e's letting 'is engines go to 'Ell."

"H'm. I noticed we were quite a bit shy on yesterday's run."

In the engine room things went from bad to worse. The Assistant Engineers, though diligently they slaved, lacked the great genius of their Chief which could make the old coffee grinder behave like clock work.

South of Kapsali they ran into dirty weather, and the poor old *Castle* took a sorry buffeting. She went rails under every roll, and the forward well-deck was a surge of green water.

Captain Ball, a notorious coal saver, had laid his course close. They were less than a mile off the thundering white breakers, when the engines sighed, wheezed, and stopped. From the gratings and ventilators came clouds of steam, and the sound of hammers and scurrying feet. Mr. Montgomery leaped to the speaking tube, and addressed the engine room. "'Urry up, you bleddy tinkers!" he screamed, "If you don't get way on 'er smartly you'll swim out through the condenser pipes!"

Captain Ball then stepped to the tube, and said a few words of his own. Those nearby could smell the rubber gums of his false teeth burning. When he had finished, he went alone into the starboard wing of the bridge and considered the situation. Things were bad—very bad. In an hour, at most, they would pile up on a lee shore. He started toward his room to gather the ship's log, his Bible, chronometers and hair tonic preparatory to ordering away the boats. Half down the ladder he was blinded by a stinging gust of spray, and as he groped on his way he encountered some one coming up.

"Hoot, Captain!" shouted Mr. Glencannon, grasping his superior officer in a joyous and drunken embrace. "I was just gaein' up to get you! Stup into my room a moment, Sir—stup into my room!"

"Hell's bones, not now!" gasped the Captain, as he dragged Mr. Glencannon into the lee of the house, "We're due to pile up any minute, man! Can't you feel that the engines are stopped?"

"I was aboot to mak' appropreeate comment on the fact," said Mr. Glencannon, feigning a polite interest, "But if you'll just come wi' me a moment, Captain, and stup into my room, I'll go below in pairson and repair them. It reminds me of a story I once heard aboot a . . ."

In desperation Captain Ball led the way across the rolling deck to Mr. Glencannon's room, and threw open the door.

"There, Captain," said the Engineer proudly, indicating the bunk with one hand and seizing a bottle with the other. "Look what the Angels ha' brought to Mary and her puir old Dad!"

On the center of the bed lay Mary Queen of Scots, feebly wagging her tail, and caressing six tiny squirming black shapes with a tender maternal muzzle.

"The reesponsibility—Ah, the reesponsibility's been terrible, Captain! But noo I'm my ain old self again. Do ye mak' yersel' comfortable for half a moment, Sir, while I just stup below and start those engines."

Weak and trembling, Captain Ball settled in a chair. This, he thought, would be as good a place to die as any. For the first time in his life he felt his years, and the tragic grief of a master about to lose his ship. Smiling bitterly, he patted Mary's hot little head. She raised it from her puppies and gratefully licked his hand. And at this instant there commenced a rhythmic throbbing underfoot! The *Inchcliffe Castle* became alive again! Mr. Glencannon, the wizard of steam, had worked a miracle with the engines!

Captain Ball arose slowly to his feet. Yes, the *Inchcliffe Castle* was ploughing along on her course. "Thank God—and three rousing cheers for Scotland!" he said.

In less than an hour, the *Castle* was around the Cape and in calm waters. Mr. Glencannon, oily, happy and thirsty, came back to his room.

"Weel, Lass!" he said, picking up the bottle, "I see that the Captain has gone. And—why, the domned old teetotal hypocrite! Look, Mary —he drank up half a pint o' Papa's Dew o' Kirkintilloch!"